STRATIGRAPHY AND SEDIMENTATION

A Geology Series

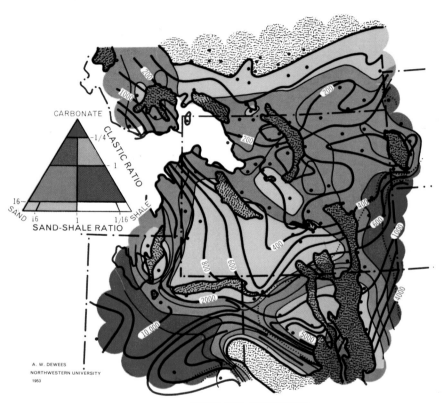

CARBONATE

CLASTIC RATIO

−1/4

1

SAND

16−

16   1   1/16

SAND-SHALE RATIO

SHALE

A. W. DEWEES
NORTHWESTERN UNIVERSITY
1953

TENSLEEP SANDSTONE
PENNSYLVANIAN OF WYOMING AREA

Department of Geology
New York University

Stratigraphy
and Sedimentation

BY W. C. KRUMBEIN AND L. L. SLOSS

DEPARTMENT OF GEOLOGY, NORTHWESTERN UNIVERSITY

Second Edition

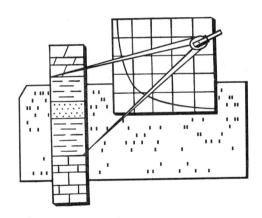

 W. H. FREEMAN AND COMPANY

SAN FRANCISCO AND LONDON

Library of Congress Catalog Card Number: 61–11422

Preface to the Second Edition

The first edition of this book appeared twelve years ago, in 1951. Revision began on the present edition in 1958, with the intention of issuing the second edition a decade after the first. But times had changed. The pace of research and publication in many fields embraced by this volume accelerated so rapidly that by the time Chapter 13 was written, the supporting materials (recast in Chapters 4–7) were already out of date. The problems of continual revision and of maintaining a balance between accepted fundamentals and newly emergent concepts have been partially resolved by condensing much of the basic material in the first part of this edition into an expository account, leaving for later chapters the integration of all that had gone before, plus expansion of some topics that had previously been treated in earlier chapters.

The net result is a book that differs little in structure from the first edition, in that stratigraphic organization and the underlying principles of sedimentation are again introduced before stratigraphic analysis and synthesis are undertaken. Within this framework, however, the present edition is more than a revision of the first; no chapter stands completely as it was, and a number have been fully rewritten—in addition, there are two new chapters. In order to maintain approximately the same size volume, much of the chapter on paleogeography has been absorbed or redistributed; similarly, the present chapter on sedimentary tectonics is a combination of two earlier chapters, with some of the material transferred to Chapter 13 of this edition.

The reader is reminded, as in 1951, that this book must be viewed as a summation of one stage in an evolutionary progression. Further, this summation emphasizes certain topics and points of view at the expense of others. These choices represent the considered, if personal, opinions of the authors, and it is not anticipated that all readers will concur. Fortunately, in the interim between editions, several books have appeared that view approximately the same ground from differing vantage points of training, experience, and inclination. In many instances the reader's attention is directed to alternative expressions or to greater detail by specific reference to other readily available texts.

v

Department of Geology
New York University

For example, the excellent treatment of sedimentary environments by Dunbar and Rodgers obviates the need for duplicating this basic material here.

Stress in this new edition continues to be laid on two cardinal points. One is the iteration and reiteration that stratigraphy is a three-dimensional field of observation—a field that is unquestionably dependent on subsurface data. The stratigraphic record consists of solid bodies that cannot be adequately analyzed from outcrop data alone. The second point is the need for continuing search for stratigraphic order and system. Without providing generalizations and integrating principles, the science of stratigraphy cannot thrive and grow.

Continuing pursuit of these objectives in this edition requires a change in the allotment of space to certain subjects. Stratigraphic mapping, for example, could be supported by only a slim bibliography in 1951, but today this subject is commonplace in academic and applied stratigraphy and is documented by numerous published examples. The field of sedimentation has also shown such a tremendous expansion between editions that a major problem consists, not in deciding what to include, but in deciding what might reasonably be omitted. This choice, difficult as it is, was dictated by the purpose of this volume, which is primarily stratigraphic analysis. International literature has also expanded at an accelerating pace, and the problems faced in including references to this literature in the first edition have become completely insoluble for this edition. This remains primarily a North American text and reference book, which, it is hoped, will be of value to readers overseas in relating their own stratigraphic studies to the principles emphasized in this book.

The high-speed electronic computer is a new element that has entered stratigraphic analysis since completion of the first edition in 1951. This important tool makes possible levels of analysis that were entirely unfeasible a decade ago. Geologic judgment, based on observation, training, and experience, is still the foundation for stratigraphic analysis, but the computer has opened new doors for the study of interrelations among stratigraphic variables, and especially for the preparation and interpretation of stratigraphic maps, as is brought out in Chapter 12.

Lithologic associations, stressed in the first edition, are now seen to be parts of a larger concept of stratigraphic models. Because these are at the forefront of current thinking, emphasis on their systematic treatment—as an integration of stratigraphic analysis—forms the last chapter of this book. Yet it is realized that this topic, as was true of some of those emphasized in the first edition, is but another stage in the development of the science, and may be expected to evolve through modification in the same manner as have other advances that added their share to the growth of stratigraphy.

The authors are again indebted beyond measure to their professional and scientific colleagues whose published and spoken thoughts are inextricably woven into the chapters of this book. The scientists of the Schlumberger Well Surveying Corporation provided illustrations and suggestions for a revised discussion of well-logging techniques in 1957, reworked these in 1959 when it became obvious that publication would be delayed, and patiently waited for still another extended period, during which their technology has inexorably advanced. The authors express their thanks to the American Commission on Stratigraphic Nomenclature and to the American Association of Petroleum Geologists for permission to reprint the Stratigraphic Code in the Appendix of this edition. To Mrs. Helen Meier go our thanks for her labors in the vital closing phases of preparation of this volume, including organization of the text material for automatic sorting and index preparation.

W. C. Krumbein
L. L. Sloss

January 1963

Preface to the First Edition

It is a remarkable circumstance that one of the most rapidly expanding fields of integrated geology, that of stratigraphy and sedimentation, has received no comprehensive textbook treatment since publication in 1913 of Grabau's *Principles of Stratigraphy,* with subsequent minor revisions. In the intervening decades, great volumes of data have been added to the record and important strides have been taken toward the establishment of new principles and interpretations.

Excellent texts and reference works on many aspects of sedimentation have appeared, and descriptive stratigraphy has achieved abundant recognition as an applied and academic science. Beyond the level of elementary historical geology, attempts at integration of the diverse components of stratigraphy and sedimentation are so widely scattered through the geologic literature that they are beyond the reach of undergraduate and beginning graduate students.

It is the purpose of this book to assemble and integrate the facts, principles, and hypotheses bearing upon stratigraphy and sedimentation in a form that may be studied and assimilated in an efficient manner. The book is the outgrowth of a combined course presented by the authors at Northwestern University. The course was designed to meet the needs of senior students in geology and to serve as an introduction in advanced stratigraphy for beginning graduate students. Prerequisites include the normal sequence of undergraduate courses in geology and related sciences. Some field experience with sedimentary rocks is assumed, preferably a formal field-mapping course.

The authors hope that the book will at least partially fulfill the need for a text in courses of this type. It is also hoped that it will be of use to the many practicing stratigraphers for whom the pressure of work prevents thorough reading of a voluminous and scattered scientific literature.

It is noteworthy that in Grabau's time there was no separation, real or implied, between stratigraphy and sedimentation. In fact, sedimentation as an independent science had not yet been born. The 1920's and 1930's witnessed the rise of sedimentation as an important field of investigation, with an accompanying trend toward separation in practice and concept between stratigraphy and its robust offshoot. More recently, the trend has been toward reintegration, and it is the intent of the authors to accelerate this trend by showing the close relation between the two domains.

The subject matters of stratigraphy and sedimentation are interwoven in the text as firmly as logical treatment will permit. The earliest chapters introduce the reader to certain basic concepts. These serve to show that his further progress in stratigraphic thinking cannot be realized without consideration of sedimentary rocks, their properties and classification, and the processes and environments which they represent. These topics, plus an exposition of the role of paleontology in stratigraphy, conclude the descriptive part of the book.

In the last six chapters, the fundamental facts and principles developed earlier are applied to the interpretation of stratigraphic data. These latter chapters explore concepts and fields which remain in an active state of flux as this is written. Therefore, the material must be viewed as a summation of one stage in an evolutionary progression which is far from complete. In this regard, the authors will consider their efforts rewarded if some of the principles expounded herein stimulate the growth of new concepts to replace them.

The present volume represents the combined efforts of the two authors. Their differences in training and experience led naturally to an apportionment of topics to one or the other. In all instances, however, individual chapters were prepared with a view toward continuity.

The level of discussion and the detail of treatment vary from chapter to chapter. Certain topics are treated in a purely descriptive manner, whereas others are given a more detailed analytic discussion. The descriptive approach is used for topics which are adequately discussed in standard textbooks and may be considered part of the common body of geologic knowledge. Here are included descriptions of sedimentary properties and of selected sedimentary rocks. Limitations of space dictate a treatment which is brief yet adequate to serve the book's purpose. Supplementary readings in standard sources are given for further detail.

Topics treated in a more expanded and analytic manner include those which are not adequately discussed in standard reference books, or which are on the forefront of current thought and require more detailed consideration. In this treatment, an effort is made to present the various sides of controversial positions wherever encountered. In as many cases as possible, however, an opinion is expressed, favoring one view or another in order to leave the reader with a clearly defined

case. The critical reader, because of wider knowledge or superior interpretation, will find himself in disagreement with some of the opinions
expressed. For this, the authors offer no apology, but hope that their
treatment is sufficiently objective to leave room for individual interpretation.

An important pedagogical purpose of this book is to acquaint the
student with the standard literature of stratigraphy and sedimentation.
This purpose is accomplished by selected readings from a number of
textbooks and periodicals. Two objectives have been kept in mind. One
is to direct the student's attention to other sources for further information on topics necessarily treated briefly; the other is to make available
to the student other points of view than those discussed in this volume.
It is the authors' hope that this approach will prepare the student more
effectively to develop his own judgment in controversial subjects.

Almost all reference material is cited from American publications,
although an attempt is made to show the influence of European thinking on the development of principles and concepts. For the most part,
the references emphasize publications of the last twenty-five years,
inasmuch as this literature is integrated, by way of bibliographies, with
accounts of earlier developments for the more advanced reader.

Very little space is devoted to purely descriptive stratigraphy, except to illustrate specific topics. It is felt that the application of principles can be made more effective if reference is made by the individual reader or class to stratigraphic sections and conditions in the area
of direct local interest. The burden of supplying the necessary col-
lateral material accordingly lies with the instructor or experienced
reader.

The authors are indebted to many individuals who have aided in
the framing of concepts, the organization of the text, and the gathering
of specific examples for illustration. Particularly are they indebted to
E. C. Dapples and other colleagues in the Department of Geology at
Northwestern University, and to F. J. Pettijohn of the University of
Chicago. The authors have benefited immeasurably from informal discussions with many petroleum geologists. It is not possible to render
individual credit to these numerous individuals, but it is hoped that
they will not be disappointed by the form in which their contributions
have been integrated and expressed. The authors are also indebted
to Mrs. C. L. Neigh for her excellent drafting of many illustrations in
this book.

An expression of gratitude is due Northwestern University, the Gulf
Oil Corporation, and the Phillips Petroleum Company for relief from

obligations to permit completion of this manuscript. The final form of the volume is due in no little measure to the efforts of W. H. Freeman and Company who have given the authors every cooperation and have been responsible for the arduous tasks of editing and book manufacture.

W. C. Krumbein

L. L. Sloss

Evanston, Illinois
November 1950

Contents

CHAPTER 1

Introduction

SCOPE OF STRATIGRAPHY AND SEDIMENTATION

Stratigraphy

STRATIGRAPHY is defined in the opening paragraph of Grabau's (1913) monumental *Principles of Stratigraphy* as "The inorganic side of historical geology, or the development through the successive geologic ages of the earth's rocky framework or *lithosphere*." The definition reflects the original concept of stratigraphy as the branch of geologic science concerned with the description, organization, and classification of stratified rocks.

The emphasis which Grabau placed on organic processes and organic factors in his book widened his definition and indicates that the scope of the science had already broadened to include most of paleontology beyond systematics and descriptive morphology. In succeeding decades the scope of the science has continued to enlarge. It may now be considered as the integrating discipline which combines data from almost all other branches of earth science in a form from which historical geology emerges as a natural product. During much of the past century and a half, the greater part of stratigraphic effort has, of necessity, been directed toward compiling data on and describing the vast volume of sedimentary rocks of the earth's crust.

Prior to World War I, stratigraphers were engaged principally in the descriptive stratigraphy of rocks observable in outcrop. This phase continues today and is still far from completion. In the past four decades, and with gathering momentum, the body of descriptive stratigraphy has been further increased by the addition of enormous volumes of data on subsurface strata, largely as a result of oil exploration and exploitation.

Past generations of stratigraphers, although primarily engrossed in the task of description, developed a number of significant principles applicable to the interpretation and analysis of sedimentary data. Many of these principles remain useful today; others, which were valid working hypotheses at one stage of stratigraphic knowledge, have failed the test of time as new data accumulated to challenge them. The influx of subsurface information, plus the development of new techniques and tools for the analysis of sedimentary materials, has required critical re-examination of time-honored concepts. In recent years, stratigraphers have been forced to modify or discard a number of earlier guiding principles, sometimes at a rate faster than they could be replaced by more acceptable ideas.

However, the re-evaluation of old principles and the consideration of new concepts have been greatly aided by the publication of several stratigraphic syntheses in book form, which are listed at the end of this chapter. Readers will note a significant difference in emphasis and interpretation between this book and others in the field. These divergences in approach and concept are symptomatic of the current healthy state of flux which exists in stratigraphy and sedimentation. A continuing period of competing and even conflicting interpretations must be expected before it will be possible to discriminate unequivocally between sound and unsound hypotheses and practices. In the meantime it should be clear to the reader that in a rapidly changing science the accepted principles of today may become the historical references of tomorrow.

Students as well as experienced professionals are obliged to inquire into the many possible conflicting positions on controversial topics expressed in parallel texts. No attempt is made in this book to crystallize the essentially fluid state of stratigraphic and sedimentologic thought; rather, an effort is made to provide a framework of sufficient flexibility to accommodate the current and future advances in data gathering and analysis which will guide the evolution of new concepts. If the approach shows merit, it will be due to the equal consideration being given to surface and subsurface geology.

Sedimentation

In a strict sense, sedimentation refers to the processes responsible for the formation of sedimentary rocks, including the origin, transportation, and deposition of rock-forming materials, their diagenesis and lithification. In the broader sense commonly implied, sedimentation encompasses sedimentary petrology and sedimentary petrography, which together cover the study, description, classification, and interpretation of sedimentary rocks.

Inasmuch as sedimentary rocks are the fundamental materials of stratigraphy, the stratigrapher is more dependent on sedimentation than on other contributing fields, with paleontology ranking as a close second. The prominent place accorded sedimentation and the lesser coverage of paleontology in this text reflect the fact that the undergraduate training of most geologists is lacking in basic sedimentation, whereas paleontology usually receives adequate attention. Therefore, emphasis is placed on those aspects of sedimentation having a direct application to stratigraphy and stratigraphic concepts.

The close relationship between sedimentation and stratigraphy is clarified by comparison with the relationship between biology and paleontology. Biology is primarily concerned with organic processes and organic patterns operating at present. Organic processes and patterns operating through geologic time have produced a paleontologic record which must be interpreted by application of biological principles. Similarly, the study of the processes governing the formation and distribution of recent sediments establishes the guiding principles used in interpreting ancient sedimentary rocks. The stratigraphic record is largely the result of the continuity of sedimentary processes through the dimension of geologic time.

The study of sediments and sedimentary processes has made great strides in recent years. New techniques have been developed for analysis of the dynamic, physicochemical, and biochemical behavior of sedimentary materials in transport and after deposition. These advances have been paralleled by the refinement of methods for measuring and quantifying a wide variety of physical and chemical attributes of sediments. In addition, the growing field of oceanographic research has provided an abundance of data to aid in the explanation of complex sedimentary patterns. It is the stratigrapher's task to apply these newer approaches to an integrated interpretation of ancient sedimentary rocks.

Academic versus Applied Stratigraphy

There has been a tendency toward a well defined cleavage between "academic" stratigraphy and "practical" or "applied" stratigraphy. Academically, the science has been directed toward analysis of the sedimentary record in terms of the reconstruction of geologic history and the description and nomenclature of various stratigraphic units. Applied stratigraphy was thought to be confined to the recognition and location, in favorable positions, of rock units associated with mineral products.

Today, the barrier between these two apparently disparate endeavors has all but disappeared. Many of the principles and concepts considered to be of purely academic interest are found to be directly applicable to the solution of practical problems. With the recognition of intensive stratigraphic research as a valid approach to oil finding, the practicing stratigraphers are among the most active in developing advanced stratigraphic concepts and principles.

ARRANGEMENT OF SUBJECT MATTER

Physical Stratigraphy and Biostratigraphy

The subject matter of the science of stratigraphy is conveniently, if somewhat artificially, divisible into two major parts, as shown in Table 1-1. **Physi-**

TABLE 1-1. COMPONENTS OF STRATIGRAPHY

PHYSICAL STRATIGRAPHY	BIOSTRATIGRAPHY
Observation and organization	
Stratigraphic column	Biostratigraphic column
Sedimentary petrology	Paleontology
Properties of sedimentary particles	Morphology
Properties of sedimentary aggregates	Properties of fossil assemblages
Classification of sediments	Classification of organisms
Sedimentary processes	Biologic processes
Analysis	
Lithologic correlation	Biostratigraphic correlation
Time-stratigraphic correlation	
Sedimentary tectonics	Organic evolution
Interpretation and synthesis	
Paleogeography	

cal stratigraphy includes all the components of sedimentation plus the physical aspects of analytical interpretative stratigraphy. **Biostratigraphy** comprises the numerous phases of biology and paleontology applicable to stratigraphic studies.

As this table indicates, practically all the components of physical stratigraphy are paralleled by analogous components in biostratigraphy. However, an important distinction must be drawn. According to the principle of uniformitarianism, it may be assumed that the materials of physical stratigraphy have remained relatively constant throughout geologic time and have responded uniformly to physical and chemical processes. The organic materials of biostratigraphy, on the other hand, have changed progressively during geologic time, under the influence of organic evolution.

Organization of Stratigraphic Data

The solution of a stratigraphic problem begins with the systematic observation and organization of the basic materials (Table 1-1), namely, the successions of sedimentary rock observable in outcrop or made available by well drilling. The history and current practice followed in organization and classification of the stratigraphic column are covered in Chapter 2.

For the reader who lacks experience and training in the various techniques used in gathering stratigraphic information, these are outlined in Chapter 3.

In Chapters 4 and 5, the properties, composition, and classification of sediments and sedimentary rocks are discussed. It is assumed that the reader has a working knowledge of elementary paleontology; for this reason the equivalent discussion of the biostratigraphic parallels to these sedimentary subjects in Table 1-1 is omitted.

The fundamental background requisite to the organization of sedimentary materials must include knowledge of the process of sedimentation as well as certain biological factors important to stratigraphy, and must include a survey of the physical and biological attributes of sedimentary environments. These topics are discussed in Chapters 6, 7, and 8.

Analytical Stratigraphy

Stratigraphic analysis involves the integration of data derived from description and organization. Such integration makes use of fundamental principles which aid in the conversion of raw data to a form amenable to interpretation. The more analytical aspects of stratigraphic investigation are introduced in Chapter 9 through consideration of vertical and lateral relationships among bodies of strata. This complex topic requires integration of much of the material in earlier chapters and is a basic prerequisite to comprehension of the complex problems of stratigraphic correlation. Correlation, the demonstration of equivalency of stratigraphic units, is discussed in Chapter 10.

The tectonic behavior of the earth's crust influences the thickness and character of accumulating sediments. The nature of the tectonic framework of sedimentation, and the integration of principles of tectonic geology with the theoretical and applied approaches to sedimentary tectonics, are presented in Chapter 11.

Chapter 12 is devoted to the consideration of numerous types of stratigraphic maps, the techniques of three-dimensional stratigraphic mapping, and the applications of these techniques to stratigraphic problems. A number of natural associations have been shown to exist among sedimentary rocks of varying types. These lithologic associations and their implications are explored in Chapter 13 as the culminating stage in analysis and presentation of stratigraphic data.

Interpretative Stratigraphy

Most stratigraphic studies are undertaken to solve some problem, or combination of problems, in paleogeography, historical geology, or economic geology. Interpretative stratigraphy is the final phase of study in which data previously gathered, organized, and analyzed are subjected to interpretation and synthesis. It is noteworthy that the words chosen by Grabau in 1913 as the final paragraph of *Principles of Stratigraphy* remain appropriate today:

"When the science of Stratigraphy has developed so that its basis is no longer purely or chiefly palaeontological, and when the sciences of Lithogenesis [sedimentation], of Orogenesis and of Glyptogenesis [gradation], as well as of Biogenesis, are given their due share in the comprehensive investigation of the history of our earth, then we may hope that Palaeogeography, the youthful daughter science of Stratigraphy, will have attained unto that stature which will make it the crowning attraction to the student of earth history."

BIBLIOGRAPHIC REFERENCES

Much of the subject matter of this book is taken from papers scattered throughout an extensive and growing scientific literature. References to significant papers are given throughout the text, and these references are arranged in a comprehensive bibliography, by chapters, at the end of the book. In addition, each chapter closes with a short annotated bibliography of supplementary reading.

Readers, especially students, should bear in mind the rapidity with which new data and revised concepts enter the fields of stratigraphy and sedimentation. The bibliography directs attention to the more important papers which appeared prior to the end of 1961. The reader should frequently review the literature for papers which supplement, modify, or replace concepts and principles which become out-dated by newer data.

The standard references, used throughout the book for supplementary reading, include works which should be available during the reading of the text. The following five books are the most frequently used sources:

1. Dunbar, C. O. and Rodgers, J., 1957, Principles of stratigraphy: New York, Wiley. (An intermediate-level text by distinguished authorities. Of particular value to readers for its excellent treatment of sedimentary environments and for its well expressed concepts and practices, many of which are at variance with those of the present authors.)
2. Lombard, A., 1956, Geologie sedimentaire; les series marines: Paris, Masson et Cie. (A well-documented and thoroughly illustrated synthesis of sedimentation and stratigraphy of particular significance to North American readers as an easily understood example of a European point of view.)
3. Pettijohn, F. J., 1957, Sedimentary rocks (2nd edition): New York, Harper. (The definitive advanced-level text and reference on sediments and sedimentary rocks, their description, classification, and interpretation. Several of the chapters in the present book have been profoundly influenced by the Pettijohn text, and readers will find repeated reference to expanded treatment of topics which cannot be fully discussed here.)
4. Twenhofel, W. H., 1950, Principles of sedimentation: New York, McGraw-Hill. (An intermediate-level textbook on sedimentary rocks and sedimentary processes; noteworthy as the culminating work of a master of American stratigraphy and sedimentation and as an exemplar of a more classical but by no means obsolete school of description and interpretation.)
5. Weller, J. M., 1960, Stratigraphic principles and practice: New York, Harper.

(An advanced-level text and reference work covering many of the same topics as the present book. Weller's text represents an integration and synthesis by an outstanding worker who has gained wide experience with both the physical and biological aspects of stratigraphy. Certain of the interpretations expressed differ markedly from those of the present book and so provide excellent examples of divergent views.)

CHAPTER 2

The Stratigraphic Column

INTRODUCTION

SEDIMENTARY rocks are the basic materials of the science of stratigraphy. Natural outcrops, excavations, quarries, mines, and well bores serve to make these materials abundantly available for study. There are over 40 million square miles of surface exposure of sedimentary rocks, and an enormous mass of stratigraphic data has accumulated, although but a small percentage of this area is known in geologic detail. This mass constantly grows as more areas are explored stratigraphically and as new data from the continental shelves and marine basins are added to the record.

Exploration for mineral resources, and their exploitation, brings to light vast quantities of stratigraphic information. Oil-well drilling accounts for nearly 60,000 wells penetrating more than 45,000 miles of sediment each year in the United States and Canada alone.

It is the task of the stratigrapher to assemble and integrate this mountain of information so that it can make a useful contribution to earth science. Such assembly and integration require three logical steps. First, the succession of sedimentary rocks which forms the **stratigraphic column** of each area must be established. Second, the stratigraphic column must be subdivided and differentiated into significant and useful units. Third, these units and the physical and biologic events they represent must be related to their proper positions in terms of geologic history.

The first step, compilation of the stratigraphic column, is a familiar operation to all geologists and needs no direct discussion at this point. Certain aspects are more appropriately covered in the following chapter and in Chapter 10. The present chapter is primarily concerned with the more controversial subjects of subdivision of the stratigraphic column and the relationship of the subdivisions to the geologic-time scale.

EVOLUTION OF STRATIGRAPHIC CLASSIFICATION

The terminology and many of the concepts employed today in subdivision of the stratigraphic column are legacies from a time when detailed geologic information was very scanty. It is necessary to review the historical evolution of nomenclature and theory in order to evaluate properly their significance today and the modifications required in the light of expanded knowledge.

Early Concepts

So far as the advancement of stratigraphic geology is concerned, the Dark Ages persisted well into the middle of the eighteenth century. Perhaps this retarded renaissance of scientific interest may be explained by the dominating influence on prevailing thought patterns of a strict interpretation of the *Book of Genesis*. Under this influence, all of geologic time was considered to amount to but a few thousand years; sediments were ascribed to the action of the Biblical Flood; and fossils were variously interpreted as evidence of creatures engulfed by the Flood, inventions of the Devil, or "figured stones."

As early as the latter half of the seventeenth century, scientific observers such as Steno, in Italy, and Hooke, in England, came close to a correct interpretation of the meaning of fossils and recognized the chronologic significance of successions of strata. (An interesting account of the period in the history of geology is given by Schneer, 1954.) However, the philosophical climate of the times did not foster a wide interest in the materials of the earth's crust, except in the search for useful minerals. Radical speculation was not encouraged, and little progress was made toward the development of stratigraphy.

First Attempts at Organization

In the latter half of the eighteenth century, a new age of enlightenment dawned, and, with it, a developing interest in man's physical surroundings, including stratified rocks. It is natural that men responsible for quarrying, coal and metal mining, and the exploitation of other mineral resources should be the first to recognize a need for working hypotheses to guide their exploration and production efforts. The writings of the time record several attempts to coordinate the data on sedimentary rocks made available by mining and quarrying operations and to express these data in logical terms.

Lehmann, Arduino, and Füchsel. Review of the scientific literature of the 1750's and 1760's reveals some of the more significant groping efforts toward a rational organization of stratigraphic materials. Among the earliest of these efforts is the work of Johann Gottlob Lehmann, a German mineralogist and mining engineer. In 1756 he published a classification of the rocks of the earth's crust, dividing them into three categories:

1. Crystalline rocks devoid of fossils and believed to be of chemical origin prior to the advent of life. These were designated by a term which may be translated as *primitive*.
2. *Secondary* rocks, fossiliferous and stratified, and containing particles eroded from older rocks.
3. Loosely consolidated surficial sands and gravels, termed *alluvial*.

It is now obvious that the connotations of relative age according to lithology implicit in Lehmann's classification are not necessarily valid. That is, types included in his primitive and secondary categories are known from all positions in the stratigraphic column. Nevertheless, the classification provided a generalized framework for the orderly study and treatment of rocks and was, therefore, a significant advance in constructive thinking.

Giovanni Arduino, Italian professor and provincial Director of Mines, appears to have been the first to apply the terms *primitive, secondary,* and *tertiary* to groupings of strata in the stratigraphic succession. He demonstrated the widespread applicability of the groupings as well as the age relationships among them.

Georg Christian Füchsel, German physician, identified and traced on a map eight "formations" or "series" of strata forming a stratigraphic succession above the crystalline rocks of the Harz Mountains and Thuringian Forest. Each grouping of strata was described in terms of its lithology and paleontology, and each was ascribed to a distinct portion of geologic time.

Werner and Neptunism. These generalizations as to the relative ages of the various rock types of the earth's crust were adopted by Abraham Gottlob Werner, the highly influential professor at the Freiberg Mining Academy. Werner was the first great organizer of geologic materials and is responsible for bringing at least a semblance of order out of the chaotic hodgepodge of mineralogic, petrologic, and stratigraphic data available to his generation. Although he published very little, his brilliant lectures dominated geologic thought during the last quarter of the eighteenth and early decades of the nineteenth centuries.

The basic concept of Werner's geologic philosophy was belief in an all-encompassing ocean which gradually receded to its present proportions while precipitating and forming all of the materials visible in the earth's crust. Because of the emphasis on an oceanic derivation for all rocks and minerals, Werner and his followers were known as the "Neptunists."

By the late 1790's, Werner had modified Lehmann's classification as follows:

1. *Primitive (Urgebirge) series.* Including what are now recognized as intrusive igneous rocks and high-rank metasediments. These were considered the first chemical precipitates derived from the ocean before emergence of land areas.
2. *Transition (Übergangsgebirge) series.* Composed of thoroughly indurated limestones, dikes and sills, and thick graywackes. These were considered the first orderly deposits formed from the ocean. With the Primitive rocks, they were thought to be "universal" in extent, extending without interruption around the world.
3. *Stratified (Flötz) series*, more commonly termed *Secondary*. Here were included the majority of obviously stratified fossiliferous rocks, plus certain associated "trap rocks." The "Flötzgebirge" were thought to represent the emergence of mountains from beneath the receding ocean, with products of the resulting erosion deposited on the flanks of the mountains.
4. *Alluvial (Aufgeschwemmte) series*, called *Tertiary* by some contemporaries. Poorly consolidated sands, gravels, and clays formed after the withdrawal of the ocean from the continents.
5. *Volcanic series.* Added more or less as an afterthought to include younger lava flows demonstrably associated with volcanic vents. Werner placed slight importance on these rocks and considered them to be merely the local effects of burning coal beds.

Werner's students applied the Neptunist concept to geologic observations throughout Europe, the more obdurate remaining steadfast in a rigid interpretation of Neptunism, even where simple objective analysis of field relationships indicated the inadequacies of the doctrine.

There is some evidence that the overwhelming dominance of Werner's views acted to retard the development of stratigraphy, since it required reference of all stratigraphic data to an unnatural framework of classification. It seems more probable, however, that the violent controversies precipitated by Neptunism greatly stimulated the gathering and study of volumes of field data that might otherwise have remained untouched for another generation.

Hutton, Uniformitarianism, and Superposition

James Hutton, a Scottish contemporary of Werner, is responsible for several of the basic principles of stratigraphy. Hutton approached geologic problems in a much more scientific and less dogmatic manner than employed by Werner, but he seems to have been a less inspiring personality, and his findings were long obscured by the dominant Neptunist philosophy.

By a combination of laboratory experiment and observation of field relationships, Hutton proved conclusively that many of the igneous rocks, which Werner insisted were marine precipitates, were cooled from a molten state. Since subterranean heat was invoked as the means of melting rocks, this concept was labeled "Plutonism." Geologic literature of the late eighteenth and early nineteenth centuries records the long and heated controversy which arose between proponents of Plutonism and Neptunism.

As a student of sedimentary processes observable in the streams, lakes, and seacoasts of his native Scotland, Hutton recognized that many of the features of ancient sediments were duplicated in modern unconsolidated deposits. These and other studies led to establishment of the principle of **uniformitarianism** which states that the "present is the key to the past," and that conditions responsible for ancient geologic phenomena are the same conditions prevailing today.

Hutton's observations of accumulating sediments demonstrated the fact that, in a sequence of strata, the older beds are successively covered by younger and younger layers. This relationship, first clearly stated by Hutton and implicit in the principle of **superposition,** is basic to most stratigraphic thinking. In Hutton's time, however, the principle was considered quite radical by geologists influenced by the Wernerian concept of oceanic precipitation above, below, or within, older rocks.

Smith and Applied Stratigraphy

During these same critical years near the turn of the eighteenth century, the science of stratigraphy was significantly advanced by William Smith, a modest and untutored English engineer: Smith paid little heed to the arguments between Neptunists and Plutonists, if, indeed, he was aware that such disputes existed. Instead, Smith demonstrated that earth-moving projects, such as canal digging and road building, were made more efficient by taking into account the stratigraphy of the terrain to be crossed.

To this end, he studied the succession of sedimentary rocks exposed in his area of interest and established a stratigraphic column subdivided into rock units. Each of these units was recognizable over broad areas by a combination of lithologic characteristics and fossil assemblages. Smith traced and mapped his units, much as he was accustomed to mapping other physical features such as streams and ridges, and prepared the first geologic maps of regional scope.

Smith's stratigraphic and mapping efforts culminated in 1815 with publication of his *Geological map of England and Wales, with part of Scotland,* showing the areal distribution of thirty-one major rock units and many subdivisions.

Lyell's Principles of Geology

Further stratigraphic investigation in England and on the Continent, plus the work of such men as Cuvier and Lamarck, who conclusively demonstrated the relationship between stratigraphic succession and paleontology, finally laid the ghost of Neptunism. The first edition of Charles Lyell's pioneer textbook, *Principles of Geology*, completed in 1833, presented a stratigraphic column which is reproduced in the first column of Table 2-1.

Lyell adopted Smith's rock units and added a few others from the Continent. The units were arranged in order of superposition and assigned to "groups" as indicated. The "groups," in turn, were subdivisions of higher categories termed "periods." It is interesting to note that terminology of the Wernerian school persisted in designation of the periods as "Primary," "Secondary," and "Tertiary."

Growth of the Catastrophist Concept

Lyell's classification set the pattern to be followed for the next 100 years. The "groups" recognized by Lyell were more commonly referred to as "systems" by other geologists and considered as fundamental groupings of strata designated by lithology (Oolitic System) or by locality of typical exposure (Jurassic System).

As the systems were identified over broad areas and their sequence established, a clear concept of the relative ages of the major rock units emerged. Gradually, the systems, which were proposed as units in a rock classification, developed an additional significance in time classification. The faunas of each of these systems were becoming well known, and it appeared that each system was represented by a group of animals and plants quite different from those above and below. It was natural, therefore, to consider each rock system an episode of earth history which closed in some sort of cataclysm, eliminating most plants and animals and paving the way for the introduction of new and different types in the rocks of the succeeding systems.

This catastrophist philosophy was supported by the occurrence of lithologic discontinuities—unconformities and other evidences of change—at system boundaries, these being the phenomena which made natural units of the systems in their type areas.

Under these circumstances, what could be more logical than a belief in repeated and synchronous changes in both physical and biological conditions? Whether one believed in repeated special creation or in the heretical evolutionary hypotheses of Lamarck, the systems appeared to represent periods of time closed by catastrophies, and separated from one another by "lost intervals" during which new species evolved or were created. Thus a strong belief developed in the principle that unconformities and lithologic discontinuities in the stratigraphic sequence represent recognizable and universal dates on the geologic calendar.

TABLE 2-1. EVOLUTION OF STRATIGRAPHIC CLASSIFICATION

	1. LYELL 1833	2. PHILLIPS 1838	3. LYELL 1872	4. DANA 1880	5. MILLER 1889
TERTIARY PERIOD / RECENT PERIOD	Newer Pliocene	TERTIARY STRATA	Post-Tertiary (TERTIARY OR CAINOZOIC)	Quaternary (CENOZOIC)	Post-Pliocene (CAENOZOIC)
	Older Pliocene		Pliocene	Tertiary	Pliocene
	Miocene		Miocene		Miocene
	Eocene		Eocene		Eocene
SECONDARY PERIOD	Cretaceous / Wealden	Cretaceous system	Cretaceous (SECONDARY OR MESOZOIC)	Cretaceous (MESOZOIC)	Cretaceous system (MESOZOIC)
	Oolite or Jura limestone group	Oolitic system	Jurassic	Jurassic	Jurassic system
	Lias				
	New red sandstone group	Red sandstone system	Triassic	Triassic	Triassic system
			Permian		
Carboniferous group	Coal measures	(SECONDARY STRATA)	Carboniferous (PRIMARY OR PALAEOZOIC)	Carboniferous (PALEOZOIC)	Carboniferous system (PALAEOZOIC)
	Mountain limestone	Carboniferous system			Subcarboniferous system
	Old red sandstone		Devonian	Devonian (PALEOZOIC)	Devonian system
	Grauwacke and Transition limestone	Silurian system (PRIMARY STRATA)	Silurian	Silurian	Upper Silurian system
PRIMARY PERIOD		Grauwacke system	Cambrian		Lower Silurian system
		Clay-slate system		Eozoic (ARCHAEAN)	Taconic system (AZOIC)
		Mica-schist system			
		Gneiss system	Laurentian	Azoic	Laurentian system

TABLE 2-1. (Continued)

6. CHAMBERLIN and SALISBURY 1905	7. SCHUCHERT 1910	8. ULRICH 1911	9. GRABAU 1913	10. PRESENT USAGE
CENOZOIC Present / Pleistocene — / Pliocene / Miocene / Oligocene / Eocene	**NEOZOIC, TERTIARY OR CENOZOIC** Neogenic / Eogenic	**CENOZOIC** Recent / Pleistocene — / Neogenic — / Eogenic	**PSYCHOZOIC OR QUATERNARY** Quaternary — **CENOZOIC OR TERTIARY** Tertiary	**CENOZOIC** Quaternary / Neogene — / Tertiary — / Paleogene
MESOZOIC Cretaceous / Comanchean — Jurassic — Triassic	Cretacic period / Comanchic period — Jurassic period — Triassic period	Cretaceous / Comanchean — Newark or Jura-Triassic — **MESOZOIC**	**MESOZOIC OR SECONDARY** Cretacic / Comanchic — Jurassic — Triassic	**MESOZOIC** Cretaceous — Jurassic — Triassic
PALEOZOIC Permian — Coal measures or Pennsylvanian — Subcarboniferous or Mississippian — **NEOPALEOZOIC** Devonian — Silurian — Ordovician — Cambrian	**NEOPALEOZOIC** Pennsylvanic – Permic period — Tennesseic period / Mississippic period — Devonic period — Siluric or Ontaric period — Cincinnatic period / Ordovicic period / Canadic period / Ozarkic period / Acadic period / Georgic period **PALEOZOIC**	Pennsylvanian — Tennessean / Waverlyan **NEOPALEOZOIC** Devonian — Silurian — Ordovician — Canadian Ozarkian / Cambrian **EUPALEOZOIC**	**PALAEOZOIC OR PRIMARY FOSSILIFEROUS OR TRANSITION** Permic — Carbonic — Mississippic — Devonic — Siluric — Ordovicic — Cambric	**PALEOZOIC** Permian — Pennsylvanian — Mississippian — Devonian — Silurian — Ordovician — Cambrian
PROTEROZOIC Keweenawan / Animikean / Huronian **ARCHEOZOIC** Archean complex	**PROTEROZOIC** — **ARCHEOZOIC**	**PROTEROZOIC** — **ARCHEOZOIC**	**PROTEROZOIC (EOZOIC)** Keweenawic / Huronic **AZOIC (ARCHAEOZOIC)** Laurentic / Keewatic	**PRECAMBRIAN** Regionally defined systems

Diastrophism as the Basis of Correlation

Much of the stratigraphic work in western Europe and eastern North America indicated that unconformities or lithologic changes exist, which make possible the physical delineation of the rock systems over wide areas. Such delineation was thought possible at the same stratigraphic horizons at which unconformities were known to bound the systems in the areas of their original designation. Thus, stratigraphers in New York, with only minor discrepancies, were able to identify widespread discontinuities of lithology and fauna to match the physical and biologic breaks separating the systems established in Great Britain.

Concurrent studies showed the stratigraphy of much of western Europe to be amenable to similar divisions. As the natural outgrowth of these findings of widespread synchronous unconformities, a belief in nearly universal orogenic episodes developed, which involved great areas simultaneously and served as the punctuation marks of geologic history.

Thus, the catastrophist hypothesis of an episodic geologic history was linked to the concept of intermittent epochs of universal orogeny or epeirogeny, during which continents were abruptly uplifted, seas withdrawn, mountain ranges formed, and biologic changes initiated. So strong was the evidence supporting this concept that it was thought that the best method of correlation of strata from place to place was with reference to unconformities, and diastrophism became "the ultimate basis of correlation" (Chamberlin, 1909).

Further Subdivision of the Stratigraphic Column

Silurian. Lyell's original classification placed certain fossiliferous strata below the Old Red sandstone and above the Primary crystallines in the Carboniferous Group of the Secondary Period. These rocks, the "fossiliferous graywackes" and "transition limestones" (note the Neptunist term), were jointly attacked by Sedgwick and Murchison in the 1830's. Murchison, starting at the base of the Old Red, outlined and described the Silurian System with sufficient clarity to influence the classification of the stratigraphic column published by Phillips in 1838 (see Table 2-1, col. 2).

Cambrian. Sedgwick, working up from the top of the basement complex, was more hesitant about rushing into print with a new system and named the Cambrian only after urging by Murchison. A dispute soon arose between the two friends as to the common boundary between their systems. No physical or paleontologic hiatus acceptable to both parties could be established, and the heated controversy raged in scientific meetings and in the literature for thirty years.

Apparently, Murchison was the more successful in presenting his case, since the Silurian reached wide application before the Cambrian was generally recognized as a valid system.

Ordovician. The issue was eventually settled in 1879 by Lapworth, who proposed the rather arbitrary erection of the Ordovician System between Cambrian and Silurian. This compromise achieved little recognition by American stratigraphers, who generally ignored the Ordovician until the end of the nineteenth century. Today, continental European stratigraphers prefer to treat the Ordovician as a series within the Silurian, while some Scandinavian workers subordinate both Cambrian and Ordovician as subdivisions of a great Silurian System.

Devonian. Sedgwick and Murchison, before they were parted by the Cambrian-Silurian question, demonstrated that a "system" of strata existed in western England, faunally distinct and separated by profound unconformities from the Silurian below and Carboniferous above. These beds they termed the Devonian System from exposures of fossiliferous marine strata in Devonshire. Tracing of the bounding unconformities to the north showed that the Old Red sandstone exhibited the same relationships and was thus part of the same system, even though it was quite distinct lithologically from the type marine Devonian.

Proof that a system may change in character from area to area, while maintaining constant relationships to unconformities and other evidences of diastrophism, served to strengthen belief in the infallibility of unconformities as universal guides to subdivision of the stratigraphic column.

The Eras

With the establishment of the Paleozoic systems noted above, the major stratigraphic units of western Europe were essentially outlined, the prominent unconformities recognized, and no further "systems" were required on physical or paleontologic grounds.

Rapid strides in stratigraphic paleontology indicated significant differences in the organisms of the Primary, Secondary, and Tertiary groups of systems. The Primary systems were found to be dominated by invertebrates and fishes, the Secondary by ammonites and reptiles, and the Tertiary by advanced mollusks and mammals. Moreover, these groups of strata appeared to be separated by unusually severe diastrophic episodes. In recognition of these factors, the times of accumulation of these groups of systems became known as "eras" of geologic history, and the terms "Paleozoic," "Mesozoic," and "Cenozoic" (with variations in spelling) were used to reflect the biologic character of each era.

Effects of Expanded Stratigraphic Exploration

As stratigraphic studies spread from England and western Europe over the rest of the Continent and to North America, previously unknown unconformities, units of strata, and fossil assemblages were encountered. It was natural that these findings should lead to the establishment of new systems and attempts to distinguish such new divisions in the areas of classical study. Table 2-1 charts the evolution of classification of the stratigraphic column from Lyell to the form now generally accepted by American stratigraphers.

By the time of publication of the Chamberlin and Salisbury text in 1905, classification and nomenclature had reached an essentially modern state. Detailed work in the Canadian Shield had led to differentiation of pre-Cambrian rocks and recognition of the Archeozoic and Proterozoic eras to represent the time of formation of pre-Paleozoic rocks formerly included in the Primary. The Cambrian-Silurian problem was effectively settled and the Permian System, established by Murchison in Russia in 1841, was widely applied, although the limits of the system were frequently debated.

American stratigraphers, impressed by unconformities and lithologic and paleontologic differences within the Carboniferous and Cretaceous, introduced and employed Mississippian, Pennsylvanian, and Comanchean as additional systems. The Chamberlin-Salisbury classification makes no reference to Tertiary, treating Lyell's Tertiary units and the additional Oligocene and Pleistocene as systems of the Cenozoic.

Continued work in America, particularly the efforts of E. O. Ulrich (1911) in the Ohio and Mississippi valleys and in the Ozark uplift, demonstrated the inadequacies of the accepted systems as fundamental subdivisions of rocks and time when applied to regions remote from the classical areas. Prominent unconformities were not found where paleontology indicated systemic boundaries should occur, and several major hiatuses were noted within the confines of single systems.

In order to satisfy these conditions, new classifications were proposed as fast as data accumulated to support them. Columns 7 and 8 of Table 2-1 illustrate the apex of the early twentieth century wave of subdivision. Note that Schuchert (1910) recognized eleven Paleozoic systems and periods without differentiation of the Pennsylvanian and Permian. Ulrich's classification is nearly as complex but ignores the Permian, places the Pennsylvanian in the Mesozoic, and lumps Triassic and Jurassic together.

PRESENT-DAY CLASSIFICATIONS

It soon became apparent that new systems established to satisfy stratigraphic patterns in one area created new problems on attempted application to other areas. The trend of the past fifty years, therefore, has been toward a simplified classification, retaining the classical systems with elimination or subordination of most of the systems proposed early in the century.

Grabau's classification of 1913 (Table 2-1, col. 9) represents one of the last efforts to continue usage of "Primary," "Secondary," etc., in a rational manner. Grabau used these terms in conjunction with the more familiar era designations ("Mesozoic or Secondary"), apparently in an attempt to justify retention of the terms "Tertiary" and "Quaternary." Use of the "-ic" suffix on system names in this column and in the earlier classification by Schuchert reflects a short-lived and generally ignored ruling of the International Geological Congress in 1900.

As Dunbar (1960, p. 352) has noted, "the words Tertiary and Quaternary are vestiges of a misconception long since outgrown, and they should be abandoned." Nevertheless, the terms persist; and "Tertiary," in particular, seems too deeply entrenched in current stratigraphic literature to permit early eradication. Shorn of its original significance, the term remains as valid and useful as "Triassic" or "Cretaceous." Column 10 of Table 2-1 reflects current North American usage; note the spelling of "Precambrian" and the abandonment of continent-wide application of Precambrian subdivisions.

NEED FOR REVISED CONCEPTS OF CLASSIFICATION

It is hoped that the preceding paragraphs have demonstrated to the reader that current concepts and terminology applied to classification of the stratigraphic column are the products of two centuries of gradual evolution. There is no justification for belief that this evolutionary process is now complete and that no further changes may be anticipated. Mid-twentieth century stratigraphers may consider themselves fortunate if their concepts withstand the test of restrospection as well as those of Hutton and Lyell.

As this book is written, the science of stratigraphy is in as great a state of flux as that precipitated by the expansion of stratigraphic exploration in the latter part of the nineteenth century and early years of the twentieth. Several things contribute to this unstable situation.

Continued Stratigraphic Exploration

Stratigraphic investigations far from the borders of the North Atlantic basin continue to raise problems in terms of the subdivision and classificacation of the stratigraphic column. Sequences of strata and assemblages of fossils unknown in the classical areas continue to replace the "lost intervals" originally considered to be universal punctuation marks of geologic history.

Concurrently, the continued discovery of more and more unconformities on all the continental masses serves to complicate the pattern still further. The German geologist, Stille (1955), for example, recognized forty-two Paleozoic and younger diastrophic episodes. These he believed were applicable to the subdivision of geologic time into relatively brief phases of mountain building and continental uplift, separated by long periods of quiescence.

Impact of Subsurface Data

Practically all of the concepts which modern stratigraphers have inherited from their predecessors are derived from studies of rocks in outcrop. It is obvious, however, that by far the greater volume of the sedimentary rocks is buried and unavailable for surface study. No stratigraphic concept which ignores this great bulk of unexposed strata can be considered complete.

Each year, tens of thousands of wells are drilled in the search for subsurface mineral resources, particularly oil and gas. Each of these wells adds to our stratigraphic knowledge by revealing previously unavailable data, until today the volume of subsurface stratigraphic information derived from drilling exceeds the studied surface data by a wide margin; and the volume is constantly increased as new areas are explored by the drill, and deeper horizons penetrated.

It is quickly apparent to the student of subsurface stratigraphy that the unconformities which may serve to subdivide the stratigraphic column in the outcrop belts become less and less distinguishable as they are traced down-dip from outcrops on the margins of sedimentary basins, until, in many cases, the unconformities disappear entirely. In other cases, where rock units are separated in outcrops by abrupt changes in lithology, complete gradations from one rock type to another are found in the subsurface, and no horizon can be selected with certainty as representing the clear demarcation observed in the surface section.

Moreover, the distinct faunal groupings, compartmented by the extinction and replacement of important faunal elements, disappear or become confused in the sedimentary basins. At the proper stratigraphic position, where the boundary between two systems should be recognizable, the subsurface stratigrapher is likely to encounter a series of transition faunas, including a mixture of supposedly diagnostic elements of both systems. Instead of a sharp break between clearly defined fossil suites, the rocks representing successive periods yield fossils which change gradually from types typical of one period to types indicative of another.

Thus, differences observed in the character of the stratigraphic column from region to region are paralleled by differences between areas of surface exposure and areas occupied by deep sedimentary basins where data are obtained largely from the subsurface.

Tectonic Control

Recent studies indicate that the depositional history of sediments and the character of their enclosed biologic elements are strongly influenced by the structural behavior, the tectonics, of the underlying crust.

Certain areas, the relatively positive or neutral shelves, tend to stand high while adjoining areas are receiving deposition. These higher areas are subject to intermittent deposition and erosion, causing numerous unconformities and hiatuses in the record.

The geosynclines follow a different tectonic pattern, sinking rapidly to receive great volumes of sediments and being repeatedly subject to mountain building, which is represented in the geosynclinal record as a series of marked angular unconformities.

Still another situation prevails in broad sedimentary basins, which sink steadily as their sedimentary filling accumulates. Intermittent emergences which expose the surrounding positive and neutral shelf areas to erosion do not normally affect the basins, and deposition and biologic evolution proceed while adjacent areas are being eroded and their sedimentary records broken. Moreover, the sediments of the basins are not commonly exposed to surface study by erosion, and in many cases their rocks may be studied only by deep drilling.

Hence, of four major environments of deposition, three—the geosynclines, positives, and shelves—bear records punctuated by numerous unconformities and breaks in the biologic record, whereas the fourth—the basins—is characterized by continuous deposition and biological continuity over long periods of time.

Examination of the outcrop areas originally studied in the establishment of the accepted systems makes it apparent that the flanks of positive areas and folded belts of geosynclines supplied most of the data. In fact, these two and the neutral shelves are responsible for the great majority of all outcrop belts of the continents.

Thus, the complex classification of the rock column and divisions of geologic time was developed from studies of stratigraphic sequences broken by numerous self-evident unconformities. With this in mind, it is not remarkable that principles and concepts developed from data obtained in certain tectonic situations fail to satisfy conditions in other tectonic environments, subject to radically different depositional histories and bearing different biologic records.

Department of Geology
New York University

DUAL CLASSIFICATION

From approximately 1930 on, stratigraphers became increasingly aware of the discrepancies between classical approaches to stratigraphic classification and established fact. Practicing stratigraphers in the petroleum industry were among the first to realize that naturally occurring units of strata cannot be forced uniformly into a man-made framework of subdivision and classification. Inasmuch as the patterns of migration and accumulation of oil and gas are dictated by the character and structural attitudes of rock units, it is natural that emphasis was placed on study of these tangible assemblages of strata, rather than on subdivisions representing portions of geologic time.

This tendency led to the development of a **dual classification** with distinct cleavage between consideration of two types of stratigraphic units: (1) objective rock units subject to tracing and mapping on the basis of observable criteria, and (2) groupings of strata differentiated with reference to their position in geologic time.

Stratigraphers in academic circles were less frequently exposed to the problems of conflicting data. Moreover, the concept of diastrophism as the fundamental basis of segmentation of the geologic calendar had proved to be a powerful pedagogical tool, as well as a potent unifying principle in historical geology. It is natural, therefore, that textbooks and the geologic literature were somewhat slower in their acceptance of a dual stratigraphic classification.

An active group of stratigraphers at Stanford University took the lead in formalizing the concept of dual classification, climaxed by a paper by Schenck and Muller (1941), which proposed recognition of the following categories of stratigraphic units:

I. Subdivisions based on position in geologic time, including:
    A. **Time units,** segments of continuous geologic time. (Eras, periods, epochs, and ages.)
    B. **Time-stratigraphic units,**[*] assemblages of strata representing deposition during distinct time units. (Systems, series, and stages.)
II. Mappable assemblages of strata, called **rock units,** distinguished and identified by objective physical criteria observable in the field and in subsurface studies. (Groups, formations, members, etc.)

[*] In their original paper Schenck and Muller (1941) offered "time-rock" as an alternative for "time-stratigraphic." "Time-rock" is concise, unequivocal, and short, and was adopted in the first edition of this book. However, recent usage, particularly that of the American Commission on Stratigraphic Nomenclature, has emphasized "time-stratigraphic" to the virtual exclusion of the shorter term, although it remains as a usable synonym.

The concept of dual stratigraphic classification has now gained general acceptance and its application has led to the resolution of many vexing problems of nomenclature. Wider application has been fostered by critical re-examination of the question of episodic diastrophism and its relation to stratigraphy (Gilluly, 1949; Westoll, 1954), and by fresh appraisal of paleontologic data which tend to refute the principle of universal and periodic changes in the rate of organic evolution (Henbest, 1952).

THE STRATIGRAPHIC COMMISSION

Problems of differentiating and classifying subdivisions of the stratigraphic column have been attacked with renewed vigor in the years following World War II. An American Commission on Stratigraphic Nomenclature, representing geologists from Canada, the United States, and Mexico, has met regularly with a view toward revision of the classical "Stratigraphic Code" as summarized by Ashley, et al., in 1933. The somewhat informal *Notes* published by the Commission (1947 and ff.) are an index to the widely divergent opinions held by active stratigraphers, and an attempt is made to reconcile the many points of view in formal *Reports* issued by the Commission (1947 and ff.). The Commission's work culminated with publication of a revised *Stratigraphic Code* (1961), the essential parts of which are reprinted in the Appendix of this volume.

As in many geologic classifications, the objectives of a codified treatment for differentiation and classification of the stratigraphic column are twofold. The first objective is largely *descriptive* and seeks a basis of agreement regarding the types or varieties of units and classification of major and subordinate units within each type. A well-conceived and mutually agreed upon set of rules, such as the revised *Stratigraphic Code,* can fulfill this primary purpose.

The second objective has a more *interpretive* quality. It involves pursuit of agreement on the geologic implications and the scope and nature of the interpretations which may be derived from each kind of stratigraphic unit. This second objective is more difficult to attain since stratigraphers' ideas regarding the implications of each class of stratigraphic units and the character of the interpretations they permit, strongly influence opinion with respect to the definitions of the units.

Not all stratigraphers will agree that the revised *Stratigraphic Code* is a completely satisfactory framework for the solution of certain problems in which interpretation has an important influence on classification. However, the code is not a rigid document and is subject to modification and emendation as the need becomes recognized. In the meantime, the revised *Code* is an invaluable guide to stratigraphic practice and is a potent force toward the achievement of uniformity in classification and nomenclature on the North American continent.

The terminology used in this book is that of the revised *Stratigraphic Code* as reproduced in the Appendix. In the discussions which follow in this and later chapters, it is assumed that readers have familiarized themselves with the *Code;* expanded treatment is given only to those topics which, because of the necessarily brief wording of the *Code,* require amplification.

EARLY CLASSIFICATIONS AND THEIR IMPLICATIONS

The very real problems of classification and the difficulty of reaching agreement on the types of stratigraphic units are more easily understood if an actual example is studied, first as it was treated in the middle of the last century, then in modern terms. The example is chosen from the relatively uncomplicated stratigraphy of the interior of North America.

The Owen Survey

In 1839 and again in the late 1840's, David Dale Owen and a corps of assistants investigated the geology, geography, and natural history of the area drained by the upper Mississippi and its tributaries, in order to evaluate the resources of the region for the General Land Office. The meat of Owen's mineral and soil evaluation was based on a geologic map, and preparation of the map required the identification and tracing of stratigraphic units.

Rock Units of the Owen Survey. The units recognized by Owen (1852) as mappable subdivisions of the stratigraphic column in the Mississippi Valley area of northeastern Iowa, southeastern Minnesota, and western Wisconsin are listed in Table 2-2.

Note that the names applied to the units by Owen and his party are purely descriptive and are derived from characteristics of lithology, nature of the contained fossils, locality of typical exposure, economic products, and relative position. The names are merely convenient "handles" like those often used informally to identify units of strata during organization of field notes and in discussions among geologists in the course of their work. Similar informal names had long been used by British and Continental stratigraphers (Inferior oolite, Rothliegende, Lingula flags, and others).

The units of strata employed by the Owen Survey are based on strictly tangible features observed in the outcrops and noted in numerous measured sections and diagrammatic lithographs which accompany the Survey report. One of these illustrations, reproduced as Figure 2-1, shows the outcrop char-

TABLE 2-2. STRATIGRAPHIC UNITS MAPPED AND DESCRIBED IN THE UPPER MISSISSIPPI VALLEY BY THE OWEN SURVEY (1839–1850)

Formation 3 (F.3)	*Upper Magnesian Limestone*	F.3.c	Coralline and pentamerous beds.
		F.3.b	Lead-bearing beds.
	St. Peter's Shell Limestone	F.3.a	Shell beds.
Formation 2 (F.2)	*St. Peter's Sandstone*	F.2.c	Sandstone, usually white and incoherent.
	Lower Magnesian Limestone	F.2.b	With veins and segregations of chert and quartz.
		F.2.a	With oolitic layers and green particles disseminated.
Formation 1 (F.1)	*Lower Sandstone*	F.1.f	Quartzose, light-colored sandstones of various degrees of induration, with intercalations of beds of Magnesian Limestone. Mammillary and botryoidal layer of white sandstone (at base). } Sixth trilobite bed
		F.1.e	Thick beds of soft, yellowish and brown sandstone, . . . passing downwards into fine-grained, soft sandstones.
		F.1.d	Ash-colored and yellowish argillocalcareous and magnesiocalcareous beds, containing *Dikelocephalus Minnesotensis*. } Fifth trilobite bed
			Green, red, and yellowish sandstones.
			Upper, brown dolomitic layers, containing *Orthis*, *Lingula*, and crinoid columns.
			Alternations of yellow, laminated sandstones, with green particles disseminated. } Fourth trilobite bed
			Fucoidal layers, and thin-bedded green and yellow sandstones
			Green and red sandstones, charged with silicate of iron.
			Loose, green sand and soft, green sandstone.
			Micaceous sandstone, containing *Dikelocephalus Meniskaensis, D. granulosa*, etc. } Third trilobite bed
			Alternations of green and ferruginous sandstones.
			Thin layers of green sand, alternating with green earth, impregnated with silicate of iron.
			Lower, brown silicocalcareous and dolomitic beds.
			Soft, thin-bedded sandstones with scales of mica disseminated.
		F.1.c	Coarse lingula grit; green, yellow, sometimes almost white.
		F.1.b	Fine grit. White and yellow sandstones. } Second trilobite bed
			Ferruginous Trilobite grits. Schistose sandstone, containing fork-tailed trilobite beds, and *Obolus* layers. } First trilobite bed
			Magnesiocalcareous rock.
			Highly fossiliferous, schistose, silicocalcareous layers, interlaminated with argillaceous, marly beds charged with sulphate of iron, the former being full of *Lingulas* and *Orbiculas*.
		F.1.a	Sandstone, with oblique lines of deposition, alternating with pebbly sandstones and coarse grits.

acteristics of a number of units below the Lower Magnesian Limestone as exposed on a bluff near Winona, Minnesota. Geologists can visit the same exposure today and readily identify the several stratal units recognized by the Owen party over 100 years ago. The original survey group followed the units along the bluffs of the Mississippi (as shown in Figure 2-1) and its tributaries, and by tracing the areal distribution of the units on a base map, a geologic map was prepared. Modern geologic maps of the same area differ only in the detail afforded by numerous subsequent observations and the use of improved base maps.

It is clear that the "formations" and their subdivisions, as established by the Owen Survey, are *tangible units based on locally evident and directly observable data.* A century later, these units, with modifications and refinements in names and boundaries, dictated by a more sophisticated system of classification and by more detailed study, remain as self-evident subdivisions of the local stratigraphic column.

Time-stratigraphic Units of the Owen Survey. Owen's rock, mineral, and fossil units sufficed for purposes of mapping, interpreting geologic structure, and indicating the distribution of soils and mineral resources. They did not establish, however, a relationship between the stratigraphy of the Upper Mississippi Valley and the rest of the stratigraphically explored world.

In the mid-nineteenth century, time-stratigraphic concepts were dominated by the Catastrophist Philosophy. The "systems" described in England by Lyell, Murchison, and Phillips were believed to involve the same successions of strata, paleontologic assemblages, and mineral deposits on all continents with only local and trivial variations. Further, each unit of rocks was thought to maintain a universally fixed position with reference to geologic time. The lead and zinc ores of the Upper Mississippi Valley, for instance, were thought to occupy the same stratigraphic and chronologic position as similar deposits in Wales—and so with the majority of Owen's subdivisions each of which was thought to represent a simultaneous and universally effective event in earth history. Strata were termed "Silurian" because they bore "Silurian fossils," and fossils were ascribed to the "Silurian" because they occurred in strata of the "Silurian System." These practices and concepts were not in obvious conflict with the state of stratigraphic knowledge of the times, and there was little necessity for recognition of the degree to which circular reasoning and inferential thinking were involved.

In this philosophical climate it was only natural that Owen and other pioneers in North American stratigraphy were little concerned with a distinction between stratigraphic units based on tangible, directly observable criteria and subdivisions related to geologic time. Both were considered evidence of the "natural order" of things and equally capable of strictly objective definition. There is no hint of debate or subjectivity in Owen's assignment of the strata between the base of the "Lower Sandstone" and the top of the "Upper Magnesian Limestone" (F.1–F.3) to the "Silurian (or Protozoic, or Primary Fossiliferous) System" of the "Paleozoic Period."

Fig. 2-1. Reproduction of a lithograph accompanying D. D. Owen's (1852) report on the Upper Mississippi Valley area. The figure shows both the succession and the outcrop character of rock units exposed near Winona, Minnesota.

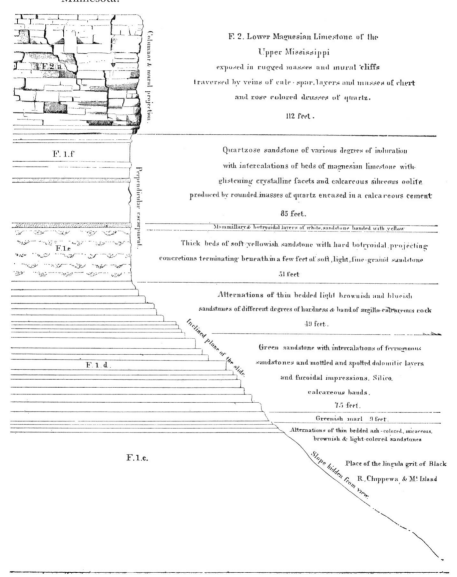

Columnar & mural projection.

F. 2. a

F. 2. Lower Magnesian Limestone of the
Upper Mississippi
exposed in rugged masses and mural cliffs
traversed by veins of calc-spar, layers and masses of chert
and rose colored drusses of quartz.

112 feet.

F. 1. f

Perpendicular escarpment.

Quartzose sandstone of various degrees of induration
with intercalations of beds of magnesian limestone with
glistening crystalline facets and calcareous siliceous oolite
produced by rounded masses of quartz encased in a calcareous cement

85 feet.

Mammillary & botryoidal layers of white sandstone banded with yellow

F. 1. e

Thick beds of soft yellowish sandstone with hard botryoidal projecting
concretions terminating beneath in a few feet of soft, light, fine-grained sandstone

51 feet

Alternations of thin bedded light brownish and blueish
sandstones of different degrees of hardness & band of argillo-calcareous rock

49 feet.

Inclined plane of the slide.

F. 1. d.

Green sandstone with intercalations of ferruginous
sandstones and mottled and spotted dolomitic layers
and fucoidal impressions. Silico-
calcareous bands.

7.5 feet.

Greenish marl 9 feet.

Alternations of thin bedded ash-colored, micaceous,
brownish & light-colored sandstones

F. 1. c.

Slope hidden from view.

Place of the lingula grit of Black
R., Chippewa, & M! Island

In the decades following the original survey, Owen's time-stratigraphic assignments have been revised repeatedly. Like the designations of the limits between rock units, the chronologic designations have been changed to meet newer fashions of classification. When the significance of Sedgwick's work became recognized in America, the Lower Sandstone (F.1) became Cambrian, whereas F.2 and F.3 remained in the Silurian. After Lapworth's Ordovician was established, the strata above the base of the Lower Magnesian Limestone and below the Coralline and Pentamerous Beds (F.3.c) were transferred to that system. Near the turn of the century, Ulrich assigned the beds from F.1.e–F.2.b to the Ozarkian System. More recently the classification has reverted to the pre-Ulrich state. Each of these shifts was introduced to bring the classification of the Upper Mississippi Valley strata into harmony with currently fashionable terminology, and no basic changes in Owen's interpretations as to the age of the strata were involved.

Changes in age assignments brought about by *reinterpretation* of the data are of a more fundamental nature. Certain quartzites which Owen included in his F.1.a are now clearly recognized as Precambrian. Other elements of the same unit (the "Red Clastic series" of the Lake Superior area) are considered to be Late Precambrian by some authorities, Cambrian by others. The precise positions of the Cambrian-Ordovician and Ordovician-Silurian boundaries have been disputed and modified almost continuously, as have the boundaries of the subdivisions of the systems. In each case the changes have been caused not by alterations in the system or framework of classification, but by the disparities in the *inferences* which different investigators can draw from the same data.

MODERN STRATIGRAPHIC CLASSIFICATION

Stratigraphers who visit Owen's area in the Upper Mississippi Valley are confronted with the implications of dual classification. The river bluffs exhibit the natural rock units which the Owen Survey observed, measured, described, and mapped over a century ago. These units have been in existence for hundreds of millions of years and have been exposed in their present state since the development of the post-glacial drainage pattern. Successive generations of geologists may apply different names to these units or shift their boundaries to facilitate mapping, but the strata remain the same. Geologists can do no more than recognize, define, and name the natural groupings of strata that are inherent in the local stratigraphic section. In each case recognition and definition are based on direct observations of the tangible features and characteristics of the strata and are independent of interpretations regarding the significance of these observations. It is convenient to refer to these natural differentiates of the stratigraphic column as **observable units.**

On the other hand, the chronologic (time-stratigraphic) classification of the same stratigraphic column can not be derived without interpretation of the strata and their contained fossils. We no longer believe, as did Owen and his contemporaries, that time-stratigraphic units are natural groupings of strata when applied outside of their areas of original establishment. Therefore, the assignment of Upper Mississippi Valley strata to age positions in terms of the European time scale becomes a matter of deduction and inference. Equally qualified observers following different paths of deduction and inferential reasoning can come to quite different, although equally sound, conclusions as to the age of the strata and positions of time-stratigraphic boundaries. The groupings of strata identified by these deductive processes are termed **inferential units.**

An outline of the classification of stratigraphic units is presented in Table 2-3. The revised *Stratigraphic Code* (see Appendix) does not distinguish explicitly between observable and inferential units, but by reference to the table the category of each class of units may be determined. Most of the classes of units are treated in the present chapter. Certain of the classes are more appropriately discussed in terms of the materials presented in later chapters and coverage of these units is deferred.

Observable Stratigraphic Units

The multiplicity of tools and techniques available to present-day stratigraphers for making observations on the characteristics of sedimentary rocks exposed in outcrop or penetrated in bore holes makes possible the recognition of a wide variety of tangible groupings of strata based on these observations. Heavy minerals, insoluble residues, electric and radioactive properties, density, and the velocity of elastic waves are some of the diagnostic features used in the differentiation of the stratigraphic column. Two classes of observable units, **rock units** based on lithologic characteristics and **biostratigraphic units** differentiated by paleontologic characteristics, have reached the widest application and have been formally treated in the *Stratigraphic Code*. Other types of observable units not specifically covered by the *Code* are discussed in Chapter 10. In the present chapter the Cambro-Ordovician stratigraphy of the Upper Mississippi Valley is drawn upon for examples which illustrate the application of the *Code* to actual cases.

Rock Units. Figure 2-2 is a diagrammatic representation of the stratigraphic section exposed on the river bluffs of southeastern Minnesota. The positions of the units identified by the Owen Survey are shown to the left of the graphic section. Experience gained, by detailed observation and

TABLE 2-3. CLASSIFICATION OF STRATIGRAPHIC UNITS

A. OBSERVABLE UNITS
 1. *Rock-stratigraphic (lithostratigraphic) units*
  a. Formal rock units
   Supergroup (rarely applied)
   Group
   Subgroup (rarely applied)
   Formation
   Member, tongue, lentil
   Bed (rarely applied as formal unit)
  b. Informal rock units
   Sequence
   Bed (oil sands, quarry layers, key and marker beds)
   Heavy mineral zone, insoluble residue zone
   Electric-log zone, radioactivity zone, velocity zone
   "Marker-defined" unit
 2. *Biostratigraphic units*
  a. Assemblage zone
   Subzone
    Zonule
  b. Range zone
   Local range zone
  c. Concurrent-range zone

B. INFERENTIAL UNITS

1. *Time-stratigraphic (chronostratigraphic) units*	*Geologic time units*
——————..........................	Eon
——————..........................	Era
System.............................	Period
Series.............................	Epoch
Stage.............................	Age

 2. *Ecostratigraphic units*
  a. Ecozone
  b. Geologic-climate unit
   Glaciation
   Stade
   Interstade
   Interglaciation

mapping, in the decades since Owen's original work, has shown that although his subdivisions of the "Lower Sandstone Formation" can continue to be applied, their usefulness is extended by differentiation into major units, which can be traced over much of the Upper Mississippi Valley area, and minor subdivisions with a more localized area of recognition. In addition, certain unit boundaries chosen by Owen have been shifted slightly to form groupings of strata with better definition and to facilitate mapping.

The four major units of strata recognized today within Owen's "Lower Sandstone" are shown to the right of Figure 2-2:

(1) At the base of the sedimentary succession, there is an obvious erosion surface cut into granites, volcanics, and metamorphic rocks. Resting on this eroded surface are beds of medium to coarse grained quartz sandstone which grade upward into fine sandstones and shaly siltstones. These, still higher in the section, grade into coarser sandstones much like those at the base.

(2) The gradational upward succession of coarse-to-fine-to-coarse sandstones gives way abruptly to a pebbly layer which marks the base of another

Fig. 2-2. Rock units exposed in the Upper Mississippi Valley. The classification of the Owen Survey is shown at the left; the formations recognized and applied today are shown at the right.

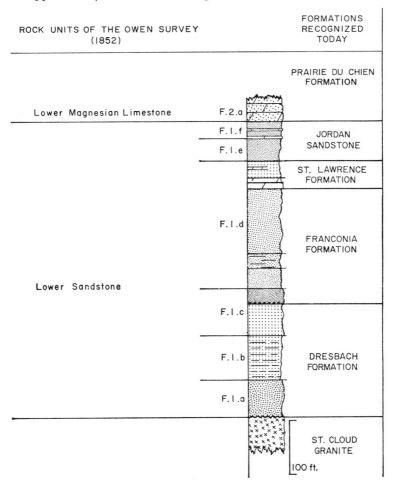

unit of sandstones characteristically colored green by abundant glauconite grains.

(3) The glauconitic sandstones are overlain by a distinct grouping of beds of dolomite and dolomitic siltstone.

(4) A prominent unit of white or yellowish coarse-grained and cross-bedded sandstones occurs next, which contains a few dolomitic beds near the top. Owen's "Lower Magnesian Limestone" is an obvious natural unit of light colored, sandy dolomites at the top of the river bluff exposures.

Formations. Each of these four groupings of strata forms a significant portion of the stratigraphic succession in the area and is distinguished by: (1) definite lithologic composition or a distinctive, interbedded or intergraded succession of lithologic types; (2) observable lithologic separation from adjacent units above and below; and, (3) traceability from exposure to exposure (or from well to well in the subsurface). These are the qualifications of **formations** (*Stratigraphic Code*, Article 16), the fundamental units of lithostratigraphy, and they are met in full measure by the Minnesota strata used as an example.

Individual formations are designated by geographic names derived from a locality or area of typical development of the unit (*Stratigraphic Code*, Article 10). The basal formation of the succession illustrated in Figure 2-2, for instance, was named the Dresbach Formation by N. H. Winchell in 1886 from exposures at Dresbach, Minnesota. The succeeding units, Franconia Formation (by C. P. Berkey, 1897), St. Lawrence Formation (by N. H. Winchell, 1874), and Jordan Sandstone (by A. Winchell, 1872), were similarly named after towns in southeastern Minnesota, and the Prairie du Chien Formation (H. F. Bain, 1906) was named after the town of the same name in southwestern Wisconsin.

When dominated by a single rock type, formations are appropriately designated by the characterizing lithology; Jordan Sandstone is an example. Other units which contain two or more rock types are designated by the word "Formation" following the geographic name, as in St. Lawrence Formation. In practice, a wide latitude of variation in the application of this principle exists, and no strong case can be made for rigid adherence to it. The Dresbach Formation of southeastern Minnesota, for instance, is commonly termed the Dresbach Sandstone in Wisconsin (where shaly beds are less prominent) and no confusion results.

It has been common practice not to capitalize rock-unit terms where used in combination with geographic names (Jordan sandstone, Dresbach formation). The Stratigraphic Commission (1961) now recommends capitalization of the initial letter of the term to conform with treatment of other geographically identified features (Mississippi River, Jordan Sandstone) used in conjunction with proper names.

Members. Formations may be subdivided into smaller groupings of strata, **members**, to provide greater detail in mapping or to single out subsidiary units of special interest (*Stratigraphic Code*, Article 7). For example, the southeastern Minnesota area in which the Dresbach Formation crops out can be mapped in significantly refined detail if the lower coarse-grained sandstone (Owen's F.1.a), middle shaly and silty sandstone (F.1.b), and upper coarse-grained sandstone (lower part of F.1.c) are recognized and traced as individual members. This usage is followed in the area and the members have received formal geographic names as shown in Figure 2-3.

The Mount Simon Sandstone, Eau Claire Sandstone, and Galesville Sandstone Members of the Dresbach Formation, as well as the other members indicated on Figure 2-3, meet the same requirements as formations in terms of mappability, lithologic distinction, and designated type sections. The only difference is that members are subdivisions of formations and may not have more than local significance as cartographic units.

Formations need not be differentiated into members. Specific members may be recognized and utilized in only part of the area of distribution of a formation, although no subdivisions at all, or other members with different names and different limits may be applied elsewhere. In the area chosen for this example the Jordan Sandstone is an undivided formation, but farther north, along the bluffs of the Mississippi, differences in grain size permit recognition of the Norwalk Member at the base of the formation and the Van Oser Member above (roughly equivalent to Owen's F.1.e and F.1.f).

Beds. Beds of economic significance, such as coal beds, quarry layers, oil or water sands, or ore horizons; and other distinct beds useful in mapping, such as bentonites or conspicuous fossiliferous horizons (for example, Owen's several "Trilobite beds"), often receive names which are locally applied, but commonly excluded from the formal body of stratigraphic nomenclature (*Stratigraphic Code*, Article 8). The application of "key beds" and "marker horizons" to problems of stratigraphic classification and correlation is discussed in detail in Chapter 10.

Groups. Two or more successive formations, related by lithology or by position with reference to unconformities, may be assembled as a **group** (*Stratigraphic Code*, Article 9). Such assemblages are useful in indicating relationships among formations and as units which can be represented on small-scale maps (such as the 1:500,000 maps of individual states and provinces). Inasmuch as groups are defined by the formations they comprise, their boundaries necessarily coincide with formation limits.

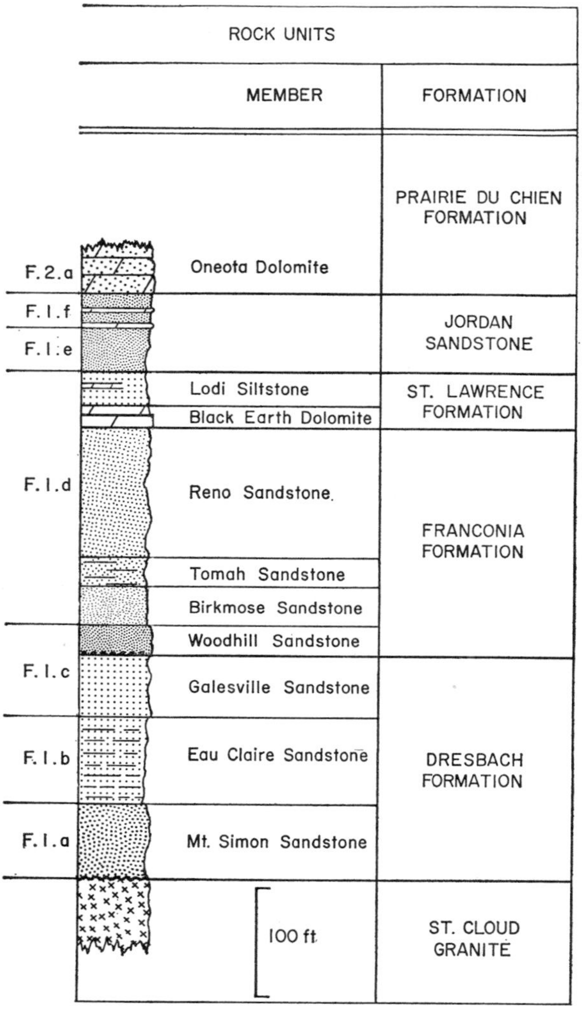

ROCK UNITS		
MEMBER		FORMATION
		PRAIRIE DU CHIEN FORMATION
F. 2. a	Oneota Dolomite	
F. I. f		JORDAN SANDSTONE
F. I. e		
	Lodi Siltstone	ST. LAWRENCE FORMATION
	Black Earth Dolomite	
F. I. d	Reno Sandstone	FRANCONIA FORMATION
	Tomah Sandstone	
	Birkmose Sandstone	
	Woodhill Sandstone	
F. I. c	Galesville Sandstone	
F. I. b	Eau Claire Sandstone	DRESBACH FORMATION
F. I. a	Mt. Simon Sandstone	
	100 ft	ST. CLOUD GRANITE

Fig. 2-3. Rock units of the Upper Mississippi Valley, showing subdivision of the formations into members. Units of the Owen Survey are at the left.

Sequences. Certain broad areas are united by a common tectonic and depositional history, such as much of the continental interior of North America. In such areas, the lithostratigraphy is marked by significant interregional unconformities, which can be traced in outcrop and in the subsurface over vast distances. The unconformities subdivide the stratigraphic record of major continental areas into groupings of strata that may include groups and supergroups in vertical succession and which are recognized over larger areas than any of their component formal rock-stratigraphic units. These unconformity-bounded masses of strata of greater than group or supergroup rank have been called **sequences** (Sloss, Krumbein, and Dapples, 1949; modified by Sloss, 1963).

Sequences, as applied in North America, closely resemble the classical systems established in western Europe, although the bounding unconformities occupy different positions in a time-stratigraphic sense. The sequences are no more than major rock-stratigraphic units, however, and have definite areal limits beyond which they are inapplicable and unrecognized.

Applications of the sequence concept are found in papers by Langenheim (1952), Scholten (1960), and Wheeler (1960).

Significance of Rock Unit Rank. Regardless of the nomenclatorial pigeon hole in which a rock unit may be placed this position must be considered one of convenience and is subject to alteration without prejudice to the physical definition and validity of the unit itself. (*Stratigraphic Code*, Article 16). The Oneota Dolomite is considered a member of the Prairie du Chien Formation in southeastern Minnesota (Fig. 2-3); in southern Wisconsin usage, the Oneota is treated as a formation of the Prairie du Chien Group, although the strata and their relationships are virtually identical in the two areas.

Biostratigraphic Units. The southeastern Minnesota strata have been differentiated lithologically into the rock units shown on the right in Figure 2-4. These same strata can also be subdivided into other observable units on the basis of their fossil content rather than on their lithologic characteristics. Stratal units defined paleontologically are called **biostratigraphic units,** and have boundaries which are drawn between successive units at stratigraphic positions marked by changes in the fossil content.

The biostratigraphic zones recognized in the Minnesota area are indicated to the left of the graphic column in the center of Figure 2-4. At the locality chosen for this example, fossil collections from the basal part of the section reveal an assemblage of trilobites characterized by the genus *Cedaria* and at least three other types. As collections are continued upward, this assemblage is found to prevail to some twenty feet above the base of the Eau Claire Sandstone Member of the Dresbach Formation. This is the upper limit of the *Cedaria* Zone, above which, careful collecting reveals a different assemblage of trilobites dominated by the genus *Crepicephalus*. These strata are identified as the *Crepicephalus* Zone, which, in turn, is succeeded by other biostratigraphic units higher in the section.

In this manner each successive biostratigraphic unit is objectively identified and delimited by the assemblage of fossil forms it contains without regard to the possible interpretation of the assemblage in terms of geologic age or depositional environment. Thus these units are tangible counterparts

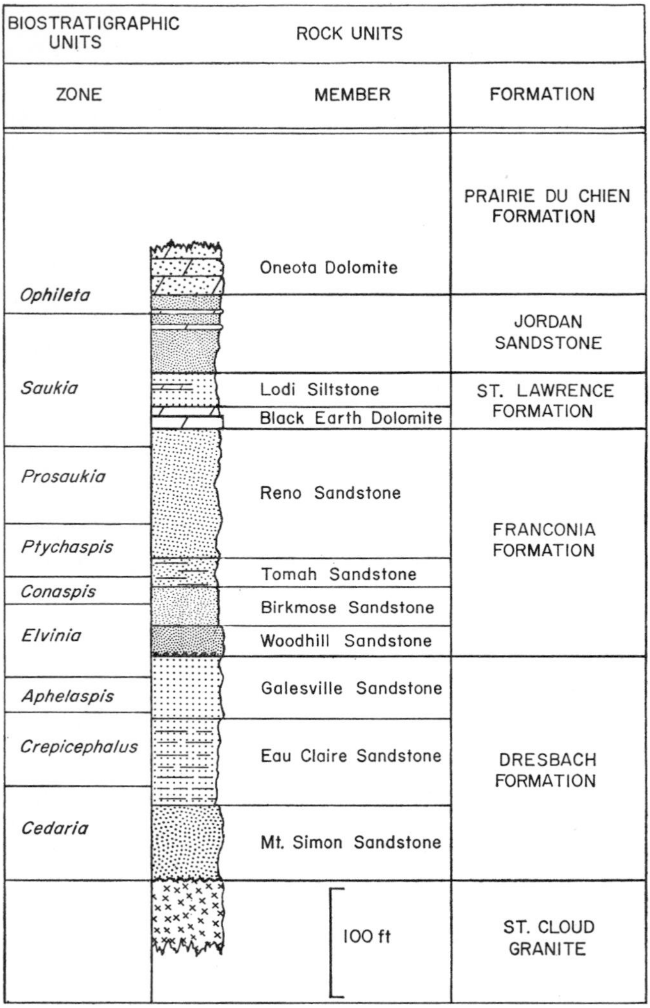

BIOSTRATIGRAPHIC UNITS	ROCK UNITS	
ZONE	MEMBER	FORMATION
		PRAIRIE DU CHIEN FORMATION
Ophileta	Oneota Dolomite	
		JORDAN SANDSTONE
Saukia	Lodi Siltstone	ST. LAWRENCE FORMATION
	Black Earth Dolomite	
Prosaukia	Reno Sandstone	FRANCONIA FORMATION
Ptychaspis		
Conaspis	Tomah Sandstone	
Elvinia	Birkmose Sandstone	
	Woodhill Sandstone	
Aphelaspis	Galesville Sandstone	DRESBACH FORMATION
Crepicephalus	Eau Claire Sandstone	
Cedaria	Mt. Simon Sandstone	
	100 ft	ST. CLOUD GRANITE

Fig. 2-4. Relationship of biostratigraphic units (assemblage zones) to rock units in the Upper Mississippi Valley. [Modified from Berg, Nelson, and Bell (1956).]

of the rock units, except that the characteristics of the fossil remains, rather than lithologic attributes, are the criteria applied.

Terminology of Biostratigraphic Units. There has been little agreement on the usage of terms applied to biostratigraphic units. An excellent review of the evolution of the terminology, including a glossary of many of the terms encountered in the literature, is presented by Teichert (1958). The revised *Stratigraphic Code* (Articles 19–25) provides a workable framework for North American stratigraphers; however, readers should bear in mind that the terms used in the Code and in this book are of relatively recent introduction and do not appear with the same connotations in the biostratigraphic literature of older date or of overseas derivation.

Assemblage Zones. The Cambrian biostratigraphic zones shown in Fig. 2-4 are characterized by groups or assemblages of fossil genera which commonly occur together. There are *assemblage zones* (*Stratigraphic Code*, Article 20) each of which is named for a prominent genus or other taxon in the assemblage although identification of the zone is not limited to strata in which the named genus is found. The *Crepicephalus* Assemblage Zone, for example, is characterized not only by the genus *Crepicephalus* but also by a number of other trilobite genera which, with the naming genus, are *guide fossils* to the assemblage zone. Neither the name given nor the other guide fossils are necessarily restricted to the zone, nor are they necessarily found in every part of it.

Subdivisions within assemblage zones are commonly recognized. The *Crepicephalus* Assemblage Zone, for example, is divisible into two *subzones*, each typified by the occurrence of guide fossils and each named for a particular species of the genus *Crepicephalus*. Some Cambrian specialists identify still smaller units, *zonules*, within the subzones.

Range Zones. The Cambrian stratigraphic column of the Minnesota area, like any succession of fossiliferous strata, is susceptible to subdivision into biostratigraphic units defined by the limits of occurrence of individual fossil taxons (genera, species, and so on). Units defined in this manner are called *range zones* (*Stratigraphic Code*, Article 22); such units commonly occur as overlapping groupings of strata that are unlike the orderly vertical succession of mutually exclusive assemblage zones. The range of the genus *Pseudagnostus,* for example, extends from within the *Conaspis* Assemblage Zone to a position above the *Prosaukia* Assemblage Zone, thus overlapping the range zones of many more restricted genera and species and extending across the boundaries of several assemblage zones and subzones. The range zone of the genus *Ptychaspis* is virtually coincident with the *Ptychaspis* Assemblage Zone, but the range zone of the species *Ptychaspis striata* is confined to the uppermost part of the assemblage zone. There is obviously a range zone for each fossil taxon recognized. The range zone of a family is of greater magnitude than that of any of its constituent genera just as the range zone of a genus typically encompasses a greater stratigraphic interval than the ranges of the individual species included within the genus.

The stratigraphic range of a given fossil taxon within any single stratigraphic section or locality is likely to be less than its maximum known range. As a result, confusion is sometimes created by the unqualified application of the term "range zone" in either a local and interregional sense. In the most commonly accepted usage, *range zone* refers to the interregional range of an individual taxon, and reference to ranges in a limited geographic area is clarified by use of the term *local range zone*.

Concurrent-range Zones. A special kind of biostratigraphic unit is defined by groups of overlapping range zones, those whose ranges have a lower stratigraphic limit and others with ranges having an upper stratigraphic limit. Thus, a unit of strata is recognized by the lowest occurrence of certain fossils and the highest occurrence of others. These *concurrent-range zones* (*Stratigraphic Code,* Article 23) are of special value in the time-stratigraphic correlation of strata. Their application to time correlation problems is discussed more fully in Chapter 10.

Inferential Stratigraphic Units

The self-evident, observable lithostratigraphic and biostratigraphic units are sufficient for depicting the *descriptive* stratigraphy of any given area. Such units do not, however, lend themselves to interpretation of the local stratigraphic column in terms of earth history. The latter purpose requires that stratigraphic units be related to geologic time, and that this relationship be expressed through some acceptable system of classification and terminology. Such a system exists in the hierarchy of time units and time-stratigraphic units, but these units are not self-evident nor directly observable; rather, they are *inferential* and are the result of complex intellectual and philosophical processes.

Time Units and Time-stratigraphic Units. The historical review presented in the early paragraphs of this chapter illustrates the evolutionary phases through which stratigraphic concepts and practices have passed to reach their present state. Three stages in this development are evident:

(1) A preliminary phase during which the concept of geologic time was given little consideration, and emphasis was placed on stratigraphic succession and recognition of the rock systems as fundamental groupings of strata.

(2) Recognition of the rock systems and their subdivisions as representing segments of geologic time separated by unrecorded "lost intervals."

(3) Realization that universally applied time units cannot everywhere be delineated by stratal boundaries, making evident the necessity for a dual classification of rocks and time.

Present usage permits consideration of **time unit** subdivisions of geologic time, differentiated without recourse to "disturbances" or "revolutions" or their effects on the sedimentary record. It may be argued that since geologic time is continuous and unbroken by pause or hiatus, any subdivisions of time are necessarily arbitrary and artificial. Nevertheless, some approach to geochronology is essential to the integration of earth history. The currently accepted time units serve this purpose as adequately as any other system of units or categories which could be devised in the light of present knowledge.

Units of geologic time, as Hedberg (1948) has pointed out, should not be considered as stratigraphic units under a rigid definition of the term, since they are not *material* bodies of strata. These units were omnipresent, but today the records of many are missing, owing to nondeposition or erosion, while others are represented by their deposits. Few stratigraphers will disagree with the concept that periods and other time units are finite intervals of geologic time, which follow one after the other, like the months of the calendar. A natural corollary of this concept is the world-wide simultaneity of the instant in time that marks the end of one time unit and the initiation of the succeeding one. Thus, the end of the Cambrian Period and the beginning of the Ordovician Period is *in concept* the same point in time everywhere.

Definition of Time-stratigraphic Units. Time-stratigraphic units, on the other hand, are material bodies of strata by definition. They are the strata deposited during finite portions of geologic time and preserved as part of the stratigraphic record. As such, these units cannot be dealt with by the application of a concept alone; instead, their delineation requires the recognition of surfaces of contact which divide the sedimentary deposits of one portion of geologic time from those of another. If time units are bounded by instants of time, then time-stratigraphic units are bounded by surfaces representing those instants. All points on the surface bounding a time-stratigraphic unit (in an unbroken succession) lie, therefore, on sedimentary laminae of identical age, that is, on *synchronous surfaces.*

No serious problems of concept or insuperable difficulties of classification affect time-stratigraphic units within their type localities. Here, each time-stratigraphic unit is also an observable biostratigraphic or rock unit bounded by unconformities or obvious lithologic and paleontologic changes. For instance, it is clear from the history of stratigraphic classification that the *systems*, now considered major time-stratigraphic units, were originally conceived as fundamental rock units. As a natural outgrowth of British and western European observation of the apparent lithologic and paleontologic individuality of the systems and the evidence of hiatus and change, which served to separate them, they later acquired chronologic significance. In due course, the time span of deposition of the systems became known as *periods.* Once the upper limit of the Cambrian System was redefined by Lapworth, in North Wales, the time span of the Cambrian Period was established.

Among other attributes that make time-stratigraphic units natural units of strata at their type localities is the common occurrence of bounding unconformities which mark episodes of nondeposition or erosion—the portions of geologic time not recorded in the stratigraphic column of the type areas. Problems arise when strata and fossils representing these time intervals are discovered elsewhere. Parallel situations exist where time-stratigraphic units were established in unfossiliferous strata.

In all areas apart from the type localities, the roles of time-stratigraphic and time units are reversed; identification of time-stratigraphic units depends on recognition of the age of the strata. The strata of the Minnesota example are not included in the Cambrian System because they form a fundamental rock unit, but because they are thought to be of the same *age* as part of the type Cambrian System of Wales. All assignments of strata to one or another time-stratigraphic unit in areas other than the type locality are made in a similar manner. No insoluble classification problem would exist were it possible to measure the age of strata with precision.

At the present time, no accurate method for determining the absolute age of sediments is available, and stratigraphers have been forced to rely on indirect and approximate means for establishing the age equivalence of physically separated bodies of strata. The most widely applied approach is one that has yielded the most valuable results; it is based on the progressive change of organisms with geologic time. Most of the accomplishments that have been achieved in integrating the geochronology of one continent with that of another, or in determining the time equivalence of strata in separate areas of the same continent have been due to the application of paleontology to time-stratigraphic problems. These advances have been made in spite of the widely recognized fact that changes in the character of fossil organisms (from one biostratigraphic unit to another, for instance) may reflect environmental factors rather than continuous change throughout geologic time.

On the following points (*Stratigraphic Code*, Articles 26–28), stratigraphers are in basic agreement: (1) The time span represented by a time-stratigraphic unit is defined by the interval of time of deposition of the unit in its type area; (2) In areas other than the type locality, a time-stratigraphic unit is defined by its geologic age; (3) Paleontology provides the most precise means of approximating the age of strata in terms of the geologic time scale. When it comes to application of these principles to the practical problem of differentiating a column of sedimentary rocks into its component time-stratigraphic units, two quite different approaches are followed in current practice. These divergent approaches may be characterized as follows:

1. Time-stratigraphic units "can be delineated (*defined*) only by their fossils" (Dunbar and Rodgers, 1957, p. 293). Thus, these units have biostratigraphic boundaries and *are*, in effect, biostratigraphic units or groupings of selected biostratigraphic units. These have been termed "practical time-stratigraphic units" (Rodgers, 1954; Jeletzky, 1956).

2. "Time-stratigraphic units are defined by time alone; their boundaries are not drawn on physical properties but are based on geologic time; that is, they [the boundaries] are isochronous surfaces" (Stratigraphic Commission, Report 2, 1952). These are the "ideal time-stratigraphic units" of Hedberg (1954).

Implications of the Definitions. The biostratigraphic ("practical") definition has powerful practical advantages. It permits the establishment of time-stratigraphic boundaries *by definition* and makes such boundaries directly observable features of the stratigraphic column. For example, a concensus of informed paleontologic opinion, on this continent, holds that the contact between the *Saukia* Zone and the overlying *Ophileta* (or *Bellefontia*) Zone closely approximates the paleontologic zoning at the type Cambrian-Ordovician boundary in Wales. This zonal boundary is uniformly applied throughout North America and establishes, as though by fiat and mutual consent, the position of the top of the Cambrian and the base of the Ordovician in the southeastern Minnesota section (Figure 2-5) and elsewhere on the continent.

In a similar fashion, once the biostratigraphy has been intensively studied and the significant zones recognized, all time-stratigraphic units can be "tagged" and delimited by appropriate zonal markers that can be identified through strictly objective observational procedures. Although debate continues on matters involving the inclusion or exclusion of certain zones with respect to a particular time-stratigraphic unit, the success with which the principle has been applied cannot be denied, and the lack of major conflicts on the limits of many time-stratigraphic units, located in widely separated areas, is a tribute to the formula. Thus, **biochronology** (dating geologic events by biostratigraphic methods) is commonly cited as the only basis for establishing operational time-stratigraphic boundaries. A searching review of biochronologic concepts and their application is given by Teichert (1958).

Note the steps in logic that are involved in the biostratigraphic definition of time-stratigraphic units. Start with the proposition that these units represent discrete portions of geologic time. Next, the basic premise is accepted that paleontology is our best, albeit approximate, means of assigning the sediments to their appropriate segments of geologic time. Finally, time-stratigraphic units are directly equated with biostratigraphy.

This somewhat syllogistic progression in logic provides a satisfactory approach to the time-stratigraphic classification of many sedimentary successions, as has been pointed out. In practice, however, two consequences emerge from the present-day application of the principle.

Consequences of "Practical" Time-stratigraphic Definition. If time-stratigraphic units are "practical" rather than "ideal" in concept, it is natural that

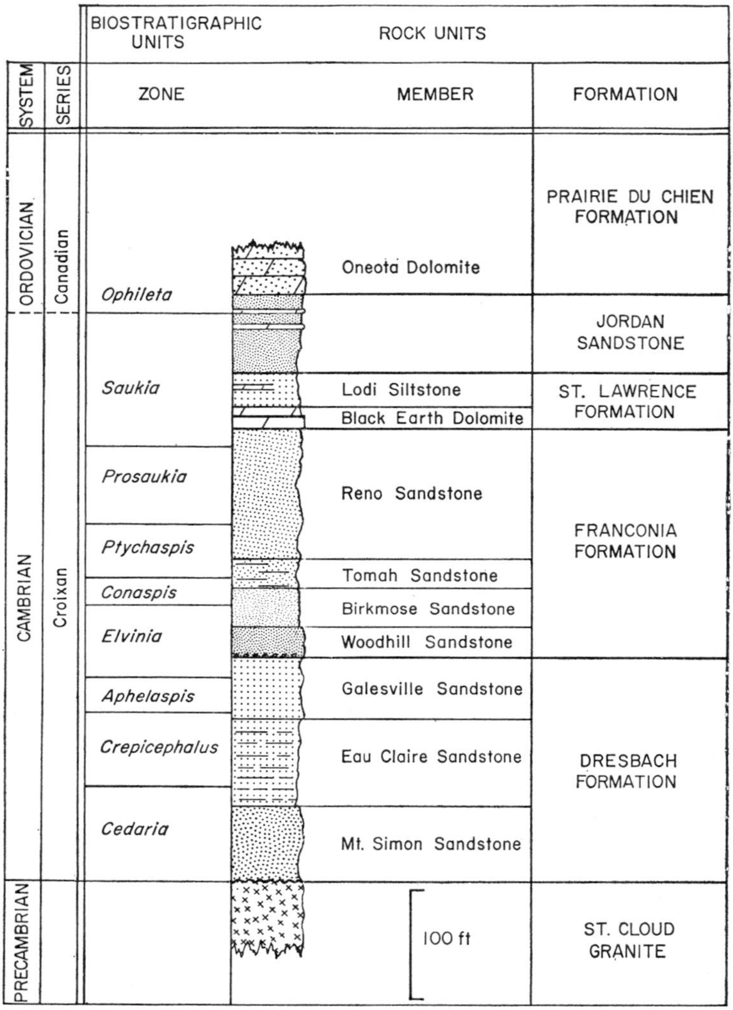

Fig. 2-5. Rock stratigraphic and biostratigraphic columns of the Upper Mississippi Valley, showing relationships of systems and series to assemblage zones. [After Berg, Nelson, and Bell (1956).]

their application to the classification of any column of sediments tends increasingly to become a matter of pragmatism, with concomitant loss of significance in chronology.

Application of Rock Unit Boundaries. In terms of practicality, rock unit boundaries are easier to recognize and follow than biostratigraphic limits. As a result, the "practical" limits of time stratigraphic units are commonly transferred from their defining paleontologic boundaries to a convenient lithic contact, even where the rock units involved suggest no evidence of parallelism with synchronous surfaces. For instance, in the southeastern Minnesota area (Figure 2-5), the base of the Ordovician System is characteristically placed at the base of the easily recognized Oneota Dolomite, ignoring the fact that the position of the defining paleontologic zone varies to a level well below the rock boundary. Other areas and other parts of the stratigraphic column provide similar examples of time-stratigraphic limits that have been arbitrarily placed at rock unit boundaries because of an assumed or extrapolated biostratigraphy.

Relationship to Assumed Synchronous Surfaces. The inconsistencies introduced by an overly pragmatic approach to time-stratigraphic classification can be avoided by a more rigid adherence to a biostratigraphic definition. Of greater consequence are the discrepancies which appear when detailed subsurface data are applied to the recognition of synchronous surfaces and to their relationships with biostratigraphic boundaries.

As noted earlier, most of our accepted stratigraphic principles are based on studies of strata in outcrop along the trends of the folded belts of mountain uplifts and around the margins of sedimentary basins. No insurmountable difficulties are encountered in these exposures in reconciliation of lithologic and paleontologic evidences of apparent isochronism. Moreover, exposures are separated, from one limb of a basin to another, for example. Hence, time-stratigraphic classification of each area of exposure can be made internally consistent without the necessity of relating the units recognized in separate areas, except in terms of biostratigraphically defined limits. Although the factor of approximation is acknowledged, a basis is nevertheless provided for time-stratigraphic assignments over large areas and a synthesis of the geologic history represented by the strata can be made.

When subsurface data from wells drilled in the interior of sedimentary basins and in the areas between mountain uplifts are taken into account, observations made down the dip of the strata are added to those made parallel to strike at the outcrop. The three-dimensional view of stratigraphy afforded by the addition of subsurface data brings to light a number of factors that are not apparent when study is confined to those beds exposed in outcrop.

Effects of More Detailed Observations. The degree to which the details of lithology can be observed and studied is greatly enhanced in the subsurface by the completeness of the section and in particular, by various mechanical logging devices. The discussion of logging methods and the implications of the data they furnish is deferred to Chapters 3 and 10. It is sufficient to note here that there are many individual beds and rock surfaces that can be traced for long distances. The systematic parallelism of these "markers" with bentonite beds and similar evidences of synchronism, suggests strongly that the "marker beds" themselves may be time-parallel.

If the biostratigraphic boundaries selected to delimit "practical" time-stratigraphic units are studied in relationship to assumed synchronous rock surfaces, the two remain essentially parallel when followed along the strike of the strata. When traced down-dip, however, the two types of surfaces commonly diverge and introduce discrepancies of tens or hundreds of feet in the basin interiors.

Paleontologically defined time-stratigraphic units recognized on one side of a sedimentary basin and traced across the basin by following apparent time-parallel "markers," have been found to emerge as beds that were assigned, on biostratigraphic grounds, to different time-stratigraphic units. This sort of occurrence generates the paradoxical situation in which strata believed to be of the same age are placed in different chronologic units, while beds of different ages are assigned to the same "practical" units. The approximations inherent in the biostratigraphic definition of units thus appear to exceed reasonable bounds.

Need for Precision in Time-stratigraphic Discrimination. The same kind of inquiry into the three-dimensional geometry of sediments that reveals the problems noted above also allows the investigation of stratigraphic patterns in a degree of detail unavailable to previous generations of geologists. Detailed cross sections and stratigraphic maps of various types are being increasingly used in the analysis, interpretation, and integration of entire depositional provinces in terms of the distribution, character, and interrelationships of sedimentary rocks and their structures. These studies are in turn applied to the interpretation of geologic history. In addition, they form the basis for predicting the distribution of mineral resources.

Attempts at detailed historical reconstruction do not yield consistent and rational results except through the recognition and analysis of stratigraphic units that closely approach "ideal" time-defined subdivisions. Similarly, the most successful predictions of the location of mineral deposits, particularly oil and gas, related to stratigraphic patterns have depended on the same approaches. In this application, the biostratigraphically defined "practical" units have not proven uniformly satisfactory. In fact, such units have been largely superseded in intraregional studies by stratigraphic subdivisions based on apparently synchronous "marker beds" or rock surfaces. Thus, the so-called "practical" biostratigraphically defined time-stratigraphic units appear to have less work-a-day practical value than units defined by other criteria. Even on the broadly interregional scale, rigid adherence to paleontologically defined units may lead to complex interpretations which are not consonant with the relatively simple patterns strongly indicated by nonpaleontologic lines of evidence. An example is the treatment of Ordovician units in the Rocky Mountain-Great Plains area as discussed by Kay (in Twenhofel, et al., 1954, p. 282).

Summary. At the moment two kinds of time-stratigraphic units are in use: Intercontinental or interregional units related to approximate "biostratigraphic time," and regional or local units related to more precise, but non-definitive "regional" or "local time markers." The latter units yield the more consistent and reasonable interpretations of regional geologic history, but this history cannot be integrated with the geologic calendar without recourse to paleontology. In this respect it is difficult to assume that either type of subdivision is pre-eminent or universally applicable to the exclusion of the other. If biochronology is designated as the sole basis for time-stratigraphic classification, further advances can be made only through refinement of paleontology. If stratigraphers adhere to the concept that time-stratigraphic units are truly time-defined subdivisions that "exist largely as ideals which can be approached but never perfectly attained" (Hedberg, 1954), the identification of such units can be thought of as *approximations* rather than rigid entities tied *by definition* to biostratigraphy alone. Thus, all future advances, including those in absolute chronology, can be applied to the continual reduction of the inherent approximations, and time-stratigraphic units can be brought closer and closer to the "ideal."

Periods and Systems. As shown by the history of stratigraphic classification, the classical **systems** were the first widely applied time-stratigraphic units. The systems, and the **periods** which represent their times of deposition, remain the fundamental units of geochronology (*Stratigraphic Code*, Articles 29 and 37).

Epochs and Series. Systems are subdivided into smaller time-stratigraphic units called **series.** Each series represents a portion, or **epoch,** of geologic time within a period (*Stratigraphic Code*, Articles 30 and 37). Many of the recognized series and epochs attained their present formal status through steps which parallel the histories of the systems and periods. At the turn of the century, when the term "series" had no special time-stratigraphic meaning, the southeastern Minnesota sediments between the Precambrian unconformity and the base of the Oneota Dolomite were termed the *St. Croix series,* with reference to a natural rock unit (Owen's Lower Sandstone) of sandstones and shales exposed in the bluffs of the St. Croix Valley. It soon became recognized that the biostratigraphic zones of the St. Croix series are widespread and that equivalent zones are found in the upper part of more complete Cambrian successions elsewhere on the continent. With this recognition, the original rock unit, the St. Croix series, became endowed with time-stratigraphic significance, and stratigraphers began to refer to Upper

Cambrian strata and Late Cambrian time by the adjective *Croixan*, meaning of or pertaining to the time of deposition of the original rock-defined St. Croix unit of strata. In modern usage on this continent, the Croixan Series and Epoch (note the capitalization of the unit terms where used with or with reference to the geographic term) have become synonymous with Upper Cambrian strata and Late Cambrian time respectively. Our Minnesota example (Figure 2-5) is drawn from a locality only a short distance removed from the type locality of the Series. Hence its time-stratigraphic limits (as inferred from the biostratigraphy) agree fairly closely with the natural rock boundaries of the original "series." The Canadian Series of the Ordovician System, to which the Oneota Dolomite and other strata of the Prairie du Chien Group of Minnesota are assigned, is named from a major natural rock unit in the Quebec area. By the same evolutionary steps this term has become applied, on the North American continent, to Lower Ordovician strata and Early Ordovician time. Since the Minnesota area is far removed from the type locality of the Series, its identification rests on biostratigraphic interpretation.

Other epoch-series subdivisions of the Cambrian Period and System are examples of the various routes that have led to formal acceptance in time-stratigraphic nomenclature. Lower Cambrian strata and Early Cambrian time are referred to the Waucoban Series and Epoch, named for a well-exposed section at Waucoba Springs in southeastern California. No rock unit of the same name preceded establishment of the time-stratigraphic unit, but reference to the Waucoba Springs locality as the type section is implicit. Middle Cambrian rocks and Middle (or Medial) Cambrian time are called Albertan in recognition of the magnificent exposures of strata of this age in the Rocky Mountains of Alberta. No reference section is specified or implied, nor is there an equivalent rock unit of the same name.

Readers should note that while the Waucoban and Albertan Epochs were represented by events in the locality of our Minnesota example, the parallel Series are not present in the Cambrian System of that area. Instead, the Early and Middle Cambrian time units are represented by the evidence of erosion at the Precambrian unconformity.

Custom and usage have developed a tri-partite subdivision of certain periods (Cambrian, Ordovician, Silurian, Triassic, Jurassic) or a simple two-way split (Cretaceous, Tertiary of some classifications). Epochs are readily identified by "Early," "Middle" (or "Medial"), or "Late" followed by the name of the period; the parallel series may be specified by application of "Lower," "Middle," or "Upper" attached to a system name. "Early Cambrian Epoch" is synonymous with "Waucoban Epoch" and stratigraphers are inclined to refer events to "Early Cambrian time" rather than to "Waucoban time." Similarly, there are many more literature references to "Upper Cambrian" than to "Croixan" strata and no ambiguity results if the time-stratigraphic value of the term is clearly implied by the context of the usage.

The same application of relative terms used to designate epochs and series cannot be carried over as simply to the period-system, which has four or more subdivisions. "Early-late Devonian Epoch" is an awkward substitute for "Senecan Epoch," and few workers would prefer "Lower-Lower Pennsylvanian Series" to the more concise "Springeran Series." Support for the latter is strengthened by the belief, held in some quarters, that the strata in question should be considered as an "Upper-Upper Mississippian Series." It seems clear that legislation for the application of geographic or relative terms in any particular case cannot prevail over clarity of expression, succinctness, and common sense.

As a natural outgrowth of their evolution in concept and practice most epoch-series names (like period-system names) are adjectives. When the temporal significance of the Cincinnati Group was recognized it was logical to refer to the time of deposition as "Cincinnatian time" or as the "Cincinnatian Epoch." Furthermore, adjectival suffixes on epoch-series names (Niagaran Series, Mohawkian Epoch, Liassic Series) served to identify these as time and time-stratigraphic units, differentiated from rock units designated by unadorned nouns. However, usage and the interests of euphony and logical spelling have forced stratigraphers to take a more flexible and less legalistic stand on this matter. (*Stratigraphic Code*, Article 32). Stratigraphers working in the Pennsylvanian will continue to use "Des Moines Series" in preference to "Desmoinesian Series"; both are acceptable by current standards. Where an adjectival suffix is used, a time or time-stratigraphic connotation is implicit. "Chesteran" always refers to late Mississippian time or Upper Mississippian strata. "Chester" used in the same sense requires the addition of "Epoch" or "Series" to eliminate confusion with the rock unit of the same name. The need for clarity of expression is reinforced by the recent trend, noted in an earlier paragraph, toward capitalization of rock-unit terms. Formerly these were uncapitalized (Chester group) and easily differentiated from time and time-stratigraphic units with adjectival geographic names and uniformly capitalized terms (Chesteran Series). A more relaxed and flexible set of carefully applied rules and regulations need not introduce misunderstanding and vagueness.

Epochs and series do not have the intercontinental status of periods and systems. Stratigraphers are striving to demonstrate a degree of equivalency between the units applied in North America and those recognized in Europe, but, with the exception of Tertiary subdivisions, the most commonly used names are confined to use on one side of the Atlantic or the other. European Tertiary epoch-series terminology is widely applied on this continent, but there is little assurance that the several series as defined in North America have more than a broadly approximate relationship to the time values of the European types. Even between the Gulf Coast and California there appear to be significant differences in definition of the Miocene Series and the Epoch it represents.

In general, the majority of epoch-series names are applied throughout the North American continent. An exception is found in the Cretaceous of the Gulf Coast where natural groupings of strata led to the temporary recognition of a new system (see Table 2-1, columns 6–9). The Comanchean has been reduced to series rank and, together with the Coahuilan Series below and the Gulfian Series above, is applied as a fundamental time-stratigraphic unit, which has no counterpart in European subdivisions nor recognition elsewhere on this continent.

Ages and Stages. Epochs of geologic time are divisible into **ages** which are represented by time-stratigraphic units below series rank, termed **stages** (*Stratigraphic Code*, Articles 31 and 37). Age-stage nomenclature has long been an important feature of European stratigraphic classification, but only in the past few decades have these units been applied widely in North America. Where the character of biostratigraphic materials permits fine discrimination among zones and where these zones give every evidence of time significance, stages are recognized and employed on an intercontinental scale. Ammonite zones, for example, are the basis for wide application of European stage names to the Mesozoic strata of North America. Paleozoic and Cenozoic stages employed in North American stratigraphy have been largely derived on this continent, and many are recognized within limited areas, such as a stratigraphic province or a single basin of deposition.

Most stages, both in the classical European areas and in North America, followed the same steps as did the systems and series in becoming established as time-stratigraphic units: first through identification as a discrete unit of rocks, then through eventual recognition as units representative of a distinct portion of geologic time. Not too long ago stages were considered, quite simply, as the "time equivalents" of formations. The Upper Cambrian stages of the Minnesota example (Figure 2-6) were derived directly from the rock-unit stratigraphy of the area ("Trempealeau Formation" was formerly used in southern Wisconsin to combine both the St. Lawrence Formation and the Jordan Sandstone). The biostratigraphic zones are closer approximations of synchronous surfaces than the rock boundaries. Hence, the working definitions of the stage limits are drawn in terms of the biostratigraphy. These limits depart from the formational boundaries to an increasing extent with distance from the type area of the stages and are identifiable hundreds, even thousands, of miles away in successions made up of entirely different rock units.

Some stage names, such as Trempealeauan, remain in current use long after their parent rock units have been renamed. The names of other stages (for example, the sub-divisions of the Miocene in California) have a synthetic origin and are not descended from rock units; this is a practice now recommended by the *Stratigraphic Code* (Art. 32). However, a great many names remain in use for both rock units and stages, which, when carelessly

Fig. 2-6. Time-stratigraphic, biostratigraphic, and rock units of the Upper Mississippi Valley, showing the Upper Cambrian stages recognized and their relationships to series and assemblage zones.

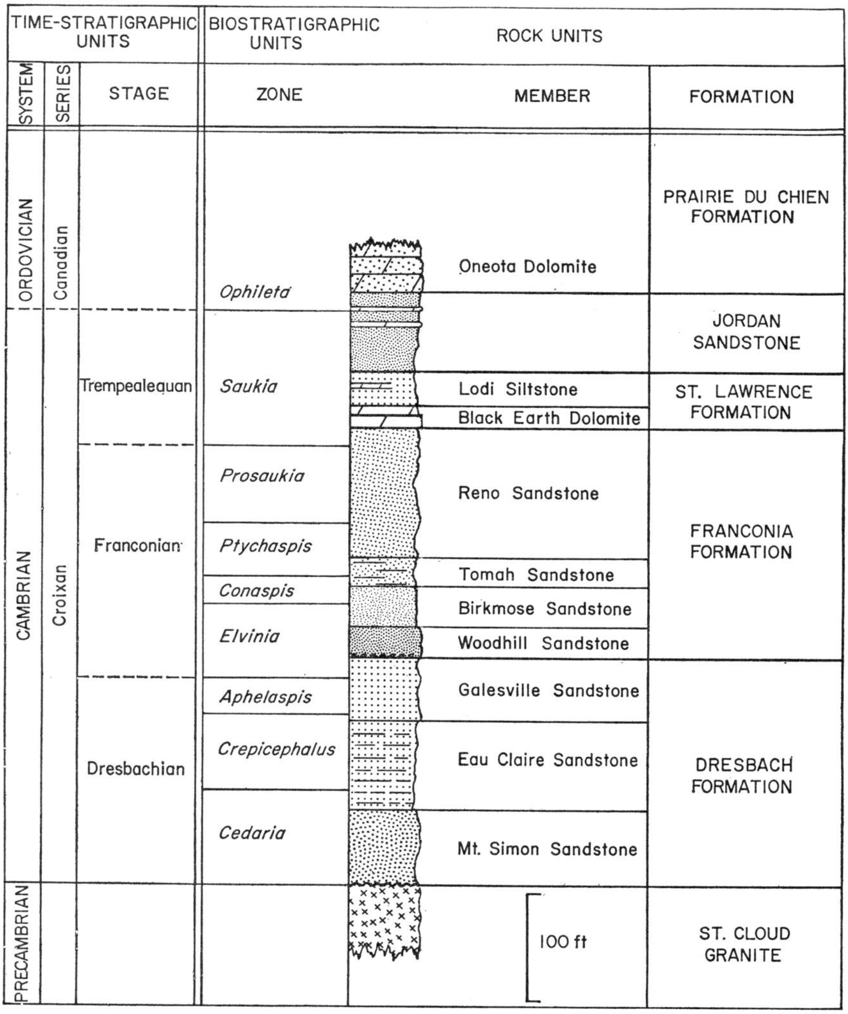

TIME-STRATIGRAPHIC UNITS			BIOSTRATIGRAPHIC UNITS	ROCK UNITS	
SYSTEM	SERIES	STAGE	ZONE	MEMBER	FORMATION
ORDOVICIAN	Canadian		*Ophileta*	Oneota Dolomite	PRAIRIE DU CHIEN FORMATION
CAMBRIAN	Croixan	Trempealeauan	*Saukia*	Lodi Siltstone	JORDAN SANDSTONE
				Black Earth Dolomite	ST. LAWRENCE FORMATION
		Franconian	*Prosaukia*	Reno Sandstone	FRANCONIA FORMATION
			Ptychaspis		
			Conaspis	Tomah Sandstone	
				Birkmose Sandstone	
			Elvinia	Woodhill Sandstone	
		Dresbachian	*Aphelaspis*	Galesville Sandstone	DRESBACH FORMATION
			Crepicephalus	Eau Claire Sandstone	
			Cedaria	Mt. Simon Sandstone	
PRECAMBRIAN				100 ft	ST. CLOUD GRANITE

applied, can create confusion. Where the names are used in a time or time-stratigraphic sense (Franconian Age, Claibornian Stage, and so forth), clarity can be gained by using adjectival suffixes, but adherence to hard and fast rules leads to "Fingerlakesian" and similar awkward constructions.

Many stratigraphers, although they grant that series and systems are units of strata bounded by time surfaces, treat stages as pure biostratigraphic units. These workers quite properly call attention to the paleontological criteria applied to the operational definition of stages and to the coincidence of stage and zonal boundaries. As identified in the field, the Trempealeauan Stage, for instance, coincides with the *Saukia* Assemblage Zone. The authors strongly believe that a system must be considered as the sum of its component series and stages, and, for the reasons developed in earlier paragraphs, the same *concept* of the "ideal" time-stratigraphic unit must be applied to all. Furthermore, it is in the highly refined technology of closely controlled local stratigraphy that stage subdivisions attain their maximum utility and meaning. Here, as explored more fully in Chapter 10, a number of criteria are available to delineate synchronous surfaces with accuracy greater than that provided by biostratigraphic zones.

Stages are divisible into subordinate time-stratigraphic units, **substages,** which are designated in the same fashion as stages and which involve the same inherent problems of definition and identification. By implication, the coordinate time term, "subage," is also available but is seldom used.

Eras. The grouping of geologic periods in larger time units, **eras,** is widely accepted and used in discussion of earth history, although no time-stratigraphic term is applied to the strata deposited during an era. In the reign of the catastrophist concept of geologic history, the eras were thought to be significant major divisions of geologic time that closed with unusual cataclysmic orogenies, or "revolutions," and were separated by long "lost intervals." Now that it is recognized that the major orogenic episodes involved long spans of time and were not simultaneous on a world-wide scale, and with the continuing discovery of sediments and faunas that fill the "lost intervals," the eras have lost much of their significance.

The era subdivisions of Precambrian time (Archeozoic and Proterozoic) have largely disappeared from current geologic literature but "Paleozoic," "Mesozoic," and "Cenozoic" remain useful categories for discussing the larger phases of the scope of earth history.

Eons. In writing and speaking of geologic history, it is frequently necessary to differentiate between Precambrian and later time. "Precambrian rocks" or "pre-Paleozoic time" effectively dispose of part of the problem. Since Precambrian eras are seldom applied, geologists cannot utilize "post-Proterozoic" for reference to later rocks and events, and most writers shrink from using the logical but awkward term, "post-Precambrian." Many ways around this dilemma have been suggested, but none has been widely adopted. Perhaps the use of "Cryptozoic Eon" for Precambrian time and "Phanerozoic Eon" for later time, as proposed by Chadwick (1930) and noted in the revised *Stratigraphic Code* (Art. 37), has the greatest possibility of successful application, but these terms are seldom encountered in geologic literature.

Ecostratigraphic Units. A stratigraphic column may be subdivided into other inferential units by consideration of the environmental significance of the rocks and their contained fossils. The environment of deposition, like the time of deposition, is not a directly observable attribute of sedimentary rocks. However, ecologic analysis and interpretation of mineralogy, depositional structures and textures, and fossil faunas make possible the recognition of vertically successive **ecostratigraphic units** or **ecozones**. Examples of the ecostratigraphic subdivision of Devonian strata in Alberta are given by Andrichuk (1958).

Although the terminology of most ecostratigraphic units has not reached formal status, the special requirements of Pleistocene stratigraphy are recognized in the codification of *Geologic climate units* (*Stratigraphic Code,* Articles 39–40). These are bodies of rock defined by inferred climatic conditions during deposition, and they comprise *glaciations* (divisible into *stades* and *interstades*) and *interglaciations.*

SUPPLEMENTARY READINGS

The subject matter of this chapter is so broad that it is difficult to recommend specific readings. The following list includes books and papers that expand some of the more important concepts, or provide supplementary background.

The periodicity of orgenic episodes and their influence on organic evolution and the subdivision of geologic time is reviewed in these papers:

1. Gilluly, J., 1949, Distribution of mountain building in geologic time: Geol. Soc. America Bull., v. 60, p. 561–590. (Address by the retiring president of the Geological Society of America, reviewing the relationship of diastrophic events to the subdivisons of geologic time.)
2. Henbest, L. G. (editor) 1952, Symposium on distribution of evolutionary explosions in geologic time: Jour. Paleontology, v. 26, p. 297–394.
3. Westoll, T. S., 1954, Mountain revolutions and organic evolution, *in* Huxley, J., Hardy, A. C., and Ford, E. B. (editors), Evolution as a process: London, Allen & Unwin Ltd., p. 251–263.

Divergent opinions on stratigraphic classification and the implications of the categories of stratigraphic units may be sampled in the following:

4. Arkell, W. J., 1956, Comments on stratigraphic procedure and terminology: Am. Jour. Sci., v. 254, p. 457–467.
5. Dunbar, C. O. and Rodgers, J., 1957, Principles of stratigraphy: New York, John Wiley & Sons, Inc., p. 250–270, 289–307.
6. Gignoux, M., 1955, Stratigraphic geology: San Francisco, W. H. Freeman and Co., p. 12–24.
7. Hedberg, H. D., 1954, Procedure and terminology in stratigraphic classification: Int. Geol. Congress, 19th Session, Comptes rendus, sec. XIII, fasc. XIII, p. 205–233.
8. Teichert, C., 1958, Some biostratigraphical concepts: Geol. Soc. America Bull., v. 69, p. 99–120.

A modern example of the procedures followed in the establishment, definition, and naming of newly designated formational units is provided by the following:

9. Hill, M. L., Carlson, S. A., and Dibblee, T. W., Jr., 1958, Stratigraphy of Cuyama Valley—Caliente Range Area, California: Am. Assoc. Petrol. Geologists Bull., v. 42, p. 2973–3000.

Interesting background material on the evolution of stratigraphic classification and on the personalities involved may be found in the following books:

10. Fenton, C. L. and Fenton, M. A., 1954, The story of the great geologists: New York, Doubleday, Doran & Co., Inc.
11. Geikie, A., 1897, The founders of geology: New York, The Macmillan Co.
12. Zittel, D. A. von, 1901, History of geology and paleontology to the end of the nineteenth century: New York, Charles Scribner's Sons.

CHAPTER 3

Stratigraphic Procedures

INTRODUCTION

AT this point it is necessary to become familiar with a number of operations and procedures used in the gathering and analysis of stratigraphic data and materials. This chapter is not intended to form a manual of field and laboratory stratigraphic techniques, but to introduce a variety of procedures constantly utilized in academic and applied stratigraphy. The subject matter of later chapters requires repeated reference to these procedures.

OUTCROP PROCEDURES

Measured Sections

Accurately measured and properly described stratigraphic sections form the basis for most studies of strata in outcrop. From measured sections are derived data used in correlations, as well as information on thickness and lithologic variations, positions of faunas, and stratigraphic relations of various rock units. The approach toward completion of stratigraphic work in any outcrop study is largely a function of the number of sections measured, studied, and analyzed.

The methods and procedures of section measurement cannot be summarized in a general fashion, since each area presents its own problems. Therefore, no attempt is made here to discuss all the possible methods of section measuring. A few examples are provided, and the reader is urged to seek further in the several textbooks and field manuals for other approaches.

Regardless of the procedure employed, a measured section is useful only if it yields the data required on lithology, paleontology, stratigraphic relations, and thickness for the particular problem in question. In reconnaissance stratigraphy, which involves the correlation of units over wide areas, it is often more important to measure ten or twenty sections in only moderate detail to establish general relationships than to spend a field season in detailed work on one section. On the other hand, when specific information on a single locality is required—for example, a mining district—the maximum benefit may result from the most searching study of a single canyon wall.

Selection of Sections To Be Measured. The proper choice of locations for section measuring is an important factor in determining the value of the results and the efficiency in procuring such results. In some areas, the choice is limited by lack of good exposures, whereas in areas of numerous exposures, choice is made on the basis of spacing between sections, amount of the stratigraphic column present, degree of exposure or cover, structural simplicity, and accessibility.

Spacing is important, since, in the stratigraphic analysis of any area, it is necessary to get as wide a coverage as possible within the time available for field work. Stratigraphic studies usually involve either the entire stratigraphic column of an area, or certain rock or time-stratigraphic units. In the first case, the sections chosen should permit the measurement and study of as much of the total column as possible. Furthermore, they should begin and end with horizons that may be correlated with adjacent sections in order that the column may be pieced together.

Where individual units, or groups of units, are involved, the selected sections should, if possible, expose the tops and bottoms of the portion of the column concerned. The most thoroughly exposed sections are to be preferred, although exposure is sometimes sacrificed in the measurement of a section which yields accurate data on overall thickness of units under conditions where there is no combination of good exposure and complete section.

Often it is also necessary to sacrifice other factors in order to choose an uncomplicated section. Gentle folding and obvious transverse faults offer no special difficulty, but complex structures are serious deterrents to accurate section measuring. The steep or overturned limbs of folds often appear to offer ideal sections for measurement, but such locations are subject to radical thinning, elimination of incompetent units, undetectable repetition, or elimination by strike faults. The dangers inherent in section measuring in areas of close or isoclinal folding are obvious. There have been published examples of sections in which units appear with abnormal thicknesses, later proven to be the result of isoclinal folding, and of other cases of sections measured and recorded upside down.

Much stratigraphic work today is a refinement of previous work. Therefore, a stratigrapher entering a known area can usually benefit from the work of his predecessors in establishing the correlation of units from adjacent areas.

Description of Measured Sections. Adequate description is required in order to extract the maximum amount of stratigraphic information from any exposed sequence of strata. The description of a measured section should include observations on the thickness of units, their stratigraphic relationships, lithology, stratification, internal structures, weathering behavior, and paleontology.

In dealing with the thickness and other attributes of strata in a measured section, reference is usually made to two kinds of "units." First there are such formal rock units as formations and members, recognizable in all or part of the area involved. Each formation or member is further divisible at the locality of section measuring according to lithology, bedding, exposure, weathering effects, or some other feature, into convenient subunits which permit the recording of differences in character within formations and members. Subunits are usually individual beds or groups of beds differentiated from those above and below by unity of color, texture, or gross appearance. Differentiation of a section into subunits is illustrated in Figure 3-1.

Subdivisions in relatively homogeneous strata are sometimes split on the basis of a horizon of chert nodules in a limestone, a covered interval, a change in the resistance to weathering, or some similar minor feature. Further work may demonstrate that certain of the subunits can be recognized over a considerable area, in which case they may be regarded as members.

Whether the subdivisions are extremely local or widely identifiable, they form a basis for detailed description and are useful in referring to finite portions of the section. Units are commonly assigned numbers. The figure 1 is given to the first unit encountered in measuring, and this number, in addition to the code identification of the section, is applied to all data, descriptions, and materials derived from the unit.

The stratigraphic relationships of all rock units, such as members and formations, at the point of section measurement should be thoroughly investigated and recorded as being transitional, sharp, disconformable, or unconformable. Shrock (1948) has summarized the characteristics of various unconformable relationships and described the features of the accompanying erosion and weathered surfaces.

The lithology of each unit is described in terms of the dominant rock type (sandstone, shale, limestone, and so forth); the texture (coarse, medium, or fine grained; sorting; shape; and roundness); the color (of fresh surface); and the mineralogy of detrital particles and cement, if any. Associated lithologies are separately recorded with mention of the percentage of each type present and the manner of its association with the dominant type. Figure 3-2 illustrates a typical field description of a measured section.

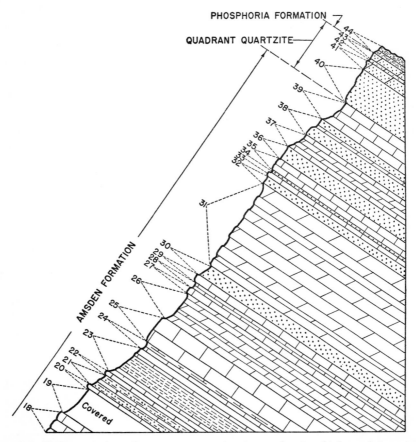

Fig. 3-1. Differentiation of an outcrop section into subunits. [Adapted from Montana Bureau of Mines and Geology, Memoir No. 24.]

Where fossiliferous units are encountered, adequate description includes a list of the faunal elements present, and some measure of the relative number of fossils representing each genus or species. Accurate paleontologic description usually requires the collection of representative fossils for later study, if they can be gathered in identifiable form. Otherwise, the description should at least note the major taxonomic categories present, and their mode of occurrence.

Lithologic Samples

In addition to observations made in the field, modern stratigraphic work requires a refinement of lithologic detail by microscopic examination and laboratory treatment. For these purposes, it is necessary to collect a sample from each subunit in the measured section. Normally, the samples need not

	Section 15-4 Samples: 15-4-1 to 15-4-73	*Sappington Canyon Sect.* *Sect 25-T1N-R2W-* *Jefferson Co. Mont.*	*Nov 5, 1944* *T.A.Hendricks* *L.S.Gardner* *L.L.Sloss*

E. side Sappington Canyon along N-P tracks &

on high ridge to E, approx. ¼ mi S. of U.S.Hwy. 10-S.

Meas. upward from top Madison Ls. with tape &

UNIT & | *Brunton, Thickness calculated in field.*

SAMPLE | | THICKNESS

1	<u>*Top Madison Ls.*</u> *Ls, gray to brownish gray, med. xyline to* *saccharoidal, massive, weathers to sandy* *textured surfaces.*	—
2	<u>*Base Amsden Fm. (?)*</u> *Basal 11' covered. Appears to rest disconform.* *on Madison with minor channelling & solution.* *Breccia, gray to pink, weathering gray to yellow-* *brown; matrix is calcareous Ss, gray, locally* *pink, med. grained calcareous; contains small* *fragments gray & brown Ls. & larger pieces* *of Ss. & Ls.*	43
3	*Ss. red & white slightly ~~~~~ aceous to*	

~~~ram rad ~~~ rops a sh.

20	*Ls, dk. gray, some brown, dense; in even beds* *as much as 3" thick separated by partings* *of non-res. clayey & silty Ls.*	3
21	*Siltstone, highly calc., yell.-gray; 3"bed* *purple & green siltstone & 2 8"beds dark-* *gray Ls nr. middle. Some poorly exposed* *green fissile shale. Ostracods &* *Brachiopods in Ls & siltst.* 　　　　　<u>*Fossil coll'n 15-4-21F*</u>	15
22	*Ls., lt. gray, fine-grained, massive, resistant;* *few fossil fragments.*	3
23	*Sh., red & green, fissile; thin layers of* *silty Ls. nr. base & gr. dense Ls nr top.* *Green sh. calc., red sh. non-calc.*	

Fig. 3-2. Example of field notes taken in section measuring. [Adapted from Montana Bureau of Mines and Geology, Memoir No. 24.]

be large—less than a handful in most cases—but even small samples become a considerable burden when thick sections involving tens or hundreds of units are studied. However, the value of "bringing the stratigraphic section into the laboratory" is more than worth the effort expended. Each sample should fully represent, in relative volumes collected, the lithologic variations in each subunit and should contain a minimum of material altered by weathering.

Some stratigraphers prefer to collect samples within five- or ten-foot intervals, rather than within natural subunits, since the regular intervals provide samples comparable to those derived from drilling. This technique is very useful in stratigraphic studies involving the comparison of surface and subsurface data, but it is not always certain that the added labor of collecting and carrying the more numerous samples is justified.

It should be noted that the systematic sampling procedures discussed above, as well as the parallel procedures for paleontologic collecting discussed below, are for the purpose of preparing a more complete description of the stratigraphic section through microscopic and laboratory analysis. Where the investigator looks forward to statistical treatment of field and laboratory data, as is increasingly desirable in modern stratigraphic studies, quite different procedures, governed by rigorous statistical design, must be employed. This subject is mentioned in Chapter 4.

Fossil Collecting

The time-stratigraphic affinities of the rock units in a measured section are most commonly determined by paleontology, and every opportunity should be taken to refine the biostratigraphic zoning of the stratigraphic column involved. It should be remembered, however, that fossil collecting during section measuring is a means to an end, and not an end in itself. Collections should be limited to representative specimens of the genera and species present and the relative abundance of each noted.

Workers familiar with the biologic elements encountered will be able to enter field identification in the notes without making extensive collections, whereas others with less paleontologic experience will have to collect more frequently for later identification. Certain fossil types, such as bryozoa, corals, and the larger foraminifera, require laboratory techniques for identification. These forms are collected by even the most expert paleontologists.

If microfossils are sought, adequate samples for later examination must be collected in addition to the smaller lithologic samples. In any case, all fossil collections should be clearly labeled with the number of the subunit from which they are derived, since such collections lose most of their stratigraphic value if their proper position in the measured section cannot be assigned.

Measuring Horizontal Strata

Measurements in horizontal rocks do not require horizontal control; therefore, any means of accurate measurement of elevation can be adapted to section measuring. A number of methods are used, the choice depending on the degree of accuracy required and the topography of the area.

One of the most commonly applied methods utilizes the hand level, the unit of measurement being the eye-level height of the worker. Figure 3-3 illustrates the method. The hand level is portable and easy for one man to use. Hand leveling is well adapted to measuring on moderate slopes, and is widely used in the flat-lying Cretaceous and Tertiary beds of the Plains states and intermontane basins of the Rockies. The method is less accurate where topographic relief is low and long "shots" are required.

Where very steep slopes or benches and cliffs are encountered, the Jacob's staff or "Jake-stick" method is applicable, as illustrated in Figure 3-4. This procedure employs a rod, usually five feet in length, which may be either specially prepared and subdivided or cut from local timber. Measurement is accomplished in a series of five-foot steps, zigzagging up the slope to avoid obstructions and covered areas. The method is particularly useful when samples are to be collected within five-foot or ten-foot intervals.

Fig. 3-3. Measuring horizontal strata with the hand level.

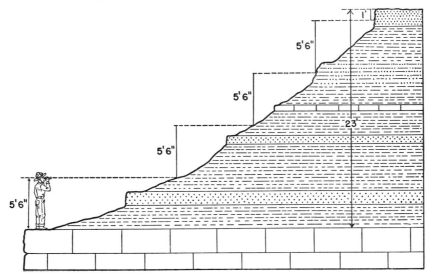

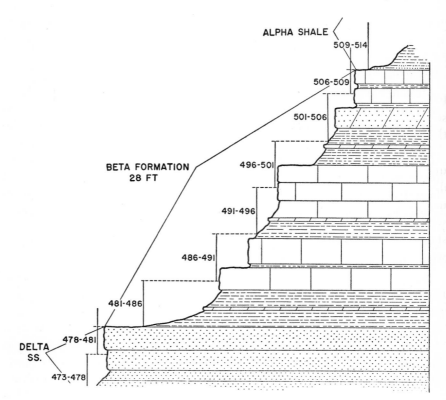

Fig. 3-4. Measuring horizontal strata with a five-foot Jacob's staff.

In areas of low relief, the necessary elevation figures are best obtained by running a traverse, either by tape and Brunton, or by plane table and alidade.

Measuring Inclined Strata

Sections measured in nonhorizontal rocks require modified methods, since the dip must be accounted for in calculation of thickness. If measurement is done on steep slopes with good exposures, the Jacob's staff can be used by holding it at right angles to the bedding and proceding by five-foot intervals. This is a simple operation in areas of blocky limestone and sandstone, since the rod can be held against joint faces, which are commonly normal to the stratification.

Kummel (1943) has described a clinometer attachment for a Jacob's staff which permits accurate five-foot readings in the absence of perpendicular joints. Frequent checks of strike and dip are necessary when this procedure is used.

The method most commonly applied in measuring inclined rocks is traversing with Brunton and tape, illustrated by Figure 3-5. Alidade-plane table traverses can be used, but have the disadvantage of keeping one man busy at the instrument and away from the stratigraphy. It is often possible to stretch the tape across the subunits at right angles to the strike to obtain the slope distance of outcrop. Then, from slope angle and dip, the stratigraphic thickness of the subunit can be readily computed, trigonometrically or graphically.

If, because of some obstruction, measurement must be made oblique to the strike, the horizontal equivalent of the slope distance is converted to distance at right angles to the strike before computing thickness. Mertie (1922) has presented equations and nomographs for the solution of such problems.

Laboratory Study of Outcrop Samples

Many details of lithology cannot be adequately studied in the field, some because of insufficient time during section measuring, others because they are not readily observable with a hand lens. Field descriptions of carbonate rocks and fine-grained clastics seldom do justice to the wealth of valuable detail these sediments can yield to microscopic study. Table 3-1 illustrates the procedure to be followed and the nature of data obtainable by binocular microscope examination of samples.

Heavy Mineral Analysis. When sandstone grains are split into heavy and light fractions by gravity separation in heavy liquids, many mineralogic details not detectable in the gross sample are exposed. Such data are useful

Fig. 3-5. Measuring inclined strata with data from Brunton-and-tape traverse.

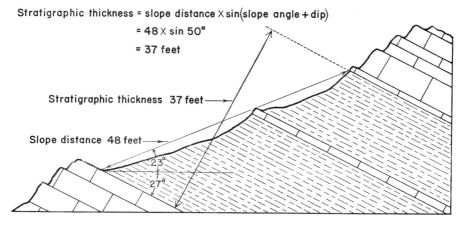

TRIGONOMETRIC SOLUTION:

Stratigraphic thickness = slope distance × sin(slope angle + dip)

= 48 × sin 50°

= 37 feet

Stratigraphic thickness 37 feet

Slope distance 48 feet

23°

27°

TABLE 3-1. CHECK LIST FOR BINOCULAR MICROSCOPE EXAMINATION OF CRUSHED ROCK SAMPLES (Modified from a form prepared by E. C. Dapples.)

Sample No. _____ Interval top _____ btm. _____ Stratigraphic unit _____
Locality or well _____ Location _____

Color _____ Fracture _____
Lamination _____ Texture
Porosities   variety _____
_____   grade sizes
_____   L _____, M _____, S _____
Hardness _____ crystal sizes
Powder of shales
_____   sorting _____
Reaction to HCl   Special Textures
_____   _____
_____   _____
Disaggregation   Mineralogy of residue
medium of _____   _____
Type of _____   _____
_____   _____
Composition   Sphericity
Grains or Xtls.   value   %
total % _____   _____   _____
quartz _____, calcite _____   _____   _____
feldspar _____, dolomite _____   _____   _____
muscovite _____, chert _____   Roundness
biotite _____, glauconite _____   value   %
chlorite _____, pyrite _____   _____   _____
pyribole _____, iron oxide _____   _____   _____
rock frag. _____, gypsum _____   _____   _____
others _____
Carbonate allochems
fossils or fossil fragments _____   Organic Remains
oolites or pisolites _____   Abundance _____
pellets _____   Condition _____
intraclasts _____   _____
lumps _____   Preservation
_____
Matrix total % _____   Kinds of organisms
_____   _____
_____   _____
_____
Cement   _____
degree _____   _____
composition _____
_____   Rock type _____

in correlation and in studies of source and depositional environments of sediment.

Insoluble Residue Analysis. Carbonate sequences which cannot be differentiated by field and microscopic study are often capable of subdivision and correlation on the basis of their insoluble residues after acid solution of the calcite or dolomite. Further treatment is given in Chapter 4. More detailed consideration of this important technique is given by Ireland (1947, 1950).

Indirect Analysis. Carbonates and shales which do not yield sufficient diagnostic detail by other methods may be amenable to certain indirect approaches to lithologic study. Quantitative spectroscopic chemical analysis of limestones, dolomites, and shales can often produce data useful in differentiating otherwise homogeneous sequences. Differential thermal and X-ray analyses of shales can be interpreted in terms of the clay minerals present and thus implement detailed lithologic description and analysis.

Textural Analysis. Many textural details of clastic rocks cannot be adequately seen in a routine microscopic examination. The particle-size distribution of sandstones, silts, and shales must be determined by mechanical analysis, usually by sieving and settling-velocity techniques. Proper evaluation of shape, roundness, surface texture, and orientation also requires special techniques, as described in Chapter 4.

Presentation of Outcrop Data

Written Descriptions. Although graphic presentation of stratigraphic data is perhaps the most useful technique, it does not portray diagrammatically all the information necessary to the full understanding of sediments. Therefore, a written description of every measured section is presented which includes all the data gathered in the field and in the laboratory for each subunit, as well as the results of paleontologic investigation. Table 3-2 is an example of the final description of the field data shown in Figures 3-1 and 3-2.

Geologic Cross Sections. Geologic cross sections conveniently illustrate both stratigraphy and the relationship of stratigraphy to structure and topography. Geologic cross sections may be used to illustrate the position and occurrence of various stratigraphic units within a mountain range or sedimentary basin. They cannot, however, show much stratigraphic or lithologic detail without great vertical exaggeration of scale and consequent distortion of relief and structure. An example is given in Figure 3-6.

Columnar Sections. Columnar sections are the most useful and familiar graphic means of expressing the stratigraphic data of measured sections.

TABLE 3-2. SAPPINGTON CANYON SECTION
(Sec. 25, T. 1 N., R. 2 W., Jefferson County, Montana)

Section of Cretaceous, Jurassic, Permian, Pennsylvanian, and Mississippian strata measured on the east side of Sappington Canyon of Jefferson River, approximately fourteen miles southwest of Three Forks, Montana. Section extends from outcrops immediately south of U.S. Highway 10S to canyon outcrops along Northern Pacific Railway tracks about one-quarter mile south. Measured and sampled by T. A. Hendricks, L. S. Gardner, and L. L. Sloss, November 5, 1944. Sample study by L. S. Gardner, January 1945.

PENNSYLVANIAN—QUADRANT QUARTZITE   *Feet*

UNIT 43. Dolomite, dark gray, dense; has many nodules of dolomite surrounded   4
by thin shells of chert; brecciated at top. Insoluble residue of silicified
brachiopod fragments and quartz silt (3%).

UNIT 42. Dolomite, light brown, weathering gray, dense, thin-bedded. Insoluble   2
residue of clay and quartz silt (10%).

UNIT 41. Sandstone, dolomitic, light yellow-brown, weathering medium brown;   7
well-sorted, median diameter approximately ⅛ mm; grains with
marked secondary enlargement, "ghost" grains with high roundness
and sphericity; heavy minerals less than 1%.

UNIT 40. Sandstone, white, massive, resistant; grades upward to gray to brown   32
quartzite at top; grain size and sorting as in 41; secondary enlargement increasing to complete cementation at top.

Total thickness Quadrant Quartzite   45

Quadrant rests conformably on Amsden with transitional contact
placed at base of lowest prominent sandstone and top of dominantly
carbonate section.

PENNSYLVANIAN AND MISSISSIPPIAN—
AMSDEN FORMATION   *Feet*

UNIT 39. Limestone and dolomitic limestone, light brown, finely crystalline;   22
forms a slope. Insoluble residue of clay and fine silt (10%).

UNIT 25. Limestone, dolomitic, saccharoidal, light brown; weathering to gray,   24
sandy-textured surfaces; contains a few 3-inch ellipsoidal nodules of
olive chert; forms a prominent ridge. Insoluble residue (8%) clay and
chalky, dolomoldic chert.

UNIT 24. Limestone, light gray, dense, weathering dark gray; grades upward   7
into nonresistant silty limestone, yellow-gray. Insoluble residue (20%)
loose quartz silt and dolomoldic clay pellets. Fossil collection 15–4–24F:
(Preservation very poor)
Chonetes sp. indet.
Composita sp. indet.
Phricodothyris sp., cf. *P. perplexa*
Punctospirifer sp., cf. *P. kentuckiensis*
Schizophoria sp. indet.

TABLE 3-2. (Continued)

UNIT 23. Shale, red, calcareous, and green, noncalcareous, fissile; thin beds of   32
silty yellow limestone with minute glauconite grains near base; gray,
dense limestone with residue of drusy silt near top.

UNIT 22. Limestone, light gray, finely saccharoidal, massive; forms prominent   3
ledge; contains few silicified, unrecognizable brachiopod fragments.
Insoluble residue (15%) of shell fragments and ooloidal chert aggregates.

UNIT 21. Siltstone, highly calcareous (40% soluble), yellowish-gray; has a 3-inch   15
bed of purple and green noncalcareous siltstone and two 8-inch beds of
dark gray highly silty limestone (insoluble residue 25%, silt) near middle of unit; a few poorly exposed beds of shale, green, fissile. Fossil
collection 15–4–21F from limestone and siltstone:
      Spirorbis anthracosis
      Gutschickia sp., cf. *G. deltoidea*
      (lowest occurrence of Pennsylvanian fossils)

UNIT 20. Limestone, dark gray, some brown, dense; in even beds to 3 inches   3
thick, separated by silty and clayey, nonresistant limestone partings.

UNIT 19. Covered. A steep slope with a few small "grass-root" outcrops of   51
greenish-gray and red fissile shale; soil predominantly red.
    Total thickness of portion Amsden Formation assigned to
    Pennsylvanian.. 366

UNIT 18. Limestone, dark gray, dense to finely saccharoidal, fossiliferous, well
bedded in layers as much as 3 feet thick: contains stringers of black
and gray chert. Upper 16 feet thin bedded, silty, with light brown
claystone partings. Fossil collection 15–4–18F:
      Linoproductus ovatus
      Spirifer increbescens
      Spirifer pellaensis
      (highest occurrence of Mississippian fossils)

Columnar sections show the sequence, interrelations, and thickness of strati-graphic units and illustrate their lithology by conventional symbols.

The selection of vertical scale makes possible the expression of whatever degree of detail is available or desired. Each unit is shown with the proper scale thickness in its proper position in the column. One hundred feet to the inch is a common scale, but some sections may require ten feet to the inch, and others may be satisfactorily depicted at 1000 feet to the inch.

Symbols expressing the chief lithologic attributes of each subunit and certain accessory features are entered within the main body of the column. The position and distribution of chert and other significant details, the spacing of bedding planes, cross-lamination, and unconformities can be

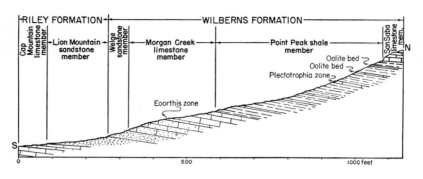

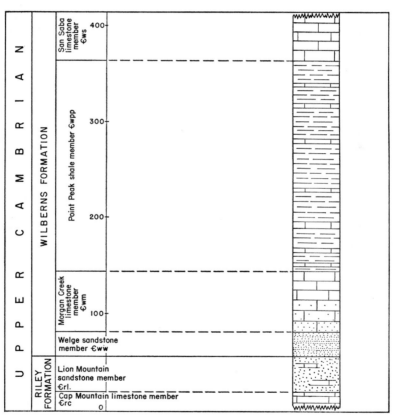

Fig. 3-6. (*Top*) Example of a geologic cross section. (*Bottom*) The same data represented as a columnar section. Note that the *Stratigraphic Code* would now require capitalization of "member" and other formal unit terms. [Adapted from Bridge, Barnes, and Cloud, 1947.]

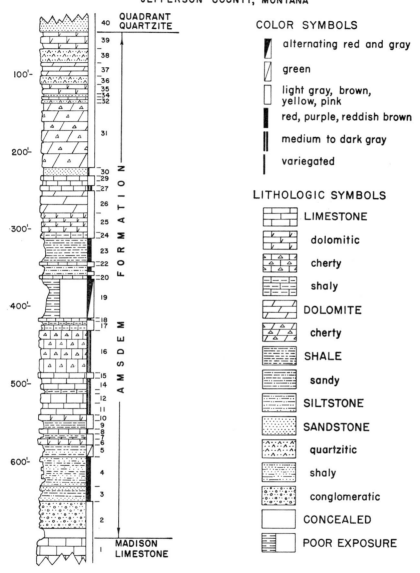

SAPPINGTON CANYON
SEC. 25, T. 1N., R. 2W
JEFFERSON COUNTY, MONTANA

Fig. 3-7. Columnar section of part of the Sappington Canyon section illustrated by Figures 3-1 and by Table 3-2. [Adapted from U. S. Geol. Survey, Oil and Gas Invest. Series, Preliminary Chart 18, 1945.]

indicated, but attempts to illustrate too many features usually result in confusing illegible columns. Figure 3-7 is an example of a columnar section representing part of the data given in Figures 3-1 and 3-2 and Table 3-2.

Color and texture are best shown by separate strips of symbols along one or both sides of the column. Where insoluble residue or heavy mineral data are available, they too require separate strips.

The range of paleontologic zones may be represented by brackets or arrows adjacent to the column, each zone being identified by its characteristic species or by a symbol referring to an annotated faunal list.

A properly organized columnar section is capable of expressing practically all the significant physical and biological data obtained from measurement and analysis of a stratigraphic section.

Stratigraphic Cross Sections. Stratigraphic cross sections differ from geologic cross sections in that they do not attempt to illustrate the topographic profile, and structure is either restored or diagrammatically expressed. Moreover, vertical scale is greatly exaggerated in order to show stratigraphic detail. Cross sections are drawn by arranging series of columnar sections side by side in proper geographic sequence. In indicating actual distance from one location to another, a uniform spacing between columns may be used, or irregular spacing may be used to show the actual separation.

If structural relationships are important in the study, the vertical positions of the columns are determined by their elevation in the field, emphasizing the influence of structure. More commonly, structure is restored, and the columns are arranged relative to some stratigraphic horizon selected as the datum. Lithologic and faunal correlations are indicated by lines connecting the proper horizons from column to column. Pinch-outs, intertonguing lithologies, and other phenomena which are inferred to be present between the positions of columns may be shown, but the distinction between inference and actual observation should be clear. Figure 3-8 is an example of a stratigraphic cross section composed of surface and subsurface columns.

Two or more lines of stratigraphic cross sections can be illustrated by arranging the various columns on an isometric map base and drawing the correlation lines to look like a network of fences viewed obliquely from the air. Such "fence diagrams" (Figure 3-9) are useful in expressing regional relationships, but very little detail can be shown, since the vertical scale must be reduced to keep the various fences from obscuring one another.

Stratigraphic cross sections are not ideal vehicles for the expression and interpretation of stratigraphy, since they give a strictly two-dimensional picture of three-dimensional bodies. Fence diagrams impart a three-dimensional aspect, but they do not express sufficient detail and cannot be drawn to cover all of any area.

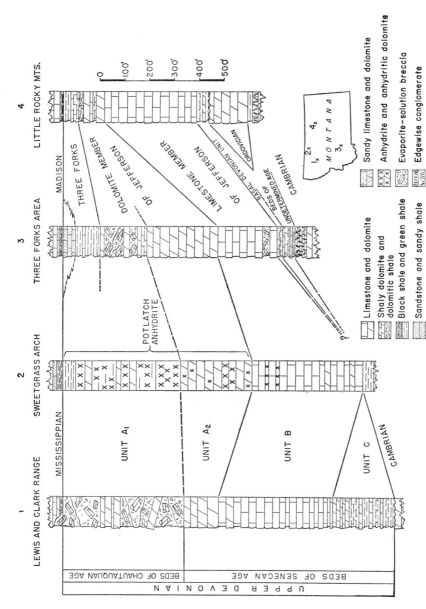

Fig. 3-8. Generalized stratigraphic cross section of Devonian strata in Montana, showing application of informal units in the reconnaissance stages of a stratigraphic investigation.

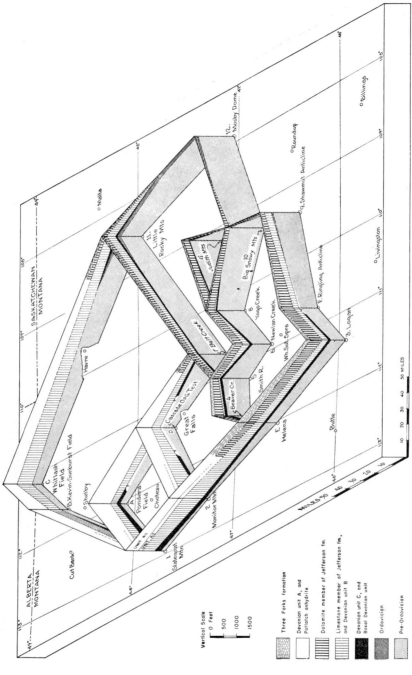

Fig. 3-9. Isometric stratigraphic diagram of the Montana Devonian strata shown in Figure 3-8. Note that the *Stratigraphic Code* would require capitalization of Three Forks Formation and Jefferson Formation, whereas the informal units would remain uncapitalized. [From U. S. Geol. Survey Oil and Gas Invest. Series, Preliminary Chart 25, 1946.]

Many misconceptions in stratigraphic thinking stem from interpretations of cross sections without consideration of conditions and relationships in other planes of the solid geometry involved. In a later chapter, ways and means of three-dimensional stratigraphic mapping are presented, but their discussion and interpretation are postponed until the reader gains a greater familiarity with certain important stratigraphic principles.

SUBSURFACE PROCEDURES

Any stratigrapher working on subsurface problems requires an intimate knowledge of drilling methods and their effects on sampling. Since there is insufficient space here to treat the subject adequately, the following summary is intended to point out the influence of the different sampling methods and is by no means a discourse on petroleum engineering. The symposium *Subsurface Geology in Petroleum Exploration*, edited by Haun and LeRoy (1958), contains over thirty papers on topics that are briefly noted in this chapter.

Cable-tool Samples

The cable-tool method is responsible for many older oil and gas wells, practically all water wells, and a considerable number of wells drilled each year in shallow oil or gas pools. Therefore, cable-tool samples available for study include a vast amount of stratigraphic data.

Cable tools (or standard tools, as they are sometimes called) "make hole" by rhythmically raising and dropping a chisel-like bit and heavy drill stem at the end of a cable. Repeated blows of the bit fracture and grind up the rocks, and at intervals the bit is withdrawn and replaced by a bailer that removes the cuttings from the hole. Samples are taken of material dumped from the bailer and are sacked and appropriately labeled.

Cable-tool wells require the casing and cementing of caving formations and artesian aquifers. Therefore, "open-hole" is carried only as long as the sides of the bore are maintained without support and excessive flows of water are not encountered. For this reason, cable-tool samples are relatively pure and include only minor amount of material knocked off uncased portions of the bore by the passage of tools and bailer.

The knowledge of horizons at which casing was set and at which water sands were encountered makes it possible to anticipate and recognize cavings in samples. Generally, the presence of caved material is obvious, and contamination does not offer a difficult problem in interpretation of cable-tool samples.

Rotary-tool Samples

In recent years, a majority of all wells have been drilled with rotary tools. In order to use and interpret the great and constantly growing mass of data obtained with this method, it is necessary to understand the influences of the drilling method on the samples.

Rotary drilling is accomplished by a cutting bit of variable design mounted at the end of the column of drill pipe. Rotation of the rotary table at the surface spins the drill pipe, causing the attached bit to cut through the strata. As drilling proceeds, joints of drill pipe are added to the top of the column. It is not necessary to remove the drill pipe and bit from the hole except to replace worn bits, to change bits, and to perform tests. In soft, nonabrasive formations it may be possible to drill several thousand feet without stopping, except to add joints of drill pipe.

During drilling, high-pressure pumps force mud down through the drill pipe, through holes in the bit, and up along the annulus between the sides of the drill pipe and the sides of the bore. The circulating mud exerts a hydrostatic pressure against the sides of the bore, maintaining them in the absence of casing, penetrating and coating permeable horizons, and preventing the uncontrolled flow of high-pressure gas, oil, or water when encountered. The specific gravity of the mud is kept at a high level by the addition of barite in order to increase the hydrostatic effect of the mud column and to make the cuttings relatively buoyant.

The returning column of mud bears the cuttings with it to the surface where the cuttings are removed by a "shale shaker." Samples of the cuttings were formerly taken at regular intervals from the ditch through which the mud circulated to pits for settling and reconditioning. Hence, the term "ditch samples" is commonly applied to rotary samples. In more recent practice a special device is responsible for continuous sampling of the cuttings from each five or ten feet drilled.

The length of time required by cuttings to rise from the bit to the surface is determined by the settling velocity of the particles and the velocity of the returning mud. Since the settling velocity of the particles varies with size and shape, some particles tend to lag behind, whereas others rise rapidly to overtake the cuttings from stratigraphically higher horizons. Rotation of the drill pipe and each removal and reintroduction of the tools cause a certain amount of caving from the sides of the bore. Therefore, rotary samples taken from a given drilled interval contain not only cuttings from the strata represented but also fragments from any horizon drilled below the lowest casing point.

When stratigraphic data are particularly important, drilling is periodically suspended while circulation of the mud continues. This removes the majority of lagging cuttings and cavings from the mud and reduces the degree of contamination in succeeding samples. This procedure is not followed as often as the geologist might wish, since it involves the relatively unproductive expenditure of "rig time."

It is common practice to sample all potential productive zones in wildcat drilling and "pay" zones in routine drilling of field wells by coring. Cores are taken with a special hollow bit which, depending on the friability of the rock, permits the cutting of cylindrical samples up to twenty feet in length. Such samples provide accurately located lithological data and material for laboratory analysis of porosity, permeability, and fluid content. These samples also recover macrofossils in identifiable form, if present.

It would be desirable to have all wells cored from surface to total depth, but coring is a very expensive process. To recover each core taken, it is necessary to remove all the drill pipe from the hole. Thus, a complete "round trip" may be required for each five feet of drilling, and at the two- to three-mile depths now current, the stratigraphic value must be weighed against the costs. These costs may be reduced under certain circumstances by use of "side-wall" cores, "wire-line" core barrel, and other devices, but expense remains high in terms of normal drilling. Therefore, the stratigrapher must continue to rely on routine cuttings supplemented by circulated samples and occasional cores.

Logging

Drillers' Logs. The records of many older oil wells and of almost all water wells consist of logs kept by the drillers, and stratigraphers are often dependent on such data in areas where modern drilling and sampling procedures have not been introduced.

Drillers' logs have certain inherent weaknesses and, even when they constitute the only subsurface data, must be used with caution in stratigraphic analysis. The old-time cable-tool driller was more often influenced by the "feel" of the action of the drill stem and the speed with which the bit was dulled than by the lithologic character of the cuttings. Moreover, the lithologic and stratigraphic terminology of driller's logs is frequently more confusing than helpful.

Sample Logs. In modern practice, a geologist is present at each exploratory well throughout the course of drilling, twenty-four hours a day, if necessary. The geologist is responsible for taking cutting samples and for recommending which intervals should be cored. While drilling continues, he compiles, from microscopic examination of the samples, a detailed log of the rocks penetrated. Such a sample log can, of course, be duplicated and elaborated or revised by later study of the samples, but the geologist "sitting" on the well has firsthand knowledge of the individual drilling problem and is often able to make the best interpretation of many factors.

Logging Cable-tool Samples. Samples from cable-tool drilling, are relatively uncontaminated and can be examined and recorded as they appear in the sample sacks. However, where two or more lithologies are present in a single sample, their mutual interrelationships must be interpreted. This problem is more pertinent to a discussion of rotary samples.

Logging Rotary Samples. When rotary samples first became available in large quantities for stratigraphic interpretation, they were viewed with considerable distrust because of their nearly inevitable contamination. Early attempts to use rotary samples resulted in the evolution of "percentage logs." These recorded all the lithologies present in each sample and gave the percentage of total sample volume represented by each lithologic type. Inasmuch as the cuttings from any interval represented by a sample may amount to 10 percent or less of the total sample, such percentage logs are distorted representations of the section penetrated.

More satisfactory logs are prepared by disregarding extraneous particles and centering attention upon material actually representative of the interval drilled. This procedure requires a certain amount of interpretation of the sample, and errors of interpretation are possible. However, to the experienced subsurface stratigrapher, this interpretive step becomes routine.

Samples must be studied in succession, from the surface down, paying particular attention to "first appearances" of different lithologies. Materials not present in previous samples represent additions to the stream of particles rising in the mud, and their presence in the sample marks the interval within which the drill passed a lithologic boundary. Thus, the presence of a few grains of sand (perhaps less than 1 percent of the total volume of the sample) in a sequence of samples composed of shale and limestone marks the top of a sandstone unit. If the sandstone is thick, the samples will gradually include larger percentages; if the unit is thin, the percentage of sand will remain small. In the latter instance, the log will show that the lithology has reverted to that encountered before the sandstone was penetrated or to a new type marking the top of a different lithology. Combination logs showing the interpreted sequence of lithologies, but including percentage data on the contaminants, are favored by some subsurface workers.

By these interpretive means it is possible to build a fairly satisfactory log from cuttings alone. Accuracy is greatly increased, however, with data from electric logs, drilling-time logs, and other mechanical logs, and also with information on casing points established during drilling, round trips, circulated samples, coring, drill-stem tests, and other operations likely to influence samples.

Cores, electric logs, and drilling-time data are particularly helpful in determining the representative portion of a sample and in locating the depth at which lithologic boundaries were penetrated. There is always a lag between the actual drilling of the rocks by the bit and the appearance of the cuttings in the samples. Thus, samples "caught" at an indicated depth of 5000 feet contain no cuttings from that depth but do contain material representative of strata penetrated a few feet higher in the hole. During slow drilling at shallow depths, the bit does not drill through fast enough to introduce a significant sample lag. However, in faster drilling at greater depths, a lag is significant, particularly when determination of the structural position of units is important.

Many stratigraphers feel that a percentage log, even one that excludes consideration of cavings and extraneous cuttings, is an unsatisfactory record for stratigraphic interpretation. A log indicating that a given interval consists of 60 percent shale and 40 percent sandstone does not state the relationships of these lithologies, which may be an important factor in correlation or facies analysis. There is therefore a growing acceptance of strictly interpretive logs where sufficient data are available. Recourse is again made to cores and electric logs which make possible the interpretation of the sample in terms of relationships between lithologies. The case of shale and sandstone mentioned above might be interpreted as "sandstone in three-foot beds interbedded with shale in two-foot beds."

Microscopic Examination. Many of the data presented in logs are derived from binocular microscope examination of samples in the same fashion described for outcrop material. Since outcrop sections are frequently partly concealed, the subsurface data may surpass the outcrop data in completeness and detail.

Other Techniques. Insoluble residue, heavy mineral, and chemical analyses are performed on picked drill cuttings in the same manner and for the same purposes as with outcrop material. McCracken (1955) and Feo-Codecido (1956) illustrate the application of these techniques to subsurface materials for purposes of differentiation of units of strata and correlation of the units from well to well.

It is sometimes possible to pick a sufficient amount of representative material from cuttings for mechanical analysis of particle-size distribution, but cores are usually required. Similarly, cores are needed for measurement of such mass properties as porosity, permeability, and fluid content. These properties are so important in petroleum technology that their determination is frequently assigned to special core analysis laboratories.

Micropaleontology. Except for the relatively rare cases of preservation of macrofossils in cores, subsurface biostratigraphic and time-stratigraphic classification must depend on microfossils, chiefly foraminifera and ostracodes, small enough to be preserved in cuttings. Therefore, micropaleontology has grown into an important science, implemented with a complex technology. Schenck and Adams (1943) have described the procedures followed in commercial micropaleontologic laboratories.

Mechanical Well-logging

The sedimentary rocks encountered in drilling for oil have widely different physical properties, and a number of these properties may be used for distinguishing among the sediments. During the past three decades, numerous mechanical methods have been developed for obtaining information on sedimentary properties from bore holes.

Electric Logs. The electric log is one of the most valuable and widely used means of obtaining information from bore holes. The log is obtained by lowering an exploring device, a sonde, attached to an electric cable. The sonde contains a system of electrodes by means of which measurements of the **spontaneous potential** (commonly called the S.P.) and the electrical **resistivity** of the strata are continuously made from bottom to top of the well. The measurements are carried to the surface and automatically recorded on photographic film as a continuous function of depth. Fig. 3-10 shows the sonde and its electrode configuration.

Spontaneous Potential Curves. The S.P. curve is measured by electrode M, Figure 3-10. Figure 3-11 illustrates the idealized S.P. curves for various types of sedimentary rocks and contained fluids. Basically, the spontaneous potential is a small electric voltage generated at the boundaries of permeable units of rock (sandstone and limestone for instance), and especially between such strata and less permeable units (shale for example). The difference in salinity between the drilling mud and the water in permeable beds is another factor in the spontaneous potential. All permeable strata contain some water, even when they carry oil or gas, and this water is generally more saline than the drilling mud. Opposite these salt-water bearing beds the S.P. curve moves negatively—to the left on the log. If the mud and formation water have the same salinity, the S.P. curve does not depart from a reasonably uniform value associated with shale readings, commonly called the "shale line." When the beds contain water less saline than the mud, the S.P. curve moves to the right of the shale line.

Resistivity Curves. The electrical resistivity of a rock (resistance per unit volume) depends primarily on the amount of fluid contained and its electrical resistivity. The amount of fluid is, of course, a function of the porosity; hence the porosity of a rock is related to its resistivity. In general terms, strata of 10 percent porosity are 10 times as resistive as those of 30 percent

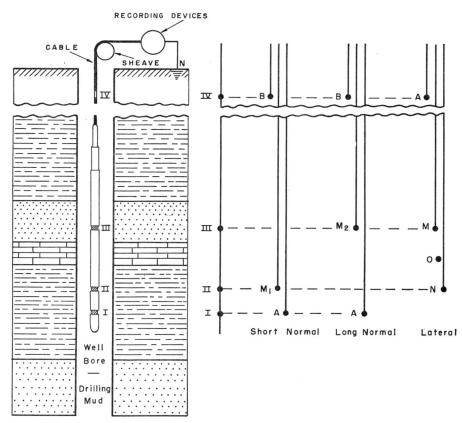

Fig. 3-10. The electric log sonde and the configuration of the electrodes for recording short normal, long normal, and lateral curves. [Courtesy Schlumberger Well Surveying Corporation.]

porosity, though both contain the same fluid. A porous sandstone filled with salt water (a good conductor of electricity) will have low electrical resistivity. The same sandstone filled with oil (a nonconductor) will have high resistivity. Dense limestones and quartzites have very low porosity and can contain little fluid of any kind, hence they have very high resistivities. These principles are illustrated by the resistivity curves of Figure 3-11.

In rotary drilling, permeable beds close to the bore hole may be invaded by the drilling mud. Since the drilling mud is usually less saline and more resistive than the formation water, a salt-water bearing unit invaded by this mud will show a high resistivity. Such a unit might be mistaken for an oil sand. To record the true resistivity beyond the invaded zone, the resistivity spacing must be increased (see Figure 3-10). Thus, in addition to a *short normal* resistivity curve of about 16-inch spacing, a *long normal* spacing of

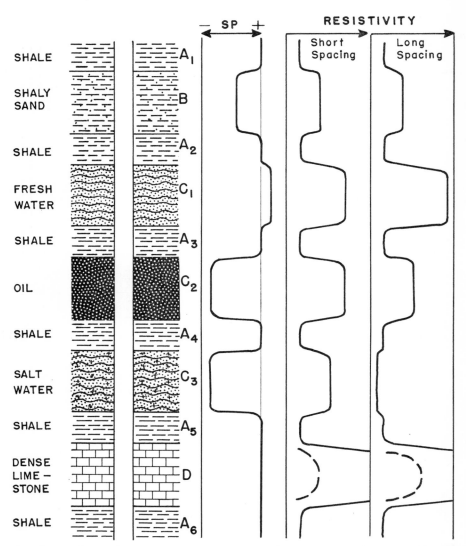

Fig. 3-11. Idealized S.P. and resistivity curves for various combinations of rock types and contained fluids. [Courtesy Schlumberger Well Surveying Corporation.]

60–70 inches is also run. An even deeper penetration measurement is the *lateral* curve, which records the resistivity between a point O (midway between two measuring electrodes) and a current electrode, A (Figure 3-10). This is a "long spacing" configuration, usually 15–18 feet, that determines the resistivity at considerable distance from the bore and well beyond the zone of mud invasion. Figure 3-12 is an electric log of a Miocene section in

Louisiana, which shows alternating shales and sands and three oil-water contacts.

Interpretation of Electric Logs. A typical electric log is shown in Figure 3-12. The S.P. curve appears on the left side of the log strip with millivolt values increasing to the left. The right side of the log bears the resistivity curves with resistivity values, expressed in ohm-meters[2] per meter, increasing to the right. The short and long normal curves are usually superimposed on the same scale, with the lateral curve on an independent scale at the right. Peaks which would plot beyond the limits of the strip are translated to the base line and may be distinctively crosshatched.

Proper interpretation of electric logs requires knowledge of a number of factors which affect the character and behavior of the various curves. The more or less empirical relationships given below are sufficient for an introduction to interpretive methods.

Permeable sandstones show a large spontaneous potential, and a thick sand is represented on the electric log by a somewhat rounded bulge on the S.P. curve which may extend outward for forty or more millivolts. The resistivity of the sandstone depends to a large extent upon the fluid it contains. If the sand contains fresh water or oil, the resistivity curves project to the right of the diagram in a double bulge on the electric log. If the sand is interbedded with shale, both the S.P. curve and the resistivity curve show numerous indentations separated by sharp or rounded peaks of width varying in proportion to the thickness of the interbedded sand beds.

Shale is typically represented by a low spontaneous potential and a low resistivity. Dense impervious limestone shows a small S.P. curve and high resistivity values, especially on the lateral curve. Porous limestone yields S.P. curves resembling those of sandstone, although, in general, it may not yield as large values in millivolts. Evaporites, such as salt or gypsum, tend to have a somewhat jagged S.P. curve with small millivolt readings, and very high resistivities, as shown by long narrow peaks on the resistivity log.

The principles of interpretation are clarified by consideration of the several groupings of strata and their electrical responses shown on the idealized log (Fig. 3-11).

Units A_1, A_2, A_3, . . . , are interpreted as shales for the following reasons:

1. The S.P. curve does not depart from the shale line, indicating a nonpermeable medium.
2. The units have a low resistivity, indicating high porosities.
3. Both short and long spacing resistivity curves have the same value, indicating that the strata are impervious to drilling mud.

Unit B is interpreted as a shaly sandstone for the following reasons:

ELECTRICAL LOG

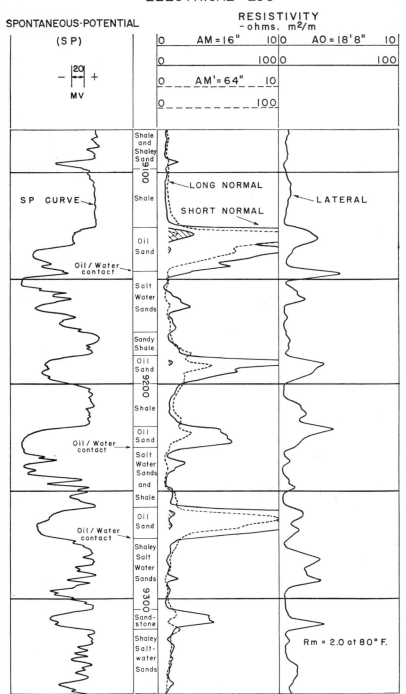

Fig. 3-12. A typical electrical log combining the S.P., normal, and lateral curves. [Courtesy Schlumberger Well Surveying Corporation.]

80

1. The S.P. has a moderate departure from the shale line.
2. Both resistivity curves show a value only slightly higher than the shale, indicating strata of moderate porosity.

Unit C_1 is interpreted as a fresh-water bearing sandstone for the following reasons:

1. The S.P. curve has a positive departure from the shale line.
2. Both resistivity curves are high because the fresh water, which saturates the sand, is poorly conductive.

Unit C_2 is interpreted as a sandstone saturated with oil for the following reasons:

1. The S.P. has a strong negative deflection.
2. The short spacing resistivity is fairly high because the part of the sand measured by that spacing contains residual oil and the invading drilling fluid.
3. The long spacing resistivity is high because the sand beyond the invaded section is principally saturated with oil, which is a poor conductor.

Unit C_3 is interpreted as salt water bearing sandstone for the following reasons:

1. The S.P. has a strong negative departure from the shale line.
2. The short spacing resistivity is fairly high because the portion of sand measured is filled with nonconductive mud filtrate, which has displaced much of the conductive salt water.
3. The long spacing resistivity is very low because this curve reaches beyond the invaded section and into the sand saturated with conductive salt water.

Unit D is interpreted as an impermeable limestone for the following reasons:

1. The S.P. has no departure, indicating a nonpermeable formation.
2. Both resistivity curves are very high; in fact the primary curves are off scale, and the reduced scales are recorded. This indicates a very dense formation containing little water.

MicroLog. An important extension of electric logging was the development of the MicroLog. (MicroLog is a trade name of the Schlumberger Well Surveying Corp.). The curves are made by electrodes in contact with the wall of the well bore and with very short spacing (one or two inches). These small spacings detect thin laminations and lithologic changes. As a result, the MicroLog shows much finer detail than the standard electric log. Permeable strata are infiltrated by drilling mud, and in the process a resistive filter cake builds up on the wall of the bore where it intersects permeable rocks. These strata are readily recognized on MicroLog curves. Furthermore, the percent of porosity can frequently be calculated from the values of two MicroLog curves. A typical MicroLog record is shown in Figure 3-13 with cross hatched bars to indicate the positions of permeable beds.

Fig. 3-13. MicroLog curves. Microresistivity curves are shown at the right. Permeable portions of the section penetrated are indicated (cross-hatched bars) by extensions of the 2-inch micro-normal curve beyond the micro-inverse. Note that the diameter of the bore, as recorded by the Micro-Log caliper, is smaller than bit size where a mud filter cake is formed at the position of permeable beds. A standard electrical log of the same stratigraphic interval is shown at the left for comparison. [Courtesy Schlumberger Well Surveying Corporation.]

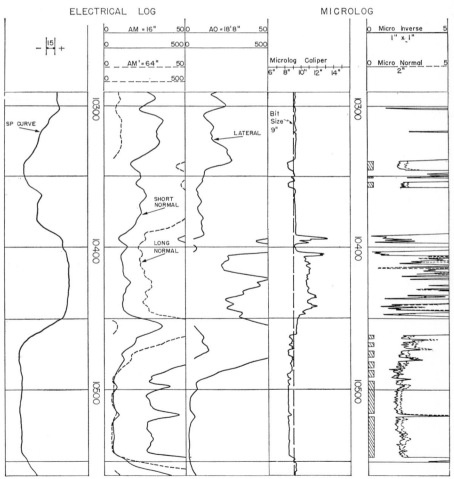

Special Focused Logs. There are some situations in which the electric log is not obtainable: in wells with no fluid in the bore hole, and in those drilled with oil base mud, high pressure gas, or air. These media are electrical insulators; thus no current is carried from the logging sonde into the strata. To log these wells, the *induction log* is used. In induction logging, the rocks surrounding the sonde are energized by an induced electromagnetic field. Secondary effects of the electromagnetic field that are related to the resistivity of the strata are measured, producing a log of the formation resistivities. A gamma ray log (discussed in a later paragraph), is usually run with the induction log in order to reveal the boundaries of stratal units. Figure 3-14, a log made in a well drilled with oil base mud, shows the induction, gamma rays and neutron curves used to detect the character of fluids contained in the rocks.

The induction log sonde beams electrical energy into the strata horizontally and thus measures only the resistivity of strata opposite the instrument. Thus, a value close to the true resistivity of the beds is read *directly*. In normal electric logging, the current flows between two widely separated electrodes and thus flows across bed boundaries. The true resistivity is obtained *indirectly* from the electric log curves, since corrections for the influence of adjacent beds must be made. Because of the advantage of direct over indirect measurement, the induction log is being used more frequently in wells drilled with conductive muds. It is of particular value in obtaining the true resistivity and is therefore a measure of the lithology and contained fluids of thin beds. The *combination electrical-induction log*, a very recent development, simultaneously records the S.P. curve, a 16-inch resistivity curve, and an induction curve of 40-inch spacing (see Figure 3-15).

An entirely different situation exists in wells drilled with salty mud. In this case the electric current tends to flow only between the electrodes on the sonde and not into the rocks. To log under these conditions, the *Laterolog* or *Guard Electrode* is used. Such a device focuses the electric current or "forces" it to enter the strata. A gamma ray log is run to replace the S.P. curve, which is usually meaningless in salty mud (formation fluid and drilling mud being of the same salinity). The *Microlaterolog*, a focused micro-device, is used in place of the MicroLog (see Figure 3-16).

Stratigraphic Applications of Electric Logs. Electric logging is the most useful geophysical tool applicable to stratigraphic investigations. Interpretation of the S.P. and resistivity curves yields precise data on the depth, thickness, and position in sequence of rock units penetrated in drilling. In many cases, interpretations can be made in terms of more minutely detailed lithology than can be derived from studies of cuttings and cores. These data are broadly applicable to such stratigraphic problems as classification and corre-

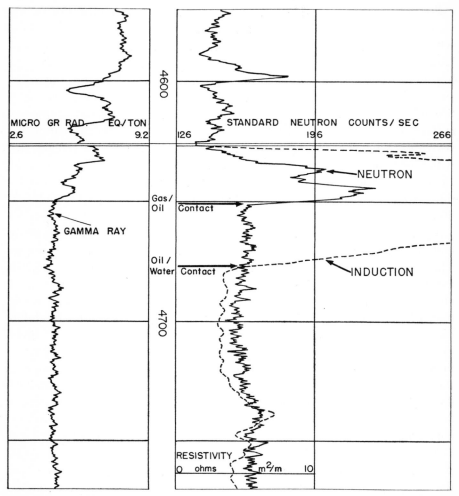

Fig. 3-14. Gamma ray, neutron, and induction curves. [Courtesy Schlumberger Well Surveying Corporation.]

lation of rock units, isopach and facies mapping, recognition of unconformities, and determination of structural attitude.

Radioactivity Logging. Radioactivity logs, another type of mechanical log, are becoming increasingly useful. They have the advantage of being obtainable through the well casing, whereas electric logs, Laterologs, sonic logs, and induction logs can be employed only in uncased wells.

Two measurements are recorded on radioactivity logs: the *gamma ray* activity and the effects of *neutron* bombardment. The gamma ray curve is a record of the natural radioactivity of the rocks. This radioactivity varies

widely among sedimentary rocks, being in general high for shales and lower
for sands and limestones. Thus, this record clearly delineates the boundaries
between stratal units and resembles, in appearance, the S.P. curve of the
electric log. It is frequently used in place of the S.P. curve as a supplement
to the induction log and Laterolog.

The neutron curve is a recording of secondary radioactive effects caused
by bombardment of the strata with neutrons. These secondary effects are
directly related to the porosity of the rocks. Thus the neutron log is very
valuable for porosity evaluation and determination of lithology. Figure 3-14
is a segment of a typical gamma-neutron log combined with an induction

Fig. 3-15. Combination electrical-induction logs. (*Left*) A standard S.P. curve.
(*Right*) Two induction curves and a standard normal resistivity curve.
The mud resistivity, used in calculations of the fluid content of porous
and permeable units, is given at the left bottom. [Courtesy Schlumberger Well Surveying Corporation.]

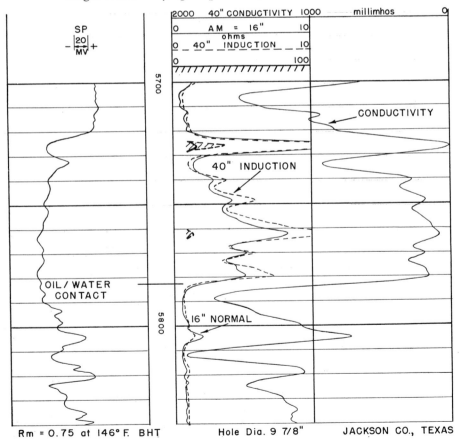

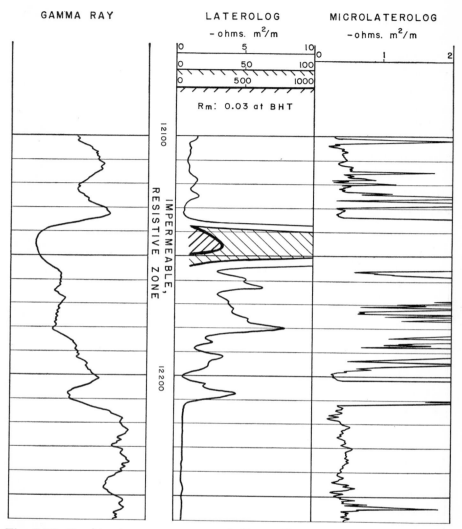

Fig. 3-16. Combination gamma ray and "focused" curves recorded by special sondes employed in the presence of conductive, salty mud. [Courtesy Schlumberger Well Surveying Corporation.]

log. Another example is given in Figure 3-16, which shows the typical responses of gamma and neutron curves to various combinations of lithology and fluid content.

In addition to their usefulness in cased wells and in wells drilled with nonconductive muds, radioactivity logs have found wide application in areas dominated by carbonate and evaporite rocks. Here, radioactivity logs are an important source of stratigraphic data, and the gamma curve, particularly, is used for lithologic interpretations in the absence of an easily decipherable S.P. curve.

Continuous Velocity (Sonic) Logs. The transmission velocity of seismic or sound waves provides still another parameter which may be measured in a borehole and related to lithology. The velocity of sonic waves propagated in sedimentary rocks is largely a function of the matrix characteristics and porosity of the rocks. In general, beds of high porosity, such as shales, are characterized by low velocities; dense nonporous rocks, such as many limestones, are typified by high velocities.

The instrument used to obtain the sonic log consists of a transmitter, which produces pulses of sound, and one or more receivers. As the instrument traverses the borehole the sound pulses, emitted at a rate of ten or more per second, travel through the adjacent strata. The transit time (travel time) is automatically recorded and expressed directly in microseconds per foot of strata or in feet per second. A continuous log is obtained, appearing as a curve plotted against well depth in the manner of other logging devices. The continuous velocity log generally includes an S.P. curve or a gamma ray curve. These curves provide additional information and establish depth control for comparison with other logs made in the same well. Figure 3-17, an example of a sonic log in a limestone section, shows the close relation between velocity and porosity as determined by core analysis.

In addition to its use in porosity estimation, the continuous velocity log is highly useful in correlation problems. Inasmuch as velocity values vary independently of resistivity or radioactivity, the sonic log permits differentiations among strata that may be less evident on other types of logs.

Caliper Logs. A fourth device for mechanical logging is the caliper log, which measures the diameter of the bore hole. Different kinds of sedimentary rocks show a greater or lesser ability to stand in vertical walls. As the borehole is deepened, some of the sediments, such as limestone, present a smooth face slightly larger than the drilling bit, whereas other sediments, such as soft shale, may have caved sufficiently to develop a borehole at least twice as large in diameter as that originally drilled. By lowering a spring caliper down the hole, it is possible to obtain a log (Figure 3-18) which shows the changes in diameter of the bore hole. This may, in turn, be used in conjunction with other types of logs to interpret the characteristics of the rock in the bore hole.

A caliper incorporated in the MicroLog sonde provides a sensitive means for measuring the diameter of the well bore. Where permeable beds are encountered, a relatively thick filter cake is formed from the penetrating drilling mud, and the hole diameter is reduced. Impermeable strata are indicated by hole diameters at approximate "bit size," and, as noted above, at the posi-

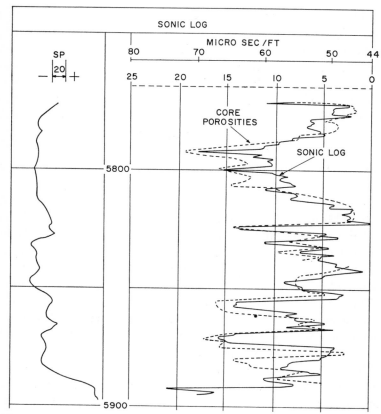

Fig. 3-17. Sonic (continuous velocity) log. The solid curve at the right indicates the velocity of sonic waves expressed as microseconds per foot; the relationship of these velocities to porosities measured in the core laboratory is shown by comparison with the broken curve. A standard S.P. curve is shown at the left. [Courtesy Schlumberger Well Surveying Corporation.]

tion of shales and other caving beds the bore hole is commonly enlarged over "bit size." These relationships are illustrated by the "microlog caliper" and microresistivity curves in Figure 3-13.

Drilling Time Logs. The drilling time log is a record of the number of feet of rock penetrated per unit of time. These data may be kept with a stopwatch or automatic device, and they show, by means of a step diagram, the relative drilling resistance of the different layers of rock. The range of drilling times in different sediments permits an interpretation of the kinds of rock penetrated. For this reason, drilling-time logs may be used to supplement other information about the lithology of the section penetrated.

Presentation of Subsurface Data

Written Logs. Written logs may be prepared from the data compiled by the sample logging procedures in much the same form as that recommended for outcrop sections. The descriptive matter is arranged in order of increasing depth with indication of thickness and depth to the top of each significant unit.

Strip Logs. In common with most stratigraphic data, subsurface data are more readily interpreted in graphic than in written form. The most commonly applied technique is the strip log. These are compiled on commercially prepared light cardboard strips, usually three inches wide. Each strip has spaces at the top for the recording of the name and location of the well and also of such essential information as elevation and completion data. The remainder of the strip bears, at the left, a half-inch column divided into hundreds and tens of feet at a scale of one inch to 100 feet for the purpose of entering lithologic symbols. The right-hand side of the strip is available for recording pertinent written data opposite the appropriate depths.

Colors are used for indicating lithologies, such as yellow for sandstone, blue for limestone, purple for dolomite, and green for siltstone. By modification of hue and shade, and by the addition of crosshatching and other symbols, it is possible to represent the great variety of textural, mineralogical, and other attributes within each major lithologic type, as well as the position and character of such items as chert, glauconite, pyrite, and phosphatic nodules.

Graphic presentation of the majority of data relieves the necessity of lengthy descriptions

Fig. 3-18

Caliper log showing comparison of bore hole diameter and electric log. [After Halliburton Oil Well Cementing Company.]

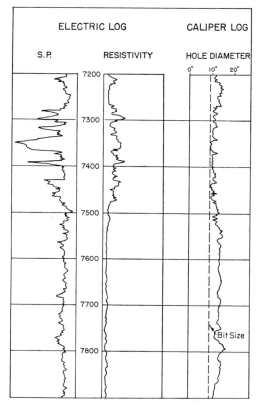

adjacent to each unit on the strip log and increases the ease with which each log may be read, interpreted, and compared with other logs.

Percentage logs are represented by considering the width of the column as 100 percent, colored in various proportions to indicate various percentages of different lithologies. A ten-foot interval represented by 50 percent sandstone and 50 percent limestone would be shown by dividing the appropriate one-tenth of an inch on the column into equal yellow and blue portions, side by side.

Interpretive strip logs illustrate, as far as scale will permit, the interbedding and other relationships of two or more rock types by horizontal bands of the colors and symbols. Even on strictly interpretive logs, however, a certain amount of percentage illustration is usually required. A silty limestone, for example, may be shown by blue with a strip of green down the middle, the width of the green strip representing the percentage of silt present in the limestone. Other lithologies which cannot be defined by a single term or represented by a single color, such as sandy shale, dolomitic limestone, and calcareous sandstone, are similarly represented by two or more colors indicating the relative proportion of each element in the mixture.

Compound Graphic Logs. Although detailed strip logs, with some description of paleontology and other features not suitable for graphic representation, are sufficient in many cases for the analysis of subsurface data, the growing importance of mechanical logs, core analysis data, and data from mineralogical, chemical, and mechanical analysis requires an elaboration of graphic treatment. A commonly used compound log is prepared by introducing a colored strip log between the spontaneous potential and resistivity curves of an electric log. Other combinations are also used, depending on the nature of the problem and the data available.

Some workers find strip logs inadequate in very detailed sample study. One technique involves the use of cross-section paper eighteen inches wide in place of three-inch strips. Various columns are devoted to details of lithology, mineralogy, texture, color, insoluble residue, and other significant attributes of each five-foot interval penetrated.

Strip logs, being colored, cannot be duplicated from tracings or published economically. For purposes of duplication or publication, subsurface data are presented, like outcrop data, by means of columnar sections. Interpretive logs in columnar section form are directly comparable to columnar sections of outcrop material, but percentage logs must be presented percentagewise by horizontal subdivision of the column. Figure 3-19 illustrates a portion of a compound graphic log which includes data from microscopic examination of samples and gamma-neutron traces, as prepared by a commercial sample logging service.

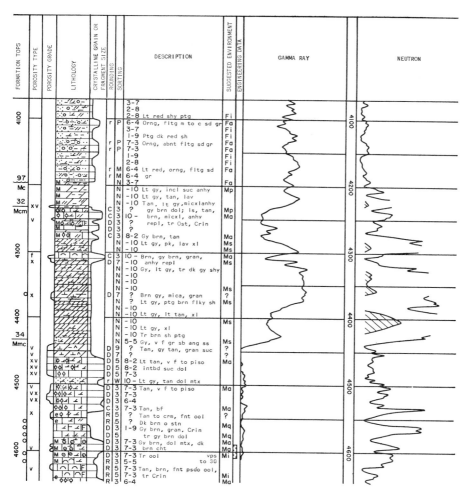

Fig. 3-19. Portion of a compound graphic log. The graphic section utilizes as many as seventy symbols to illustrate lithologic details, supplemented by abbreviated description; other details on textures and mass properties are given by symbols and numbers in adjoining columns. A coded environmental interpretation is shown at the center, and a standard gamma-neutron log at the right. [Courtesy American Stratigraphic Company.]

SUPPLEMENTARY READINGS

1. Feo-Codecido, G., 1956, Heavy mineral techniques and their application to Venezuelan stratigraphy: Am. Assoc. Petrol. Geologists Bull., v. 40, p. 984–1000.

2. Haun, J. D. and LeRoy, L. W., 1958, Subsurface geology in petroleum exploration: Colorado School of Mines, Golden. Parts 2, 3, 4, and 6 of this well known

symposium contain papers of special merit as extensions of the synoptic treatment of subsurface methods presented in this chapter.

3. Lahee, F. H., 1961, Field geology: New York, McGraw-Hill Book Co., Inc. This classic and repeatedly revised reference book on field methods covers a number of topics related to surface and subsurface methods.

4. LeRoy, L. W. and Low, J., 1954, Grahic problems in petroleum geology: New York, Harper and Brothers. A manual on the methods of presentation of stratigraphic data. Problems 1–5 and 16–18 provide illustrations and exercises covering the material of this chapter.

5. McCracken, E., 1955, Correlation of insoluble residue zones of the upper Arbuckle of Missouri and southern Kansas: Am. Assoc. Petrol. Geologists Bull., v. 39, p. 47–59. Gives examples of insoluble residue logs and their application to the establishment and correlation of insoluble residue zones.

6. Mertie, J. B., 1922, Graphic and mechanical computation of thickness of strata and distance to a stratum: U.S. Geol. Survey, Prof. Paper 129. An original reference covering the mathematical and graphic treatment of thickness data.

7. Milner, H. B., 1962, Sedimentary petrography: New York, The Macmillan Co. This fourth edition of a standard British reference work contains a number of chapters that amplify many of the topics touched upon in this chapter, and includes contributions by other outstanding authorities. Publication of the two-volume revised edition during the late stages of preparation of the present book made it impractical to enter many appropriate references in the body of the text.

8. Schenck, H. G. and Adams, J. E., 1943, Operations of commercial micropaleontologic laboratories: Jour. Paleontology v. 17, p. 554–583. A description of practical micropaleontologic methods.

CHAPTER 4

Properties of Sedimentary Rocks

INTRODUCTION

AN important part of applied stratigraphy is the description, classification, and interpretation of sedimentary rocks—a study known as **sedimentation** or **sedimentology.** A distinction is made between **processes of sedimentation** (weathering, transportation, deposition, and lithification) and **products of sedimentation,** the sedimentary rocks. A **sediment** is a deposit of solid material on the earth's surface from any medium (air, water, ice) under normal conditions of the surface. A **sedimentary rock** is the consolidated or lithified equivalent of a sediment.

A description of any sedimentary rock delineates its texture, structure, and composition. **Texture** refers to the characteristics of the sedimentary particles and the grain-to-grain relations among them. Larger features of a deposit, such as bedding, ripple mark, and concretions, are **sedimentary structures. Sediment composition** refers to the mineralogical or chemical make-up of a sediment.

Most sediments are mixtures of two main components, a **detrital fraction** (pebbles, sand, mud), brought to the site of deposition from some source area, and a **chemical fraction** (calcite, gypsum, and others) formed at or very near the site of accumulation. The components may be mixed in any proportions, yielding sediments ranging from pure types (such as quartzose sandstone) to intermediate types (such as shaly limestone).

A **clastic** rock (conglomerate, sandstone, shale) is composed predominantly of detrital material, whereas a **nonclastic** rock (limestone, dolomite, gypsum) is composed mainly of chemically or biologically formed material. Some clastic rocks are composed of transported and reworked nondetrital material such as fossil fragments.

The study of sediments—both present-day deposits and ancient sedimentary rocks—has grown enormously during the past decade. Much of this new knowledge has immediate and direct bearing on stratigraphic analysis, and has paved the way for a continuing, closer integration of stratigraphy and sedimentation. This is especially true for the concepts of "facies models," discussed in Chapters 12 and 13. The present chapter, and those immediately following, accordingly summarize some aspects of sedimentary petrology that are further developed in the more integrative treatment of the closing chapters of this book.

TEXTURE OF SEDIMENTARY ROCKS

Detrital rocks commonly have **fragmental texture,** whereas chemical rocks usually have **crystalline texture.** Fragmental texture is characterized by broken, abraded, or irregular particles in surface contact, crystalline texture by interlocking particles, many having crystal faces or boundaries (see Figure 4-1). Fragmental texture may at times include some crystal borders, owing to secondary enlargement of the grains or to the presence of post-depositional cementing material. Similarly, crystalline textures may include some fragmental or abraded particles.

Mass Textural Features

Within the general categories of fragmental and crystalline aggregates, three components give a rock its mass textural characteristics. These are: the **particles** themselves, the **matrix** of finer material which fills the interstices among the particles, and the **cement** which may bind particles and matrix together.

Particles and matrix form a relative association—for example, sand grains in a clay matrix, or pebbles in a sand matrix. If all the particles are of similar size, as in dune sand, no distinction is made, inasmuch as the term matrix is restricted to the noticeably finer material associated with a distribution of

Fig. 4-1. Diagrammatic representation of sedimentary textures. (*Left*) Crystalline texture of dolomite. (*Right*) Clastic texture of sandstone.

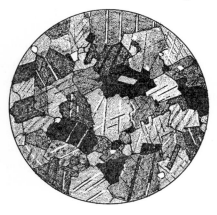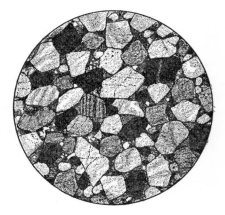

larger particles. Cement is a postdepositional chemical precipitate in the interstices among grains and matrix. The most common cementing materials in sedimentary rocks are silica, calcite, dolomite, and siderite. The introduction of cementing material into a clastic sediment may give it a partially crystalline texture. Silica cement in sandstones is deposited as quartz in optical continuity with the quartz particles, and the rounded grains develop small crystal faces. As cementation continues, the crystals may grow until they form an interlocking mass. Recrystallization of lime mud also forms crystalline aggregates.

Particle Properties

The detailed texture of a sedimentary rock is largely determined by the size and shape of the particles and by their arrangement in the aggregate. In mechanically transported sediments (clastics, detrital rocks), six properties of the particles influence the final texture of the deposit:

1. size,
2. shape (sphericity),
3. roundness,
4. surface texture,
5. orientation,
6. mineralogical composition.

The first five properties are textural, and the last is compositional. However, certain physical and chemical properties also play important roles under special conditions: density in transportation, solubility in some postdepositional changes, and so on.

The particle properties of a sediment are closely related to certain aggregate properties that characterize the rock as a whole; both are important in the study of sediments. Griffiths (1961) has defined the basic properties of sedimentary rocks to be particle composition, size, shape, orientation, and packing. Packing is a measure of the degree to which individual particles are in contact with or interlocked with their neighbors. According to Griffiths, recognition of these fundamental attributes of sediments is necessary and sufficient for a unique description of a rock.

Chemical or nonclastic rock particles also have the properties listed above, but they may not have the same significance in the interpretation of chemical rocks as they have in detrital rocks. The occurrence of large detrital particles in a clastic sediment carries certain implications of the strength of current necessary to transport them, whereas a coarse crystal of calcite in limestone may be more a reflection of physical and chemical conditions at the site of deposition, and after burial, than of transportational effects.

TEXTURE OF CLASTIC ROCKS

Particle Size

Particle size is an important textural element in clastic rocks because it is related to the dynamic conditions of transportation and deposition. The most common method of measuring particle size is **sieving**. When a sample of sand is shaken in a nest of sieves the particles are sorted into size groups according to the sieve openings. Another method of determining the size of small particles is establishing their **settling velocity**. Small spheres settle in accordance with **Stokes' law**, which states in its simplest form that the settling velocity varies as the square of the particle diameter.

Intercepts are used to express particle size. The longest dimension of a particle is the maximum intercept, and shorter dimensions are termed intermediate and short intercepts. For large particles, the **volume** may be used as an expression of size, converted to its **nominal diameter** by computing the diameter of a sphere having the same volume as the particle. **Microscopic methods** are adaptable to size measurement of particles in the sand range and smaller. Grains are measured along the maximum and intermediate intercepts, or the area of the grain images may be measured.

Wentworth Grade Scale. A **grade scale** is a systematic division of a continuous range of sizes into classes or grades, and the Wentworth grade scale (1922) provides a means of standardizing terminology. Wentworth's scale is shown in Table 4-1. Each size grade or class differs from its predecessor by the constant ratio 1/2, and each has a specific name to identify particles falling within it.

By virtue of the constant ratio between classes, Wentworth's scale is a **geometric grade scale**. Geometric grade scales are well adapted to the de-

TABLE 4-1. WENTWORTH'S PARTICLE SIZE CLASSIFICATION

GRADE LIMITS (Diameters in mm)	NAME	GRADE LIMITS (Diameters in mm.)	NAME
Above 256	Boulder	1/2–1/4	Medium sand
256–128	Large cobble	1/4–1/8	Fine sand
128–64	Small cobble	1/8–1/16	Very fine sand
64–32	Very large pebble	1/16–1/32	Coarse silt
32–16	Large pebble	1/32–1/64	Medium silt
16–8	Medium pebble	1/64–1/128	Fine silt
8–4	Small pebble	1/128–1/256	Very fine silt
4–2	Granule	1/256–1/512	Coarse clay
2–1	Very coarse sand	1/512–1/1024	Medium clay
1–1/2	Coarse sand	1/1024–1/2048	Fine clay

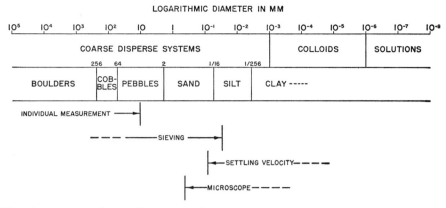

Fig. 4-2. Range of particle size in clastic sediments, and methods of mechanical analysis applicable to various size ranges.

scription of sediments because they give equal significance to size ratios, whether the ratios occur in gravel, sand, silt, or clay. The difference of one centimeter in the size of a boulder is negligible, whereas a difference as small as one micron in the size of a colloidal clay particle may be sufficient to double or halve it.

Size Distribution of Sediments. The process of analyzing a sediment for the range of sizes present is called **mechanical analysis,** and the numerical or graphical result is the **size distribution** of the sediment.

Mechanical analysis is performed in any of several ways, using the size definitions given above. Figure 4-2 shows the applicability of the methods to specific size ranges. Individual measurement methods are used for pebbles and larger particles. Sieving methods extend from about 30 mm to 0.05 mm. Settling velocity methods are used in the silt and clay range, which is the range of applicability of Stokes' law. Microscopic methods are most effective in the range from medium sand to clay. Composite methods may be used with sediments which range from pebbles to clay. Details of analytic methods may be found in Krumbein and Pettijohn (1938) and in Twenhofel and Tyler (1941). Consolidated sediments usually require preliminary treatment to separate the particles, or they may require thin-section analysis.

Milner's classic volume on sedimentary petrography, completely revised, was published while this book was in the proof stage. Volume 1 contains material that bears strongly on this and succeeding chapters, and the reader is urged to refer to the sections of Milner's book that correspond to each of the main divisions of this chapter. The annotated bibliography at the end of this chapter lists some of the pertinent items.

Most methods of particle size analysis determine the weight percentage of grains in each size class rather than the number of grains in the class. Milner's treatment follows the weight-frequency point of view, but the reader's attention is called to the problem of expressing particle size distributions by count. Several references dealing with this subject are: Herdan (1953, chapter 6), Marschner (1953), Berman (1953), Wolman (1954), and Griffiths (1961). Berman gives an example of this problem in the study of heavy minerals.

The purpose of mechanical analysis is to obtain graphic or numerical data about the particle sizes in a sediment. These data form the basis for textural descriptions, for comparisons among samples, for developing or testing theories of sediment behavior during transport and deposition, for interpreting the conditions of sediment formation, and for mapping sedimentary variations. Nearly all of these uses are important in some aspects of stratigraphy.

Graphic Representation of Size Distribution Data. Two graphic procedures are commonly used in presenting the data of mechanical analysis. A **histogram** is a block diagram which gives the percentage of grains in the grade sizes present in the sediment. A **cumulative curve** of the sediment is prepared by adding the percentages in succeeding grades, and drawing a smooth curve through the points. Figures 4-3 and 4-4 show histograms and cumulative curves of four typical sediments.

Histograms present a factual picture of the abundance of grains in each grade size, in a readily visualized form. However, they cannot be used di-

Fig. 4-3. Histograms of four sediments.

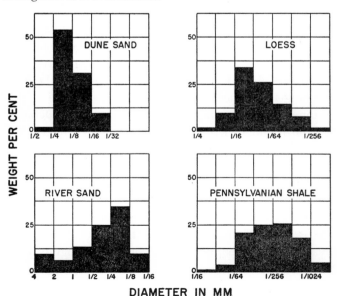

DIAMETER IN MM

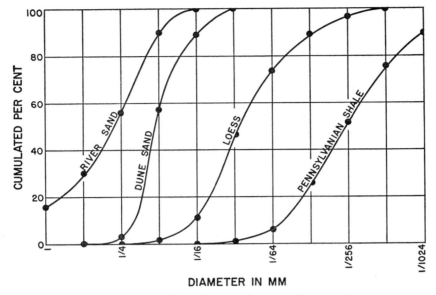

Fig. 4-4. Cumulative curves of the sediments shown in Figure 4-3.

rectly for numerical summaries of the data. Therefore, the corresponding cumulative curves are used as graphic devices for determining average particle size and other properties.

A **frequency curve** may be obtained graphically from the cumulative curve. It is equivalent to a smooth curve drawn through the histogram. Details are given in Krumbein and Pettijohn (1938). A large quantity of literature has accumulated on the graphic analysis of particle size data, as summarized below. In addition, various writers have discussed the nature of cumulative curves (Tanner, 1958, provides an example), the nature of the size distributions (Rogers, 1959), methods for direct measurement of particles in terms of the phi scale, described below (Grender, 1961), and various methods for illustrating textural studies of sediments (Shepps, 1958).

Statistical Analysis of Size Distribution Data

Quartile Measures. One of the simplest methods for the statistical summary of sediments is based on **quartiles** obtained graphically from the cumulative curve. The quartiles are determined by following the 25, 50, and 75 percent lines on the graph to the right to their intersection with the cumulative curve, then reading the values on the size scale which lie directly below the intersections. Figure 4-5 shows the method of reading these values from the cumulative curve. The graph paper is semi-logarithmic to facilitate reading interpolated values.

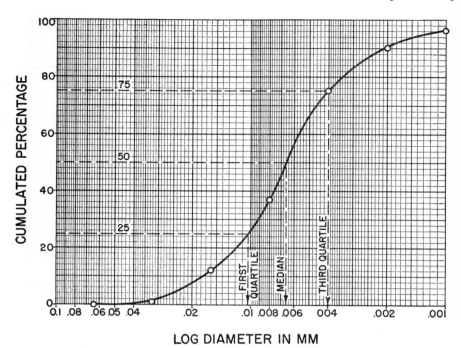

Fig. 4-5. Cumulative curve of loess on semilogarithmic paper, showing the method of reading the median and the quartiles.

Median Diameter and Sorting Coefficient. The second quartile, associated with 50 percent line, is called the **median diameter.** Inasmuch as the median diameter represents the middlemost grain, with an equal weight frequency of grains on both sides, it is the **average grain diameter** of the sediment.

Two sands may have the same median diameter, yet one sand may have a much wider size range than the other. The **degree of sorting** is a measure of the spread of the distribution. It is defined statistically as the extent to which the grains spread on either side of the average. The wider the spread, the poorer in the sorting. The **sorting coefficient,** S_o, developed by Trask (1932), is defined as the square root of the ratio of the larger quartile (the 25 percent value, Q_1) to the smaller quartile (the 75 percent value, Q_3):

$$S_o = \sqrt{Q_1/Q_3}.$$

The more nearly equal the two quartiles are, the more closely the sorting coefficient approaches 1.0. The sorting coefficient of the loess shown in Figure 4-5 is $\sqrt{0.010/0.004} = 1.58$. Its median diameter is 0.0066 mm, which is finer than the loess in Figure 4-4.

The sorting coefficient exemplifies the use of size ratios in describing sediments. When one quartile is divided by the other, the size dimension cancels out, and the sorting coefficient applies equally well to gravel, sand, silt, or clay.

Significance of Median Diameter and Sorting Coefficient. The median diameter and sorting coefficient give some clues to the conditions of formation of clastic sediments. The former is associated with the strength of the current that moved the material to the site of deposition. The latter is an index of the range of conditions present in the transporting fluid (range of velocities, degrees of turbulence) and to some extent is indicative of the distance of transportation. According to Trask (1932), well-sorted marine sediments have S_o values less than 2.5, moderately sorted sediments range from 2.5 to 4.0, and poorly sorted sediments have values larger than 4.0.

Skewness and **kurtosis** are additional statistical measures of distribution curves. The first is a measure of the asymmetry of the distribution; the second is a measure of the peakedness of the distribution. These attributes can be expressed as quartile measures (Krumbein and Pettijohn, 1938), though graphically determined moment measures, described below, appear to be more commonly used.

Moment Measures. Quartile measures are paralleled by **moment measures,** which are computed from the original percentage data or read from special types of cumulative curves. Moment measures are related to the center of gravity of the size frequency curve, and they have some advantages over the quartiles in studies of the dynamic conditions of sediment transport. Because of the need for a geometric grade scale in particle size analyses, moment measures are usually expressed in logarithmic form. The average diameter in the logarithmic moment method is the **phi mean,** which may be converted to its antilog, the **geometric mean diameter in mm.** The degree of sorting is expressed as the logarithmic standard deviation, **sigma phi,** or its antilog, the **geometric standard deviation.**

Quartile and moment measures are approximately equivalent, and they have very nearly the same geologic significance. Moment measures are generally more useful in detailed statistical analyses, but their application is limited, owing to an early lack of graphic methods in their determination. Otto (1939) developed graphic methods for moment measures much like those used for quartiles, and more recently Inman (1952) proposed a method that permits simultaneous graphic treatment for both quartile and moment measures. Inman's method is illustrated in Figure 4-6, using the same data given in Figure 4-5. The cumulative curve is plotted on probability paper, which sometimes tends to straighten out the curve, permitting more convenient interpolation.

In Inman's method the diameter scale is expressed as its negative logarithm to the base 2, which yields the arithmetic **phi scale** (Krumbein

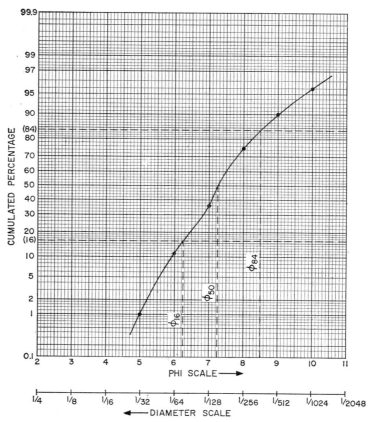

Fig. 4-6. Cumulative curve of the loess shown in Figure 4-5, drawn on probability paper with phi scale.

and Pettijohn, 1938). Here, the phi values for the 16, 50, and 84 percent intercepts are read graphically. The phi value associated with the 50 percent line is the **phi median.** The **phi mean** is half the sum of the phi values associated with the 84 and 16 percent lines, and **sigma phi** is half the difference between these same values:

$$\text{Phi median, } Md_\phi = \phi_{50} = 7.25$$
$$\text{Phi mean, } M_\phi = (\phi_{84} + \phi_{16})/2 = (8.50 + 6.25)/2 = 7.38,$$
$$\text{Sigma phi, } \sigma_\phi = (\phi_{84} - \phi_{16})/2 = (8.50 - 6.25)/2 = 1.13.$$

These measures are logarithms, and they may be converted to their diameter equivalents by use of charts (Krumbein and Pettijohn, 1938, p. 244), Page's conversion table (1955), or the tables of Griffiths and McIntyre (1958). Here, the diameter equivalent of the phi median is 0.0066 mm, which agrees with Figure 4-5. The geometric mean diameter, equivalent to the phi mean, is 0.0060 mm, which is slightly smaller than the median diameter. Sigma phi is commonly used directly in its logarithmic form as a measure of the degree of sorting of a sediment.

Skewness and kurtosis are discussed at some length by Inman (1952). One measure of skewness, α_ϕ, is based on the extent to which the mean and the median separate as a curve becomes asymmetrical (in a symmetrical curve they coincide):

$$\alpha_\phi = (M_\phi - Md_\phi)/\sigma_\phi$$

For the sediment shown in Figure 4-6, the skewness is $\alpha_\phi = (7.38 - 7.25)/$ $1.13 = +0.115$, indicating a tail extending in the positive phi direction, toward smaller grain sizes. Inman introduced a second measure of skewness, based on the 5th and 95th percentiles, that is more sensitive to the extremes of the distribution. Similarly, kurtosis is measured by contrasting the sorting in the central part of the distribution with that of the extremes to obtain a measure of the degree to which the particles are concentrated near the center. Details and an example are given by Inman (1952, p. 138). Mason and Folk (1958) suggest variants of Inman's measures, based on additional percentile values, in order to improve the graphic estimation of the statistical measures. Plumley and Davis (1956) demonstrate that the mean, median, sorting, and skewness of sediments can also be estimated graphically from triangle diagrams of sand, silt, and clay percentages.

Comparison of the exact geometric meaning of quartile and moment measures is complicated by the need for logarithmic analysis. The theory underlying the graphic method for moment analysis is not discussed here, but it may be found in Otto (1939) and Inman (1952). Cadigan (1954) pointed out some shortcomings of graphic methods and recommended use of computational methods; these methods are treated in Krumbein and Pettijohn (1938).

It was partly the need for implied logarithmic treatment of particle size data that gave rise to the widespread use of quartile measures in sedimentary petrology. When there is no need for logarithmic transformation, moment methods are more widely used.

Published values on size analyses include both quartile and moment data. The numerical values of the median and the geometric mean may be used interchangeably, but the logarithmic standard deviation is smaller than the sorting coefficient for the same sediment, owing to differences in computation methods. Table 4-2 lists the size data of some sediments and provides approximate conversion values for the two measures of sorting.

Application to Series of Samples. It is not always possible to interpret a single sample from its size data. Beach sand and dune sand have very

TABLE 4-2. PARTICLE SIZE DATA OF SELECTED SEDIMENTS

SEDIMENT	MEDIAN mm	SORTING, S_0	GEOMETRIC MEAN, mm	STANDARD DEVIATION*
Dune sand, Recent, Porter County, Inc.			0.19	0.33
Dune sand, Recent, Coffins Beach, Mass.	0.22	1.18		
Beach sand, Recent, Half Moon Bay, Calif.			0.68	0.65
Stream gravel, Recent, Los Angeles County, Calif.			4.70	2.48
Lagoonal silt, Recent, Barataria Bay, La.	0.012	4.20		
Glacial till, Edgar County, Ill.	0.094	4.76		
Pleasantview sandstone (Pennsylvanian), Fulton County, Ill.	0.08	1.72		
Macoupin sandstone (Pennsylvanian), Fithian, Ill.	0.13	1.40		
Berea sandstone (Mississippian), Elyria, Ohio			0.15	0.57
Red bed shale (Triassic), Conchas Dam, N. M.	0.013	2.45		
Santa Rosa gray shale (Triassic), Las Vegas, N. M.	0.032	3.10		
Francis Creek shale (Pennsylvanian), Fulton County, Ill.	0.05	2.00		
St. Peter sandstone (Ordovician), Ottawa, Ill.			0.29	0.68

* The standard deviation is a logarithmic moment measure instead of a direct ratio. Rough conversion values for this measure and S_0 are as follows: When S_0 is 1.0, 1.5, 2.0, 3.0, and 4.0, the log standard deviation is approximately 0.0, 0.5, 0.8, 1.3, and 1.6, respectively.

similar size distributions, even though they are formed by different geologic agents. When a series of samples is available, the summarized data often eliminate some interpretations, and graphs or maps of the variation in particle size and degree of sorting afford clues to the agent which formed the deposit. Figure 4-7 gives data for samples collected from a known beach environment in the direction of transport. Note the systematic decrease in average grain size, and an improvement in sorting, in the direction of movement.

The interpretation of such graphs involves a study of the rate at which the size properties of one type of sediment change in comparison with that of other types. The curve of average grain diameter in Figure 4-7 is an **exponential curve** (Krumbein, 1937), which is commonly observed when mean particle size is studied as a function of distance from source.

The similarity of beach and dune sands has given rise to numerous papers discussing the ways to distinguish between them. Skewness and kurtosis afford the best discrimination, according to Mason and Folk (1958), in that the tails of the distribution curves are a highly sensitive measure of conditions of transport. The observational evidence of numerous samples favors the inference that dune sands are more positively skewed than beach sands. Among other writers who have examined this problem pro and con are Keller (1945), Shepard and Young (1961), Friedman (1961), and Folk (1962).

Fig. 4-7. Change in average particle size and degree of sorting of beach sand with distance from source. [Generalized data from Half Moon Bay, California.]

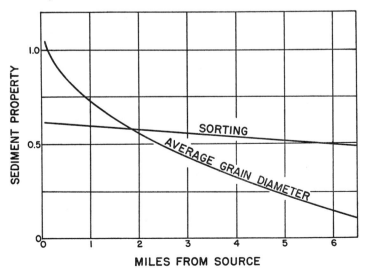

Particle Shape

A description of the shape or geometric form of a particle involves several separate but related geometric concepts. On the one hand, there are those shape factors which depend upon the relative lengths of the particle intercepts; on the other, particle angularity or roundness. These two geometric aspects of particle shape are important in the study of sediments, but in different ways. The form, or relative intercept relations of the particle, partly controls its behavior during transportation and deposition, whereas angularity or roundness reflect the distance and rigor of travel.

Sphericity. The relation of the particle intercepts to each other may be expressed as the sphericity of the particle. The original concept of sphericity, as defined by Wadell (1932), is

$$\text{True sphericity} = \frac{\text{Surface area of the particle}}{\text{Surface area of sphere of same volume}}.$$

In practice the measurement of the true sphericity of an irregular particle is not feasible, and Wadell (1933) proposed a practical operational definition that may be expressed as

$$\text{Operational sphericity} = \sqrt[3]{\frac{\text{Volume of particle}}{\text{Volume of the circumscribing sphere}}}.$$

The second equation has been made the basis for most measurements of sphericity. Wadell developed a method for large particles in which the volume of the particle is measured by water displacement and may then be expressed as a sphere with nominal diameter d: $(\pi/6)d^3$. The circumscribing sphere has a diameter equal to the maximum intercept through the particle, and hence has a volume $(\pi/6)a^3$. By substituting these relations in the operational definition, and cancelling common terms, the sphericity becomes simply

$$\text{Operational sphericity} = d/a.$$

Thus the sphericity of the particle is the ratio of the nominal diameter (d) to the maximum intercept (a) through the particle.

In 1935 Zingg showed that if the ratio of the intermediate to the maximum intercept (b/a) of a particle is plotted against the ratio of the shortest to the intermediate intercept (c/b), the particle may be classified according to its shape. Figure 4-8, left, is a diagram of Zingg's classification. It shows four shape classes and provides an easily visualized manner of grouping particles according to their shape.

The operational sphericity of a particle can be related to Zingg's classification in terms of particle intercepts. The particle may be expressed as a triaxial ellipsoid with axes equal to the pebble intercepts, a, b, and c. The

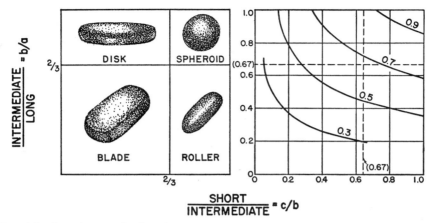

Fig. 4-8. (*Left*) Zingg's classification of pebble shapes, based on ratios of intercepts. (*Right*) Relation of intercept sphericity to Zingg's classification of pebble shapes.

volume of the ellipsoid is $(\pi/6)abc$. This may be substituted for the numerator in the defining equation, with $(\pi/6)a^3$ in the denominator as before, to obtain an expression relating sphericity to the (b/a) and (c/b) ratios of Zingg's shape classification (Krumbein, 1941). The resulting equation may be plotted as a series of curves on the grid of Zingg's chart to obtain lines of equal operational sphericity (called the **intercept sphericity**), as shown in Figure 4-8, right.

The fact that the lines of equal operational sphericity swing across the chart as hyperboloid curves indicates that particles of decidedly different appearance to the eye may have the same numerical value of sphericity. Comparison of the figures shows that the 0.5 line sweeps through the disk, blade, and roller classes. Inasmuch as sphericity is important in particle dynamic behavior, particles with the same sphericity behave in a similar manner under given conditions if their nominal diameters and densities are the same. Hence, disk-shaped or roller-shaped pebbles can be stable in the same environment, on beaches, for example.

In its original form, true sphericity expresses a relation between the surface area of a particle and its corresponding sphere. For a given volume a sphere has the least surface area of any shaped particle, and as the shape departs from spheroid the ratio of surface area to volume increases. This relation affects the resistance a particle offers to movement by a fluid. Although direct measurement of true sphericity does not seem feasible, Aschenbrenner (1956) showed that true sphericity may be approximated by using, as a reference form, a tetrakaidekahedron of 14 faces instead of a triaxial ellipsoid. The surface area of the tetrakaidekahedron may be computed from measurements of the particle intercepts, thus affording an estimate of the particle surface area. Aschenbrenner developed a chart similar to Figure 4-8 that permits graphic determination of the "true sphericity." The lines differ in their placement on the graph, although the hyperboloids sweep across the field in like manner. In 1958 Sneed and Folk set up a maximum projection sphericity defined as the cube root of the ratio c^2/ab—the cube root of the ratio of the square of the shortest intercept to the product of the long and intermediate intercepts. The maximum projection sphericity shows a higher linear statistical correlation with observed settling velocity than does the operational sphericity of Wadell, suggesting that the cross sectional area may be an important control in the shape behavior of particles.

Sphericity measurements are conveniently made on pebbles, which are large enough to be handled individually. Microscopic methods for obtaining the intercepts of sand grains are available (Rittenhouse, 1943; Aschenbren-

Fig. 4-9. Histogram and cumulative curve of sphericity distribution of river pebbles. The broken lines show the 16th, 50th, and 84th percentiles on the cumulative probability graph.

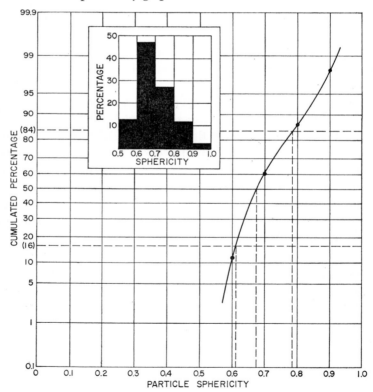

TABLE 4-3. COMPUTATION OF MEAN SPHERICITY AND
SPHERICITY STANDARD DEVIATION

CLASS MIDPOINT, m	FREQUENCY, f	fm	fm^2
0.55	12	6.60	3.6300
0.65	48	31.20	20.2800
0.75	27	20.25	15.1875
0.85	11	9.35	7.9475
0.95	2	1.90	1.8050
Totals	100	69.30	48.8500

Mean sphericity $= 69.30/100 = 0.69$
Sphericity standard deviation $= \{[48.85 - (69.3)^2/100]/100\}^{1/2}$
$$= \sqrt{(48.85 - 48.02)/100} = \sqrt{0.0083}$$
$$= 0.09$$

ner, 1955; Curray and Griffiths, 1955; Wright, 1957). Two-dimensional methods have also been used (Riley, 1941).

Just as the particle size properties of a sediment may be expressed statistically, so the sphericity data may be expressed as a sphericity distribution. Figure 4-9 shows a sphericity histogram and a cumulative curve.

The cumulative curve is drawn on probability paper, as in Inman's method for particle size, except that the abscissa (sphericity) is not transformed to logarithms. Use of the 16, 50, and 84 percent lines provides data for obtaining the average sphericity either as the **median sphericity** or the **mean sphericity,** and for computing the degree of shape sorting as the **sphericity standard deviation:**

Median sphericity $= X_{50} = 0.68$;
Mean sphericity $= (X_{84} + X_{16})/2 = (0.78 + 0.61)/2 = 0.69$;
Sphericity standard deviation $= (X_{84} - X_{16})/2 = (0.78 - 0.61)/2 = 0.08$.

The mean sphericity is more commonly used than is the median sphericity. If computational methods are preferred, the mean and standard deviation may be computed as shown in Table 4-3. The midpoints of the classes are entered in the first column, and the percentage frequency is entered in the second column. The third column gives the product fm, obtained by multiplying the midpoint by the frequency for each class. The fourth column shows fm^2, obtained by again multiplying the values in the third column by the class midpoint. The last three columns are totaled as shown. The mean sphericity is obtained by dividing the sum of the third column by the total frequency to obtain the value 0.69.

The standard deviation is computed by squaring the sum of the third column, dividing by 100, and subtracting the quotient from the sum of the fourth column. The remainder is divided by the total frequency, N, and the square root is taken, as shown in Table 3. The equation used is

$$\text{Sphericity standard deviation} = \left\{ \frac{\sum fm^2 - \left[\left(\sum fm \right)^2 / N \right]}{N} \right\}^{1/2},$$

where $\sum$ indicates summation.

The difference between the graphic and computed values is not large in this example, but it illustrates that the two methods may lead to somewhat different results, especially with the standard deviation. In general, computational methods provide better estimates of the statistical values than do graphic methods. In the past more than at present, geologists preferred graphic methods because of their greater convenience. As the tendency toward more complete statistical analysis increases, computational methods will supersede graphic methods. Curray and Griffiths (1955), for example, present a comprehensive statistical treatment of particle sphericity in sandstone, using formal statistical designs.

The theory and additional details for computational methods is given in Dixon and Massey (1957, p. 20), in Hoel (1957, p. 52), and in Krumbein and Pettijohn (1938). In the present example the convention of using one less than the total frequency for computing the standard deviation is not used (see Hoel on this point in computing moments).

The average sphericity of particles in clastic sediments changes systematically in the direction of transport—owing, in part, to changes in average stream velocity, degree of turbulence, and initial particle shape. In general, the sphericity of pebbles increases with distance of travel. Russell and Taylor (1937) observed a decrease in sphericity of Mississippi River sands downstream from Cairo, Illinois.

Roundness. Particle roundness is expressed in a two-dimensional manner by arranging a particle such that its maximum projection area is visible. Sand grains sprinkled on a cover glass and lightly tapped tend to arrange themselves with the shortest intercept approximately vertical and their longest and intermediate intercepts showing from above. The grains may be photographed or traced to obtain images for measurement. The radii of curvature of corners and edges are then compared with the radius of the largest circle inscribed in the image.

By definition, roundness (Wadell, 1932) is expressed as

$$\text{Roundness} = \frac{\text{Average radius of corners and edges}}{\text{Radius of maximum inscribed circle}}.$$

When the corners and edges are sharp, their average radius is small, and the roundness is low; but when the average radius of the corners approaches that of the inscribed circle, the roundness value approaches 1.0.

The eye may be trained to estimate particle roundness from a set of roundness images, and this rapid method has largely superseded the more laborious method of image measurement. Figure 4-10 is a combined roundness and sphericity chart applicable to sand grains. The sphericity is related to the proportion between length and breadth of the images, and the roundness by the curvature of the image edges. Separate charts are used for pebbles, because low-roundness sand grains have fewer secondary surface projections (Krumbein, 1941). For rapid stratigraphic analysis, a scattering of sand grains under the microscope may be compared with the visual chart.

Visual estimates of particle sphericity and roundness are subject to some variation when different observers make the estimates. This effect, known as **operator variation,** has been studied statistically by Rosenfeld and Griffiths (1953) and summarized by Griffiths and Rosenfeld (1954). In general, although estimates of individual grains may vary significantly, average values based on 50 or more particles tend to be similar because the errors of estimation are largely compensating in the absence of strong operator bias.

Particle roundness (and sphericity) receives continuing attention in terms of new or improved methods and scales of measurement (Powers, 1953;

Fig. 4-10. Chart for visual estimation of roundness and sphericity of sand grains. Compare this with the excellent half-tone in Powers (1953, p. 118).

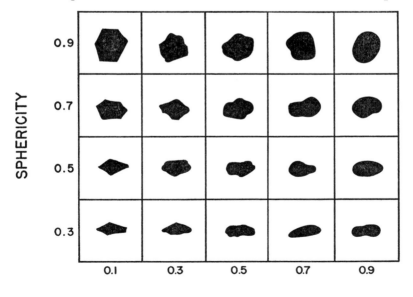

ROUNDNESS

Robson, 1958; and Waskom, 1958), as well as in terms of their environmental significance (Curray and Griffiths, 1955; Beal and Shepard, 1956).

For more detailed roundness studies the data may be grouped into classes to obtain the roundness distribution shown by the histogram and cumulative probability graph of Figure 4-11. As with size and sphericity data, the **mean roundness** and the **roundness standard deviation** may be determined graphically or by computation. The gravel analysis presented in Figure 4-11 has a computed mean roundness of 0.38 and a computed roundness standard deviation of 0.07. Curray and Griffiths (1955) provide examples of particle roundness studies in arkose, graywacke, and quartzose sandstones.

Pebble roundness increases in the direction of transport, in the absence of severe breakage. Large, angular particles tend to round more rapidly than small ones. The rapidity of rounding depends, in part, on the hardness of the particles. Limestone pebbles round very rapidly, whereas chert pebbles may remain relatively angular for great distances of travel.

Fig. 4-11. Histogram and cumulative curve of roundness distribution of river pebbles. The dashed lines show the 16th, 50th, and 84th percentiles on the cumulative probability graph.

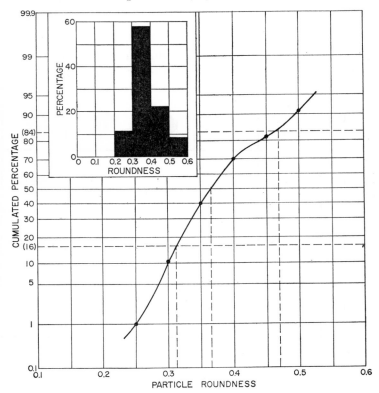

TABLE 4-4. PARTICLE ROUNDNESS AND SPHERICITY
OF SELECTED SEDIMENT SAMPLES

SEDIMENT	AVERAGE SPHERICITY	AVERAGE ROUNDNESS
Dune sand, Recent, Cook County, Ill.	0.75	0.70
Beach sand, Recent, Cook County, Ill.	0.83	0.64
Beach gravel, Recent, N. Shore, Lake Superior	0.64	0.61
Stream gravel, Recent, Los Angeles County, Calif.	0.71	0.34
Glacial till pebbles, Cary, Ill.	0.72	0.54
Glacial outwash gravel, Cary, Ill.	0.75	0.58
Pleasantview sandstone, (Pennsylvanian), Fulton County, Ill.	0.73	0.54
Francis Creek shale (Pennsylvanian), Fulton County, Ill. (Silt only)	0.80	0.30
St. Peter sandstone (Ordovician), LaSalle County, Ill.	0.83	0.77

Table 4-4 shows the average roundness and sphericity of selected samples and indicates the range of values observed in common sediments.

Particle Surface Texture

The **surface texture** (surface roughness) of a sedimentary particle is the aggregate of its minute surface features. These surface features may reflect the abrasional history of the particle (striations on ice-transported pebbles), or they may reflect postdepositional changes (incipient solution after deposition).

Although surface texture has been studied for many years, satisfactory methods for numerical measurement are difficult to devise. An important step in this direction is the method of Porter (1962), who applied electron microscopy to the problem. Porter recognized five surface-texture groups:

1. abraded (chipped or ground),
2. lobate (cobbled appearance),

3. corroded (material removed by solution),
4. smooth (no pronounced markings),
5. faceted (crystal planes).

The relative proportions of these groups can be counted in a set of grains, permitting description and comparison of sediments. Interpretations of some surface textures are tentative, but Porter's work shows that in the Winchell Formation (Pennsylvanian) of north central Texas the proportion of grains in the five classes diminishes in the order of listing. Moreover, each group is related to grain size over the range studied in the samples (0.015–0.500 mm).

Particle Orientation and Sedimentary Fabric

Under some conditions of deposition, particles assume a fixed orientation at the instant of coming to rest. Stream pebbles may be **imbricated** by successive pebbles overlapping their predecessors in an upstream direction. Pebbles embedded in glacial till have their maximum intercepts oriented in the direction of ice movement, and roller pebbles on beaches tend to align themselves with their longest intercepts parallel to the water line.

Sedimentary fabric represents the orientation of the aggregate of particles in a deposit. Fabric is important in controlling certain attributes of a sediment, such as the pore space. If particles are packed systematically, the pore space may be much less than if they are arranged in a haphazard manner.

Sedimentary fabric is a response of particles to the dynamics of sedimentary conditions, and it is modified by particle-shape factors which more or less insure that certain preferred orientations will result. This topic is further discussed under sedimentary processes in Chapter 6. The measurement of particle orientation is largely confined to pebbles and sand grains because of difficulties in measuring the orientation of very small particles. Methods for pebbles are described in Krumbein (1939), in Karlstrom (1952), and in Harrison (1957). For sand grains, the early work of Dapples and Rominger (1945) was followed by the introduction of additional methods by Nanz (1955), Curray (1956), Martinez (1958), and Nairn (1960). Martinez developed a photometer method which measures the mean orientation of grains in a thin section, thus avoiding the need for measuring individual particles and averaging their individual orientations. A recently developed "axiometer" (Schmoll and Bennett, 1961) permits accurate location and measurement of pebble axes by means of a pebble clamp and a track-mounted caliper, greatly reducing the time required in macrofabric studies.

Particle orientation data may be treated in a manner similar to that used for particle size, sphericity, and roundness, although complexities arise, owing to the angular nature of the measurements. Figure 4-12 shows a histogram of the orientation of long axes of till pebbles arranged on a half cylinder, over a range of 180°. Where a distinct modal class is present, the distribution may be "unwound" with this class in the center. In such cases the corresponding cumulative curve of the distribution in a plane may be used for graphic or computational determination of the **mean orientation** and the **degree of preferred orientation** (Krumbein, 1939). The distribution in Figure 4-12 has a mean orientation of N 85° E, and a degree of preferred orientation (standard deviation) of 35°. For more rigorous analysis, vector methods are required, as discussed in Krumbein (1939), Pincus (1956), Curray (1956), and Harrison (1957).

Additional aspects of particle orientation are brought out by **petrofabric diagrams,** which illustrate the orientation in polar coordinate terms, as is common in the description of metamorphic rocks. Harrison (1957) shows examples of sedimentary petrofabric diagrams.

In addition to its importance in reconstructing sedimentary petrofabric processes, particle orientation in oil sands has an important effect on preferential flow of fluids through the sand body. Orientation of the grains parallel to the bedding results in greater permeability parallel to bedding planes than across them.

Particle fabric (such as long axis orientation) is an example of a **vector property** in sediments. Other vector properties include cross-bedding, ripple-mark, and orientation of fossils. Inasmuch as vector properties have both magnitude and direction, they are of value in reconstructing paleocurrents,

Fig. 4-12. Histogram of orientation of long axes in pebbles of glacial till.

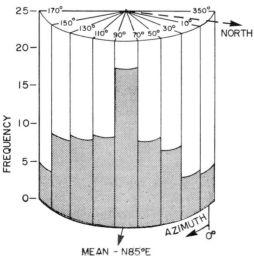

ancient shore line trends, and similar features. These aspects are treated in Pettijohn (1957, pp. 577 ff.), and are further discussed in Chapter 6 of this text. In contrast to vector properties are **scalar properties** of sediments, which have magnitude only. Particle size and shape are examples of scalar properties.

Some relations among scalar and vectorial properties are important in determining the degree to which a vectorial property may be generated. In particle orientation, for example, the degree of orientation observed in a deposit is partly dependent on particle sphericity, in that perfect spheres have no orientation, whereas lath-shaped grains with marked intercept differences respond strongly to orienting forces.

TEXTURAL ELEMENTS OF NONCLASTIC ROCKS

The textural elements of nonclastic (chemical, nondetrital) sediments carry different implications from those of the clastics. Particle roundness in clastic sediments is a function, in part, of particle wear, but it may have no relation to particle abrasion in true nonclastic rocks. Thus, some constituents of nonclastic rocks may be formed in a rounded state, such as oolites or pellets. Some carbonate rocks, such as highly fossiliferous limestones, may show rounded fossil fragments, indicative of some transportation of the materials before final deposition.

Textures of nonclastic rocks, especially the carbonates limestone and dolomite, have received considerable attention during the past decade because of the need for detailed classification, especially in connection with subsurface exploration for reefs and other porous types of carbonate rock. The classification of nonclastic rocks as a whole is deferred to the following chapter, and emphasis here is placed on textural elements that have been useful in the description and interpretation of limestones.

Crystal size in carbonate rocks is commonly expressed in terms of Wentworth's grade limits; in addition, some special scales adapted to thin-section work have been proposed. Alling (1943) discusses this subject in some detail. Table 4-5 summarizes textural terms that are commonly applied to carbonate

TABLE 4-5. TEXTURAL GROUPING OF CARBONATE ROCKS

GRAIN SIZE	TEXTURAL TERMS	EXAMPLES
Greater than 2 mm (coarse)	Calcirudite	Coquina and crinoidal limestone
$2-\frac{1}{16}$ mm (medium grained)	Calcarenite	Oolitic limestone and foraminiferal limestone
Less than $\frac{1}{16}$ mm (fine grained)	Calcilutite	"Lithographic limestone"

rocks. The subdivision into coarse, medium, and fine, in the first column, is based on the corresponding Wentworth grade limits associated with gravel, sand, and silt plus clay. The textural terms are shown in the second column, and several examples in the third column permit ready visualization of the terms.

Textural Components of Carbonate Rocks

The textural groups of Table 4-5 are too general for identification of specific carbonate rocks. Within the past few years Folk (1959) and Wolf (1960) have proposed classifications of limestones based upon the nature and amount of the coarser components in contrast with the finer grained matrix. The coarser components, referred to as **allochem grains,** are of several kinds. Folk discusses four allochemical constituents: **Intraclasts** are fragments of weakly consolidated carbonate sediments that have been eroded from adjoining parts of the sea bottom and reincorporated into newly formed calcareous deposits. **Pellets** are rounded aggregates of fine grained calcareous material, devoid of internal structure. In contrast with pellets, **oolites** are spherical to elliptical bodies that show either a radial or concentric internal structure. It may be mentioned parenthetically that oolites are commonly classified as sedimentary structures rather than as textural elements. **Fossils and fossil fragments,** which constitute an important part of the coarser components in some carbonate rocks, are Folk's fourth allochem. A fifth coarse component of carbonate rocks was introduced by Wolf, who uses the word "**lump**" to represent composite oolites or composite pellets.

Two kinds of interstitial material are recognized by Folk. **Micrite** is a semi-opaque matrix material with very fine subcrystalline texture, such as comprises the bulk of lithographic limestone. In contrast with this is the more coarsely crystalline though fine textured and transparent calcareous spar that makes up the **sparite** of the rock. Sparite may, in part, represent fine grained material that accumulated during the deposition of the carbonate, or it may have been introduced later as a cement. These textural elements obviously have a strong compositional implication, and they are discussed further in connection with limestone classification in Chapter 5.

An additional aspect of the texture of carbonate rocks needs to be emphasized, though it is not explicitly developed in the foregoing. Some limestones are composed almost entirely of worn or broken shells, crinoid columnals, or sand-sized dolomite rhombs, commonly well bedded or even cross-bedded. These "clastic limestones" are relatively more common than was earlier believed, and they indicate transportation and sorting of the organic remains or chemically precipitated particles after deposition. It is believed, however, that such transportation is essentially local compared to the much greater distances that some detrital fragments travel from source to final site of deposition.

Some fine-grained crystalline limestones are believed to have formed from lime muds transported after deposition, but their study is rendered difficult by extremely small particle sizes, complicated by subsequent recrystallization. Chalky textures, being finely crystalline or cryptocrystalline, differ from most limestone textures and show much less lithification.

MASS PROPERTIES OF SEDIMENTARY AGGREGATES

The association of particles in aggregates (as in a sandstone core) endows the whole with certain mass properties. One mass property is **porosity**, a measure of the pore space present. Another is **permeability**, a measure of the ease of fluid movement through the aggregate. Additional properties of the aggregate include plasticity (in clays), compactibility, and others, summarized in Table 4-6. The following text selects several for further discussion.

Porosity

The percentage of pore space in a rock is its **porosity**. Total porosity is the total percentage of void space, whereas effective porosity is the percentage of connected void space. The distinction is important in oil geology, since it is the connected pore space that governs the recoverability of the contained oil. Unconsolidated sediments have the same total and effective porosity, but consolidated sediments may have significant differences in the two, depending on the degree to which pores are sealed by cementing material.

The porosity of sedimentary rocks may be measured in a number of ways. A common method involves withdrawing air from pore spaces under vacuum, and measuring the volume of displaced air at atmospheric pressure. The porosity is computed from the volume of air and the known bulk volume of the test piece. This method and some others use variants of the fundamental equation for porosity, which may be stated as:

$$\text{Porosity} = 100 \left(\frac{\text{Bulk volume} - \text{Grain volume}}{\text{Bulk volume}} \right)$$

Porosity is a function of the uniformity of particle size and shape, and of the state of packing of the particles. The more loosely packed in random orientation the particles are, the greater the amount of pore space. Poorly sorted sediments are less porous than well sorted sediments. Theoretically, porosity is independent of size for spheres. Similarly shaped particles, with a given packing and a given degree of sorting, should exhibit the same porosity

TABLE 4-6. SUMMARY OF MASS PROPERTIES OF SEDIMENT*

Cohesiveness. The property of cohering or sticking together by surface forces. Displayed by unconsolidated, fine-grained sediments under 0.01-mm particle diameter.

Color. The over-all hue of a sediment, caused by combinations of grain color, surface coating, matrix color, and cement.

Compactibility. Decrease of volume under load, commonly expressed as a decrease in porosity. Shown most strongly by fine grained, unconsolidated sediments. Shale decreases from about 50 percent to 5 percent porosity by burial to 5,000 feet.

Density. Mass per unit bulk volume of the rock. Values range from about 2.1 for sandstone, 2.3 for shale, 2.4 for limestone.

Elasticity. Capability of a strained body to recover its size and shape after deformation. Elasticity is important in controlling the velocity of seismic waves in geophysical prospecting. Young's Modulus ranges from about 2×10^{11} dynes/cm^2 for shale, through values of about 5×10^{11} dynes/cm^2 for sandstone, to about 6×10^{11} dynes/cm^2 for limestone.

Electrical Resistivity. A measure of resistance to the passage of an electric current. It depends upon the nature of the sediment and the fluid content in the pores. For sandstone, the resistivity is of the order of 10^4 ohm-cm. The relative resistivity of sedimentary rocks penetrated in a well is shown on the "lateral curve" of electric logs.

Magnetic Susceptibility. A measure of the magnetic properties of rocks. In sediments, the susceptibility is largely a function of the amount of magnetite present. In c.g.s. units, 90 percent of sediments have a magnetic susceptibility less than 0.001. (By comparison, basic lava flows show values greater than 0.001 for 90 percent of samples.)

Permeability. A measure of the ease of fluid flow through rocks. (See text for discussion.)

Porosity. A measure of the pore space in a rock, expressed in percent. (See text for discussion.)

Packing. A measure of the mutual spatial relationships among the grains of a rock. It is a measure of the degree to which grains are in contact with or interlocked among their neighbors.

Radioactivity. Radioactivity of sediments is expressed in units equivalent to 10^{-12} grams of radium per gram of rock. Measured values average about 4.1 for pure sandstones, 4.0 for limestone, 11.3 for gray shale, and 22.4 for dark gray to black shale.

Thermal Conductivity. A measure of the ease of heat flow through rocks. The conductivity K, expressed in calories/sec cm deg is of the order of 0.005.

* Much of the numerical data in this table is taken from Birch, et al. (1942).

regardless of average grain size. In practice, it is generally found that fine grained sediments have higher porosities than coarse, but this is partly a function of differences in packing and orientation. The effects of packing on porosity are discussed by Graton and Fraser (1935). Rosenfeld and Griffiths (1951) made a comprehensive study of porosity measurement, using statistical design to test differences of method. Murray (1960) and Weyl (1960) discuss the origin of porosity in carbonate rocks; Gaither (1953) and Rogers and Head (1961) studied relations between porosity, median grain size, and sorting of sands. Methods for measuring or estimating porosity are given in Levorsen (1954, pp. 98–99). Russell and Dickey, in Trask (1950), also discuss the subject.

Permeability

One of the most important mass properties of a sediment is its **permeability,** which controls the relative ease of fluid flow through the rock pores. Unlike porosity, permeability is strongly influenced by particle size. Coarse gravel has large openings among the pebbles, affording easy passage for fluids. As the particles become smaller, the pores also become smaller, and a greater force or a greater length of time is required to move a unit volume of fluid through a sediment.

TABLE 4-7. POROSITY AND PERMEABILITY OF SELECTED OIL SANDS

NAME OF SAND	POROSITY, PERCENT	PERMEABILITY, MILLIDARCIES
"Second Wilcox" (Ordovician), Oklahoma County, Okla.	12.0	100.0
Clinch (Silurian), Lee County, Va.	9.6	0.90
Strawn (Pennsylvanian), Cooke County, Texas	22.0	81.5
Bartlesville (Pennsylvanian), Anderson County, Kan.	17.5	25.0
Olympic (Pennsylvanian), Hughes County, Okla.	20.5	35.0
Nugget (Jurassic), Fremont County, Wyo.	24.9	147.5
Cut Bank (Cretaceous), Glacier County, Mont.	15.4	111.5
Woodbine (Cretaceous), Tyler County, Texas	22.1	3390.0
Eutaw (Cretaceous), Choctaw County, Ala.	30.0	100.0
O'Hern (Eocene), Duval County, Texas	28.4	130.0

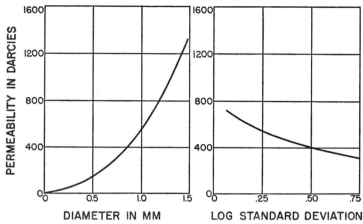

Fig. 4-13. Variation of sand permeability with average particle size and degree of sorting for unconsolidated sand.

In petroleum production, it is the effective porosity which determines how much oil a unit volume of reservoir rock may ultimately yield, but it is the permeability which determines how readily the oil may be recovered.

Permeability may be measured by various methods. One procedure is to drive gas or liquid through a small rock core under a known pressure differential. The permeability is one **darcy** when 1 sq. cm. of rock surface releases 1 cc. of fluid of unit viscosity in 1 sec. under a pressure differential of 1 atmosphere/cm. The permeability of a consolidated sand 1/2 mm in average diameter is approximately 1 darcy. Table 4-7 lists the permeabilities of typical sediments. The porosities are included for comparison.

Permeability is influenced by particle size and degree of sorting, by particle shape, by sedimentary fabric, and by the state of packing. The experimental data of Figure 4-13 shows how rapidly permeability increases with increasing grain diameter if the sorting remains constant. The effect of poorer sorting in sands of equal average grain diameter is a decrease in the permeability, and well sorted, fine grained sand may have the same permeability as less well sorted, coarser sand. Particle shape has an intermediate effect, with some shapes favoring permeability more than others. Tickell and Hiatt (1938), Krumbein and Monk (1942), and Pettijohn (1957) discuss these relations more fully. Levorsen (1954, p. 102–106) describes methods for measuring permeability.

A complex statistical relationship exists between permeability and porosity. In general, more highly porous rocks of a given grain size have a larger permeability than less porous rocks. Fine grained sediments may have high porosity, but the fineness of the pores reduces the permeability and retards fluid flow.

Packing

The **degree of packing** may be defined as the mutual spatial relationships among the grains of a sediment. Kahn (1956) set up two operational definitions by which packing may be measured. The first of these is the **packing proximity,** equal to the total percentage of grain to grain contacts along a traverse measured on a thin section of the rock. The second characteristic is the **packing density,** defined as the cumulated grain intercept length along a traverse in a thin section. The packing proximity is thus an estimate of the number of grains that are in contact with their neighbors, and the larger this proportion is, the greater the degree of packing will be. The packing density is a measure of the extent to which grains occupy the gross volume of the rock in contrast to spaces between the grains. Gaither (1953) reviewed the relations between porosity and grain attributes, partly on the basis of the number of contacts per grain, thus relating porosity with a packing effect.

Statistical Design in Sedimentary Textural Studies

Some aspects of statistical treatment of textural and mass properties of sediments were discussed in previous sections, but no sharp distinction was made between descriptive and analytical statistics. In the former the sample data are used directly for geological generalizations, whereas in the latter the sample data are used to make statistical inferences about the larger class of phenomena from which the samples are obtained. Thus, in most papers on sedimentary texture, the discussion is based almost wholly on the properties of individual samples rather than on the statistically inferred attributes of the geological "populations" from which the samples are obtained. A sample is of value only to the extent that it gives insight into the population.

The application of formal statistical design in sedimentary studies has expanded widely during the past decade, largely through the use of conventional **analysis of variance** designs. These provide methods by which the total variability observed in samples can be related to identifiable statistical and geological factors. Griffiths and co-workers are leaders in this area, but the literature is quite extensive. The following references are selected as an introduction to the subject:

1. General information on statistics in geology (populations, sampling)—Miller, 1953; Krumbein, 1960; Griffiths, 1961; Steinmetz, 1962.
2. General information on analysis of variance—Dixon and Massey, 1957, Chapter 10; Krumbein and Miller, 1953.
3. Analysis of variance of particle properties and mass properties of sediments—Swineford and Swineford, 1946; Rosenfeld and Griffiths, 1951;

Griffiths, 1953; Rosenfeld and Griffiths, 1953; Griffiths and Rosenfeld, 1954; Krumbein and Slack, 1956; Pincus, 1956; Flinn, 1958.

Chapter 16 in Milner (1962), prepared by Griffiths, provides an excellent introduction to statistical methods in sedimentary petrography.

COLOR OF SEDIMENTS

Color is perhaps the most obvious and readily observed characteristic of a sedimentary rock. However, the exact description of the color, on an objective basis, is usually possible only by the use of color charts or a color dictionary. In general, four factors control the color of a sediment (Krynine, 1948): The total mass effect of the colors of the component mineral grains; the color of the finer grained matrix or of the cement; the color of any coating on the grains, such as iron oxide on quartz particles; and the degree of fineness of the sedimentary grains.

Very fine grained sediments are usually darker than coarser ones of similar composition because of the more even distribution of the coloring matter. Various pigmentary materials, usually in the matrix, but also associated with grain surfaces, may be present. These include iron oxides, glauconite, organic material (such as bitumen), iron sulphide, and others.

Common color terms are used in the informal description of sediments, but for detailed studies of stratigraphic intervals, it may be important to observe slight color changes indicative of corresponding changes in mineral assemblage, in texture, or in other properties. The color chart issued by the National Research Council (1948) provides small color chips that permit detailed description and comparison of sedimentary hues in detail.

The significance of color in sediments has received much attention, especially in connection with "red beds" and black shales. Red sediments owe their color to the presence of iron compounds, whereas black shales may owe theirs to iron compounds or organic carbon content. Tomlinson (1916) showed that red, purple, green, and black slates range in total iron content from about 3 to 6 percent, but that the ratio of ferric to ferrous iron varies from one extreme to the other. In red slates, ferric iron is four times as abundant as ferrous, whereas in black slates it is only 0.2 percent as abundant. More recently, Van Houten (1948) examined the phenomenon of red coloration and found that factors in addition to the ratio of ferric to ferrous iron are involved. It is generally agreed that red color indicates either derivation from red soils or accumulation of sediments in oxidizing conditions. Krynine (1949) discusses the problem in terms of weathering and sedimentation and concludes that four main conditions are responsible for red coloration. These are discussed more fully in Chapter 13 in the section on red bed associations.

Black colors in sediments may be caused by finely disseminated iron sulphide, as in some black shales, or by abundant organic matter (bitumen and related substances). Trask and Patnode (1942) found that sediments range from light to dark over a range of organic carbon from essentially none to about 5 percent. Keller (1953) reviews the subject and shows that in some sediments green color is associated with illite and montmorillonite in the clay fractions. Weller (1960, p. 129–141) has an excellent discussion of sedimentary colors, which is recommended for detailed reading.

SEDIMENTARY STRUCTURES

Sedimentary structures include the larger features of a sediment, which are better seen in outcrop than in hand specimens. Sedimentary structures depend more on relations between sedimentary aggregates than on the grain to grain relations that control texture.

Classification of Structures

Structures are commonly classified as **syngenetic** and **epigenetic**. Syngenetic structures are formed contemporaneously with the sediment. They include bedding, ripple mark, organic features, and others. Epigenetic structures are formed after deposition. Certain concretions, compaction features, and large-scale features, such as folds and faults, belong in this category.

Sedimentary structures, whether syngenetic or epigenetic, may also be classified as **external** or **internal**. The external structure or morphology of a rock mass includes its size and shape, the nature of its boundaries (whether conformable or unconformable), and the types of folding it exhibits. Internal structures include bedding, ripple mark, concretions, fossils, and others.

Table 4-8 is a classification of sedimentary structures based on syngenetic or epigenetic origin, with subdivisions into physical, chemical, or organic mode of origin, and with reference to their external or internal nature. The following topics, selected from the table are arranged according to external and internal features. The selection is based largely on the importance of the structural features in stratigraphic and sedimentary analysis. More detailed discussion can be found in Shrock (1948), Twenhofel (1950), Pettijohn (1957), and Weller (1960).

External Structures. Sedimentary bodies in the geologic column are three-dimensional solids of finite size, have some kind of geometric form, and exhibit sharp or gradational contact relations with their neighbors.

TABLE 4-8. SEDIMENTARY STRUCTURES

A. MAINLY SYNGENETIC (PRIMARY)
    1. *Mainly physical*
        a. External structures
            Size and shape of sedimentary body
        b. Internal structures
            Bedding and lamination
                Normal current bedding
                Cross-bedding
                Graded bedding
                Rhythmic bedding
            Features of bedding planes
                Ripple mark
                Mud cracks
                Raindrop prints
                Swash and rill marks
                Flute casts
                Load casts
            Deformation structures
                Postdepositional slump features
                Intraformational conglomerates
    2. *Mainly organic*
        a. External structures
            Biostromes
            Bioherms
        b. Internal structures
            Fossils

B. MAINLY EPIGENETIC (SECONDARY)
    1. *Mainly physical*
        a. External structures
            Nature of boundaries (comformable or nonconformable)
            Folds and faults
         b. Internal structures
            Clastic dikes
    2. *Mainly chemical or organic*
        a. Internal structures
            Corrosion zones
            Concretions
            Stylolites
            Cone-in-cone
            Crystal molds and casts
            Veins and dikes

Size and Shape of Sedimentary Bodies. The external configuration or shape of a sedimentary body may be described as a **sheet, lens, wedge, fan, delta,** or **shoestring.** The shapes of sedimentary bodies, especially buried sand bars, stream channels, and porous layers in limestone or dolomite, are highly important in oil and gas exploration, because they commonly provide conditions for stratigraphic traps. A classification of shapes is developed in Chapter 8.

Nature of Boundaries. Some sedimentary bodies abut abruptly against their neighbors vertically and laterally, whereas others may show continuous gradations from one type of deposit to another. The vertical relations give rise to **conformable** and **unconformable** contacts, as well as purely gradational contacts. Laterally, the deposits may **intertongue** abruptly with their neighbors, or they may **intergrade** in an imperceptible fashion from one deposit to another.

Unconformable relations among sedimentary deposits are very important in stratigraphy since they are the criteria upon which time intervals between the deposition of successive formations are recognized. Hence, fuller discussion of the subject is deferred to Chapter 9 of this text.

Fig. 4-14

Comparison of two classifications of bedding thickness.

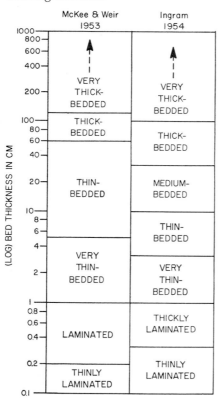

Internal Structures. Internal Structures occur within the body of a sedimentary rock. They are readily visible in outcrop, but the larger internal structures may become obscure when well cuttings or thin sections are examined.

Bedding and Lamination. Most sedimentary rocks are arranged in layers or strata. According to Payne (1942), a **stratum** is an individual layer of rock 1 cm. or greater in thickness, and is separated from strata above and below by a discrete change in lithology or a physical break (plane of separation). A **lamina** is similar to a stratum, but is less than 1 cm. in thickness. A **bed** is a rock unit composed of several strata or laminae. Alling (1945) developed a classification of shaly bedding based upon the ease of breaking along bedding planes. McKee and Weir (1953) developed a classification of stratifiefd units, that employs thickness limits similar to those defined by Payne. Figure 4-14 shows a comparison of McKee and Weir's classification with the geometric grouping of Ingram (1954).

Strata may be very uniform in thickness and composition over great areas, or they may change very rapidly, developing lenslike forms. Widespread shallow seas tend to develop deposits remarkably uniform in bedding and composition, whereas deposits in geosynclines and other rapidly subsiding areas may show much local variation in thickness and extent of their strata.

Thickness Distributions of Beds. Measurements on sets of beds have shown in several instances that the distribution of bed thickness tends to be lognormal. Pettijohn (1957, p. 160) shows several examples. This implies that although most beds in a series tend to be of moderate thickness, there is a finite probability for the occurrence of markedly thicker beds in the series. Subsurface studies of sandstone thicknesses based on electric logs are useful in disclosing relations between bed thickness and oil or gas occurrence. Figure 4-15, drawn from Potter and Siever (1955, Table 4) shows the thickness distribution of Lower Pennsylvanian sandstone beds in a part of the Illinois Basin. This distribution closely approximates log-normalcy. Note that although most of the beds are less than 16-feet thick, some are thicker than 150-feet.

This apparent log-normal thickness distribution justifies Ingram's use of geometric class limits to define bed thicknesses. Kelley (1956) also proposed a scale for statistical grouping of bed thicknesses, and Bokman (1957) used a geometric series based on the ratio 2 to facilitate computation of the logarithmic mean and standard deviation of sets of beds.

Graded bedding is typical of some sandstones in geosynclinal sequences, in contradistinction to **current bedding**, found in widespread, thinner sandstones. In graded bedding, which is apparently the result of relatively rapid pulsational sedimentation under unstable tectonic conditions, the particles grade from coarse to fine from bottom to top of the bed. Figure 4-16 (from Bailey, 1936), shows the distinction between current bedding and graded bedding.

Kuenen and Migliorini (1950) advanced the hypothesis that graded bedding may be caused by density currents (turbidity currents) moving down relatively steep slopes and depositing their material in graded form. The rocks thus formed are commonly called **turbidites.** Some of the characteristics that permit interpretation of the conditions under which they were deposited are described under bedding plane and deformation structures. Kuenen (1953) presents an excellent summary of the attributes of graded bedding.

PROPERTIES OF SEDIMENTARY ROCKS [CHAP. 4]

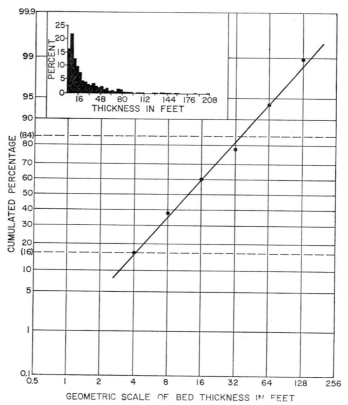

Fig. 4-15. Histogram and cumulative curve of thickness of 898 Lower Pennsylvanian sandstone beds. Bed thickness is plotted on an implied logarithmic scale, and the straight line on the probability paper indicates a distribution essentially normal in terms of the logs of thickness. [Inset adapted from Potter and Siever (1955). Copyright by the University of Chicago.]

Cross-bedding is an arrangement of laminae transverse to the planes of stratification in straight sloping lines or concave forms. The angles of inclination are usually 30 degrees or less. Cross-bedding is made by water and wind and, in many instances it is not possible to distinguish the two types. Both show cross laminations tangential to the lower stratification plane and truncated at the top, but water cross-bedding is more likely to have the upper stratification plane roughly parallel to the lower plane; while wind cross-bedding is more likely to have inclined or curved upper surfaces, giving a wedge shape to cross-bedded units. Shrock (1948) includes illustrations of numerous bedding types. McKee and Weir (1953) proposed a threefold classification of cross-bed types, as shown in Figure 4-17, adapted from their paper. Cross-bedding and other primary structures were further discussed by McKee in 1957.

Inasmuch as cross-bedding is a vector property of sediments, it has been extensively used for the study of paleocurrent directions. Reiche (1938) studied the directions of cross-lamination in the Coconino sandstone (Permian) of Arizona, and more recently, Potter and Olson (1954) used formal statistical design in the sampling, measurement, and interpretation of cross-bedding direction in basal Pennsylvanian sandstones of the Eastern Interior Basin. Potter et al. (1958) show that cross-bedding along the outcrops of Chester sands (Mississippian) in southern Illinois agree with subsurface trends of the sands.

Bedding Plane Markings. Bedding surfaces of sedimentary rocks show much variation in smoothness and roughness. Some bedding planes are characterized by **ripple mark,** the subparallel ridges and hollows formed by waves or currents. **Oscillation ripple mark** is caused by the orbital motion of water waves, a to-and-fro motion along the bottom. Irregularities on the bottom develop small eddies which rearrange the loose material into symmetrical parallel ridges. Oscillation ripples are stationary, and their amplitude and height are functions of wave characteristics and water depth.

In addition to these long recognized and widely described features of bedding surfaces, considerable information has been gained during the past decade on bedding plane features associated with turbidity currents. Many

Fig. 4-16. Contrast of current bedding and graded bedding. [Adapted from Bailey (1936).]

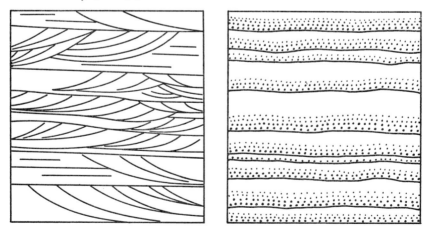

CURRENT BEDDING   GRADED BEDDING

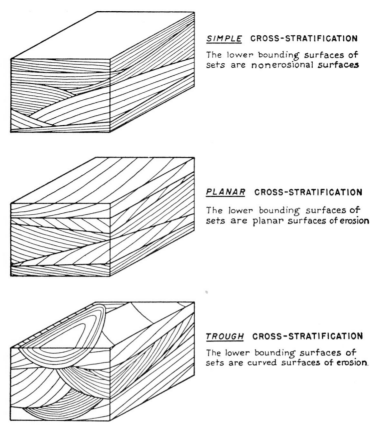

SIMPLE CROSS-STRATIFICATION

The lower bounding surfaces of
sets are nonerosional surfaces

PLANAR CROSS-STRATIFICATION

The lower bounding surfaces of
sets are planar surfaces of erosion

TROUGH CROSS-STRATIFICATION

The lower bounding surfaces of
sets are curved surfaces of erosion.

Fig. 4-17. Basic elements in McKee and Weir's (1953) classification of cross-stratification.

of these are important vectorial properties that establish the direction flow of the current that deposited the rocks.

Figure 4-18 shows three typical bedding plane features in addition to a slump structure, which are characteristic of turbidites, reproduced from Ten Haaf (1959). The upper left illustration shows **flute casts**, characterized by steep bulbous upstream ends from which the casts flatten toward downstream portions of the casts. The upper right illustration shows **groove casts**, elongated parallel grooves or scratches oriented in the direction of current flow. **Load casts** are deformations of a bedding plane caused by the partial sinking of a heavy plastic layer into a softer substratum. Load casting commonly occurs when turbidites are deposited on unconsolidated mud. These features appear to be most common during the onset of deposition rather than higher up in the turbidity current deposit. As the figure shows, the underlying plastic material may be squeezed upward into the sandy bed of the turbidite.

Current ripple mark, formed either by wind or water, is asymmetrical, with a gentle slope in the upcurrent direction, and a steeper slope downcurrent. In water, the grains roll up the gentle slope and down the other side, so that the ripple as a whole moves downstream. The ripple wave lengths and amplitudes correspond to varying conditions of current and grain size. Wind ripples are the result of saltation movement of sand grains, in which the grains leap and bound along the surface. Bagnold (1941) has shown that wind ripple wave length is a function of the mean length of the saltation path for grains of a given size. Bucher (1919) and Shrock (1948) treat ripple mark in some detail. An excellent series of photographs of ripples on beaches is given by Trefethen and Dow (1960); Tanner (1960) also describes shallow-water ripple mark.

Among finer sediments, which shrink on drying, **mud cracks** may be formed. Mud cracks form polygonal patterns of varying length and width.

Fig. 4-18. Bedding plane and slump structures. (*A*) Flute casts, current from left to right; (*B*) upcurrent ends of groove casts; (*C*) load casts, current direction shown by arrow; (*D*) slump structure in shale (shown as black); the sandstone (white) has slipped to the left in the upper part of the diagram. [From Ten Haaf (1959).]

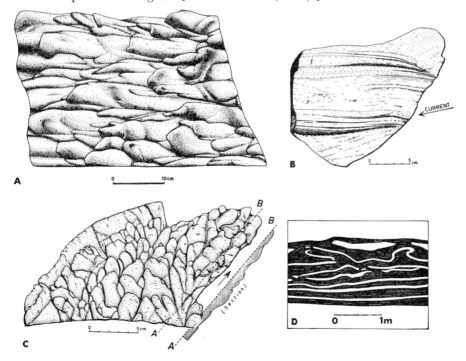

The pattern is in part determined by the accidental occurrence of foreign materials in the mud, and by the degree to which the mud dries out. Mud cracks in ancient sediments are assumed to indicate exposure to the air, apparently a safe inference in many instances. Mud cracks are more common in continental sediments than in marine sediments because of the greater opportunities for drying. Marine mud cracks occur mainly in tidal flat or estuarine deposits.

Deformation Structures. Many sediments display intricately folded beds or laminae, sometimes accompanied by breccia, strongly suggesting that deformation occurred during or shortly after deposition.

Increased interest in turbidity current deposits has shed considerable light on a variety of deformation structures. The lower right illustration in Figure 4-18 represents a **slump structure;** shale layers are shown in black and sandstone seams in white. Such structures commonly occur when a relatively thick turbidite bed slips or slumps relative to the more plastic and clayey bed immediately below.

Some deformation structures apparently occur in deposits laid down on inclined slopes independent of the action of turbidity currents. Inasmuch as some fine grained sediments contain up to 80 percent water when freshly deposited, such loosely aggregated material may readily yield to forces and slide down a relatively gentle slope or shear under gentle stresses. The original bedding becomes intricately folded during the sliding, and stiffer materials in the beds may break into angular fragments, developing **intra-formational conglomerates.** Sliding may readily occur at the edges of coral reefs and along the seaward margins of deltas, as well as over the much more gentle slopes down which turbidity currents may flow.

Deformation during compaction arises when fine grained sediments are deposited over hills or other irregularities on the depositional surface. Overlying beds compact the lower material, and mold it to the shapes of the buried hills. Coral reefs may act as such irregularities, developing structures which drape over the reefs. Some Devonian oil-bearing structures in the Illinois Basin have been found associated with underlying Silurian coral reefs.

Concretions. **Concretions** are aggregates of inorganic material within the body of sediments. They show wide variations in size, shape, density of distribution, and composition. Concretions range in size from minute spheres to structures many feet across. In shape, they range from perfect spheres to flattened, rounded objects, sometimes in combinations of tangentially united globular masses.

Concretions usually show radial or concentric structure, but some appear structureless, such as the large "nigger-heads" in some shales associated with coal. Concretions may be formed of calcite, chert, siderite, limonite, pyrite, gypsum, and other substances.

Among the more common concretionary forms are **oolites**. Pisolites are larger, usually of pea size. Other common concretions are irregular, structureless chert concretions and masses appearing in some limestones and dolomites. Iron oxide and siderite concretions, usually small, are common in some sandstones, and gypsum concretions are common in some shales. Weeks (1953) discusses the origin of carbonate concretions in shale.

A number of origins have been assigned to concretions. Some bear evidence of having been formed at the time of, or shortly after, deposition of the enclosing sediment; others show definite proof of having been formed some time after deposition. Concretions in limestone and shale seem, on the whole, to be formed contemporaneous with deposition, as exhibited in their relation to fossils and to the bedding planes. In sandstones, the concretions appear, in most instances, to have been formed later by cementation of the sand grains.

Oolites are formed in saline waters under agitated conditions along shores or in shallow places where waves break. Calcareous oolites represent more or less even deposition of calcite on nuclei, which are tossed about by the agitation of the water. The oolites may accumulate in the local area where they form, or they may be transported mechanically, forming bedded and cross-bedded deposits typical of the clastic sediments. Oolites may later be replaced by chert, iron oxide, or other secondary minerals. Eardley (1938) describes the formation of oolites in Great Salt Lake, Utah. Rusnak (1960) and Freeman (1960) present recent papers on this subject.

In ancient sediments, oolites are sometimes found associated with limestone reefs. Apparently the shallow, agitated water of the reef is suitable for oolite formation. In part, the oolites are deposited locally, but the remainder may be swept along in the lagoonal areas among the reefs, developing "oolite trends."

Corrosion Surfaces. Corrosion surfaces, which occur in limestones and dolomites, represent modified bedding planes. It is believed that corrosion zones develop during interludes of nondeposition in carbonate producing environments, when some of the previously deposited calcareous material is redissolved.

Corrosion surfaces may be pitted in an irregular manner; they may be coated with a black manganese oxide stain, or, more commonly, a residue of relatively stable material such as pyrite grains, phosphatic nodules, and shells, as well as some detrital grains. Pettijohn (1926), Weiss (1954), and Prokopovich (1955) describe and discuss corrosion surfaces.

Other Internal Structures. A number of other internal structures, including stylolites, cone-in-cone, swash marks, and rill marks, are not treated in detail here. They are described by Twenhofel (1950) and Shrock (1948).

Organic Structures. Fossils are typical organic structures. They are among the most important for interpreting the age of the formation and its conditions of deposition. Larger organic structures, such as coral reefs, are called **bioherms.** They represent accumulations of organic remains and debris formed under conditions of prolific life.

A type of organic structure without the prominent size and steep walls of the typical bioherm is the **biostrome,** a zone of organic structures or remains spread as a blanket or in localized sheets or lenses through a formation. Some oyster reefs are biostromes; coal seams represent fossil plant biostromes. These and other organic structures are so important in stratigraphic analysis that further consideration is given them in later chapters.

COMPOSITION OF SEDIMENTARY ROCKS

Composition of sedimentary rocks is expressed in mineralogical or chemical terms. Composition is the third important property of sediments, and together with texture and structure, it comprises the aggregate characteristics of the rock.

Composition provides an important basis for grouping sediments into related classes. Sedimentary classifications commonly give first rank to composition in the naming of a rock, and a secondary rank to texture or structure.

Mineralogical Composition of Sediments

Some sedimentary rocks are very uniform in mineralogical composition. The St. Peter sandstone (Ordovician) is composed of more than 99 percent quartz grains. More commonly, sediments are mixtures of several minerals, and some, such as glacial till, have a large variety of minerals and rock fragments.

More than 150 mineral species have been identified in sedimentary rocks. Most of these are relatively rare and depend on the accidental inclusion of parent rock minerals with altered debris. Some 20 minerals compose about 99 percent of the bulk of sedimentary rocks, according to Krynine (1948). Table 4-9, adapted from Krynine, shows the commonest minerals arranged according to their relative abundance in sediments. Rock fragments, though not listed in the table, are also important components in sedimentary rocks. They are discussed in relation to sandstone classification in Chapter 5.

TABLE 4-9. THE COMMON MINERALS OF SEDIMENTS

COMMONLY OVER 10 PERCENT OF ROCK	COMMONLY LESS THAN 10 PERCENT OF ROCK	LESS THAN 1 PERCENT OF ROCK (ACCESSORY MINERALS)
	DETRITAL MINERALS	
Quartz	Detrital chert	"Iron ores"
Clay minerals	Coarse grained micas	Zircon
Fine grained micas	Feldspars	Tourmaline
		Epidote
		Garnet
		Hornblende
	CHEMICAL AND AUTHIGENIC MINERALS	
Calcite	Chert	Anatase
Dolomite	"Secondary" quartz	Authigenic feld-
	Gypsum	spar and mica

Detrital and Nondetrital Minerals

The first group in the table includes the **detrital minerals,** which consist of broken and abraded particles brought to the site of deposition by mechanical transport. The detrital minerals form the bulk of the clastic sediments, and, as Table 4-9 shows, the most abundant minerals in these rocks are quartz, clay minerals, and fine grained micas. Less common are detrital chert, feldspar, and coarse grained micas. The **accessory minerals** are least abundant and are particles of higher density derived from the parent rock.

Figure 4-19 shows the common size range of the detrital particles in clastic sediments. Quartz and mica extend through most of the size range, whereas the clay minerals are more typically associated with shale.

The **nondetrital minerals** are precipitated from solution by chemical or biological agents. Accumulation occurs at, or generally close to, the site of precipitation. This group also includes authigenic minerals formed in the sediment after deposition.

The most common minerals in the nonclastic rocks are calcite and dolomite. Chert, secondary quartz, and gypsum (or anhydrite) are less common. Small amounts of anatase, and rare occurrences of accessory minerals may be found in the nonclastics.

The composition of all sedimentary rocks may be expressed in terms of the two groups of components shown in Table 4-9. These components may be mixed in any proportions in specific sediments. For example, a limestone may be wholly composed of the nonclastic minerals calcite and dolomite, or it may have enough detrital clay mineral to classify it as argillaceous lime-

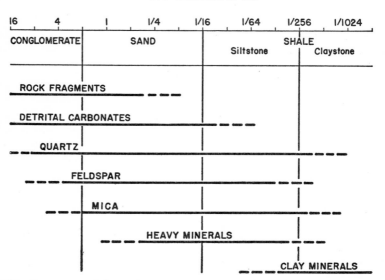

Fig. 4-19. Size range of detrital particles in clastic sediments.

stone. The classification of sediments, including those of mixed composition, is treated in Chapter 5.

In any sediment, the composition of the detrital fraction depends upon the kind of source rock, the degree of weathering of the source rock, and the distance and processes of transport. Similarly, the composition of the non-detrital fraction depends upon the physical and chemical processes taking place at the site of deposition.

Authigenic Minerals

In addition to the detrital and nondetrital minerals that constitute original sedimentary deposits, other components may be introduced after deposition. These are **authigenic minerals,** formed in place within a sediment.

A large number of authigenic minerals is known. Among the more common are chert, formed in limestone after deposition; calcite cement in sandstone; pyrite in dark shales; feldspar crystals in limestone; gypsum crystals in clay; and many others. Glauconite is commonly considered an authigenic mineral, and apparently forms on the sea bottom and where it may be incorporated into sediments. Glauconite commonly occurs as grains in some sandstone, and as disseminated material in some clay shale.

It is not always feasible to distinguish authigenic minerals from non-detrital minerals. Calcite may form simultaneously with the deposition of clean quartz sands to yield calcareous sandstone, or the calcite may be introduced later as a cement. Similarly, the process of dolomitization of limestone may occur contemporaneously with deposition, or it may occur later. The line drawn between typical nondetrital minerals and authigenic minerals may have to be arbitrary in some instances.

Authigenesis is one aspect of the broader subject of postdepositional changes in sediments, called **diagenesis.** Diagenetic changes in sediments have been studied intensively in the light of geochemical principles, and the subject is more fully treated in Chapter 7, under the heading of diagenetic environment.

The End-member Concept

The detrital and chemical fractions are commonly designated as **end members,** and sedimentary rocks may be classified according to whether they consist of 50 percent or more of detrital end members, or 50 percent or more of chemical end members. The former are detrital (clastic) rocks, and the latter are chemical (nonclastic) rocks.

The end-member concept was developed by Krynine (1948) and extended by Pettijohn (1949). In its extended form, it is possible to express the composition of any rock in terms of particular end members (such as quartz, calcite, and others), or groups of end members (such as quartz plus feldspar, calcite plus dolomite, and others) to bring out systematic variations among classes of sediments.

The end-member concept provides an important tool for classifying and interpreting sedimentary rocks. It is possible to select groups of related end members to bring out certain genetic relations among sediments and to show variations in composition as the rocks approach pure end members. This topic is treated in greater detail in Chapter 5.

Table 4-10 provides a summary of the more abundant minerals in sedimentary rocks. Common occurrences as primary or authigenic components of sediments are indicated. Types of source rocks which may provide the detrital minerals are also suggested.

Accessory Minerals

The accessory minerals listed in Table 4-10, deserve more detailed treatment because of their importance in indicating the source rocks of sediments. Accessory minerals are the least abundant in the clastic rocks. They were derived from the parent rocks, having survived the weathering and transportation cycles. The accessory minerals have a greater density than the more abundant quartz and feldspar in sediments and, accordingly, they are called **heavy minerals.**

TABLE 4-10. SUMMARY OF COMMON SEDIMENTARY MINERALS

QUARTZ	Occurs as detrital fragments and rounded grains, or as authigenic quartz in secondary enlargement. Common sources are quartz-bearing, coarse grained, igneous rocks (granite), metamorphic rocks (gneiss), or reworked sediments.
CHALCEDONY	Occurs as detrital chert (as in salt-and-pepper sandstones), chert nodules or beds in limestone or dolomite, silica cement in sandstone. Some chert probably forms as a primary chemical precipitate.
FELDSPAR	Occurs as detrital fragments and grains, or as authigenic feldspar in limestone. Potash feldspar is more common than other varieties. Derived from granitic areas under conditions of rapid erosion and rapid burial.
MICA	Occurs as detrital flakes commonly oriented along bedding planes in sandstone and shale. Derived from micaceous igneous and metamorphic rocks (such as pegmatite, gneiss, schist). *Muscovite* is more common than *biotite*. Authigenic mica occurs in fine grained aggregates or microscopic flakes or shreds, called *sericite*. *Chlorite* is common in some graywacke sandstone.
ACCESSORY MINERALS	Occur as typical minor constituents in sandstone such as magnetite, ilmenite, tourmaline, garnet, zircon, and rutile. (See further under section on "Heavy Minerals" in this chapter.)
CLAY MINERALS	Occur typically in shale or as matrix in other clastic sediments. Derived from weathering of igneous or metamorphic rocks, or from reworked shale.
IRON OXIDES	Commonly occur as cement, coatings on grains (as hematite in red sandstone), or as earthy masses.
CALCITE	Occurs as crystals, fossil fragments, oolites, cement, etc. Mainly formed at site of deposition by chemical or biological agents, but may be detrital in part. Cements are authigenic.
DOLOMITE	Occurs mainly as a replacement of calcite, although primary dolomite believed to occur with evaporites. Dolomite rhombs, of sand size, commonly cross-bedded, develop "clastic dolomites."
EVAPORITES	Gypsum and anhydrite most common; halite less so. Occur as bedded masses from evaporation, as disseminated crystals or masses (authigenic), and as cement.

Heavy Mineral Analysis

Detailed study of the mineral composition of clastic rocks, especially sandstone, affords information on the **provenance** or source area of the detrital material. The heavy minerals in sediments are most important in this connection.

Separation of Heavy Minerals

The heavy minerals may be separated from lighter minerals in several manners. A common method uses a liquid of specific gravity 2.9, such as bromoform, $CHBr_3$, which is poured into a separatory funnel into which the sand grains are introduced. The lighter minerals, such as quartz and feldspar (specific gravity about 2.7), float on the liquid, whereas the heavier minerals, such as magnetite (specific gravity 5.2), zircon (specific gravity 4.6), and tourmaline (specific gravity 3.5 to 4.3), sink to the bottom.

After separation, the heavy minerals at the bottom of the funnel are washed in filter paper, dried, and weighed. The percentage of heavy minerals in the sample is computed, and the grains mounted on microscope slides for identification and counting.

For more detailed work, other methods of further separation may be used, among which are magnetic electrostatic methods. Specific details of heavy mineral analysis are given by Krumbein and Pettijohn (1938) and by Twenhofel and Tyler (1941). Poole (1958) discusses methods of separation and the use of statistical tests in evaluating the data. Bates and Bates (1960) evaluate heavy mineral separation by study of artificial mineral samples.

The heavy minerals in sediments include unaltered grains from igneous and metamorphic rocks, some reworked grains from previously existing sediments, and some authigenic minerals formed in the sediment after deposition.

Heavy Mineral Associations

Table 4-11 lists the common heavy mineral associations of sediments, arranged in terms of the parent rocks from which the sediments were derived. First-generation sediments, formed from freshly exposed igneous or metamorphic terrain, tend to have clean angular to subangular heavy mineral grains, with some cleavage and crystal faces preserved. The heavy mineral assemblage may contain some unstable minerals, such as hornblende and biotite.

Sediments derived from pre-existing sediments tend to have well rounded, heavy mineral grains composed of the most stable heavy minerals, such as tourmaline and zircon. Such features indicate reworking and elimination of less stable components.

As Table 4-11 indicates, some thirty heavy minerals are fairly diagnostic of the source rocks, especially when they occur in associated groups. Many sediments contain minerals from more than one source, however. The full interpretation of heavy mineral data requires consideration of relative proportions of the mineral groups, degree of rounding of the grains, effects of differential solution, and other factors.

Heavy minerals have been used in stratigraphic correlation, as discussed in other chapters of this book. More recent work has tended to emphasize the areal distribution of heavy minerals as they relate to dispersal agents and

TABLE 4-11. DETRITAL MINERAL SUITES CHARACTERISTIC
OF SOURCE ROCK TYPES

SILICIC AND INTERMEDIATE IGNEOUS ROCKS	PEGMATITES	MAFIC AND ULTRAMAFIC IGNEOUS ROCKS
Apatite	Cassiterite	Anatase
Biotite	Fluorite	Augite
Hornblende	Topaz	Brookite
Monazite	Tourmaline	Chromite
Muscovite	Wolframite	Hypersthene
Titanite		Ilmenite
Zircon (euhedra)		Leucoxene
		Olivine
		Rutile

METAMORPHIC ROCKS	REWORKED SEDIMENTS
Andalusite	Glauconite
Garnet	Iron ores
Glaucophane	Quartz
Hornblende (blue-green variety)	Rutile
Kyanite	Tourmaline
Sillimanite	Zircon (rounded)
Staurolite	

probable source areas, as well as to post-depositional changes in heavy mineral composition of sediments. Some references that bear on these aspects are Goldich (1938), Pettijohn (1941), Smithson (1941), Allen (1949), Potter (1955), Pettijohn (1957), Poole (1958), and Van Andel and Poole (1960). Van Andel (1959) has written an excellent summary on the interpretation of heavy mineral analysis. The subject of heavy mineral dispersal and interpretation will be discussed again in Chapters 7 and 12.

Insoluble Residue Analysis

Paralleling heavy mineral analysis in detrital rocks is the study of **insoluble residues** in nonclastic rocks such as limestone and dolomite. The insoluble materials in carbonate rocks include a wide variety of substances, ranging from detrital sand and silt grains to secondary minerals, commonly chert replacements of original minerals or fossils.

Crushed rock samples are digested in dilute hydrochloric acid until the carbonates are dissolved. The residue is washed, dried and weighed, and preserved in glass vials or microscope slides for detailed examination. Ireland (1950) describes the technique and provides a classification of insoluble residues.

In many instances, insoluble residues occur in typical associations or relative abundances which render them useful for correlation purposes. Limestone and dolomite low in fossil content, and uniform in gross aspect through great thicknesses (such as the Ellenburger of Texas), may show certain zones in which the insoluble residues are alike over appreciable areas (Crowley and Hendricks, 1945). In 1959 Bisque and Lemish studied the relations between insoluble residues and the magnesium content of carbonate rocks. Carpenter and Schmidt (1962) present a detailed discussion of stratigraphic correlation with insoluble residues, including statistical treatment of the data.

CHEMICAL COMPOSITION OF SEDIMENTS

Complete chemical rock analysis is time consuming and requires special technical skills. Among coarse grained sediments, the identification of the minerals is usually sufficient to indicate gross chemical composition.

For fine grained sediments like shale, it is difficult to identify all the minerals by ordinary microscopic means. In such instances, chemical analysis may be the only accurate method of classifying the rock according to its lithologic type.

O'Neil (1959) discusses a number of procedures for chemical analysis of fine grained sedimentary rocks, in which major elements are determined by rapid semimicro methods, trace elements by spectrochemical procedures, and iron and molybdenum by a fluorescent X-ray spectrochemical method. Hirst and Nicholls (1958) describe techniques in sedimentary geochemistry for separating detrital and nondetrital components in limestone by spectographic procedures. These papers reflect the rapid increase in the use of geochemical methods for studying the composition of sediments—methods that are increasingly being used to supplement conventional mineralogical analyses. See Haun and LeRoy (1958) for spectrographic and other methods.

In addition to complete chemical analysis, analysis of trace elements, and study of particular components such as organic matter [see Orr and Emery (1956) on the use of chromatographic methods in this connection], other chemical or physicochemical attributes of sediments are being examined. **Thermoluminescence** is an example. This property is shown by certain solids that emit light during thermal stimulation. Parks (1953) describes the phenomenon and the equipment used, and Johnson (1960) discusses the thermoluminescence of biogenic limestones. The subject is further treated

TABLE 4-12. CHEMICAL ANALYSES OF SANDSTONE, SHALE, AND LIMESTONE

	ST. PETER SANDSTONE OTTAWA, ILL.	FRANCIS CREEK SHALE DAYTON, ILL.	PLATTEVILLE LIMESTONE OTTAWA, ILL.
SiO_2	98.47	61.11	0.80
TiO_2	0.05	1.13	—
Al_2O_3	0.75	20.26	1.19
Fe_2O_3	0.08	4.64*	1.67*
FeO	—	—	—
MgO	0.08	1.54	8.31
CaO	0.21	0.93	43.73
Na_2O	—	0.67	Trace
K_2O	0.06	4.26	Trace
P_2O_5	—	—	—
S	—	0.05	0.12
H_2O+	—	—	—
H_2O-	—	0.30	0.02
CO_2	0.47	0.96	43.72
Ignition loss	—	5.66	44.13†
Totals	100.17	100.25	99.95

* Includes FeO. Data for all samples from Wilman and Payne (1942).
† Omission of this ignition loss yields a total of 99.56.

in Chapter 10, since thermoluminescence is used in stratigraphic correlation.

The average sedimentary rock contains about 58 percent SiO_2, 13 percent Al_2O_3, 6 percent CaO, 5 percent combined FeO and Fe_2O_3, 5 percent CO_2, and less than 5 percent each of other constituents such as MgO, K_2O, and Na_2O. As may be expected, the average sediment has a composition which suggests a mixture of sandstone (mainly SiO_2), shale (mainly Al_2O_3 and SiO_2), and limestone (mainly CaO and CO_2).

The chemical composition of the average sediment differs from that of the average igneous rock in the greater amount of CO_2 present, a much lower percentage of Na_2O, and a higher ratio of Fe_2O_3 to FeO. These differences are due mainly to additions from the atmosphere, loss of soluble salts to the ocean during weathering, and a high degree of oxidation during weathering.

The chemical composition of specific sedimentary rocks is in part an index of the selective effects of the depositional agent. Table 4-12 lists the chemical composition of pure quartz sandstone, clay shale, and dolomitic limestone. The simple composition of the sandstone reflects the great predominance of quartz, due to long sorting action by the transporting agent. The more complex composition of the shale indicates the presence of clay minerals and a larger variety of components other than the sandstone. The dolomitic limestone is mainly calcium carbonate with a moderate amount of magnesium, and only minor amounts of other substances.

Trace Elements in Sedimentary Rocks

The development of new techniques for the spectrographic detection and identification of minor chemical components in rocks has given rise to a considerable amount of data on trace elements in sedimentary rocks. These trace elements, which may range from less than one part per million to several hundred parts per million, are useful in the geochemical interpretation of sedimentary deposits. Sometimes a given trace element may suggest the occurrence of ore bodies by its association with the ore mineral. Vanadium is commonly associated with uranium and may thus afford a method for geochemical prospecting for uranium.

Table 4-13 shows the geometric mean content, in parts per million, of

TABLE 4-13. AVERAGE COMPOSITION OF URANIUM ORE AND UNMINERALIZED SANDSTONE*

ELEMENT	URANIUM ORE	UNMINERALIZED SANDSTONE
Aluminum	2.48	1.20
Iron	0.90	0.24
Magnesium	0.68	0.23
Calcium	1.97	3.30
Sodium	0.091	0.089
Potassium	0.27	0.3
Titanium	0.104	0.051
Zirconium	0.0237	0.0103
Manganese	0.031	0.022
Barium	0.084	0.034
Strontium	0.0122	0.0049
Beryllium	0.0001	0.0001
Boron	0.0015	0.0008
Scandium	0.001	0.001
Vanadium	0.49	0.0010
Chromium	0.00169	0.00066
Cobalt	0.00104	0.0002
Nickel	0.00084	0.0002
Copper	0.0086	0.0013
Zinc	0.0116	0.0053

* This table shows the first twenty trace elements in Table 2, from Shoemaker, et al. (1959, p. 32). It illustrates the kind of detailed information obtainable by trace element analysis.

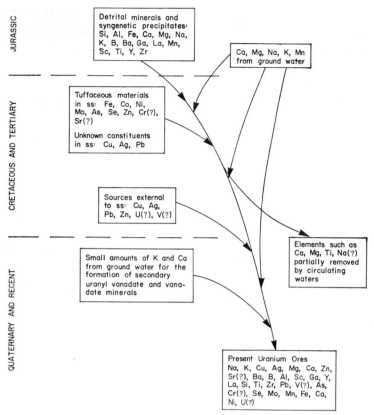

Fig. 4-20. Flow from various sources of the elements involved in the formation of the present uranium ores. The oldest events are at the top. [Data from Miesch (1961).]

some trace elements in unmineralized sandstone and in uranium ore of the Morrison formation, as reported by Shoemaker, et al. (1959). Note that the aluminum, iron, and magnesium are more abundant in the uranium ores, whereas calcium content is higher in the unmineralized sandstones. Other elements, such as sodium, may occur in about the same concentration in both kinds of rock. The strong association of vanadium with the ore is shown in the table.

Recent work by Miesch (Ph.D. Dissertation, Northwestern University) has shown that the trace elements in some uranium deposits can be assigned to several groups. The first includes the elements originally present in the local body of rock. The other groups represent contributions caused by the rearrangement of elements contained in or associated with the original sediment, as well as contributions from external sources.

Figure 4-20 shows the relations graphically. The uranium appears to have been precipitated by pyrite and carbonized plant remains in the sandstone. This example of geochemical analysis has obvious applications for the study of postdepositional changes in sediments, even in the absence of economic concentrations of ore. Equally important in the study of such processes is consideration of elements that may have been completely or partially removed from the original deposit. The likelihood that such changes occur is suggested by one of the arrows in Figure 4-20.

Statistical Analysis of Composition Data

Graphic and statistical analysis of heavy mineral data differs from that of textural data of sediments. The diameters of sandstone particles differ from each other by infinitesimal amounts. For this reason, the size distribution represents a continuous range of diameters. Mineral composition, on the other hand, is discontinuous between species. Between zircon and garnet, for instance, there is no continuous gradation in composition. Moreover, when mineral grains are counted, the count is always in integers. Thus, heavy mineral data are discrete rather than continuous. Bar graphs can be used to show heavy mineral data in percentage form, as shown in figure 4-21, but since the measurements are discrete and have no necessary rank implications, the position of the bars is arbitrary. Changes in heavy mineral composition in the direction of sediment transport may be studied by computing and plotting ratios of one mineral to another. The ratio of an unstable mineral, such as hornblende, to a stable mineral such as garnet, com-

Fig. 4-21. Heavy mineral frequencies in two sandstones. (*Left*) St. Peter sandstone, Wisconsin. (*Right*) Basal Pennsylvanian cyclothem sandstone, Illinois.

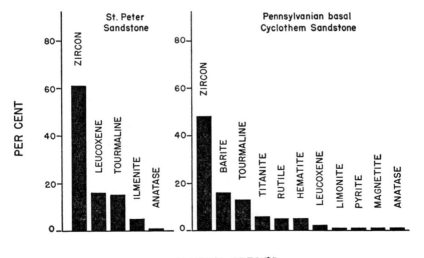

monly decreases away from the source area, in the absence of additions from tributary sources, as shown in 1931 by Pettijohn. An early map of heavy mineral distribution in the bottom sediments of Barataria Bay, Louisiana, is included in Caldwell (1940). Recent examples of such maps are included in Van Andel and Poole (1960), for several minerals and ratios in the Gulf of Mexico. The interpretation of such maps is considered in Chapter 6.

Variations in heavy minerals, insoluble residues, or chemical constituents in a stratigraphic sequence may be shown on strip logs, as described in Chapter 3. Such strip logs are of value in stratigraphic correlation.

Frequency distributions of individual rock components tend to be **binomial** when the mineral is abundant, and **Poisson** when the mineral is rare (see Dixon and Massey, 1957, pp. 228–231 for definitions). The two histograms in Figure 4-22 were prepared by collecting 100 subsamples of 10 pebbles each

Fig. 4-22. Histograms illustrating the number of beach pebbles of a given composition observed in 100 subsamples of 10 pebbles each. See the text for discussion.

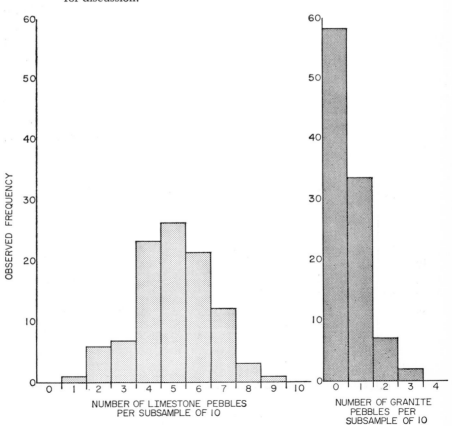

from a limited area of beach gravel (Krumbein, 1954), and counting the number of occurrences of limestone and granite in each subsample. Limestone pebbles constituted about 50 percent of the gravel, whereas granite pebbles made up only about 5 percent.

The limestone pebble histogram is typically binomial with a central maximum dropping away symmetrically on each side. The granite pebble histogram is more nearly a Poisson distribution. This histogram is highly asymmetric, and it illustrates how variable small samples may be—thus, when a rock or mineral makes up only a small part of an aggregate, it will most commonly not be observed in a single, small sample. In the present example, the chances of observing one or more granite pebbles in a sample of 10 pebbles are only 42 out of 100, even though the pebbles are actually present to the extent of 5 percent.

Griffiths (1960) has developed the topic of frequency distributions in accessory mineral analysis in considerable detail; the reader is referred to his paper for further details. In addition to the greater emphasis on mineral frequency distributions in recent years, some geologists have applied formal statistical design to the study of mineral variation. Carroll (1957), for example, compared the mineral contributions of two major source areas to the South River near Waynesboro, Georgia. The statistical design permitted contrast of the variability within and among tributaries, as well as of the contributions from two source areas. Rogers and Powell (1958) examined the grain-size distributions of heavy minerals and presented histograms of zircon grains, which are well sorted and show little or no skewness. An important and basic paper by Manning (1953) discusses the use of sample data in establishing confidence intervals and in testing hypotheses for heavy mineral analysis.

Statistical methods have also been applied to the data of chemical analyses of sediments. Many of these represent applications of the conventional statistical methods used by chemists. An excellent introductory reference is Youden (1951). Miesch et al. (1960) and Miesch and Riley (1961) include frequency distribution analyses of elements and statistical correlation and regression analyses as applied to geochemical investigations of uranium deposits in the Colorado plateau. These papers provide an introduction to the subject. Problems on the nature of the frequency distributions of trace elements are discussed by Miller and Goldberg (1955), based on earlier analysis by Ahrens (1954).

SUPPLEMENTARY READINGS

The following text and reference books are recommended as a supplement to the material presented in this chapter. Each author presents his material in a slightly different way, and the shift in emphasis from one book to another can benefit the reader. The references mentioned in the text are given in the comprehensive bibliography at the end of this book.

1. Krumbein, W. C. and Pettijohn, F. J., 1938, Manual of sedimentary petrography: New York, D. Appleton-Century Co., Inc.

   Particle size, shape, roundness, orientation, surface texture, and analysis: Chapters 4, 5, 6, 10, 11, 12.
   Graphic and statistical methods: Chapters 7, 8, 9.
   Mass properties: Chapter 20.
   Mineral analysis: Chapters 13, 14, 15, 18.

2. Twenhofel, W. H. and Tyler, S. A., 1941, Methods of study of sediments: New York, McGraw-Hill Book Co., Inc. An introductory textbook on methods of sedimentary analysis.

   Particle size analysis: Chapter 4.
   Mineral analysis: Chapters 5, 6.
   Graphic methods: Chapter 7.
   Other properties of sediments: Chapters 9.

3. Shrock, R. R., 1948, Sequence in layered rocks: New York, McGraw-Hill Book Co., Inc.

   Sedimentary structures: Chapters 4, 5.

4. Twenhofel, W. H., 1950, Principles of sedimentation: New York, McGraw-Hill Book Co., Inc., 2nd edition.

   Sedimentary structures: Chapter 14.
   Texture and color: Chapter 15.

5. Weller, J. M., 1960, Stratigraphic principles and practice: New York, Happer and Brothers.

   Textures, Structures, and Colors of Sediments: Chapter 5.

6. Pettijohn, F. J., 1957, Sedimentary rocks: New York, Harper & Brothers, 2nd edition.

   Textures: Chapter 2.
   Composition: Chapter 3.
   Sedimentary structures: Chapter 4.

7. Dunbar, C. O. and Rodgers, J., 1957, Principles of stratigraphy: New York, John Wiley and Sons, Inc.

   Stratification: Chapter 5.

8. Dixon, W. J. and Massey, F. J., 1957, Introduction to statistical analysis: New York, McGraw-Hill Book Company, Inc., 2nd edition.

Histograms, mean and standard deviation, median and quartiles: Chapters 2, 3, 6.
Binomial distribution: Chapter 13.

9. Milner, H. B., 1962, Sedimentary petrography, Vol. 1: New York, The Macmillan Company.

Laboratory techniques, texture and mineral composition: Chapters 3–7.
Chemical analysis: Chapters 8–10.
Spectrographic, fluorescence, X-ray, electron microscope, and nuclear methods of analysis: Chapters 11–15.
Statistical methods: Chapter 16.

10. Haun, J. D. and LeRoy, L. W. (editors), 1958, Subsurface geology in petroleum exploration: Colorado School of Mines, Golden.

Insoluble residues, Electron microscope, X-ray, and thermoluminescence analysis: Part II, Chapters 5, 8, 9, 10.

CHAPTER 5

Classification and Description of Sedimentary Rocks

INTRODUCTION

THE properties of sedimentary rocks provide a basis for classification according to similarities in texture, composition, or other characteristics. The observable properties may be used directly in **descriptive classifications,** or the conditions of sedimentary origin may be inferred from the properties to develop **genetic classifications.**

Several sedimentary classifications have been proposed. Descriptive groupings are based on textural properties of the sediment, or on chemical or mineralogic composition. Genetic classifications include those based on agent of deposition (wind *vs.* water), process of deposition (mechanical *vs.* chemical), environment of deposition (marine *vs.* nonmarine), or on the tectonic framework of deposition.

The most comprehensive scheme of sediment classification was proposed by Grabau (1904, 1913). Each rock name expresses the texture and chemical composition, as well as the agent mainly responsible for deposition of the sediment. A pure quartz sandstone deposited in water is a hydrosilicarenite, whereas a lime-mud rock deposited in water is a hydrocalcilutite. Grabau introduced many new names, which hindered the full adoption of his system. His concepts, however, have to some degree colored subsequent classifications. Especially significant was his recognition that sediments are either **exogenetic** (derived from some outside source area), or **endogenetic** (derived from material in solution at or near the site of deposition).

MODERN CLASSIFICATIONS

A close relation exists between genetic and descriptive factors in the classification of sedimentary rocks. The descriptive element is necessary in order that observable or measurable criteria may be used to place a specimen in its proper classification. Ideally, once the rock has been classified,

150

its position in the classification scheme should shed some light on its origin. The observable descriptive characteristics of the rock are defined where possible in a manner that relates them to their conditions of origin.

Factors Important in Sedimentary Rock Classification

It is generally impossible to select a single group of characteristics that adequately allows classification of all sedimentary rock types. For this reason, some attributes of clastic rocks, which permit their classification and shed light on their origin, differ from the corresponding attributes of non-clastic rocks. In general, the clastic rocks are characterized by their **mineral composition,** an important factor in determining their **provenance;** by their **maturity,** expressed in their uniformity of texture and composition; and by such **textural** and **structural** properties as may shed light on the nature of the transporting agent or on the environment of deposition.

On the other hand, the attributes of nonclastic sediments that are of primary importance in classification are related to the chemical and biological conditions under which these sediments form. Thus, properties indicative of **oxidizing** versus **reducing** conditions and **acidic** versus **alkaline** conditions are of importance in interpreting the conditions that control chemical and biological deposition.

In any scheme of classification, decisions must be made regarding the relative importance to be given to composition, texture, and associated sedimentary structures. Composition is commonly ranked first in modern classifications. Texture is usually superimposed on composition, leading to such categories as coarse grained, medium grained, or fine grained sediments. Sedimentary structures are important for interpreting conditions of origin of clastic sediments as well as direction of transport. Some special sedimentary structures developed by turbidity currents may be highly diagnostic in interpreting such deposits.

General and Special Classifications

In contrast to broad general classifications that embrace all sedimentary rocks, there are special classifications limited to particular groups of rocks. These special classifications may include sandstones only, or carbonates only, and in part they are a response to the importance of these rocks as reservoirs in oil and gas exploration. In addition, the sandstones especially are useful in evaluating the influence of tectonic events during their accumulation, as will be brought out later.

Although specialized classifications are important in detailed description and interpretation of particular groups of sediments, recognition of the broader interrelationships among sedimentary rocks as a whole is a desirable prerequisite to the establishment of any specialized kind of classification. The broader aspects of sedimentary classification are perhaps best expressed in terms of the **end member concept.** Most sedimentary rocks are mixtures of detrital (exogenetic) and chemical (endogenetic) components. These two main groups of components comprise the detrital and chemical end members described earlier. The main detrital end members are quartz and clay minerals. The principle chemical end members are calcite, dolomite, chert, and the evaporites (gypsum and anhydrite).

Inasmuch as most sediments are mixtures of no more than three end members, it is convenient to show the relations among the principle constituents of sedimentary rocks by means of simple triangle diagrams. The more general case involving rocks with four end members may be illustrated with a tetrahedron, in which the four triangular faces each represent a three component mixture. The simpler two component mixtures are then represented by the edges of the tetrahedron, and pure end member sediments are represented by the corners.

The Tetrahedron as a Classification Device

Use of the tetrahedron for showing the composition of sediments, as developed by Pettijohn, is illustrated in Figure 5-1, left. This tetrahedron represents one of the commonest major families of sedimentary rocks, and it is based on the four very commonly occurring end members quartz, clay, carbonate, and chert.

In this tetrahedron, the quartz vertex represents sandstone, the clay vertex represents shale, the carbonate vertex (calcite and dolomite) represents limestone, and the chert vertex represents chemically formed silica sediments.

Any sediment having significant amounts (5 percent or more) of these four end members may be represented as a point inside the tetrahedron. Any single face of the tetrahedron includes all sedimentary rocks having significant proportions of the three end members indicated at the apices of that face. Figure 5-1, right, shows one face of the tetrahedron, with carbonate, quartz, and clay apices. Rocks whose composition is shown at or near an apex are relatively pure end-member sediments.

Between and among the end-member sediments are rocks composed of different proportions of the end members. For example, calcareous shale and argillaceous limestone lie between the clay and carbonate apices. Mixtures of these two end members are shown along the edges of the triangle.

In practice, the composition of a sediment is expressed as the percentage of the several end-member minerals present. A sandy calcareous shale may have 60 percent clay minerals, 25 percent carbonates, and 15 percent quartz

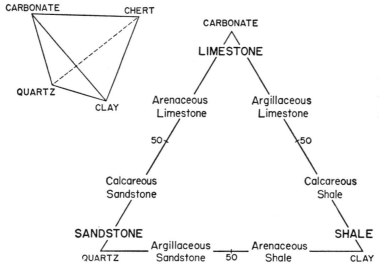

Fig. 5-1. The fundamental tetrahedron for classfying sedimentary rocks. The carbonate-quartz-clay face is shown in detail.

grains. These percentages are plotted along axes of the triangle which bisect the corresponding apex angle, and result in a point on the diagram, which expresses the composition in terms of the three end members.

The boundaries between the several lithological types represented on the triangular faces are somewhat arbitrary. Theoretically, such boundaries may be drawn between fields of maximum density of observed points to attain classifications based on actual occurrence of specific rock types.

COMMON SEDIMENTARY FAMILIES

Quartz, Carbonate, Clay, Chert

Figure 5-2 shows the four triangular faces of the tetrahedron of Figure 5-1. The upper left triangle (carbonate-clay-quartz) includes the most common types of sediments in the stratigraphic column. The three end-member sediments, **sandstone**, **shale**, and **limestone**, are familiar to all students. Such triangles were originally developed by Pirsson and Schuchert (1920). The relations of intermediate rock types to the end members are clearly brought out by the triangle.

The three triangles with chert apices in Figure 5-2 include **siliceous** and **cherty limestone, siliceous shale**, and **cherty sandstone**. Toward the chert apex is a less common sediment, **porcellanite**, a dense, massive cherty rock. Porcellanites have a predominance of chert or other chemically precipitated

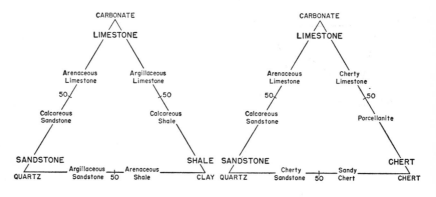

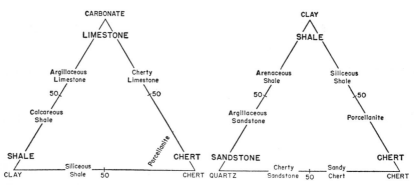

Fig. 5-2. Four faces of the tetrahedron shown in Figure 5-1.

silica, with varying amounts of detrital quartz, clay minerals, or calcite. **Novaculite,** a dense and massive or bedded form of silica, belongs in this group as an end member.

Quartz, Carbonate, Clay, Organic Matter

The fundamental tetrahedron of Figure 5-1 may be altered to show other end members, as shown in Figure 5-3. Organic matter may be substituted for chert to represent sediments with significant organic content. The organic matter may include both humic and bituminous material. Humic material is coaly, high in carbon and oxygen, and low in hydrogen. Bituminous material is high in carbon and hydrogen and low in oxygen. Asphalt is a typical bitumen.

The triangle in Figure 5-3 includes **bituminous** (and humic) **shale, bituminous limestone,** and such end-member sediments as **coal** and **bitumen.** There is a complete range from slightly organic to highly organic sediments. Distinctions between humic and bituminous sediments are not always clear because gradations from purely humic coaly sediments to cannel coal involve all degrees of change from humic to bituminous material.

The triangular faces not represented in Figure 5-3 include bituminous and humic sandstones, as well as the common sediments shown in Figure 5-2, upper left. As long as the carbonate-clay-quartz corners are not changed, the three-component system of the front face of the tetrahedron is not changed. In fact, if the two tetrahedra of Figures 5-1 and 5-3 are placed face to face along the carbonate-clay-quartz plane, a double tetrahedron is formed, which extends from chert at one extreme to organic matter at the other, passing through limestone, sandstone, and shale along the common face.

Quartz, Carbonate, Clay, Sulfate

The substitution of sulfate for chert in the fundamental tetrahedron shows some of the relations between normal sediments and evaporites. Figure 5-4 shows the tetrahedron and its carbonate-clay-sulphate face. Intermediate sediments include **gypsiferous limestone** and **gypsiferous shale**, and calcareous or argillaceous gypsum rocks, leading to **gypsum** and **anhydrite** as end members. In a more general diagram, both sulphates and chlorides may be combined in the end member, to develop a series including salt (**halite**) in the end member, and additional saliferous intermediate varieties.

Fig. 5-3. The fundamental tetrahedron with organic matter substituted for chert. The carbonate-clay-organic-matter face is shown in detail.

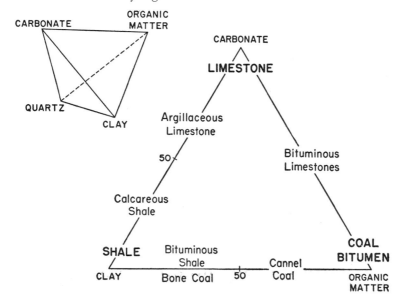

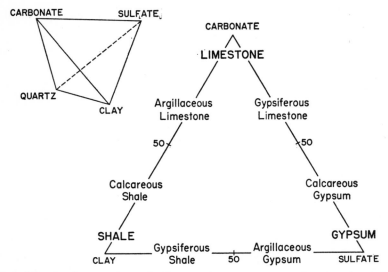

Fig. 5-4. The fundamental tetrahedron with evaporites (sulfates) substituted for chert. The carbonate-clay-sulfate face is shown in detail.

The triangular faces not shown in Figure 5-4 include the common sedimentary family of the upper left triangle of Figure 5-2, as well as sediments intermediate between sandstone and evaporites, such as **gypsiferous sandstone.**

Less Common Sedimentary Groups

Among the many additional sedimentary families which may be illustrated with tetrahedra are those containing phosphatic, ferruginous, manganiferous, and other special end members. The relations of these sedimentary groups to the commonest family may be seen by substituting each new end member successively for the chert corner in Figure 5-1.

Relations among other groupings of the preceding end members may be studied by substituting more than one end member in the fundamental tetrahedron. If organic matter is substituted for the chert corner, and iron oxide (or iron carbonate) for the quartz corner, associations among limestones, shales, organic sediments, and ferruginous sediments may be seen.

Other Applications of Tetrahedra

Segration of End-member Sediments. The quartz corner of the tetrahedron of Figure 5-1 represents sandstone in general, but it does not distinguish among the many varieties of sandstone. Special sets of end members may be drawn at the apices of a triangle to divide the sandstone into several types, as shown in Figure 5-5. The left triangle is adapted from

Krynine (1948), and the one on the right from Pettijohn (unpublished chart, 1944).

Krynine's sandstone triangle is formed by grouping quartz and detrital chert at one apex, micas and chlorite at the second apex, and feldspar and kaolin at the third. In this choice of end members, the matrix material is in part segregated in terms of its genetic association with the coarser grains. Thus, feldspar and kaolin represent a composite end member consisting partly of grains and matrix, whereas quartz and detrital chert will, in general, consist of grains rather than matrix material. With these selected groups of end members, several classes of sandstone can be segregated. At the top of the triangle is **orthoquartzite,** relatively free of fine grained matrix material. As the triangle is followed downward to the right, the amount of feldspar increases, as does the amount of clay matrix and the sandstone becomes **arkose.** Similarly, the addition of increasing amounts of mica and chlorite forms **low rank graywacke** and **high rank graywacke,** depending upon the amount of feldspar present. **Impure arkose** is a transitional rock. In Pettijohn's triangle (Figure 5-5) the coarser grains are separated from the matrix material by placing all matrix material in the upper end member of the triangle, with feldspar at the lower left and quartz plus detrital chert at the lower right. In subdividing this triangle, Pettijohn selected 75 percent matrix material as the basis for distinguishing between sandstones and shale. The group of rocks containing between 20 percent and 75 percent matrix material are classified as **graywackes.** The special subdivision of **subgraywacke** is represented by that part of this block in which the content of feldspar is 10 percent or less.

Sandstones with less than 20 percent matrix material are classified in Pettijohn's triangle on the basis of the feldspar content. **Arkose** contains

Fig. 5-5. Triangular (three-end-member) classifications of sandstone. [(*Left*) Krynine (1948); (*Right*) Pettijohn (unpublished chart, 1944).]

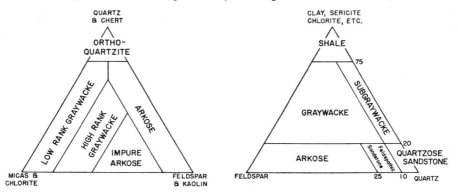

more than 25 percent of that component, and pure quartzose sandstone (**orthoquartzite**) less than 10 percent. The intermediate group is **feldspathic sandstone,** containing between 10 percent and 25 percent feldspar.

Although Krynine's and Pettijohn's sandstone triangles appear to differ markedly, both schemes classify sandstones into similar categories. As a result, the subgraywacke in Pettijohn's triangle is equivalent to low rank graywacke in Krynine's. Similarly, arkose falls into corresponding blocks in both triangles. Differences in detail arise, inasmuch as Pettijohn's graywacke includes parts of Krynine's high rank graywacke and impure arkose. Pettijohn's triangle is used here as an illustration only, since his present classification utilizes four end members, as will be described later. In addition to the use of triangular diagrams for sandstone classification, they may also be used for nonclastic and chemical sediments, as illustrated later in this chapter under the topic of carbonate rock classification.

Textural Classification of Sediments. The lithologic tetrahedron is also used to indicate the textural relations among sediments. Figure 5-6 shows a tetrahedron with gravel, sand, silt, and clay end members. These may be mixed in any proportions to form typical textural classes of detrital rocks.

Some of the transitional groups are shown in the sand-silt-clay face of the tetrahedron. The admixture of silt with sand yields such intermediate textures as **silty sand** and **sandy silt.** The several other possibilities are indicated between the sand and clay and clay and silt apices.

Fig. 5-6. Application of the tetrahedron to textural classification. The sand-silt-clay face is shown in detail.

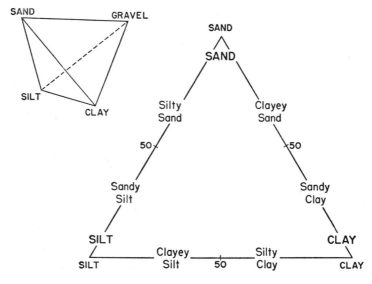

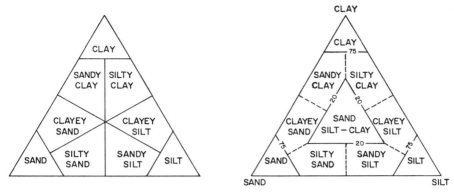

Fig. 5-7. (*Left*) Sand-silt-clay face from Figure 5-6. (*Right*) Improved textural class limits introduced by Shepard (1954).

Construction of the other faces of the tetrahedron, with gravel at one apex, displays the textural classes among the coarser sediments. Such common sediments as **sandy gravel** and **pebbly sand** lie between the sand and gravel vertex. Less common mixtures, such as **pebbly clay** and **silty gravel,** occur between appropriate vertices. **Glacial till, fanglomerate,** and other relatively poorly sorted sediments with a wide range of particle size are included in these categories.

The textural triangle of Figure 5-6 includes three pure end-member sediments plus six intermediate kinds. In this general case the six intermediate classes would meet at the center of the triangle, as shown by the illustration on the left of Figure 5-7. Note that for sediments containing approximately equal amounts of sand, silt, and clay, a slight compositional difference in the sediment results in a complete change of its name. Inasmuch as some "mudstones" contain roughly equal parts of these end members, classification of a large number of samples may distribute these equivalent sediments over six classes, sometimes wholly as a result of relatively small errors in measurement.

To overcome this disadvantage, Shepard (1954) developed a modified end-member triangle having a triangular area at its center, as shown on the right of Figure 5-7. This modification provides a convenient separate class for those sediments that tend to fall within the central part of the end-member triangle. An additional advantage is that the six intermediate mixtures of Figure 5-6 now have more restricted areas allowing more discrimination between them. Shepard's triangle is useful for showing the overall composition of sets of sedimentary samples, and it has been extensively used in the description of Mississippi delta sediments.

Summary of End-member Groupings

The foregoing illustrations of the end-member concept demonstrate that the fundamental tetrahedron may be used for a variety of classification purposes. All possible mixtures of composition and texture occur among sediments, and these may be studied by the proper selection of compositional and textural end members. The name assigned to a sedimentary rock relates the rock to the adjoining classes of sediments in the tetrahedron, or to the end members that form it.

The fundamental tetrahedron provides a convenient means of assigning names to sediments, and for studying the relations among associated sediments. By developing interlocking tetrahedra, entire families of sediments with a variety of end members may be readily visualized.

DESCRIPTIONS OF SELECTED CLASTIC SEDIMENTARY ROCKS

Triangle diagrams and lithologic tetrahedra are largely descriptive in that they represent measurable compositional and textural data. In more detailed descriptions of sediments, attention is also given to color, type of bedding, roundness or sphericity of grains, and other characteristics not conveniently shown on tetrahedra.

Detailed descriptions of sediments should include some information on origin, which requires interpretation of the observed data. For this purpose it is convenient to separate clastic and nonclastic sediments, and to present each group on a textural basis.

Consideration of clastic sediments in a textural framework has the advantage of showing segregation of the textural classes as rocks grade from conglomerate to shale. In general, conglomerate as a class represents a mixture of pebbles, sand, and some silt or clay. Sandstones represent mixtures of sand and silt, with some clay, and shales are mainly silt and clay.

Each of the textural classes carries certain groups of properties, some of which are more significant than others for interpreting conditions of sediment origin. Sandstones, for example, are among the most diagnostic of certain conditions of origin, and they have received much study from this point of view.

The remainder of this chapter is devoted to a description of the more commonly observed sedimentary rocks. The purpose is to provide a reference section in which sediment properties may be reviewed as they are discussed in other connections in later chapters. To a large degree, the material is descriptive and may be considered mainly as a series of definitions. The processes which form these sediments, their environments of occurrence, and their associations with other sediments are treated at greater length in later chapters.

Inasmuch as the subject of sedimentary rock classification is in a state of flux, the descriptions which follow include both the common names of the rocks and some more specialized terms that have arisen from recent or current classification schemes. In order to include a fairly representative number of sedimentary rocks the descriptions are necessarily brief, and the reader is urged to consult Pettijohn (1957) for added detail regarding the specific rocks covered in this chapter.

The topics of sandstone and limestone classification are developed in more detail than are other categories of sediments. This has been done to emphasize some of the factors that have influenced the development of current classifications that endeavor to combine descriptive and genetic implications of the rocks.

Coarse Grained Clastic Sediments

Conglomerate is a clastic rock composed of rounded fragments or pebbles larger than 2 mm in diameter. Breccia is distinguished from conglomerate on the basis of fragment angularity. Breccia fragments commonly have a roundness of 0.2 or less. The terminology of coarse grained sediments is given in Wentworth (1935).

Conglomerate is distinguished from sandstone on the basis of particle size, although in practice, the distinction is commonly made on the proportion of pebbles in the rock. There is no universal agreement on what this proportion should be. Willman (1942) suggested that gravel must contain at least 50 percent pebbles. Pettijohn (1949) suggested that the term conglomerate be applied if the rock contains more than 10 percent of pebbles greater than 2 mm in diameter. More recently, Folk (1954) applied the term gravel to mixtures containing 30 percent or more of pebbles. Another distinguishing criterion, though not used extensively in practice, is based on the average particle size of the sediment in contrast to its proportion of pebbles. On that basis, conglomerate would be characterized by particles having an average diameter in excess of 2 mm.

Conglomerates and breccias may be classified according to several bases. The grouping followed here is based on composition of the pebbles, proportion of matrix, and degree of size sorting.

It is commonly true that well sorted Recent gravels have relatively little matrix, and tend to have only a single peak in their size-distribution curves (see Fig. 5-8, left). Moreover, such gravel commonly has only a few rock types represented by its pebbles.

Among ancient conglomerates of the same general type, there is usually

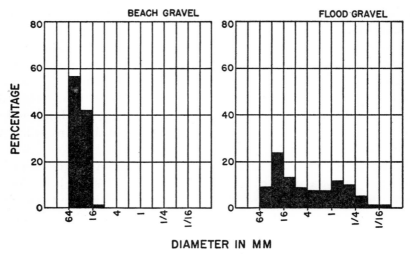

Fig. 5-8. Comparison of size distributions of well sorted beach gravel and poorly sorted alluvial gravel.

a sandy matrix, believed to have been introduced after deposition. A well sorted "open-work" gravel provides large interstices for infiltration of sand after burial. The ancient counterpart of the well sorted gravel may, accordingly, contain well sorted homogeneous pebbles in a matrix of clean sand. The size-distribution curve in such instances has two distinct peaks.

In contrast to well sorted gravel and conglomerate are others with poor sorting, with relatively large amounts of matrix, and with two or more irregular peaks in their size-distribution curves (see Fig. 5-7, right). These conglomerates commonly also have a wide range of lithologic types in their pebbles, forming a more heterogeneous deposit than the well sorted kind.

Exceptions to the foregoing types are conglomerates with simple lithologic composition, poor sorting, and abundant matrix. It is not implied, therefore, that all conglomerates fall into two simple classes, but to the extent that they do, certain genetic inferences may be drawn from them.

The well sorted, lithologically homogeneous conglomerates are typical of widespread basal deposits that mark transgressive seas. Poorly sorted lithologically heterogeneous conglomerates tend to occur in thick wedge-like deposits, typical of rapidly subsiding depositional areas. Many of the wedge-like deposits appear to be mainly fluvial, and represent a pouring of coarse clastic material into geosynclines from rapidly eroding uplifted source areas. Within such sedimentary masses are turbidite conglomerates, which were formed by turbidity currents moving down unstable depositional slopes. These turbidity currents, described more fully in Chapter 6, give rise to deposits that show textural grading from bottom to top, and are more common than was formally supposed. The pioneer work of Kuenen and Migliorini (1950) stimulated a widespread interest in more detailed examination of bedding and bedding plane features for evidence of deposits formed by turbidity currents.

Several exceptional deposits do not fit into the relatively simple classification of well sorted and poorly sorted conglomerates described above. Among these are certain volcanically derived conglomerates and breccias, which may have homogeneous lithological composition, with poor sorting and abundant matrix. Another exception is glacial till, marked by very heterogeneous composition and showing no evidence of sorting action.

Pettijohn (1957, Chapter 6) subdivides conglomerates into **orthoconglomerates** and **paraconglomerates**. The orthoconglomerates are generally interpretated as originating from deposition under highly turbulent conditions, such as those prevailing in streams and along shores in the zone of breaking waves. Paraconglomerates, on the other hand, represent "conglomeratic mudstones," in that they contain more matrix material than pebbles. Paraconglomerates include glacial till, some laminated mudstones in which cobbles or boulders may be embedded among somewhat distorted bedding planes, and some relatively structureless clay or shale bodies in which pebbles or cobbles are randomly distributed, possibly as a result of ice rafting. Miller (1953) discusses conglomeratic mudstone, and Pettijohn (1957, Chapter 6) summarizes present information on the subject.

To some extent, the several classes of conglomerate may be related to corresponding sandstones. The sands represent segregations of matrix material from unsorted clastic debris, thus certain types of sandstone are associated with particular conglomerates. Well sorted quartz-pebble conglomerate, for example, commonly occurs with pure quartz sandstone. Granite-pebble conglomerate, with abundant matrix, occurs interbedded with arkosic sand. These common associations, and others, are more fully developed later in this chapter.

Well Sorted, Lithologically Homogeneous Conglomerates. Several varieties occur, among which **quartz-pebble conglomerate, chert-pebble conglomerate,** and **limestone-pebble conglomerate** are typical. Table 5-1 lists the properties of quartz-pebble conglomerate, which may be taken as typical of the class.

Quartz-pebble conglomerate represents relatively stable material derived from eroded granitic or metamorphic terrain, with a winnowing-out of finer textures and less stable lithologic types. Chert-pebble conglomerate may be derived from a weathered limestone terrain in which the chert occurs as residual fragments. Limestone-pebble conglomerates apparently require special conditions which permit preservation of relatively unstable lithologic

TABLE 5-1. QUARTZ PEBBLE CONGLOMERATE

MINERAL COMPOSITION:	90 percent or more of quartz pebbles; may be vein quartz, meta-quartzite, and so on. Minor amounts of chert pebbles or other stable types.
GROSS CHARACTER:	Light color, bedding and cross bedding may be prominent.
TEXTURE:	Average particles in fine or medium pebble size; pebbles well sorted, highly rounded, high sphericity.
MATRIX AND CEMENT:	Matrix commonly a well sorted, clean, quartz sand (introduced after deposition?). Cement may be silica or calcite. Glauconite matrix rare.
FOSSILS:	Rare, fragmental.
EXAMPLE:	Baraboo conglomerate (Animikian).

types. Rapid erosion of a limestone terrain without prolonged weathering and rapid burial after short transport appear to be requisites.

The well sorted, lithologically homogeneous conglomerates commonly occur as relatively thin, widespread, or patchy sheets, interbedded with quartz-type sandstones, representative of the basal deposits of transgressive seas.

Poorly Sorted, Lithologically Homogeneous Conglomerates. This class includes conglomerates derived from special sources areas, deposited under conditions of rapid burial without complete sorting, or formed in special depositional environments. Examples are **granite-pebble conglomerate, intraformational conglomerate, volcanic conglomerate** and breccia, and **collapse breccia,** which represent several extremes in conditions of origin.

Granite-pebble conglomerate commonly occurs interbedded with arkosic sandstone in thick wedgelike deposits. These were derived from tectonically active areas under conditions of fluvial transport and rapid burial in subsiding basins. As a result, the matrix content is high, and consists of quartz and feldspar grains, with some finer kaolinitic material. This type of conglomerate therefore belongs with the poorly sorted type, but is exceptional in its relatively homogeneous lithologic composition. Table 5-2 summarizes its properties.

Intraformational conglomerate and breccia represent locally formed accumulations, in which previously deposited material is broken and shifted about shortly after deposition. The fragments are commonly of a single lithologic composition, angular or slightly rounded, and enclosed in a matrix of finer material.

Typical intraformational conglomerates are found in limestone, where they occur as interbeds of thin, angular fragments randomly arranged in a calcareous matrix. It is believed that thin layers of lime mud, lithified by cementation or exposure above tide level, may be broken and slightly shifted during storms producing a layer of angular fragments that becomes incorporated in muds which later accumulate on the surface.

Intraformational conglomerates are also typical of sand-shale sequences. Thin layers of mud, compacted or lithified, are similarly broken and incorporated into a sandy or silty matrix as deposition continues. Intraformational deposits may be classified either as conglomerate or breccia, depending upon the angularity or rounding of the fragments.

Volcanic conglomerate and breccia include coarse, pyroclastic deposits, composed of volcanic material in a matrix of tuff or volcanic glass. These deposits grade from unbedded to bedded. The bedded deposits are the result of local reworking by streams or of deposition in bodies of water.

Collapse breccias are representative of another group of coarse sediments formed by special processes. Exposures of interbedded limestone and gypsum commonly show limestone breccia formed by collapse of limestone beds as the gypsum is leached away. The breccia is lithologically homogeneous but contains many very angular fragments, some of which show solution markings.

Poorly Sorted, Lithologically Heterogeneous Conglomerates. This class of conglomerate and breccia includes coarse deposits with a wide variety of lithologic types embedded in abundant matrix. **Fanglomerate** and **glacial till** are two examples.

Fanglomerate is representative of coarse conglomerates deposited in alluvial fans, where the high gradient of the mountain stream is abruptly

TABLE 5-2. GRANITE PEBBLE (ARKOSIC) CONGLOMERATE

MINERAL COMPOSITION:	Mainly fragments and pebbles of granite with sand and silt matrix of quartz, fresh feldspar, mica, and alteration products such as kaolin, sericite, and chlorite.
GROSS CHARACTER:	Color dependent on source rock: granites high in potash-feldspar yield pink aggregates; syenites and granodiorites yield gray aggregates. Truncated cross bedding prominent.
TEXTURE:	Particles range in size from small boulders to sand grains; poor sorting; moderate values of sphericity and roundness.
MATRIX AND CEMENT:	Sand and silt composed of quartz and feldspar; clay mainly kaolin; cement rare, mainly secondary silica or calcite.
FOSSILS:	Very rare, fragmental if present.
EXAMPLES:	Fountain Arkose (pink type); Weber grit (gray type), (both Pennsylvanian).

TABLE 5-3. GRAYWACKE CONGLOMERATE

MINERAL COMPOSITION:	Cobbles, pebbles, and fragments of phyllite, gneiss, schist, igneous rocks, chert, limestone, quartzite, and others may be present. Pebbles and larger fragments usually constitute less than 40 percent of the rock. The matrix of sand and finer material exceeds 15 percent.
GROSS CHARACTER:	Color predominantly gray to gray-green. Massive to graded bedding typical; cross bedding rare or absent.
TEXTURE:	Very poorly sorted. Particles range from boulders and cobbles to sand, silt, and clay. Cobbles and pebbles may be moderately round; finer particles more angular. Particle sphericity moderate to low.
MATRIX AND CEMENT:	Matrix is heterogeneous mixture of sand, silt, and clay. Quartz, feldspar, chlorite, sericite, and mica prominent. Cement is usually secondary silica.
FOSSILS:	Rare, fragmental.
EXAMPLES:	Wood River conglomerate (Pennsylvanian) of Idaho; Ogishke Conglomerate (early Precambrian) of the Lake Superior region.

checked. The material deposited under such circumstances is poorly sorted and may contain representatives of all the lithologic types crossed by the stream. The texture of this kind of conglomerate is shown in Figure 5-8, right.

Thick deposits of poorly sorted, lithologically heterogeneous conglomerate are associated with poorly sorted sandstone and silty shale, indicating rapid deposition in subsiding areas. The matrix of such conglomerates is silty or clayey, with chlorite sometimes abundant. **Graywacke conglomerate,** summarized in Table 5-3 is an example.

Glacial till is properly classed as a conglomerate or breccia, inasmuch as it contains, on the average, more than 10 percent of pebbles or rock fragments. The size-distribution curve has several peaks, and the lithologic composition is varied. Pettijohn (1957, p. 266) lists a number of detailed criteria for recognizing till.

Tillite is indurated glacial till. Induration of the matrix produces a dense, dark rock in which some embedded pebbles and cobbles have characteristic glacial forms and striae.

Medium Grained Clastic Sediments

Sandstone. Sandstones are classified into four main types, some of which have important subtypes. Certain implications regarding the conditions under which they were formed are found in each type. These genetic implications play a part in sandstone classification, although the definition of sandstone types is commonly based on directly observable properties of the rocks.

The problem of sandstone classification is not a simple one, as attested by the large amount of literature devoted to the subject that has accumulated during the past decade and a half. In part, differences in classification arise from the choice of end members or other criteria used in classification, as well as from the choice of limits used to define the several sandstone classes. It is evident from the literature that the whole subject is in a state of flux. Among the many discussions of the subject, the following were used in developing the present treatment: Krynine (1948), Pettijohn (1st edition, 1949), Tallman (1949), Dapples, Krumbein, and Sloss (1953), Folk (1954), Pettijohn (1954, 1957), Williams, Turner, and Gilbert (1954), Packham (1954), Bokman (1955), and Folk (1956).

Sandstone classifications have been based in part on end-member triangles, typified by Krynine's triangle (1948), and Pettijohn's (1944), both of which are shown in Figure 5-5. It subsequently became apparent that triangular arrangements were not wholly satisfactory, and that some of the rock definitions did not adequately describe rocks in particular genetic categories. As an extension of the classifications, tetrahedral representations came into use. The generally accepted end members appear to be **quartz + detrital chert, feldspar, rock fragments,** and **matrix,** which includes the argillaceous and other fine detrital components of the rock.

One problem in subdividing the tetrahedron into sandstone classes is determining the amount of matrix material permissible in "clean" sandstones as against "dirty" sandstones. This amount has varied from 20 percent (Pettijohn, 1944) to 10 percent (Williams, Turner, and Gilbert, 1954); later, Pettijohn (1954) revised this to 15 percent. A second problem is choosing rock names for various mixtures of three or four of the end members.

A distinction has been drawn between two major categories of sandstone, which are being increasingly referred to as **arenites** and **wackes.** An arenite is a relatively "clean" sandstone. It has a relatively simple mineralogical composition, is relatively well sorted, and contains little if any matrix material. A wacke is an impure ("dirty") sandstone that may contain a variety of mineral and rock fragments. Wackes are commonly poorly sorted and contain an appreciable amount of matrix material. Apparently the terms arenite and wacke will play an increasing role in sandstone classification, inasmuch as the terms carry connotations related to sandstone genesis.

The growing emphasis on the use of arenite as a basic term represents, in a real sense, a return to some parts of Grabau's work mentioned earlier in this chapter, as well as the revitalization of an old word, wacke, which goes back to early times as representing a large stone or "stoniness" in general.

Figure 5-9 shows two current classifications represented on tetrahedra, oriented like pyramids to give equal area to the faces of main interest. The end members in the tetrahedra are essentially the same, but the class limits and rock names differ as shown. Tetrahedron A is based on Pettijohn's percentage classification of 1954, and tetrahedron B is based on Williams, Turner, and Gilbert's 1954 diagrams. In tetrahedron A the class limits are set up largely on the percentage of quartz + chert and the percentage of matrix, with the distinction between **arkose** and **subgraywacke** on the left face determined by a feldspar-rock fragment ratio of 1. In tetrahedron B the classes are primarily based on the limiting percentages of feldspar, rock fragments, and matrix. The distinction between **arkosic** and **arenite lithic arenite** on the left face of B (and the corresponding wackes within the tetrahedron) is also based on the ratio of feldspar to rock fragments.

These recent developments in sandstone classification emphasize the sharper distinctions that can be made among sandstones by the use of four end members rather than three. Because sandstone classification is still in a stage of flux, a combination terminology is used in this book, taking into account recent changes in sandstone classification, but retaining some earlier classes of sandstones that have been subjected to severe reclassification. One of the most important changes in terminology is the reclassification of Pettijohn's "subgraywacke." The definition of this important class of sandstones was discussed by Tallman (1949) and Folk (1954) among others, each of

Fig. 5-9. Sandstone classification tetrahedra. [Left figure adapted from data in Pettijohn (1954); right figure adapted from Williams, Turner, and Gilbelt (1954).]

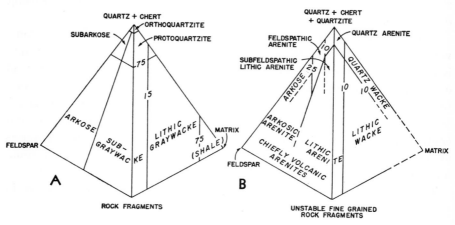

whom suggested some changes in the definition. Pettijohn (1954) modified his original definition of "subgraywacke" (a sandstone containing *more* than 20 percent matrix and less than 10 percent feldspar, as shown in Figure 5-5) to one that includes rocks composed of *less* than 15 percent matrix and in which rock fragments exceed feldspar in content, as shown in Figure 5-9. This change arose from the unsatisfactory genetic relation of the original "subgraywacke" to graywacke and other associated sandstones, as pointed out by Pettijohn (1957, footnote, p. 317). The original "subgraywacke" is now included in the larger group of **lithic graywackes** in Pettijohn's revised classification.

To avoid confusion due to changed terminology, the term **quartz wacke** is used in this book for sandstones having the composition of "subgraywacke" as originally defined by Pettijohn. Pettijohn's present definition of subgraywacke is included in the **lithic arenite** class of Williams, Turner, and Gilbert (1954).

Mention may be made here of two other sandstone terms, **flysch** and **molasse,** that have been discussed in recent literature. These terms refer not so much to particular kinds of sandstone as to their associations and conditions of occurrence. Flysch is commonly referred to as the Graywacke Suite (Pettijohn, 1954, p. 615) because of its apparent occurrence in many geosynclines, whereas molasse refers (Pettijohn, 1954, p. 618), to a Subgraywacke Suite, a product of the erosion of essentially penecontemporaneous uplifts during orogenic cycles. These associations are treated more fully in Chapter 13.

Quartzose Sandstone (Orthoquartzite, Quartz Arenite). Quartzose sandstone has a simple mineralogical composition, with a dominance of quartz and a minor amount of matrix. The average particle size ranges from medium to coarse sand, with a high degree of sorting. Heavy minerals constitute a few percent of the rock, and are commonly very stable types, such as tourmaline and zircon.

Quartzose sandstone occurs as widespread blanket sands, seldom exceeding several hundred feet in thickness. Cross bedding may be prominent, and fossils are relatively rare. The sandstone represents stable conditions of sedimentation, with very mild subsidence during accumulation, and with considerable transport and winnowing action before final accumulation. Quartzose sandstone is typical of basal sands developed by encroaching seas. It commonly occurs in association with widespread unconformities.

Several varieties of quartzose sandstone are recognized, depending upon the minerals associated with the dominant quartz. The type sandstone of this group, **pure quartz sandstone,** contains 95 percent or more of quartz grains. **Quartz-glauconite sandstone** is a subtype, containing an appreciable amount of glauconite. **Quartz-iron oxide sandstone** has its quartz grains coated with a thin film of hematite. This type of sandstone commonly occurs in association with red beds, as in the Magdalena formation (Pennsylvanian) of New Mexico.

Quartz-muscovite sandstone is another variety, with 10 percent or more muscovite flakes. **Feldspathic sandstone** has from 10 to 25 percent feldspar, mainly potash feldspar. This variety is here included as a quartzose type, although it is commonly shown as a separate category in triangle diagrams.

Table 5-4 summarizes the properties of pure quartz sandstone, which may be taken as typical of the group.

Arkose. **Arkose** generally contains more than 25 percent feldspar, and less than about 15 percent matrix. Feldspar is more abundant than rock fragments. The matrix is commonly kaolinitic. Average particle size ranges from coarse to fine sand, with angular to subrounded grains. The degree of sorting is moderate and depends upon the amount of matrix present. Some arkose is essentially a **granite wash,** and consists of granitic debris in a kaolinitic matrix. Oriel (1949) discusses definitions of arkose.

Arkose commonly occurs in thick sedimentary bodies of limited extent. Less commonly, it occurs as thin blanket sands in association with feldspathic sandstone. Thick arkose deposits represent rapid burial in rapidly subsiding depositional basins or fault troughs. Source areas are strongly uplifted granitic terrains, subject to rapid erosion.

Climatic conditions appear to play only a minor role in the formation of arkose. Rapidity of erosion and burial are the important factors, as Krynine (1935) has shown.

Thin blanket arkose represents the reworking of residual granitic material by transgressing seas. This arkose displays evidence of some winnowing action, and is commonly associated with quartzose and feldspathic sandstone

TABLE 5-4. PURE QUARTZ SANDSTONE

MINERAL COMPOSITION:	95 percent or more of clear quartz grains; heavy minerals mainly stable types: tourmaline, zircon, magnetite, and others.
GROSS CHARACTER:	Light color; cross bedding prominent; bedding massive or obscure.
TEXTURE:	Average particle size commonly in coarse or medium sand grade; excellent sorting; well rounded grains; sphericity high; frosting, pitting, quartz enlargement common.
MATRIX AND CEMENT:	Matrix less than 5 percent, commonly lacking; cement minor, silica, calcite, or dolomite.
FOSSILS:	Rare, commonly fragmental.
EXAMPLES:	St. Peter Sandstone (Ordovician).

TABLE 5-5. ARKOSE

MINERAL COMPOSITION:	Quartz and feldspar dominant, with feldspar exceeding 25 percent. Minor amounts of mica and pyribole. Less than 15 percent kaolinitic matrix.
GROSS CHARACTER:	Color usually pink or gray. Massive to well bedded and cross bedded.
TEXTURE:	Moderately well sorted; particle sizes range from coarse sand to silt. Particle roundness and sphericity moderate to poor.
MATRIX AND CEMENT:	Matrix composed mainly of kaolin, iron oxides, and fine silt. Generally unconsolidated or loosely cemented with calcite, rarely with secondary silica.
FOSSILS:	Rare, usually fragmental if present.
EXAMPLE:	La motte Sandstone (Cambrian).

(for example, **subarkose** or **feldspathic arenite**). Table 5-5 lists the characteristics of a typical arkose.

Graywacke. **Graywacke** is the general name applied to poorly sorted sandstones containing more than 15 percent matrix. Graywackes may be divided into **feldspathic graywacke** and **lithic graywacke,** dependng upon whether feldspar is more abundant than rock fragments (Pettijohn, 1957). The matrix is composed of clay minerals, chlorite, and sericite. Mineral cement is usually absent.

Average particle size in graywacke ranges from fine to coarse sand. The degree of sorting is generally poor. Unstable types (amphibole, biotite) and stable types (zircon, tourmaline) of heavy minerals may occur.

Graywacke occurs as thick lenticular masses in large sedimentary bodies associated with linear geosynclines. Fischer (1933) described it as a "poured in" type of sediment, derived from the rapid erosion of tectonic source areas, and buried rapidly under geosynclinal conditions. The high matrix content implies lack of sorting or winnowing action.

Many Precambrian and early Paleozoic graywackes are partially metamorphosed and consist of dense, dark rocks best studied in thin section. Pettijohn (1943) describes several early Precambrian graywackes. Mesozoic and later graywacke may be only partially indurated, but all types show the general characteristics of the group, which include massive or obscure bedding in the thicker units, graded bedding in the thinner beds, and associated thin-bedded silty and siliceous shales or slates. Kuenen (1953) discusses the attributes of graded bedding.

It was assumed by some earlier writers that graywacke is the "basic" equivalent of arkose. That is, whereas arkose is derived from granitic terrain,

TABLE 5-6. GRAYWACKE (FELDSPATHIC WACKE; LITHIC WACKE)

MINERAL COMPOSITION:	Quartz 30 to 40 percent; feldspar 10 to 50 percent; rock fragments and detrital chert 5 to 10 percent; chlorite-sericite matrix greater than 20 percent. Minor amounts of carbonate and pyrite.
GROSS CHARACTER:	Color predominantly gray to gray-green. Usually massive graded beds; may be interbedded with chlorite shale. Cross bedding rare.
TEXTURE:	Sorting usually very poor. Particle size ranges from pebbles or very coarse sand to fine silt or clay. Particle roundness and sphericity low to moderate.
MATRIX AND CEMENT:	Matrix composed mainly of a "paste" of chlorite, sericite, biotite, and illite. Cement mainly secondary silica.
FOSSILS:	Rare.
EXAMPLES:	Siamo Formation (Animikian); Jackfork Formation (Pennsylvanian).

graywacke was considered to be supplied by areas of basic igneous rocks. This inference is not tenable, inasmuch as graywacke fails to show the mineralogic composition required, and rock fragments present show derivation from a varied source area. Pettijohn (1957) considers the evidence in some detail.

Table 5-6 lists the properties of typical graywacke.

Quartz Wacke (Original "Subgraywacke" of Pettijohn, 1944). This important class of rocks, subjected to severe reclassification as described earlier, is retained here as a group that carries some important genetic implications. As may be seen from Figure 5-9B, the class contains less than 10 percent feldspar, less than 10 percent unstable, fine grained rock fragments (generally shale fragments, bits of coal, and other sedimentary types), and more than 10 percent matrix. This agrees fairly well with Pettijohn's original usage of subgraywacke, except that the matrix content of the original class exceeds 20 percent rather than 10 percent. In this textbook, the lower limit of matrix is taken to be 15 to 20 percent, a slight modification of Williams, Turner, and Gilbert's usage as shown in Figure 5-9.

The particles in quartz wacke are angular to sub-rounded and are composed of abundant quartz, some feldspar, and coarse muscovite flakes. Various heavy minerals occur, including some unstable types. The matrix may include clay minerals, chlorite, or sericite. Carbonaceous flakes are common in some quartz wackes. Unstable fine grained rock fragments (bits of shale, coal, and the like) may be abundant in some rocks of this general class, in which case the term "lithic wacke" is perhaps more appropriate. Quartz wacke is commonly fine grained, and sorting varies from poor to fair. The content of rock fragments in quartz wacke is generally less than 10 percent; in lithic wacke it may locally rise to 40 or 50 percent.

The average quartz wacke contains less matrix than the average graywacke; apparently some quartz wackes represent "washed" graywacke, in which some winnowing action occurred during transportation producing a slightly cleaner type of sand. Quartz wackes show less graded bedding than graywacke.

Quartz wacke occurs under conditions of moderate subsidence in unstable depositional areas, and in sedimentary basins where the rate of burial is rapid enough to prevent thorough winnowing action during transportation. Common associations include silty shale and thin, nodular limestone. Many Pennsylvanian coal measure sandstones are quartz wackes. Table 5-7 summarizes the properties of a typical Pennsylvanian example.

Tuff and Tuffaceous Sandstone. An important subdivision of sandstone includes those of volcanic origin. **Tuff** is a stratified rock composed of sand-size particles expelled from volcanoes and deposited on the land surface or in water. Tuff is composed of igneous rock fragments, volcanic glass, and crystals or fragments of quartz, plagioclase, biotite, and hornblende.

There is a complete gradation from tuff, composed wholly of volcanic

TABLE 5-7. QUARTZ WACKE*

MINERAL COMPOSITION:	Predominant mineral is quartz, ranging up to 80 percent; feldspar less than 10 percent; minor amounts of rock fragments or detrital chert. Muscovite may be prominent along bedding planes; sericite abundant in matrix.
GROSS CHARACTER:	Gray to buff in color. Massive to thin bedded; cross bedding may be common locally.
TEXTURE:	Sorting moderate; particle sizes range from coarse sand to fine silt. Particle sphericity and roundness moderate.
MATRIX AND CEMENT:	Matrix constitutes more than 20 percent of rock; principally sericite and clay minerals. Minor amounts of cement, mainly secondary silica; calcite rate.
FOSSILS:	Relatively uncommon; carbonaceous flakes or plant fragments may occur.
EXAMPLES:	Atokan Series sandstones (Pennsylvanian); numerous basal cyclothem sandstones of the Midcontinent and East Central States.

* This term is used throughout the remainder of this book to represent rocks having the composition of subgraywacke as originally defined by Pettijohn.

material, to detrital sandstone. Intermediate varieties, called **tuffaceous sandstone,** receive specific names based on the relative abundance of volcanic and detrital grains. Tuffaceous varieties are typically associated with graywacke and subgraywacke. Terminology of the pyroclastic rocks is given by Wentworth and Williams (1932). Hay (1952) suggested a revision of the fine grained, detrital volcanic rocks on the basis of the content of volcanic material. In 1956 Hay applied this to his study of detrital basic breccia in the Absaroka Range, Wyoming.

Fine Grained, Clastic Sediments

Shale is a fine grained, laminated or fissile sedimentary rock, with a predominance of detrital components. Unconsolidated varieties are silt and clay. Silty shale (**siltstone**) has an average grain size between 1/16 and 1/256 mm, and clay shale (**claystone**) has an average size less than 1/256 mm. Some shale is massive or blocky, without lamination. Twenhofel (1937) discusses terminology of the fine grained sediments.

Shale represents accumulation of the finest products of rock weathering. It is winnowed from the coarser, unsorted debris of weathering by geologic agents. Under conditions of less effective sorting action, the silt and clay components form the matrix of coarser sediments. Inasmuch as matrix is commonly related to its associated grains, the shales, as a class, display characteristics which relate them to corresponding sandstones. This relation provides a logical basis of shale classification.

Shale classification is based on the silt minerals, which correspond in mineralogical composition to the four main types of sandstone. Very fine shales that contain essentially no silt minerals are classified on the basis of chemical analysis, or on known associations with sandstone types.

The descriptions which follow emphasize the more common shales of the stratigraphic column. Certain special varieties, such as black organic shales, are described later under organic sediments. Residual clays, formed by weathering processes at the site of accumulation, are not expressly considered. Details may be found in Pettijohn (1957).

Quartzose shale is composed dominantly of rounded quartz grains in the silt sizes. Feldspar grains are not common, although the shale may be calcareous, glauconitic, ferruginous, or carbonaceous.

Quartzose shale ranges from sandy siltstone to claystone, with finer textures more common. The shale is green or gray, with brown, red, and black less common. In structure, the shale may range from well laminated to massive or blocky.

These shales represent the reworking of residual clays as transgressive seas encroach on old land areas. Their common association with quartzose sandstone is evidence of such origin, and their association with normal marine limestones suggests deposition under relatively stable conditions with gentle rates of subsidence.

Feldspathic shale (also called **kaolinitic shale**) is characterized by a feldspar content greater than 10 percent in the silt size, and by a finer matrix of kaolinitic clay minerals. Subangular to rounded quartz grains may be common.

The shale ranges from sandy silstone to silty claystone, with coarser textures common. The color may be gray, green, red, or chocolate. The shale is usually well laminated, but massive to blocky varieties also occur.

Feldspathic shale is commonly associated with arkose. It represents a winnowing out of finer material from coarser arkosic debris, and its deposition represents quieter phases of the same general conditions which produce arkose deposits.

Chloritic shale contains a variety of minerals in the silt size, including unstable types. The silt grains are typically angular to sub-round. Feldspar is usually abundant in the silt, and may exceed quartz. Chlorite may be abundant in the finer matrix.

Chloritic shale ranges from sandy siltstone to silty claystone, with coarse varieties more common. Color varies through gray, green, brown, red, or black; and the shale may be calcareous, carbonaceous, siliceous, or pyritic. Lamination is not prominent.

Chloritic shale is associated with graywacke and represents accumulation of relatively finer detritus under conditions of rapid deposition. Unlike quartzose shale, chloritic shale represents silt and clay derived from rapidly eroded orogenic source areas. Like its corresponding sandstone, chloritic shale is literally "poured" into rapidly subsiding depositional areas.

Micaceous shale has abundant muscovite flakes along its lamination planes, and finer grained sericite in its clay matrix. Silt minerals include abundant quartz and minor amounts of feldspar, commonly subangular to round.

Micaceous shale ranges in texture from sandy siltstone to claystone, with medium and coarse textures common. The color is usally gray or brownish gray, with red and green subordinate. The shale is usually well laminated, although massive varieties with obscure lamination and ellipsoidal parting are not uncommon.

Micaceous shale is commonly associated with quartz wacke, and, like its corresponding sandstone, it represents detrital deposition under moderately unstable conditions in the sedimentary basin.

NONCLASTIC SEDIMENTARY ROCKS

The most important nonclastic sediments are limestone and dolomite. Others, less common, are the evaporites (gypsum, salt, anhydrite), and ferruginous, phosphatic, siliceous, and organic sediments, all of which are important in some aspects of stratigraphic analysis.

Limestone and dolomite contain more than 50 percent of the carbonate minerals, calcite or dolomite. Several varieties are recognized, depending upon textural differences or upon inferred conditions of origin. **Autochthonous limestone** is formed in place by the accumulation of organic remains, or by chemical precipitation, and **allochthonous limestone** represents an accumulation of transported fossil fragments, calcite rhombs, or oolites.

Most dolomite represents a postdepositional alteration of limestone, although some crystalline dolomites associated with evaporites appear to be primary chemical deposits. Dolomitization is a replacement process, commonly accompanied by recrystallization, producing a rock in which some of the original limestone structures and textures are lost.

Dolomitization may occur in any limestone, although some types are more subject to such changes than others. Evidence is not clear whether dolomitization is an early or late postdepositional process. If time and depth of burial are important, it may explain why Paleozoic limestones are more commonly dolomitized than later deposits.

Classification of Carbonate Rocks

As pointed out in Chapter 4, the classification of limestone is a rapidly expanding topic in sedimentary petrology. The several allochems (coarse elements), as described in the preceding chapter—**intraclasts, pellets, oolites, lumps, fossils,** and the interstitial materials **micrite** and **sparite**— have been used as a basis for the development of formal limestone classifications. As with sandstone classification, limestone classification is in a state of flux.

The end-member concept, illustrated in Figure 5-10A by Pettijohn's triangle (1944) based on calcite, dolomite, and silica, has been extended by Folk (1959) in the manner shown in Figure 5-10B. Allochem grains are used as the top end member; the two lower end members are micrite and sparite, representing the interstitial material. This somewhat generalized triangle was supplemented with another by Folk as shown in Figure 5-10C. Here the allochem components (intraclasts, oolites, and a combined group of fossils and pellets) were selected as the end members. This latter triangle classifies the limestones in which allochem components exceed in amount the interstitial material. The principal dividing line in this triangle is at 25

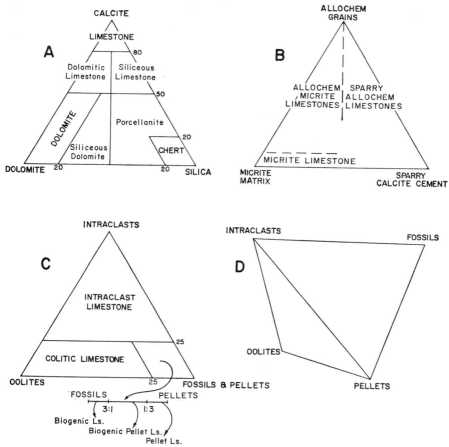

Fig. 5-10. End-member groupings of carbonate rocks. (*A*) Generalized limestone-dolomite-chert grouping, unpublished chart, Pettijohn (1944); (*B*) generalized grouping based on coarse and fine components; (*C*) Folk's basic classification; (*D*) generalized tetrahedral grouping of Folk's end members. [Both (*B*) and (*C*) are from Folk (1959).]

percent intraclasts. A further subdivision is made at 25 percent oolites for those rocks having less than 25 percent intraclasts. If the content of intraclasts is greater than 25 percent, it is called **intraclastic limestone.** If the rock contains less than 25 percent intraclasts, but more than 25 percent oolites, it is called **oolitic limestone.** When the limestone contains less than 25 percent intraclasts and less than 25 percent oolites, the name assigned to it depends upon the relative proportions of fossils and pellets in the rock. As shown by the scale in Figure 5-10C, Folk recommends that when fossils are more than three times as abundant as pellets, the rock be called **biogenic limestone;** if pellets are more than three times as abundant as fossils, the rock is **pellet limestone.** Intermediate compositions have the combined name **biogenic pellet limestone.**

The advantages of the end-member concept are made apparent in earlier parts of this chapter; it is evident that end members may be chosen in various ways, in terms of the kinds of rock that the classification tends to emphasize. As a rule, tetrahedra tend to replace triangles in classification, inasmuch as four end-member systems seem to be more fundamental than the three end-member systems. Folk's classification can be set up as a tertahedron, as shown in Figure 5-10D. This scheme segregates pellets and fossils into separate end members, which results in the transfer of Folk's auxiliary scale between pellets and fossils to a new triangular face, and permits further subdivision of pellet-fossil-intraclast limestones if desired. It is interesting to note in this connection that Wolf's (1960) introduction of **lumps** as an additional textural feature of limestones does not lend itself to Folk's end member grouping, inasmuch as lumps consist of composite pellets or oolites, the end member combination used in Folk's triangle (Figure 5-10). However, this regrouping of end members in terms of individual entities as opposed to composite entities may be justified if it can be shown to aid classification or to facilitate genetic interpretation of limestones.

Folk and Wolf have each proposed a limestone classification. Folk's is based on the triangle in Figure 5-10C, and is given in detail in his paper (1959, p. 14). Wolf's classification differs from Folk's in that lumps are included as an additional allochem component, and the class limits used by Folk are changed by placing the major subdivisions at 90, 50, and 10 percent rather than mainly at 25 and 10 percent, with the additional 3:1 and 1:3 limits of Figure 5-10C. Wolf's classification is given in detail in his 1960 paper (p. 1415).

Folk's classification is widely used, and Wolf's inclusion of lumps has been generally adopted. Table 5-8 is an attempt to develop a somewhat generalized classification that combines Folk's and Wolf's concepts, without stating any specific class limits. The allochemical grain types are listed across the top, with subdivisions into interstitial micrite or sparite making up the two rows of the table. The general class name for those limestones in which the allochemical components predominate is indicated in the top line within the columns. The two subdivisions in each column represent limestone types in which interstitial material predominates, and the resulting composite names reflect the main kind of interstitial material present.

The lack of class limits in Table 5-8 is a concession to the rapidly expanding literature on the subject of carbonate rock classification, and does not imply that either Folk's or Wolf's limits are unsatisfactory. Folk's groupings have, in fact, been widely accepted, as have the names he proposed for limestone classes. In this light, Table 5-8 is to be regarded as a guide to the main classes of limestones, for which limits and possible further subdivision or simplification of components will be determined by general usage as limestone classification is refined.

Important further contributions to limestone classification, as reported by Bissell and Chilingar (1961), include a structural classification by Teodorovich and a genetic classification by Shvetsov. Teodorovich presents two main classes based on predominance of the main mineral mass or of cementing material. The first of these is further subdivided according to whether the content of cementing material is less than 10 percent, or lies between 10 percent and 40–50 percent. In each of these subdivisions the limestones are grouped as normal-granular, crusty (as in stalactites), and ray-aggregated (as in radiolitic limestone). The second class, in which cementing material predominates, is divided into biogenic, biochemical, and chemical types.

This classification, as well as that of Shvetsov, is given in Bissell and Chilingar's paper. Shvetsov's genetic classification has two main classes based on preservation or alteration of the original components. Where these are identifiable, the classification includes several biogenic and chemical types such as fossiliferous, oolitic, etc. Where the original components have been altered, Shvetsov's main classes include limestones with identifiable vestiges of the primary material as against cryptogenic limestones in which the original material has been reworked or recrystallized.

The reader is referred to the symposium on the classification of carbonate rocks, included in the annotated bibliography at the end of this chapter.

The problem of classifying dolomite has been in part examined by Folk (1959). Primary dolomites are classified in the same manner as limestones, whereas the replacement dolomites are classified according to whether they contain allochem "ghosts" or not. The problem of dolomite classification is more severe than that of primary limestones, inasmuch as important

TABLE 5-8. CARBONATE ROCK CLASSIFICATION BASED ON COMPONENTS

INTERSTITIAL MATERIAL	FOSSILS OR FOSSIL FRAGMENTS	OOLITES AND PISOLITES	PELLETS	INTRACLASTS	LUMPS
	Biogenic limestone	Oolitic limestone	Pellet limestone	Intraclast limestone	Lump limestone
Micrite	Crinoid (etc.) biomicrite	Oolite micrite	Pellet micrite	Intraclast micrite	Lump micrite
Sparite	Coral (etc.) biosparite	Oolite sparite	Pellet sparite	Intraclast sparite	Lump sparite

changes in texture and components may occur as a result of recrystallization and other phenomena that accompany dolomitization.

Teodorovich, as reported by Bissell and Chilingar (1961), has also proposed a classification of dolomite with three main classes based on predominance of the main mineral mass, the cementing material, or the cavernous-porous nature of the rock. The first class is further subdivided on the basis of whether the rock contains more or less than 10 percent of positive relics. Still further subdivisions are made on the basis of whether the texture is clear-grained or micro-grained. The cavernous dolomites have negative relic structure, and are also subdivided on their clear- or micro-grained texture. Lastly, where cementing material predominates, subdivision is based on inorganic fragmental structure (sandy dolomites) and on relic-chemical or relic-organic structures, such as oolitic and biomorphic dolomites, respectively.

Although it is probably premature to standardize the classification and description of carbonate rocks in view of the rapid advances being made in this subject, the following descriptions of some limestone types follows the general class names given in Table 5-8.

Biogenic Limestone. This major class of limestones includes a number of varieties, which may be either authochtonous or allochthonous. **Coquina limestone** is a common example of an authochtonous accumulation, composed of shells of pelecypods and other bottom-dwelling forms. Some coquinas show preservation of delicate organic structures, evidence of accumulation without subsequent transportation or agitation of the articulated form.

Crinoidal limestone, consisting almost entirely of crinoid columnals, is an allochthonous variety, commonly showing evidence of sorting action. Such allochthonous limestones do not necessarily imply long distances of transport. Local movement on shallow bottoms under wave or current action is apparently sufficient to rearrange and sort the fossil fragments. Crinoidal limestone is common in the Osagian (Mississippian) of the Illinois Basin.

Foraminiferal limestone is composed of tests of bottom-dwelling and floating foraminifers. Numerous Missourian and Virgilian (Pennsylvanian) fusulinid limestones of the Midcontinent are typical. These biogenic limestones, lacking a fine grained matrix, are the **biosparites** of Folk's classification.

A major group of biogenic limestones includes those with a significant admixture of fine grained carbonate material filling the spaces between organic tests and fragments. Limestones of this type are termed **biomicrites** by Folk.

Limestone characterized by an organic framework of carbonate laminae that bind allochem grains as a rigid structure are typical of the cores of organic reefs, as is discussed in Chapter 13. Folk's classification places such limestones under the general heading of **biolithites.**

Oolitic Limestone. This class of limestone is typified by carbonate rocks composed almost wholly of relatively uniform oolites, with virtually no interstitial material. Such oolitic limestones have an even texture, and are usually light gray or buff in color. The absence of interstitial material gives the limestone a high primary porosity and permeability. Some oolitic limestones are important oil reservoirs, such as the St. Genevieve (Mississippian) of Illinois, the Strawn (Pennsylvanian) of north Texas, and the Smackover (Jurassic) of southern Arkansas. These are the **oosparites** of Folk.

Oolitic limestone ranges from the clean type just mentioned, to relatively dense and dark types in which the oolites may be scattered through the body of the rock with interstitial micrite between the oolites, the **oomicrites** of the Folk classification. Parts of the Smackover limestone in Arkansas and Louisiana are of this type.

Pellet Limestone. Pellets, as defined earlier, are rounded masses without internal structure contained in the body of the carbonate rock. Pellet limestones, according to Folk, are relatively common in lower paleozoic strata, but they are usually so fine grained that it is difficult to distinguish them from micrite limestone in the field. Folk interprets pellets as being fecal matter, and infers that the environment of deposition of pellet limestones is one in which organisms may be relatively common. Because of this apparent biological origin of pellets, Folk groups fossils and pellets into one end member as shown in Figure 5-10C. Silurian limestones recognized in West Virginia contain approximately equal portions of fossils and pellets. The interstitial material in pellet limestones is most commonly sparite, forming **pelsparite,** although pellet limestones with fine interstitial material (**pelmicrites**) are not uncommon.

Intraclast Limestone. This class of limestones includes **edgewise conglomerates,** which are formed when fragments of existing carbonate deposits are disturbed and reincorporated into newly forming limestones. Folk (1959, p. 5) considers that the most common mode of intraclast formation is by the erosion of fragments from a widespread layer of semiconsolidated carbonate sediment, with erosion reaching only shallow depths. The eroded fragments may become rounded to somewhat irregular shapes, before reincorporation into the newly forming carbonate deposits.

Intraclastic limestones of the edgewise conglomerate type are very common. Cambrian and Orodovician limestone terrains in many parts of the world are characterized by intraclastic limestone layers, commonly with fine interstitial material forming **intramicrite.**

Lump Limestone. This term has been introduced by Wolf to include a number of limestones in which the allochemical constituents consist of aggregates of pellets or oolites in a matrix of micrite or sparite. The Bahama grapestone aggregates, described by Illing (1954), are cited by Wolf as an example, although this same sediment is classified in the intraclastic group by Folk (1959). In some lump limestones, the aggregates may form the nucleus of oolitic or pisolitic masses, with a superficial coating of finely layered calcite that produces a parallel concentric structure. Wolf cites parts of the Nisku Limestone (Devonian) of Alberta, Canada as an example of this type. Some parts of the Smackover Limestone (Jurassic) of southern Arkansas and northern Louisiana also show composite oolites in a matrix of micrite.

Micrite Limestone. Some limestones have few or no allochemical components, in which case the rock is called micrite limestone, or, simply, **micrite.** **Lithographic limestone** is characteristically of this type.

Evaporites

Evaporites are a group of sedimentary deposits which owe their origin mainly to the evaporation of restricted bodies of sea water. Evaporites include gypsum, anhydrite, salt (halite), and chemically precipitated limestone and primary dolomite. Evaporite deposits are discussed in Chapter 6, 7, and 13.

Gypsum and Anhydrite. Gypsum is a hydrated variety of calcium sulfate, whereas **anhydrite** is the anhydrous salt. Either gypsum or anhydrite may be precipitated during evaporation of sea water, depending upon physical conditions. The normal deposit at temperatures above 30° C. is anhydrite, whereas gypsum is formed at lower temperatures. Most subsurface occurrences are anhydrite, and it is believed to be the primary deposit in most instances, owing to the high temperatures normally associated with evaporation.

Anhydrite typically occurs as uniformly bedded deposits with uniform dense to saccharoidal texture. Color varies from translucent to white, pink, or tan.

Gypsum occurs in uneven masses, or in beds with disturbed bedding, due to expansion during hydration. Some gypsum has undisturbed bedding, and is apparently formed as a primary deposit. Fine to medium grained texture is common, and color ranges from translucent to white, pink, or tan.

Anhydrite is rare in outcrop because hydration occurs on exposure to ground-water circulation. The resulting gypsum may be exposed, but in some instances the occurrence of collapse breccia, caused by solution of the gypsum, is the only evidence of its former presence.

Salt (Halite). Beds of sodium chloride, often of remarkable purity, occur in evaporite associations. The salt occurs in transparent to translucent beds, colorless, white, pink, or tan. Texture is coarsely crystalline. Because of its great solubility, salt is seldom found in outcrop.

Gypsiferous Shale and Limestone. Some shales interbedded with evaporites may contain disseminated grains or crystals of gypsum or anhydrite. These intermediate sediments represent admixtures of detrital and chemical end members and are normal sediments in the association. However, gypsum is also a common authigenic mineral, and may occur as selenite crystals in shales and in clays not associated with evaporites. These crystals develop from later infiltration of gypsiferous waters, and the gypsum crystals and stringers show evidences of secondary origin. Some fire-clays associated with coal beds contain abundant selenite crystals, derived from oxidation and leaching of sulphides present in the coal.

Chemical Sediments

A wide variety of other nonclastic sediments is known. Many of these represent special responses to particular sedimentary environments, and to a large degree, they are controlled by chemical or biochemical processes. These sediments may be grouped into classes according to their tendency to form under various combinations of acidity or alkalinity as well as of oxidizing or reducing conditions in the environment.

These conditions are considered in more detail in Chapter 6, but for completeness of the present chapter, a brief statement of a number of such rock types is included here. As stated near the beginning of this chapter, these descriptions are included primarily to enlarge the reader's vocabulary of sedimentary rock types, even though some of the processes by which these rocks are formed are not discussed in detail here. Discussion of these processes is deferred until chapters 6, 7, and 13.

Siliceous sediments, represented mainly by chert, are very common in the stratigraphic column. Phosphatic, ferruginous, and organic sediments, as pure end members, are relatively rare. However, admixtures of these end members with shale or limestone are abundant, forming a wide variety of sedimentary types, some of which were illustrated in the tetrahedral groupings shown earlier.

Several examples of each type are described here, to illustrate the wide range of sediments important in stratigraphy. Further details may be obtained in Twenhofel (1950) and Pettijohn (1957).

Siliceous Sediments. Chert, flint, and novaculite represent silica end-member sediments. Some occurrences of these sediments strongly suggest primary deposition of silica by chemical processes. The most common occurrences, such as chert nodules and concretionary layers in limestone, are demonstrably secondary, as shown by silicified fossils and definite replacement structures in the limestone.

Novaculite and similar bedded cherts, as illustrated by the Woodford (Devonian) of western Arkansas, are considered to be a result of primary deposition of silica under geosynclinal conditions. Some difference of opinion exists regarding depth of water, source of silica, and other factors, but the common occurrence of strongly siliceous sediments in geosynclinal tracts suggests a primary genetic relationship.

Chert. Chert is a dense, hard rock with dull to semivitreous luster, ranging in color from white through brown and gray to black. It typically occurs as nodular masses or concretionary beds in many limestones and dolomites. Evenly bedded varieties are less common and occur interbedded with dark, siliceous shale.

Some chert occurs in brecciated masses, left as residual deposits as the enclosing limestone is weathered. Thick accumulations are found in the subsurface at the top of the Mississippian limestone along the Central Kansas Uplift, attesting to prolonged exposure and weathering before Pennsylvanian seas moved in.

Detrital chert pebbles and grains are common in some conglomerate and sandstone. These sediments represent "second cycle" deposits in their chert content. The "salt and pepper" Bow Island Sandstone (Cretaceous) of Alberta is an example.

Siliceous Shale and Limestone. Accumulations of diatom and radiolarian tests develop **siliceous shale,** such as occur in the Tertiary of California (Bramlette, 1946). After deposition, original textures and structures may be modified by solution and alteration, to develop more nearly structureless siliceous shale. Other siliceous shales, such as the Mowry (Cretaceous) of Wyoming, represent normal shales fortified by siliceous material from volcanic ash (Rubey, 1929). Dark, splintery shale is common in geosynclinal associations, and is believed to represent primary silica precipitation during times of clay deposition, developing shales in which silica is intimately associated with clay minerals.

Siliceous limestone represents an admixture of two chemical end-members. The silica may be intimately associated with the carbonate to produce a dense, dark rock, commonly thin bedded. This type of limestone is also found in geosynclinal associations, and is believed to represent simultaneous accumulation of carbonates and chemically precipitated silica. All gradations are recognized, however, between these extremes and the more common silicified limestone, which bears evidence of metasomatic replacement of calcite by silica.

Phosphatic Sediments. The term **phosphorite** is applied to phosphatic material of composition similar to collophane. Relatively pure phosphatic sediments are represented by residual accumulations from phosphatic limestone, as in the Florida phosphate beds.

The phosphorite in the Phosphoria Formation (Permian) of western Wyoming occurs as oolitic, concretionary, or fine grained masses and beds associated with shale and limestone. The phosphatic beds contain relatively few fossils, consisting of orbiculoid brachiopods, small gastropods, and some fish remains.

Phosphorite is gray, brown, or black. Associated impurities include quartz grains, pyrite, and marcasite. Oolitic phosphorite ranges from minute spherules to coarse-sand size. Most oolites have concentric structure, but some are structureless.

The origin of the phosphorite is uncertain, but accumulation is inferred to take place under conditions of slow sedimentation in partially restricted areas, or the phosphate may have resulted from wholesale destruction of organisms through development of hydrogen sulfide or other noxious substances in the environment. There is some evidence that phosphorite was deposited as colloidal material, and that phosphatic replacement of other sediments occurred during or shortly after deposition. Both processes probably occurred simultaneously.

Most limestone formed by biological agents contains some phosphorus contributed by invertebrate shells. Differential leaching of the calcite, accompanied by some secondary enrichment, produces **phosphatic limestone.** The phosphatic material may be intimately associated with the calcite, or it may occur as discrete nodules and other masses within the limestone beds.

Phosphatic shale, representing mixtures of primary or secondary phosphate and clay minerals, occurs in association with phosphorite and phosphatic limestone.

Phosphatic Nodules. Small phosphatic concretions are widely distributed throughout the geological column. They range in size from small grains to "pebbles" an inch or more in diameter. The nodules are irregular rounded and flattened bodies, black, with a high surface luster.

Concentrations of phosphate nodules have been observed in many unconformities, especially in the Cretaceous of the Gulf Coast, where they are found at the base of the Eagle Ford. The nodules occur in a thin clay or shale zone associated with fish teeth, glauconitic material, and a restricted invertebrate fauna.

Ferruginous Sediments. The most common iron minerals in sedimentary rocks are hematite, limonite, greenalite, siderite, glauconite, and pyrite. The occurrence of pure end-member sediments is relatively rare, although they are prominent in the Precambrian iron formations of the Lake Superior district.

The ferruginous sediments considered here are limited to several commonly occurring types. James (1954) discusses the iron-bearing sediments in some detail, classifying them into carbonates, silicates, oxides, and sulfides.

Glauconite is a potassium-iron silicate, which has widespread occurrence in the geological column. **Glauconitic sandstone** is a quartzose variety, with detrital glauconite grains. Other occurrences include disseminated grains in limestone, and relatively concentrated associations with phosphate nodule zones. Glauconite apparently forms under conditions of slow sedimentation in partially restricted environments (Galliher, 1935), but, once formed, it may be transported and sorted as detrital grains. Cloud (1955) reviews the general subject, and concludes that glauconite formation requires marine water and reducing conditions, the latter favored by high organic content. The presence of glauconite is considered a sound criterion of marine origin of the enclosing sediment.

Mixtures of iron-bearing end members (iron oxides, siderite) with clastic end members are common among sediments. **Ferruginous shale** and **ferruginous sandstone** are examples. The iron minerals may be hematite or limonite, present as cement or thin coatings on sand grains (as in quartz-iron oxide sandstone). **Ferruginous limestone** has part of its calcite replaced by siderite or iron oxide, forming typical brown or reddish sedimentary rocks. Complete replacement of fossiliferous limestone by hematite yields ores of the Clinton type. Clinton ore contains fossils, oolites, and granular or concretionary masses replaced by the iron oxide.

Relatively pure deposits of limonite occur as **bog iron ore,** formed in fresh-water lakes under restricted conditions, presumably through bacterial or biochemical action. Bog ores are yellow or brown, concretionary, pisolitic, or irregular spongy masses mixed with sand and clay.

Iron sulfide, especially pyrite, is one of the most common minor minerals in sediments. It occurs in black shale, in some limestone (as in the Greenhorn Limestone, Upper Cretaceous, Wyoming), and is associated with phosphatic nodules and glauconite in some zones along unconformities.

Iron-bearing concretions, called **clay ironstones,** are important in many shales. They range in size from fractions of an inch to more than a foot in diameter; the larger ones are commonly referred to as "niggerheads." The concretions have a dense internal texture, and are dark gray to black. They are believed to represent segregations of iron minerals (mainly siderite and iron oxide) formed during or shortly after deposition of the enclosing muds.

Clay ironstones are abundant in some Pennsylvanian micaceous shales.

The Cherokee Shale of eastern Oklahoma has numerous occurrences, commonly arranged as nearly continuous bands of concretions along bedding planes. Large niggerheads occur in associated black fissile shale. Similar concretions, with associated high manganese content also occur, as in the Pierre Shale (Cretaceous) of South Dakota.

Organic Sediments. Organic sediments arise from the accumulation and preservation of organic matter of plants and animals. Preservation is mainly dependent upon rapid burial of soft parts, or accumulation under anaerobic conditions, which prevent oxidation.

The occurrence of organic sediments as pure end members is rare in the geologic column. The most important occurrences, from a stratigraphic viewpoint, are **coal** and **peat,** because of their importance as marker beds. The LaSalle No. 2 coal of the Liverpool cyclothem in Illinois, for instance, has been traced over an area which extends from eastern Oklahoma, through Missouri and parts of Iowa, to the Illinois Basin and parts of Indiana and Kentucky. Some Tertiary lignites can be traced for considerable distances in the subsurface.

Coal is typically black, exhibits conchoidal fracture and is uniformly bedded. Lignite may be brown and relatively soft or earthy in appearance. Coal has been the subject of considerable study, summarized by Cady (1942), Thiessen (1920), Twenhofel (1950), and Pettijohn (1957). Conditions of coal origin are treated by Jeffrey (1915).

In general, megascopic examination of coal reveals four main constituents: vitrain, fusain, clarain, and durain. Vitrain and clarain occur as bright glossy bands in coal. Fusain and durain have a dull luster; the luster of the former is somewhat charcoal-like. Thiessen (1920) describes two basic microscopic constituents, anthraxylon and attritus. The former constituent is formed from the woody parts of plants, and constitutes the bright bands. Attritus is macerated plant material, forming duller bands in the coal.

Coal and peat typically occur in association with subgraywacke sandstone, micaceous shale, and thin nodular or fossiliferous-fragmental limestone. The coal seldom exceeds a few percent of the aggregate thickness of the stratigraphic section. The stratigraphic relations of coal beds are described more fully in Chapter 13, under cyclothems.

Mixtures of organic and clastic or chemical end members are very common among sedimentary rocks. **Carbonaceous shale** and **bituminous shale** are examples. Distinction is made between humic organic matter, composed of plant fragments or carbonaceous flakes, and bituminous organic matter, composed of more oily substances such as pollen grains, animal matter, and resins.

Carbonaceous shale contains humic material, and is generally formed under conditions in which plant stems or leaves may be incorporated into the sediment. This presupposes deposition on alluvial plains, in lakes, or in shallow lagoons and estuaries. Bituminous shale is typically marine or brackish, and associated fossils commonly are bottom-dwelling forms.

Increase of bituminous material in shale causes darkening, and some black shales have 10 percent or more of organic matter. Iron sulfide may produce black shale also, so that color alone is not a satisfactory criterion of organic content.

Black shale, with appreciable organic content, is widespread in the geologic column. The Chattanooga Shale (Devonian-Mississippian) of the central United States is of this type, and has been considered an important source rock of petroleum. Other black shales, of more limited extent, occur in coal-bearing sequences. Twenhofel (1950) discusses the origin of black shales at length, and the subject is further touched upon in Chapter 6, 12, and 13.

Some limestone is dark, dense, and has a fetid odor when freshly broken. This is **bituminous limestone,** of which the Bone Spring Limestone (Permian) of west Texas is an example. These limestones are believed to have formed under stagnant conditions, in which abundant organic matter is preserved. The limestones are associated with organic-rich, black shale.

Petroleum may be considered as a liquid organic end member. The subject of petroleum genesis, important as it is in certain aspects of stratigraphy, cannot be given justice in a volume of this scope. The reader is referred to Levorsen (1956) for a summary of the subject. Trask and Patnode (1942) discuss technical aspects of source rocks. Cox (1946) presents a summary of geological controls on petroleum origin. Orr and Emery (1956) examined the hydrocarbon distribution in recent sediments in southern California offshore basins.

SUPPLEMENTARY READINGS

1. Grabau, A. W., 1913, Principles of stratigraphy: New York, A. G. Seiler & Co.

   Classification of sediments: Chapter 6.

2. Pettijohn, F. J., 1957, Sedimentary rocks: New York, Harper & Brothers.

   Classification of sediments: Chapter 5.
   Coarse grained clastic sediments: Chapters 6, 7.
   Fine grained clastic sediments: Chapter 8.
   Limestone and dolomite: Chapter 9.
   Siliceous, ferruginous, and other nonclastic sediments: Chapter 10.

3. Twenhofel, W. H., 1950, Principles of sedimentation (2nd edition): New York, McGraw-Hill Book Co., Inc.

Classification of sediments: Chapter 7.
Clastic sediments: Chapter 8.
Carbonate sediments: Chapter 9.
Chemical sediments (siliceous, ferruginous, etc.): Chapters 10, 11, 12, 13.

4. Dunbar, C. O. and Rodgers, J., 1957, Principles of stratigraphy: New York, John Wiley & Sons, Inc. Sedimentary rock nomenclature: Chapter 8. Description and interpretation of sedimentary rocks: Chapters 9–14, inclusive.

5. Weller, J. M., 1960, Stratigraphic principles and practice: New York, Harper & Brothers.

Classification and composition of sediments: Chapter 4.

6. Levorsen, A. I., 1956, Geology of petroleum: San Francisco, W. H. Freeman and Co.

The origin of petroleum: Chapter 11.

7. Williams, H. Turner, F. J. and Gilbert, C. M., 1954, Petrography—an introduction to the study of rocks in thin sections: San Francisco, W. H. Freeman and Co.

Pyroclastics: Chapter 8.
Sandstone, argillaceous rocks, calcareous rocks: Chapters 15, 16, 17.

8. Ham, W. E. (editor), 1962, Classification of carbonate rocks—a symposium: Am. Assoc. Petroleum Geologists, Memoir 1, Tulsa, Okla. This volume, which appeared when this book was in proof, is an indispensable reference on the subject. It contains papers on carbonate rock classification, on the interpretation of carbonate textures, on mappable aspects of carbonate rocks, and it concludes with an application of factor analysis in the classification of Bahamian carbonate deposits.

CHAPTER 6

Sedimentary Processes

INTRODUCTION

WEATHERING, transportation, deposition, and lithification are the elements of sedimentation. The process begins at the instant when fragments are dislodged from the parent rock by weathering.

The stratigrapher draws heavily on principles of sedimentation in his study of the distribution and character of ancient sediments. Several lines of inquiry may be followed in sediment interpretation. Composition of the rocks sheds light on source areas; textures and structures reflect the dynamics of transportation and deposition; and associated fossils permit age determination of beds and reconstruction of sedimentary environments.

The purpose of this chapter is to examine present-day sedimentary processes and to show their bearing on sediment interpretation. Much of the material is based on fairly well established principles, and is reviewed without specific literature references with the exception of some basic papers that support specific technical points.

Sedimentary processes that involve movement of clastic particles by turbulent agents have received more study than the chemical and biological processes by which nonclastic sediments are formed. Advances in geochemistry during the past decade, however, have shed considerable light on processes of nonclastic deposition, and some of these newer developments are included in the discussion. On the physical side, the importance of density currents in contrast to normal turbulent agents, such as streams, has been increasingly recognized in recent years.

ROCK WEATHERING

Rock weathering is a phenomenon of the interface between atmosphere and lithosphere. Rocks from deep-seated environments, such as granite, become adjusted to surface conditions through weathering processes. In essence, weathering causes a change from a massive to a clastic state, breaking solid rocks down to chemically stable debris.

190

Kinds of Rock Weathering

Rock weathering is a complex of physical, chemical, and biological processes, as shown in Table 6-1. **Physical weathering** changes the particle size, surface area, and bulk volume of the parent rock, with no significant change in composition.

Chemical weathering causes a complete change in physical and chemical properties, accompanied by an increase in bulk volume caused both by the lesser density of new compounds, and by additional porosity of the weathered aggregate. Principles of chemical weathering are given in Keller (1955).

Biological weathering is similar to chemical weathering, in that changes in both the state of aggregation and in chemical composition occur. Physical and biological weathering contribute much less than chemical weathering to most soils.

The products of weathering include two groups of substances. Soluble materials (and some colloids) are removed by circulating ground water, and residual material accumulates at the site of weathering. The segregation of these is illustrated in Figure 6-1. Insoluble clay minerals, original quartz, some secondary quartz or chert, such accessories as zircon, and some soluble material, remain at the site of weathering.

The "weathering complex" is the end product of weathering. It is the main source of detrital material swept away mechanically and formed into

TABLE 6-1. WEATHERING PROCESSES

TYPE OF WEATHERING	EXAMPLES	SUMMARY
Physical	Unloading (expansion of rock during erosion) Thermal expansion Frost action (ice wedges) Colloid plucking (pulling effect of gels)	Generally of secondary importance. Net effect is particle size reduction; increased surface area; no change in chemical composition.
Chemical	Solution Hydration, hydrolysis Oxidation (with or without valence increase) Reduction Carbonation (exchange reactions in part)	Complete change of chemical and physical properties; net increase in volume.
Biological	Wedge work of roots Plant acids	Combination of chemical and physical effects.

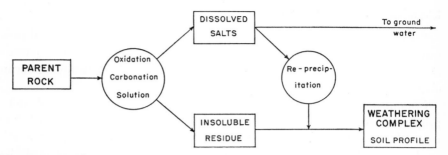

Fig. 6-1. Development of weathering complex from parent rock.

clastic sediments by geologic agents. The dissolved material is carried away by ground water and streams and is ultimately added to the salts in the ocean.

The Soil Profile

Several zones develop from the surface downward as the weathering complex accumulates. These zones constitute the **soil profile.**

The uppermost zone is the **A-horizon,** from which colloids and soluble material have been leached. Below this is the **B-horizon,** in which leached material from above is reprecipitated to form a dense colloidal zone. The **C-horizon** lies below the B-horizon, and is partially weathered parent rock, extending down to unaltered fresh rock below.

Soil profiles have a very direct application to stratigraphy, inasmuch as ancient soil profiles occur along some unconformities and disconformities. Where larger structural features of the rock are obscured in the subsurface, recognition of fossil soil profiles may be important in demonstrating the presence of unconformities.

Soil-forming Processes

Three main soil-forming processes are recognized, two adjusted to temperate zones and one to the tropics. The following paragraphs, adapted from Reiche (1950) summarize their main characteristics.

Podsolization is the normal process in temperate, humid climates with a forest cover. It concentrates iron or iron and aluminum compounds in the B-horizon. Calcium, sodium, and magnesium are thoroughly leached, and silica may be removed in colloidal form. Kaolinitic clay minerals are the normal end products of the process. Soil formed by this process is called a **pedalfer.**

Calcification occurs in dry climates with brush or grass cover. It concentrates calcium and magnesium carbonates in the B-horizon. A distinguishing feature is the whitish "caliche" zone commonly associated with the profile. Chemical weathering is seldom complete, and the clay mineral associated with the process is montmorillonite. Soil formed by this process is a **pedocal.**

Laterization is the normal, soil-forming process in the tropics. It concentrates iron or aluminum oxides, or both, in the B-horizon, at the expense of the silica, which is leached out. Chemical weathering is rapid. Kaolinitic clay minerals are normal end products in some circumstances but, in others, the clay minerals are not stable. Where clay breakdown occurs, silica is removed, and the aluminum remains behind as a hydrate. Soil formed by this process is **laterite.**

Buried Soil Profiles

The extent to which soil profiles are modified during burial beneath an unconformity is not fully understood. It is believed that zones of concretions are preserved. Ratios of aluminum to iron, aluminum to silica, or potassium to sodium, may remain fixed. Each of these ratios depends on the degree of weathering and depth below the surface in the soil profile.

Some authorities believe that variegated shales (green, red, purple) may be the end products of ancient soils after long burial and modification, perhaps including some reworking. Thin beds of red shale in an otherwise normal section are considered, by others, as signs of weathered zones. The identification of unconformities in the subsurface may depend upon recognition of such criteria, in the absence of other clear-cut evidence. Features associated with unconformities are described in Chapter 9.

Clay Minerals

Among the most important constituents of soils and sediments are the **clay minerals,** mainly hydrous aluminum silicates. Owing to their small particle size, clay minerals have great surface activity, represented by ionic adsorption, cohesiveness, and other properties. The clay minerals have been studied in great detail because of their scientific and economic importance. The brief treatment given here includes only a few properties and occurrences of the clay minerals as they relate to the main theme of this book. It is assumed that the reader has had course work or has literature on the mineralogy and crystal structure of the clay minerals.

The clay minerals, mainly formed during weathering processes, become important constituents of clastic sediments. Shale derives many of its distinctive properties, such as fine lamination, from its clay content. The clay minerals are also a common insoluble residue in argillaceous limestone, and they form part of the matrix of poorly sorted sandstone.

The Kaolinite Group. Kaolinite occurs in the pedalfers, and it is commonly present in laterites. It is also abundant in shale. Kaolinite occurs in soils in flakes down to about 0.3 micron in diameter. The mineral has small ion absorption, small water absorption, and a low degree of compaction compared to other clay mineral groups.

The Montmorillonite Group. Montmorillonite occurs in the pedocals, and is present in bentonites developed from volcanic ash. The mineral also occurs in recent marine sediments. Montmorillonite commonly occurs in flakes smaller than 0.2 micron in diameter. It has large ion-adsorbing capacity and large water absorption. The clay swells markedly when wet, and shows corresponding shrinkage on drying. Montmorillonite has small permeability and large plasticity, compared with kaolinite.

The Illite Group. Illite is a common mineral in marine shale, and is common in some desert soils. It occurs in flakes as small as 0.1 micron in diameter. The clay has intermediate values of ion-adsorption capacity, water absorption, permeability, and plasticity, in comparison with the extremes of kaolinite and montmorillonite.

The Chlorite Group. The chlorite clay minerals, which may be thought of as magnesium-rich derivatives of the montmorillonite group (Keller, 1955), have been recognized as an important constituent in recent and ancient marine sediments. These clays occur as flakes that may be smaller than 0.1 micron in diameter. As with illite, the chlorite clays lie between the extremes of kaolinite and montmorillonite in their physical properties.

Table 6-2 summarizes some properties and modes of occurrence of the clay minerals (adapted largely from Grim, 1953).

Importance in Stratigraphy and Sedimentation. The properties of clays change markedly with the nature of absorbed ions. Common absorbed ions include calcium-ion, sodium-ion, and hydrogen-ion. Calcium clays are more permeable than the corresponding sodium-clays, but sodium-clay is more plastic than calcium-clay.

The kinds of clay minerals present in sediments and the nature of their absorbed ions are important in determining the properties of fine grained clastic sediments. The specific clay minerals observed are a reflection of some combination of conditions that existed in the area of weathering of the parent rocks and, later, in the area of accumulation. The **alkalinity** or **acidity** of associated fluids; presence of **oxidizing** or **reducing** conditions; character and amount of **dissolved salts**; **temperature**; and the presence or absence of **organic material** appear to be involved. Clay minerals carried to the sea by streams have a given composition and contain certain absorbed ions inherited from the weathering site. During transportation some changes may occur in clay mineral composition, but the presence of dissolved salts in

TABLE 6-2. SUMMARY OF CLAY PROPERTIES AND OCCURRENCE

ITEM	KAOLINITE GROUP	ILLITE GROUP	CHLORITE GROUP	MONTMORILLONITE GROUP
Particle size (in microns)	4.0–0.3	0.3–0.1	0.3–0.1(?)	0.2–0.02
Relative ion exchange	Slight	Moderate	Moderate	Large
Relative water adsorption	Slight	Moderate	Moderate	Very large
Relative permeability	Large	Moderate	Moderate	Small
Relative plasticity	Slight	Moderate	Moderate	Large
Occurrence in soils	Pedalfers Laterite	Pedocals	Present in some	Pedocals
Occurrence in recent sediments	Common	Abundant	Common	Common
Occurrence in ancient sediments	Common	Abundant	Common	Common

ocean waters may produce additional changes during and after deposition on the sea bottom.

The relative importance of conditions at the weathering site, in contrast to those at the site of deposition, are difficult to evaluate. Weaver (1958) contends that clay minerals are mainly detrital in origin, and tend to reflect the character of their source areas, although they are subject to some alteration in fluviatile and subaerial environments. Grim (1951) has suggested that montmorillonite especially is subject to postdepositional alteration to other clays (illite). In a review of the problem Grim (1958) points out that clay minerals are more "at home" in some environments than in others. Changes that occur when a clay mineral is subjected to a new environment depend upon the nature of the new environment and on the specific type of clay mineral involved, and the changes appear to occur relatively quickly.

Although the subject of clay-mineral response to environment is presently in a state of flux (as are many other aspects of geology as they affect stratigraphy), there is little doubt that clay minerals can provide important information on their origin and environment of deposition, especially as more definitive methods of analysis are developed. Among recent papers bearing on the problem are Keller's (1956) discussion of clay minerals and environments and Weaver's areal study (1958) of the origin and petrology of clays in Upper Mississippian and Lower Pennsylvanian sediments in the Central United States. Van Houten (1953) points out that an "inheritance factor" is present, in that the dominant clay minerals in many soils are the same as those in the parent rocks.

TRANSPORTATION OF SEDIMENTS

Under normal conditions, erosion proceeds at about the same rate as rock weathering. The unconsolidated debris left by weathering is available for movement by fluids, and constitutes the main source of sedimentary detrital components.

Once they are made available to geologic agents, the detrital particles are transported in accordance with certain laws of fluid flow. Knowledge of the behavior of particles in fluids and an understanding of the laws of transportation and deposition have been greatly increased by experimental study.

The two fundamental aspects of sediment transportation are the settling velocity of the particles, and the laws of fluid motion. These aspects apply to all sediments, but they can be illustrated more readily with the detrital sediments.

Settling Velocity of Spheres

The most fundamental property of a particle in its behavior during transportation is its settling velocity. It is determined by the size, sphericity, and density of the particle.

The physical laws governing the settling of spheres are well known, and the theory can be extended to include the irregular particles which compose sediments. Two laws of settling are important for sediments, one applicable to fine particles, and the other to coarse particles. Details of the derivation of these laws are given by Rubey (1933).

Stokes's Law. A sphere of any diameter d and of given density, settling in water, is pulled downward by a force which depends on the particle volume, the acceleration of gravity, and the difference between the density of the particle and the fluid. If the sphere is very small (of the order of less than 0.1 mm diameter in water), the resistance offered by the fluid is proportional to the product of the diameter and velocity of the particle, times the viscosity of the fluid. By equating these relations for small particles, it can be shown that the settling velocity (v) is proportional to the square of the particle diameter,

$$v = C_1 d^2,$$

where the various constants (particle density, fluid density, acceleration of gravity, fluid viscosity) are included in C_1. This expression is the simplest form of **Stokes's Law.**

Impact Law. If the sphere is too large for control of its settling velocity by fluid viscosity, the resistance to its motion is proportional to the product of the sphere density, the square of its diameter, and the square of its velocity. Viscous forces become negligible. By equating the downward force to the new resistance, it can be shown that for large particles the settling velocity is proportional to the square root of the particle diameter,

$$v = C_2 \sqrt{d},$$

where the various constants, as above, are included in C_2. This second relation is the simplest form of the **Impact Law.**

Stokes's Law plots as a concave parabola, and the Impact Law as a convex paraboloid, as shown in Figure 6-2. Observed data on the settling of quartz grains (the heavy curve in the figure), show that very small grains follow Stokes's Law, whereas larger grains behave according to the Impact Law. In a transition zone extending from about 0.1 mm to 1.0 mm in diameter, the experimental data agree with an average of the two laws, indicating their mutual effect.

The physical meaning of the curves in Figure 6-2 is that small particles (mainly silt and clay) settle under conditions of viscous resistance, whereas larger particles (sand and pebbles) settle under inertial conditions. If the particles are considered to be held in suspension by upward currents, it is evident that very feeble currents could maintain the smaller particles in suspension, whereas a pebble 10 mm in diameter would require an upward current of nearly 3 ft/sec. Even among small particles, there is a significant difference in settling velocity. A clay particle of diameter 0.001 mm settles 0.0001 cm/sec, which is 1 foot in about 3 days. A silt particle with diameter 0.02 mm settles 0.04 cm/sec, which is 1 foot in 10 minutes.

Effect of Particle Shape. Most quartz grains have sphericities of 0.7 and above, and only occasional sedimentary grains, like hornblende or mica, depart markedly from spheroidal shapes. As long as the particles have sphericities of the order of 0.7 and above, the settling velocity changes in roughly the same proportion as the sphericity.

A quartz particle with sphericity of 0.8 settles about 0.8 times as fast as does a quartz sphere of the same volume. Therefore, in applying settling velocity laws to sedimentary particles, no adjustments need be made in the

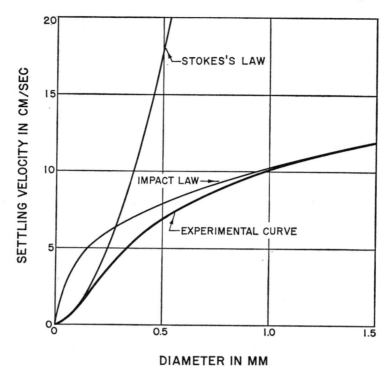

Fig. 6-2. Comparison of experimental data on settling velocity with Stokes's Law and the Impact Law. [Data adapted from Rubey (1933).]

reasoning, except to recognize that nonspherical particles have smaller settling velocities than the corresponding true spheres.

On the assumption that particle shape influences setting velocity approximately as a direct proportion, Stokes's Law may be stated as follows:

The settling velocity of small particles is directly proportional to the difference between particle and fluid density; inversely proportional to fluid viscosity; directly proportional to particle sphericity; and directly proportional to the square of the particle diameter.

The Impact Law, similarly modified by the influence of particle shape, may be expressed as follows:

The settling velocity of large particles is independent of fluid viscosity; it is directly proportional to the square root of particle diameter, directly proportional to particle sphericity, and directly proportional to the difference between particle and fluid density divided by fluid density.

From the similarities and differences of these two laws, it is apparent that, whereas the rate of settling of a silt or clay particle is influenced by the viscosity of the medium (air as against water), larger particles settle independently of this effect. The settling velocities of both small and large particles are influenced by particle density, sphericity, and diameter.

Importance of Settling Velocity. The sorting action of a current is related to the settling velocity of the particles carried by it. If a load of suspended silt and clay is fed to a slow lake current by a stream, the clay particles can be carried much greater distances than the silt particles; moreover, if the current conditions remain constant, there is a regular gradation (sorting) of particle size away from the source, as the larger particles settle to the bottom, always leaving finer material in suspension.

In contrast to long-continued suspension of fine particles even in slow currents, coarser particles settle to the bottom almost immediately, unless upward currents are sufficient to keep them in suspension. As will be seen, turbulent motions in the fluid provide the upward velocity components which keep the particles in suspension.

Many problems in sediment interpretation are related to settling velocity phenomena. It is possible, for example, to visualize a suspended load where smaller highly spherical particles settle out more rapidly than larger low-sphericity particles, thus apparently increasing particle size in the direction of transport.

Micaceous sands, composed of high-sphericity quartz grains and low-sphericity mica flakes, are often difficult to interpret because they first pose the problem of whether the mica is primary or secondary, and, if primary, whether deposition occurred under the same conditions as the sand, or during quiet intervals between deposition of individual sand layers. Such problems can be solved by a study of the size, shape, and density of the two minerals in terms of their relative settling velocities.

In a similar manner, the problem of whether a sandy gravel represents simultaneous deposition of pebbles and sand, or whether the sand later infiltrated the gravel, may be solved by application of settling velocity laws.

Important as settling velocity laws are in the solution of sedimentary problems, full interpretation must take account of the motions of the fluid. In nearly all problems of sediment transportation and deposition, the interaction among particles and moving fluids controls the characteristics of the final deposits.

Fluid Flow

Laminar and Turbulent Motion. Fluid flow is of two general kinds. **Laminar flow** is a relatively slow motion in which each "thread" of liquid retains its identity and flows smoothly alongside its neighbors. It is a type of streamline motion which curves smoothly around irregularities in its path, rather than setting up whirls and eddies as it moves past.

The second motion is **turbulent flow** in which small, random, velocity fluctuations occur across the line of flow. The cross fluctuations are caused by eddies generated as the fluid moves past obstacles or along rough boundaries. Figure 6-3 illustrates the paths of laminar and turbulent flow past an obstacle. A small particle suspended in a turbulent current does not follow a smooth path, as it would in laminar flow, but fluctuates up and down and from side to side as it moves along.

Turbulent flow develops when the velocity exceeds the restrictions of viscous forces. For water flowing in a pipe 15 cm in diameter (6 in.), laminar flow requires a velocity less than 1.4 cm/sec.

A very extensive literature is available on fluid flow and particle movement. The following selection is largely geologically oriented: Gilbert (1914), O'Brien (1933), Rubey (1933), Leighly (1934), Rubey (1937), Hjulstrom (1939), Bagnold (1941), Kalinske (1942), Rittenhouse (1943), Inman (1949), Einstein and Chien (1953), Leopold (1953), Bates (1953), Finkel (1959), and Kuenen (1959). Bagnold and Finkel emphasize wind deposits, and Bates applies jet-stream theory to the mouths of sediment-laden rivers, as in the Mississippi delta. Kuenen provides a classification of marine conditions of transport. The other references are concerned mainly with stream phenomena.

Turbulence Intensity. Turbulence is studied experimentally by measuring the instantaneous velocity variations in the flow. Drops of fluorescent fluid of the same density as water are introduced into a pipe filled with flowing water, and recorded by a motion picture camera under ultraviolet light. The cross fluctuations of the drops are read from the film and average values are computed. **Turbulence intensity** is defined as the relative magnitude of the velocity cross fluctuations in the current.

A visual representation of the cross fluctuations may be had by introducing a "thread" of dye into the moving fluid. Figure 6-4 shows the paths of dye introduced into pipes with laminar and turbulent flow. In laminar flow, the thread retains its identity along a single streamline. In turbulent flow, the cross fluctuations of the water current disrupt the thread of dye and diffuse it across the section of flow.

Fig. 6-3. Lines of fluid flow past a cylinder. (*Left*) Laminar flow. (*Right*) Turbulent motion.

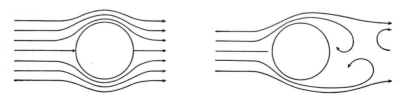

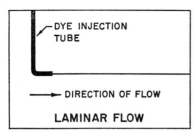 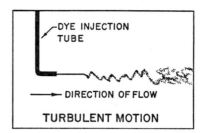

Fig. 6-4. Contrast of laminar and turbulent motion as shown by injection of dye into a pipe. The cross-fluctuations in turbulent motion are related to the intensity of turbulence. [Drawing on the right is from a photograph by Kalinske and Van Driest (1938).]

Turbulence Scale. Turbulence is related to intensity and rapidity of eddy motion. **Turbulence scale** is a measure of average eddy size in the flow. Small eddies rotate more rapidly than large eddies for any given state of flow. However, average eddy size may be large or small in turbulent flow of any intensity. The turbulence scale is separate from the intensity, and both features must be known in order to measure the turbulence completely.

Turbulence Diffusion. An important feature of all turbulent motion is its high rate of transfer of heat, momentum, energy, and suspended solids across flow lines. The cross fluctuations of turbulent motion result in a thorough mixing of the fluid. When a turbulent current flows over a sand bottom, sand grains may be lifted by the instantaneous vertical velocity fluctuations, and diffused over the entire cross section of the channel.

Turbulence diffusion or cross fluctuation is related both to the intensity and scale of the turbulence. Transfer of the suspended load throughout the stream cross section depends upon the relative concentration of material in suspension, and on the lifting of additional particles from the stream bed.

Turbulent motion is displayed by wind, streams, and shore waves and currents. The laws of sediment transportation by these agents are fundamentally contingent upon the principles of turbulent flow and the principles of settling velocity.

Although there are differences among turbulent geologic agents in their effect on particles they transport, these differences arise more from differences in density, range of velocity, and physical limitations of flow (channels *versus* broad sea floors, for instance) than from any fundamental differences in the physical laws which apply. It is known that many transportation phenomena of streams have their analogues in wind and current transport. Principles of stream transportation may accordingly be applied to other agents.

Movement of Particles

Particle movement is initiated in streams when the drag of the moving fluid overcomes gravitational and cohesive forces on the particle. The displaced particle thus rolls along with the fluid, or if the momentary vertical velocity fluctuation is greater than its settling velocity, the particle is swept upward into suspension.

This statement implies that small particles are set into motion more readily than large ones because they offer less resistance to the forces. This is not strictly true because of the increasing effect of cohesive forces in small particles, and because large particles shed eddies as the turbulent fluid moves past them.

Particles larger than approximately 0.2 mm act as individual obstacles on the stream bottom and form eddies. As long as the particle sheds eddies, it concentrates upon itself forces which would otherwise be distributed over a larger area of the stream bottom. When these forces exceed a critical value, the particle is set into motion along the stream bed or swept into suspension.

If the particles are too small to form eddies, the fluid forces are applied to the stream bed as a whole. A paradoxical situation thus arises, in that individual large particles may be moved by velocities which do not disturb a bed of finer material. It requires increasingly vigorous conditions to initiate movement on beds of fine material, both because of the lack of forces concentrated on individual particles, and the increasing cohesiveness of fine silt and clay.

Once movement is initiated, the subsequent behavior of the particles is largely a function of their settling velocity. For example, although it requires a greater force to set clay particles than small sand grains into suspension, the sand grains settle rapidly, but the clay remains in suspension because of its smaller settling velocity.

Hjulstrom's Diagram. Hjulstrom (1939) formalized these hydrodynamic relations in the manner shown in Figure 6-5. The upper curve shows the critical velocities necessary to initiate particle movement for different diameters. Velocities greater than 100 cm/sec are required for particles 1 micron in diameter. The critical velocity diminishes to a minimum value of about 20 cm/sec. for diameters between 0.1 and 0.5 mm. For sizes larger than this, the critical velocity again increases to more than 100 cm/sec. for pebbles 10 cm in diameter.

The lower sloping line on the graph, the settling velocity curve, expresses the velocity conditions under which a particle comes to rest because its settling velocity exceeds either the forward motion of the stream or the effect

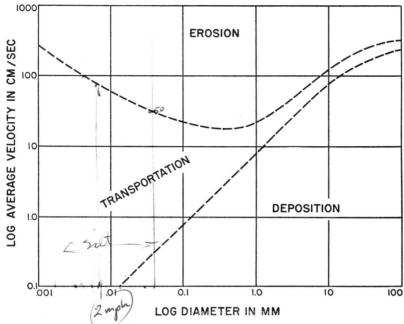

Fig. 6-5. Hjulstrom's diagram of the relations among erosion, transportation, and deposition of sedimentary particles. [Adapted from Hjulstrom (1939).]

of cross fluctuations. The settling velocity curve rises to the right, and approaches the curve of initial movement in the upper right hand side of the graph.

The area above the upper curve is the **erosional regime** within which particles are set into motion. The area below the lower curve is the **regime of deposition,** within which particles in transport come to rest. The broad, wedge-shaped area between the two curves is the **regime of transportation.** Transportation continues as long as the velocity, with its implied turbulence intensity and scale, lies between the limits of the two curves.

CLASSIFICATION OF STREAM LOADS

In detail, there are three modes of stream transport, which are not explicitly distinguished in Hjulstrom's diagram. The first is **traction transport,** in which particles roll, slide, or tumble along the bottom. **Saltation** is a mode of transport in which particles bounce along the stream bed in a series of short interrupted leaps. In **suspension transport,** the particles are swept along entirely free from the stream bed.

Suspension Transport

Suspension transport occurs when the turbulence intensity is greater than the settling velocity of the particles set into motion by lift and drag forces. Stream bed particles vary in size, shape, and density, and the smaller, less spherical, and least dense of these particles are lifted into suspension.

Although very small particles are more difficult to dislodge than fine sand grains, the movement of large particles along the bed usually dislodges finer particles which join the suspension load.

Observations on suspended material in streams show that the concentration of particles is much greater near the stream bed than near the top. Moreover, the relative concentration of different particle sizes varies through the stream section. The concentration of very fine material may be very nearly the same from top to bottom, whereas coarser particles, such as silt and fine sand, show definite **concentration gradients** from top to bottom of the stream.

Figure 6-6 illustrates the concentration gradients of coarse sand, fine sand, and fine silt in a stream. It shows that during suspension transport, materials with greater settling velocity tend to move in lower parts of the stream than those with smaller settling velocities.

Fig. 6-6. Concentration gradients of coarse sand, fine sand, and fine silt in a stream. [Adapted from Hjulstrom (1939).]

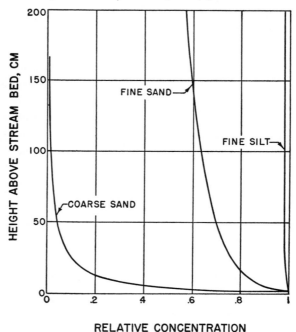

RELATIVE CONCENTRATION

For any given diameter, the amount of material coming down is equivalent to the product of the concentration gradient times the settling velocity. The amount of material rising depends upon turbulent diffusion of the more concentrated suspension near the bottom into less concentrated areas above. When the upward movement due to turbulence equals the downward movement due to settling, equilibrium exists, and the concentration curves assume the form shown in the figure.

In suspension transport, one may imagine the graph of Figure 6-6 moving downstream at the average velocity of the stream. As long as equilibrium is present between factors that keep the material in suspension and factors which tend to settle out the material, transportation continues in a balanced state. That is, as much new material is picked up as settles out over any unit area of stream bottom.

Deposition occurs when turbulence intensity and scale diminish. A decrease in turbulence intensity means that the concentration gradient becomes unbalanced in favor of particles settling as against particles rising. Hence, a new state of balance is reached, with a change in the concentration gradient proportional to the amount of material dropped out of the stream. Turbulence intensity decreases as average stream velocity decreases, which results in deposition in the quieter parts of stream channels.

Traction Transport

The traction transport of particles is related to shearing forces along the stream bottom, developed by the moving stream. The effect of shearing forces on particles is strengthened by lifting forces of the turbulent motion. It has been shown experimentally that the ease with which particles are set into motion along the bed is partly a function of their settling velocity. Thus, settling velocity plays a part in both suspension and traction movement, even though in the latter, the particles are not actually lifted from the bed. The traction load usually consists of coarser particles than does the suspension load. Nevin (1946) discusses traction and suspension loads in relation to settling velocity.

Highly spherical particles roll more readily than less spherical ones; hence, spheroidal particles are favored during traction movement. Particle size and density are also involved, resulting in a traction load adjusted to the flow conditions. As long as conditions of flow remain the same, traction transport continues in a balanced state. When there is a reduction in average stream velocity, or in the intensity of turbulence, the larger, denser, or lower sphericity particles are left behind.

The movement of the traction load, confined as it is to the bed of the stream, is somewhat more sensitive to velocity and turbulence conditions than is the suspension load. Inasmuch as the degree of turbulence tends, in general, to vary with stream velocity, factors which affect the velocity exert a controlling effect on transportation.

Stream velocity varies as the square root of the product of the stream gradient times the "hydraulic radius," divided by a "friction factor," which is related, in part, to the roughness of the stream bed:

$$\text{Stream velocity} = (\text{const.}) \sqrt{\frac{\text{Gradient} \times \text{Hydraulic radius}}{\text{Friction factor}}},$$

where the constant depends partly upon channel shape. The hydraulic radius of the stream is the cross-sectional area divided by the wetted perimeter.

Decrease in the numerical value of the stream gradient or of the hydraulic radius, or an increase in the value of the friction factor, causes a decrease in velocity and part of the load is deposited. Similarly, reverse conditions increase the transporting capacity of the stream.

Although the traction load is more sensitive to slight changes in velocity conditions than the suspension load, the latter also responds by adjusting the concentration curves of Figure 6-6.

Saltation Movement

Saltation movement may be considered an intermediate phase between traction and suspension transport. Particles not large enough to remain in traction on the stream bed nor small enough to be swept into true suspension may be lifted momentarily above the bottom, and acquire the velocity of the stream, moving forward in a series of leaps or bounds.

The relative height of particle rise during saltation depends upon the specific gravity of particle and fluid (Kalinske, 1942):

$$\text{Height of jump} = (\text{const.}) \left[\frac{\text{Specific gravity of particle}}{\text{Specific gravity of fluid}} \right].$$

The effect of saltation in air and water may be illustrated by a quartz sphere (specific gravity 2.65). The ratio of specific gravities in air (2.65/0.0012) is 2,200; in water, the ratio (2.65/1.00) is 2.65. Thus, the rise of the quartz particle in air is of the order of 800 times as great as the corresponding jump in water.

This relation accounts for the observed fact that wind movement of sand is mainly by saltation, whereas movement of sand by rivers and water currents is mainly by traction or suspension.

Bagnold (1941) studied sand movement by wind and found that the sand grains describe a parabolic trajectory during saltation, rising steeply at first and then descending gradually. The height and length of the trajectory vary with grain size and wind conditions, but, in general, the saltation movement is confined to a shallow zone above the sand surface. Occasional grains may rise as high as five feet, but the average is much less than one foot. Concentration of the main load near the surface means that the saltation load responds much as the traction load to changes in velocity and turbulence conditions.

SELECTIVE TRANSPORTATION AND ABRASION

Selective Transportation

The discussion of settling velocities showed that, for given particle size, spheres settle faster than disks, and heavy minerals settle faster than less dense minerals. When a cloud of material is swept into suspension, the flatter particles rise higher or stay in suspension longer than the spherical particles. As suspension transport proceeds, the heavier and more spherical particles in any size range sink near the bottom or settle out. The net result is that particles with relatively low sphericity are favored during suspension transport.

In traction movement, on the other hand, spheres roll most readily and outstrip lower-sphericity particles of given size and density. The net effect of the interplay of these factors, combined with varying intensity and scale of turbulence, is a complex sorting of material during transportation, on the basis of particle size, shape, and density. This sorting process is called **selective transportation,** or **selective sorting.**

A result of selective sorting is that geological agents show systematic changes in the characteristics of the moving load and of the deposited material as they are followed downstream, down beach, or down wind. These systematic changes include a downstream decrease in average particle size, an increase in average particle sphericity, and some changes in average density.

Debris available for erosion at sites of weathering includes a wide range of particle sizes, shapes, and densities, whereas the final sediments observed in nature consist of relatively well sorted gravel, sand, silt, and clay. It is apparent from this that the process of sedimentation is at least partly one of selective transportation and deposition. The continued segregation of particles according to size, shape, and density during transportation suggests that the best-sorted sediments are those which have been subjected to long-continued movement by geological agents.

The curves in Figure 6-7 show the changes which may occur in particle properties under ideal conditions of traction transport. Average size of the

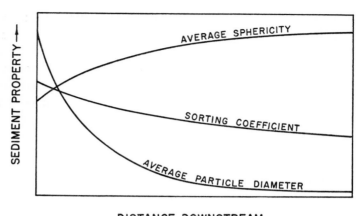

Fig. 6-7. Changes in sediment properties during selective transportation in a stream.

particles decreases in the direction of transport. This is partly the result of a gradual diminution in turbulence intensity downstream. The numerical value of the sorting coefficient decreases downstream, as the degree of sorting improves. Average particle sphericity increases downstream.

Selective transportation has its largest effect on average particle size, an intermediate effect on particle sphericity, and a lesser effect on particle density. This is the same order in which settling velocity is controlled by the particle properties.

In nature, many complexities occur in the simple curves of Figure 6-7, owing to the effects of new material fed into the stream by tributaries, recurrent changes in stream conditions, such as floods, and because of breakage and other changes in the particles during transport.

Particle Wear during Transportation

Concurrent with changes in average attributes of the sedimentary load through selective transportation, is a series of changes which take place when particles strike or abrade each other during transportation, especially during traction movement. As particles roll and slide along the bottom, edges are knocked off or abraded and particle roundness increases very rapidly in the early stages of transportation. If conditions are extremely vigorous, the particles may shatter, giving rise to rough edges, as well as abrupt changes in particle size and shape. Under normal conditions of transportation, breakage is less important than abrasion.

Systematic studies made of abrasion during traction movement show that roundness is the most strongly affected particle property. Figure 6-8 is a graph of experimental data on abrasion of limestone fragments. Roundness increases rapidly at the start of the experiment and then levels off to a more uniform value. The sphericity increases, but less markedly than the roundness. A continuous diminution in average particle size is shown, which is relatively rapid at first and which slows as transportation continues.

The nature of the experimental curves and their underlying theory show that rounding occurs much more rapidly than size reduction due to abrasion. The much higher rate of rounding is accounted for by the fact that an angular particle increases its roundness significantly when very small corners and edges are abraded, whereas particle size is hardly changed by this small removal of material. Roundness increases rapidly as long as corners remain to be removed, but when these are gone, more surface area must be removed to increase roundness significantly.

Relative Importance of Particle Selection and Wear

Study of the size characteristics of many recent sediments shows that average particle size decreases downstream more rapidly than can be accounted for by abrasion alone. This suggests that selective transportation is more important in producing the observed changes than is abrasion. It is believed by some authorities that perhaps 90 percent of the observed changes in sedimentary deposits from source to final resting place are effected by selective transportation, and perhaps 10 percent by particle wear. Pettijohn (1957, Chapter 12) treats selection and abrasion in considerable detail, and the reader is referred to that source for additional data.

Fig. 6-8. Changes in sediment properties during stream abrasion. Compare with Figure 6-7, especially on average particle diameter.

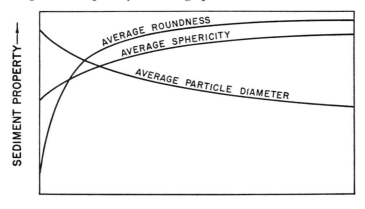

Sediment Maturity

The **maturity** of a clastic sediment is defined by Pettijohn (1957, p. 508) as the degree to which it "approaches the ultimate end product to which it is driven by the formative processes that operate upon it." Mature sandstone, for example, is well sorted, has highly rounded particles, and contains only stable mineral components. Such sand is the end product of a dispersal history that started initially from poorly sorted, weathered, crystalline rock debris with dominantly angular grains, and with an assortment of stable and unstable minerals.

Plumley (1948) applied the concept of maturity to stream gravel carried out of the Black Hills, and showed that in relatively short distances the stable components (quartz, quartzite, and chert) increased as the less stable components diminished. Hence, the percentage of the stable pebbles served as an index of maturity. In 1951 Folk developed a classification of four stages of textural maturity based on the removal of clay, the sorting of the non-clay portion, and the progressive rounding of grains, all related ultimately to the total input of energy by the operative agents.

The concept of sediment maturity has been widely applied to the interpretation of sandstones, and as mentioned in Chapter 5, is one basis for sandstone classification. The question whether first-cycle sands (that is, sands derived directly from a crystalline terrain) may become fully mature, or whether several stages of reworking are required has also been discussed. Potter and Pryor (1961) discuss this point in their study of dispersal centers of clastics in the Upper Mississippi valley.

DEPOSITION OF CLASTIC SEDIMENTS

The deposition of clastic sediments is controlled by the same laws as transportation. Average velocity, turbulence scale and intensity, combined with particle settling velocity, determine the movement of particles by suspension, saltation, or traction. The same factors, acting in an opposite sense, control deposition. Hjulstrom's diagram (Fig. 6-5) shows these intimate relations between transportation and deposition and emphasizes the interplay between particle-settling velocity and conditions of fluid flow in controlling the two processes.

The stratigrapher, in examining his sections, finds only the sediment deposited at each point, and has no direct data on the load which passed his point of observation. However, study of progressive changes in sediment properties over the depositional area affords many clues for reconstructing the essential elements of the story. Moreover, the physical similarity of the laws controlling transportation and deposition by all turbulent agents permits reasoning by analogy from one type of sediment to another.

Comparison of Wind and Water Deposition

It is instructive, in this connection, to compare the deposition of sand and dust by wind with deposition of sand and mud by shallow marine currents. Wind blowing across a dry floodplain may acquire a load of sand and dust. The sand moves mainly by saltation, and the dust is swept upward into suspension. The flow of sand is halted along valley edges by surface obstacles or by vegetation, but the higher suspension load of dust is swept past the surface obstructions. As the wind continues its movement, its velocity and turbulence normally decrease. Part of the suspended load settles out selectively, with the coarser silt particles near the source, and finer grained deposits down wind.

The resulting sedimentary pattern consists of sand dunes marginal to the floodplain, and a blanket of loess that extends for a number of miles down wind. The loess decreases systematically in thickness and particle size with distance from source. Figure 6-9 is a sketch map of these relations along the Illinois Valley in Illinois. The inset graphs indicate the observed changes in loess thickness and particle size along the line of sampling.

The same principles may be applied directly to transportation and deposition by currents in shallow seas. Sand and mud fed into currents from shore processes will be segregated into traction and suspension loads. The coarser sand in the traction load is confined mainly to more turbulent zones along the shore, whereas the suspension load of silt and clay may be carried for great distances seaward. The suspension load settles mainly in accordance with Stokes's Law, which means that viscosity is an important factor.

The viscosity of water is much greater than that of air, which explains why under similar conditions, mud will remain suspended in water much longer than dust in wind. Even with slow marine currents, mud may be carried great distances in shallow seas. It is believed that certain widespread shales, such as the Chattanooga, were deposited over large areas of shallow sea floor by slow circulating currents, in part associated with spreading of the sea itself. The wide extent of such muds or shales suggests that the sediment pattern shows a more gradual decrease in sediment thickness and particle size than corresponding wind deposits.

A factor of some importance in the deposition of fine clastic sediments is the effect of coagulation by dissolved ions in sea water. Clay particles in suspension in fresh water carry certain adsorbed ions which may be exchanged for others in a saline solution. This ionic exchange may result in

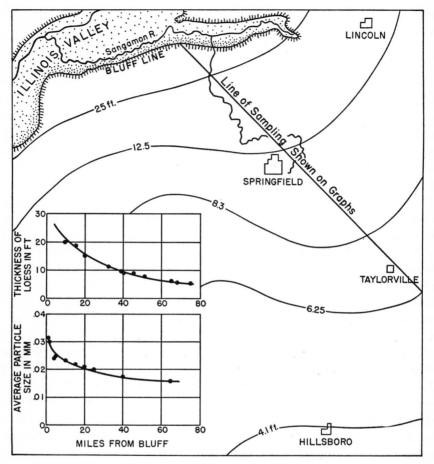

Fig. 6-9. Variation in thickness of Peorian loess southeastward from the Illinois River in central Illinois. The inset graphs show thickness and average particle size along the line of sampling. Map scale is about 17 miles per inch. [Data from Smith (1942).]

the clay particles forming aggregates that settle more rapidly than the individual clay flakes. As a result, the clay is deposited more rapidly than would normally occur if the particles settled individually.

The extent to which coagulation hastens the settling of clay in marine water is partly a function of the strength and direction of currents near shore. Although the clay aggregates settle faster than individual particles, the settling velocity is still much less than that of sand or silt grains. Hence, even coagulated clay aggregates may be carried for considerable distances from land.

Deposition of Sand and Gravel

In contrast with finer sediments, sand and gravel settle in accordance with the Impact Law, and, in general, require more turbulent conditions for transportation. High degrees of turbulence occur along shores or in stream channels. Ancient sandstones commonly occur in linear zones or lenses within beds of shale. The "shoestring sands" (Pennsylvanian) in eastern Oklahoma are examples. These suggest deposition in stream channels or along barrier beaches in zones of high turbulence associated with quieter conditions on either side. Bass (1936) describes the features in detail, and concludes they are old barrier beaches. The abundance of subsurface data available from oil and gas exploration during the past two decades has made possible much more detailed studies of the form and distribution of buried sand bodies. These are described in detail in Chapter 13, but some preliminary remarks are appropriate here. Siever (1951), for example, describes the sandstone channels along the Mississippian-Pennsylvanian unconformity in the Illinois Basin. Interest has also been focused on problems of distinguishing water-laid and eolian sand bodies from the study of surface and subsurface data. Shepard and Moore (1954), Bradley (1957), and Mason and Folk (1958) are pertinent.

All sandstones are not localized sand bodies, however. Widespread blankets of sandstone, such as the St. Peter (Ordovician) and the Tensleep (Pennsylvanian) cover large areas, and are relatively uniform in texture and thickness. To develop such widespread sheets of well sorted sand, it is necessary that turbulent conditions occur over the entire area of deposition. An unusually agitated sea would be required for such a sheet of sand to be formed simultaneously over a large area. It is more likely that these sandstones represent deposits formed progressively in the turbulent shore zone of encroaching seas. Eolian reworking of the sand probably also occurred. Keller (1945) and Dapples (1955) discuss the St. Peter sandstone in this context.

Turbidity Currents

Turbidity currents, also called density currents, are tongue-like masses of debris-charged water that flow downslope beneath clearer water by virtue of their greater density. Turbidity currents may be generated by discharge of a muddy stream into a body of standing water. The stream water, with its greater content of suspended material, flows downslope along the bottom without seriously disturbing the clear water above. Currents of this type were studied by Bell (1942) and Knapp (1943), who showed that this phenomenon may occur as underflows in lakes and reservoirs, as dust storms, as descending clouds of volcanic dust (*"nuees ardentes"*), and in other ways.

More recently, Kuenen and Migliorini (1950) showed experimentally that turbidity currents are capable of transporting large rock fragments by virtue of their high viscosity. Within the turbid current, a vertical gradient of particle sizes exists. For this reason, the deposits left by such currents commonly show graded bedding. Successive density currents, passing over previous deposits, may lay down additional graded beds without seriously disturbing the relatively fine upper surface of previous layers. Markings and other structures may occur, however, as noted under Sedimentary Structures in Chapter 4, resulting in the use of these associated structures as criteria for the recognition of turbidites. Kuenen (1953) describes the important features of graded bedding.

Many field studies undertaken during the past decade have shown that turbidity currents may be one of the most important mechanisms responsible for the deposition of graywacke in geosynclines. The currents are generated by slumping along slopes on which rapid sedimentation occurs. Slumping may be triggered by an earthquake shock, or may occur when semi-fluid deposits become unstable on inclined surfaces. Apparently the slope along which such currents move may be relatively gentle, and yet coarse clastics may be carried to bathyal or abyssal depths. Menard and Ludwick (1951) applied hydraulic theory to the study of turbidity currents, and Kuenen (1956) discusses differences between sliding and turbidity flow. Shepard (1961) points out that some deep water sand deposits associated with submarine canyons appear not to have been deposited by turbidity currents.

The general name **turbidites** has been applied to deposits left by turbidity currents. They have been widely identified in geosynclinal areas, and the suggested mechanism of transport provides a logical basis for explaining the poor degree of sorting, the "poured-in" appearance, and the associations of graywacke with other deep water sediments. Kuenen (1958) points out that such deposits seen along the axis of a geosyncline may be derived either from the sides or the ends of the subsiding area. Knill (1959) concluded that graywackes tend to be deposited by axially oriented turbidity currents during geosynclinal fill. He cites the lower Paleozoic geosyncline of Wales as having accumulations derived from both axial and lateral sources of supply, thus supporting Kuenen's argument.

Summary of Coarse Clastic Deposition

The growing body of evidence supporting the interpretation that some sandstone and shale sequences with intercalated conglomerate beds have been formed from turbidity currents, requires that the study of coarse clastic deposits be considered from two somewhat contrasting points of view.

The physical principles of transportation and deposition of coarse clastics by turbulent agents, described earlier, are well established. Such transportation represents, in large part, a relationship between the settling velocity of particles in quiet water and the upward and forward components of movement in the turbulent fluid. On the other hand, the occurrence of relatively coarse clastics bearing evidence of deposition in water too deep to have significant turbulence, requires recognition that coarse particles can be carried in suspension when the medium of transport is made relatively viscous by the presence of abundant suspended clay and silt. In the latter case, the characteristics of the resulting deposits are different from those transported and deposited by turbulent streams. These differences, already mentioned, include graded bedding, poor sorting, and associated turbidite structures on the one hand, in contrast to cross bedded and well sorted deposits on the other.

As a result of the two major mechanisms for transporting coarse clastic particles, the field geologist is faced with the need for careful and critical examination of numerous sedimentary features in order to infer correctly the origin of a given deposit. These features include composition, texture, and sedimentary structure, all or some of which may be determined by the modes of transport and deposition. That some deposits will be erroneously interpreted is to be expected when the balance of evidence is not completely clear. In this connection the reader is referred to Boswell's (1960) comments on the term graywacke, including both its descriptive characteristics and the genetic processes that are inferred to have occurred during its deposition.

Sedimentary By-passing

The laws of selective transportation show that some sedimentary particles may travel faster or farther than others, owing to size, shape, or density differences which favor continued movement. Eaton (1929) applied the term **by-passing** to instances where one particle passes another simultaneously transported, or continues in motion after the other has come to rest.

The normal decrease in average particle size of sediments away from source areas is a common example of by-passing. Evidently, the finer particles continued their movement after the coarser ones came to rest.

The term by-passing is also applied to circumstances in which coarser particles travel farther than fine particles. Evidence of such reverse by-passing is seen in coarse gravel found along the edge of the continental shelf, beyond areas of sand or finer sediment. In the subsurface, there is evidence that sand may sometimes by-pass mud toward the center of a depositional basin. Density currents may also be responsible for such occurrences.

Hjulstrom's diagram (Fig. 6-5) may aid in explaining some reverse by-passing phenomena. Mud deposited on a broad alluvial plain or tidal flat may become firm by cohesion or partial compaction relatively soon after deposition. A firm mud surface requires high velocities to initiate transportation of the particles. It is possible that sand could be moved slowly across the plain or tidal flat without seriously disturbing the surface.

Experimental verification of by-passing phenomena has been obtained in the laboratory (Straub, 1940). A mixture of sand and medium sized pebbles is introduced into a flume under fixed conditions of water velocity and turbulence. Critical adjustments made on the slope of the flume and on the upper surface of the moving sediment determine whether the pebbles outstrip the sand or lag behind. Control of the experimental conditions thus permits development of reversed size-gradients, in which the moving load shows an increase in average particle size in the direction of transport.

The hydrodynamic explanation of this phenomenon is not fully understood, but its occurrence is well established. Increasing evidence of reverse by-passing indicates that the required conditions may have existed on numerous occasions in the past. Recognition of reverse by-passing depends upon detailed study of surface and subsurface data to demonstrate that the coarser sediments traveled farther from the source than associated finer sediments.

Interpretation of Vector Properties of Sediments

The preceding sections on transportation and deposition of clastic particles are based mainly on particle behavior, as controlled by such scalar properties as particle size, shape, and density. From the study of these properties, it is possible in many instances to infer **provenance,** the **transporting agent,** and the **conditions of deposition** of the sediment. Of equal importance, the **specific directions of movement** can be inferred from vectorial properties of the rocks, as defined in Chapter 4. During the past decade increasing attention has been given to these properties, as methods of measurement have developed and as formal statistical analysis of the data has been applied.

Sandstone Cross-bedding. Cross bedding in sandstones is widely used as an indicator of the direction of transport. The dip-direction of current-generated cross bedding can be plotted on a map to show the prevailing movement of sand. Figure 6-10, from Potter and Olson (1954), represents one of the earliest large-scale projects of this sort that was based on the specific use of sampling design in obtaining and evaluating the data. The dip-direction arrows show the direction of movement at the moment of deposition, and indicate the regional slope of the depositional surface. Interpretation of such maps is facilitated by study of the heavy minerals in the sandstones, which

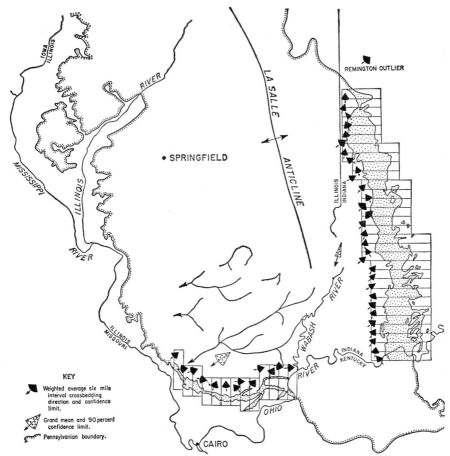

Fig. 6-10. Regional cross-bedding patterns in basal Pennsylvanian sandstones. The weighted average directions are based on tiers of townships in Indiana and on columns of ranges in Illinois. The La Salle Anticline and the subsurface channels on the Mississippian-Pennsylvanian unconformity are included to suggest regional slopes. [From Potter and Olson (1954). Copyright by the University of Chicago.]

are indicative of the ultimate source area. Thus, the basal sands of the Pennsylvanian, as shown in Figure 6-10, have been correctly interpreted by Potter and his co-workers as having been derived largely from the Appalachian area rather than wholly from the Canadian shield, as extrapolation of the cross-bedding arrows alone would imply. McKee (1957) and McKee and Sterrett (1961) have studied the forms of bedding and cross-bedding produced under given conditions in laboratory experiments.

Sand-grain Orientation. Significant advances have been made in the use of sand-grain orientation as a vectorial property indicative of the direction of transport. The use of grain orientation for this purpose depends ultimately on an understanding of the physical processes that control the orientation. Schwarzacher (1951) divided depositional conditions into three kinds, the first being sedimentation in a quiet liquid where gravity is the only active force. The second condition is sedimentation in flowing water, where both gravitational and current vectors are involved. The third condition is that in which deposition is followed immediately by sliding down a dip face. Rusnak (1957) concluded from his theoretical and experimental analysis of grain orientation that the long axes of sand grains tend to align themselves parallel to the direction of fluid flow, with the highest degree of orientation shown by elongate grains. Imbrication is in the upstream direction, and the angle of imbrication is larger during turbulent flow over a rough bottom surface than over a smooth bottom surface.

DEPOSITION OF NONCLASTIC SEDIMENTS

Introduction

The laws governing deposition of nonclastic sediments differ from those of clastic sediments. The detrital components of clastic rocks are carried mechanically to the depositional site, whereas the components of nonclastic sediments are formed by chemical or biological agencies from material in solution. Hence, for nonclastics, the physicochemical and biochemical conditions in the medium play a more important part than purely physical factors such as turbulence.

Fundamentally, the treatment of nonclastic sediments starts with normal sea water, which is the chemical medium in which the bulk of them are formed. Normal sea water contains a number of ions in various concentrations, as shown in Table 6-3. These ions, in appropriate combinations, are

TABLE 6-3. DISSOLVED IONS IN SEA WATER*

ION	PERCENT BY WEIGHT OF TOTAL SOLIDS	ION	PERCENT BY WEIGHT OF TOTAL SOLIDS
Chloride (Cl^-)	55.04	Magnesium (Mg^{++})	3.69
Bromide (Br^-)	0.19	Calcium (Ca^{++})	1.16
Sulfate ($SO_4^=$)	7.68	Strontium (Sr^{++})	0.04
Bicarbonate (HCO_3^-)	0.41	Potassium (K^+)	1.10
Boric acid (H_3BO_3)	0.07	Sodium (Na^+)	30.61

*The data in this table were taken from Lyman and Fleming (1940). Certain ions, present in trace amounts, are not included. Among these the phosphate ion (PO_4) is geologically important.

extracted from solution by biological or chemical changes, to form the corresponding chemical end members of the nonclastic rocks. The physics, chemistry, and biology of sea water are treated by Sverdrup, Johnson, and Fleming (1942).

Normal sea water may change its properties in response to geological controls. Restriction of sea water in a lagoon with excess of evaporation over inflow results in hypersaline solutions which precipitate combinations of ions suited to those special conditions. If restriction occurs in a humid climate, a different set of ions may provide combinations adjusted to stagnant conditions with high hydrogen sulphide concentration.

Figure 6-11 is a schematic diagram of several variations that may occur in sea water. Nonclastic sediments may be formed in each. With free circulation and no restrictions on currents, normal sediments of the open ocean are formed. Differences in depth, commonly associated with relative remoteness from clastic sources, produce some differences in the resulting sediments. Hence, shallow and deep conditions have been segregated in the figure.

Circulation may be restricted by barriers or other features that impede currents. As stated, chemical sediments formed under restricted conditions may differ markedly according to climatic conditions in the restricted area, as shown by the blocks in Figure 6-11 that separate humid from arid conditions.

Movement of fresh water into marine bays or lagoons develops brackish conditions, with reduced concentration of dissolved salts. Brackishness covers a wide range of concentration and, theoretically, extends from nearly normal sea water to essentially fresh water. Consequently, a number of sedimentary types may be formed, especially if the entire range from one extreme to the other is considered.

Each bracket in the diagram includes certain ions important in nonclastic sedimentation. The ions shown are not always the most abundant, however. Normal sea water contains only traces of phosphate ion, but this is important to organisms which produce limestone. Other ions, such as bromide, though present in measurable quantity, occur only in special sediments, and are not considered in this treatment.

Chemical Controls on Nonclastic Deposition

The chemical end members that form under given depositional conditions are controlled in large part by the acidity or alkalinity (**hydrogen ion concentration,** *p*H) of the medium, and by the oxidizing or reducing qualities (**oxidation-reduction potential, Eh**) of the medium. The *p*H scale extends from 0 to 14. Neutrality is 7 on the scale; smaller numbers indicate increasing acidity, and larger numbers indicate increasing alkalinity. The Eh is

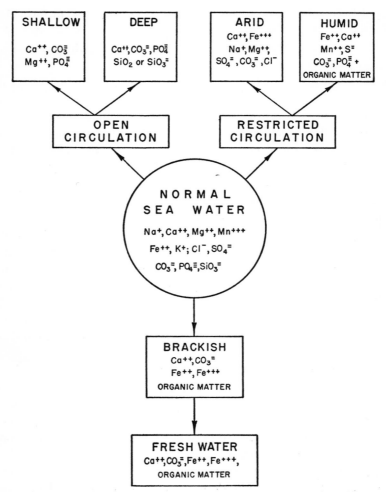

Fig. 6-11. Diagram showing ions important in nonclastic sedimentation for varying conditions of concentration and circulation.

positive under oxidizing conditions, and negative under reducing conditions.

In terms of Figure 6-11, normal sea water under open circulation conditions has a pH between 7.5 and 8 and a small positive Eh, indicating the presence of slightly alkaline and mildly oxidizing conditions. When circulation becomes restricted under arid conditions, the pH tends to increase, although generally the evaporating medium remains mildly oxidizing. Under humid restriction the pH may decrease to 7 or even less in the bottom waters. Similarly, the Eh tends to become negative in the bottom waters, due largely to lack of oxygenation.

Figure 6-12 is a schematic diagram showing the Eh–pH regions under

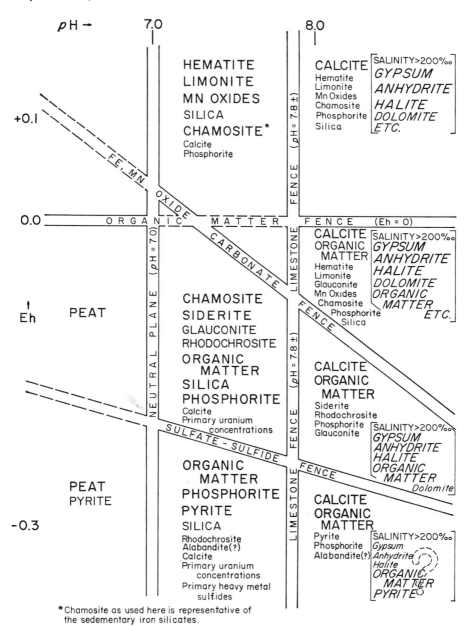

*Chamosite as used here is representative of
the sedementary iron silicates.

Fig. 6-12. Fence diagrams showing relations of chemical sediments to Eh and
pH controls for normal sea-water conditions. Associations in brackets
refer to hypersaline solutions. [Adapted from Krumbein and Garrels
(1952). Copyright by the University of Chicago.]

which some chemical end members of nonclastic sediments are formed. The "Limestone Fence" at $pH = 7.8$ separates a region to the right in which abundant calcite may form, from one on the left where conditions are less favorable for calcite formation. The limestone fence is independent of Eh, as shown by its vertical position. The "Organic Matter Fence" at Eh = 0, separates a region above, in which oxidizing conditions prevail, from one below, with negative Eh. Organic matter, in general, can be preserved most effectively under negative Eh conditions. The "Iron Oxide-Carbonate Fence" separates regions in which the conditions favor hematite and limonite formation from regions in which siderite is the dominant iron-oxide formed. This fence slants, indicating that this boundary is sensitive to both Eh and pH. The region below the "Sulfate-Sulfide Fence" represents conditions under which abundant pyrite may form. This fence is also sensitive to Eh and pH.

Recognition of the conditions that favor the occurrence of specific chemical end members provides a basis for the interpretation of the conditions under which ancient nonclastic sediments may have formed. Such reconstruction is complicated in part by postdepositional changes, which are treated in the next chapter.

Chemical Sedimentation in Open and Restricted Circulation Conditions

The material presented in Figures 6-10 and 6-11 can be used as a framework for discussing the conditions under which nonclastic (chemical) sediments are formed. The following treatment uses the main subdivisions of Figure 6-11 as its framework, and relates the conditions of circulation to the chemical controls operative in terms of Figure 6-12.

Free Circulation (Open Ocean). A wide range of sedimentary conditions exists in the open ocean, extending from those under which purely clastic deposition along beaches occurs to those under which fine mud and siliceous ooze of the deep sea are formed. Two typical situations are selected for discussion because of their importance in forming ancient, nonclastic sediments. These are shallow, open waters, as typified by wide epicontinental seas of the past; and deep conditions, characteristic of present ocean deeps and some phases of geosynclinal deposition. Only the nonclastic components are treated in detail, although, in nature, various combinations of detrital and chemical end members occur. These are mentioned where appropriate.

Shallow Water. Shallow water includes depths to about 600 feet below sea level. Shallow water with free circulation is characterized by adequate mixing and current movement to maintain proper oxygenation of the water for the development of floating, swimming, and bottom-dwelling organisms.

Limestones of Biological Origin. Several processes of nonclastic deposition may occur. Organisms extract calcium carbonate from the sea water to form shells and tests. Important lime-secreting organisms include foramini-fera, brachiopods, corals, bryozoa, and algae. The shells of bottom-dwelling forms may accumulate rapidly in areas where life is prolific. Crinoids have been so abundant locally that their columnals form thick accumulations of limestone.

If accumulation occurs in sufficiently shallow water, the shell fragments may be swept about by currents and partially abraded before coming to final rest. The resulting limestones are the fossiliferous-fragmental varieties mentioned in Chapter 5. In places such shell-fragment limestones accumu-late as extensive shoals or banks; these are the carbonate banks treated in greater detail in Chapter 13.

Where sediment-binding organisms (such as certain bottom-dwelling calcareous algae) are present, shells, tests, and fragments are bound to-gether in rigid, wave-resistant masses (the biolithites noted in Chapter 5) which may grow to significant size as biostromes and reefs, as discussed further in Chapter 13. Floating algae and certain bacteria also contribute to the precipitation of calcium carbonate through biochemical action near the surface of the sea. The precipitated material accumulates on quiet bot-toms as a fine carbonate mud, which later recrystallizes to form micrite limestone.

The chemistry of calcium carbonate precipitation in sea water through organic agencies and through the inorganic reactions touched upon below is developed in some detail by Revelle and Fairbridge (1957).

Limestones of Inorganic Origin. Calcium carbonate may be precipitated from sea water by inorganic chemical processes. Changes in atmospheric partial pressures of carbon dioxide produce corresponding changes in carbon dioxide solubility. Because of these relations, there is a direct connection be-tween atmospheric carbon dioxide and the amount of dissolved calcium ion in sea water.

If the carbon dioxide dissolved in sea water decreases, some bicarbonate ions change to carbonate, thereby causing precipitation of calcium carbon-ate. The precipitate forms a fine, crystalline cloud which settles to the bottom.

Observations show that surface water in some warmer parts of the ocean is saturated with calcium carbonate. This suggests that, at present, the warmer seas are potentially large limestone accumulators. That similar con-ditions may have existed in the past is attested by numerous limestones having relatively dense crystalline texture and a paucity of fossils. The pos-sibility that such limestones were formed by bacteria or obscure, lime-secret-ing algae must also be entertained, however.

Oolites may be formed in shallow parts of the open sea, where wave or current action is sufficient to agitate the bottom. Calcite is precipitated around sand grains or fossil fragments as nuclei. The widespread extent of some oolitic limestones (such as the Smackover of Jurassic age in Arkansas and Louisiana) suggests that oolites can form in shallow seas with free circulation.

Summary of Ions Extracted. The composition of limestone formed in shallow seas with open circulation indicates that the principal ions extracted from sea water by the processes enumerated are calcium, magnesium, carbonate, and phosphate. Although neither magnesium nor phosphate is abundant in typical calcitic limestone, measurable amounts of these components are usually present. Most invertebrate shells contain some calcium phosphate.

Deep Water. Sediments now accumulating in the deeper parts of the oceans are mainly red-clay deposits and oozes. The oozes constitute the organically formed sediments. Oozes are divided into calcareous ooze (*Globigerina* and pteropod ooze), and siliceous ooze (diatom and radiolarian ooze).

In a general way, calcareous ooze is typical of depths under 12,000 feet, whereas siliceous ooze occurs at greater depths. Both types of deposit are formed from floating organisms, but the stability of calcite and silica differs at depth. In the cold waters of the oceanic deeps, calcite is more soluble than at lesser depths, in part accounting for re-solution of such calcareous tests as may settle toward the bottom.

Absence of light penetration to great depths and other factors inhibit growth of bottom-dwelling forms. As a result, the sediments consist almost exclusively of tests from the surface zones, plus such fine dust as may be blown to sea.

Deposits in some ancient geosynclines suggest deposition under deep-water conditions. Highly siliceous sediments, including bedded chert, thin siliceous limestone, and dark siliceous shale, appear to be typical. During times of high detrital inflow, the deposits may be largely dominated by turbidites as discussed earlier.

The origin of bedded chert has been much discussed in the geologic literature. Though a deep-water origin is favored by some writers, the placement of silica in Figure 6-12 in terms of the several "fences" suggests that the formation of primary chert is controlled by the physicochemical conditions of the environment, whether the water be shallow or deep. In any event, the ions most affected by deep-water conditions are silica (or silicates), calcium, and, to a lesser degree, carbonate.

Restricted Circulation. A number of geologic factors may cause isolation of parts of the sea, developing enclosed lagoons, barred basins, relict seas, or other features in which free access to the open ocean is restricted. The restrictions may be due to biological, physiographic, or tectonic controls. Rings of reefs may form along the edges of subsiding basins, producing enclosed lagoons separated from the sea except for narrow inlets. Barrier beaches, developed along coasts with small tidal range, may also develop restricted lagoons. Arms of the open sea, slightly deeper than fronting offshore waters, may be left behind as relict seas during regression of the strand line.

Whatever the cause for restriction, two broad sets of conditions may result. If the climate is arid, evaporation exceeds inflow, and the water becomes hypersaline. If the climate is humid, the restricted sea may retain its volume, but stagnate.

Restriction in Arid Climates. Under conditions of aridity, the restricted sea has adjacent lands with little or no stream action other than torrential episodes which may occasionally wash in detrital material. The sea may attain high temperatures, with excessive evaporation, and development of salinity greater than that of the open ocean. Excessive evaporation produces a lowering of water level, and induces a permanent inflowing current of normal sea water across, or through, the restricting barriers.

The Gulf of Karabugas, along the east coast of the Caspian Sea, affords a case in point. The shallow water of the gulf is subject to rapid evaporation in the arid climate. As a result, the water level is lowered below the level of the sea, and a permanent inflow current from the Caspian passes through the narrow inlet which connects gulf and sea.

If it were not for the continued inflow current, the history of restricted seas in arid climates would be short. The water would completely evaporate, leaving behind a relatively thin coating of saline residue. Maintenance of inflow from the open sea provides a continuous supply of dissolved salts, and a balance is reached between evaporation and inflow for given conditions. Inevitably, the concentration of salts within the restricted area is increased and may reach the saturation point for some. Emery (1956) and Morris and Dickey (1957) describe present-day evaporite environments in the Persian Gulf and in Peru, respectively.

Precipitation of Evaporites. The sequence of salts deposited from sea water is a complex response to physicochemical relations involving temperature, pressure, relative solubilities, and other factors. Laboratory experiments on the evaporation of sea water show that when the volume is reduced by approximately half, calcium carbonate is precipitated, along with a trace of iron and aluminum hydroxide. When the volume is reduced to about one-fifth, calcium sulfate is formed and continues to precipitate as the volume is further reduced. Sodium chloride, accompanied by magnesium sulfate and magnesium chloride, appears when the original volume is reduced to about one-tenth. Clarke (1924, p. 220) gives the sequence in detail.

Lithological associations of evaporites and a brief review of earlier literature on the origin of evaporites is summarized by Krumbein (1951). In 1953 Scruton considered the subject from the viewpoint of the physicochemical processes active during the formation of evaporites, and some of his conclusions are summarized here. Large restricted basins remote from the open sea appear to be most satisfactory for evaporite formation. Circulation in depositional basins is similar to that in estuaries, producing a continuous inflowing surface current that is in part counterbalanced by an outgoing underflow of concentrated brine. The restrictions preventing escape of the deep brine may be physical barriers, or may be a result of the interrelations of pressure, as well as friction, developed between currents flowing in opposite directions. A horizontal salinity gradient develops, with the salinity increasing from the point of entrance to the head of the evaporating area. From knowledge of this gradient, an approximate prediction can be made regarding the vertical sequence of evaporites formed in the basin.

Briggs (1958) extended Scruton's analysis to the Salina Formation of the Michigan Basin. He set up hypothetical conditions in a model evaporating basin and developed a pattern of idealized evaporite deposition with its associated carbonate rocks. Briggs developed the paleogeographic map of Figure 6-13 by comparing the idealized relations with the observed occurrences of evaporites and carbonates in the Michigan Basin and adjoining areas. These observed relations permitted inference of the circulation pattern in the seas during times of high salinity, as shown by the arrows in Figure 6-13. Brigg's model basin is treated in Chapter 13, along with further discussion of evaporite associations.

Natural evaporites occur under a variety of conditions, which are described more fully in Chapter 13. Sometimes the deposits are cyclical; in other instances, detrital sand or mud may be washed into an otherwise wholly chemical sequence. Oolites are common in some evaporite associations, and the formation of oolites seems to be favored by agitation of concentrated solutions. The precipitated evaporites may be reworked by waves and currents, segregating certain sizes or compositional classes and moving them toward the basin center, where abnormally thick deposits of a single evaporite may accumulate. Cyclical aspects of evaporites are discussed by Sloss (1953).

Biological factors may be of minor importance in contributing to the formation of evaporites. In some instances, organisms are swept into the restricted seas by the inflowing current, but the high salinity normally

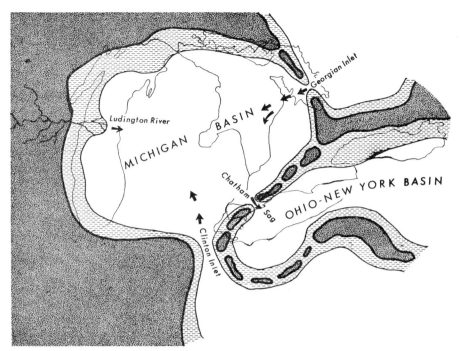

Fig. 6-13. Paleogeographic map of Michigan Basin and Ohio-New York Basin during Salina (Upper Silurian) time, showing inferred patterns of circulation.

destroys them. The faunas found in evaporites are typically depauperate, or aberrant, and mainly include forms with a high tolerance for saline conditions.

Summary of Ions Extracted. In the purely inorganic processes that predominate during evaporation, the principal ions extracted from sea water are calcium, magnesium, sodium, ferric iron and carbonate, sulfate, and chloride. True evaporitic limestone is more commonly dolomitic than calcitic, and the calcium sulfate commonly forms anhydrite rather than gypsum. Water temperature has an influence on the form assumed by the calcium sulfate, with anhydrite appearing when brine temperature exceeds 30° C.

Evaporites formed from sea water differ from **saline residues** left behind as lakes evaporate. Lake deposits more commonly include sodium sulfate than gypsum, although halite also occurs.

Restriction in Humid Climates. In humid climates, the reduction in volume associated with excess evaporation does not normally occur. Instead, varying degrees of stagnation of the bottom waters may ensue, depending upon the extent to which circulation is impeded.

Stagnant conditions in the Black Sea and in some Norwegian fiords have been studied (Fleming and Revelle, 1939). In both instances, relatively deep bodies of water are isolated from sea by barriers that are mainly submerged rock sills. The surface waters are normally oxygenated and support floating and swimming organisms. At depth, however, oxygen is deficient, and sulfate-reducing bacteria develop hydrogen sulfide, which may completely inhibit bottom-dwelling organisms.

The organisms in the surface waters contribute organic matter and tests to the bottom, but the absence of a bottom fauna, with its inevitable scavengers, preserves the organic matter as an integral part of the accumulating sediment. The presence of hydrogen sulfide causes precipitation of ferrous sulfide, which blackens the organic-rich accumulations.

Bottom-dwelling organisms in humid restricted environments may range from essentially none to nearly normal faunas. The more tolerant species persist in all except extreme conditions, but they show numerous adaptations. The forms may become depauperate, developing an aberrant fauna consisting of phosphatic brachiopods, annelid worms, and some cephalopods. Calcium carbonate, in the form of shells and tests, may be added to the accumulating sediments by the organisms.

Some of the conditions associated with humid restriction are shown on the chart of Figure 6-12, below the "organic-matter fence," with a wide range in pH. Table 6-4, from Krumbein and Garrels (1952), illustrates one manner in which these conditions may be summarized. The original reference has similar tables for normal marine open-circulation conditions and for arid restrictions.

Bituminous Shale. Some black bituminous shale shows evidence of deposition under stagnant conditions. It is believed that prolific growth of kelplike algae, such as occurs locally at present, may have inhibited circulation near the bottom of some ancient shallow seas.

Life processes of the algae flourish at the surface, but the intertwined fronds below may essentially stagnate the bottom waters. Dead algal fronds, settling to the bottom with other contributions from floating organisms, accumulate as a rich organic mud. Restriction of bottom faunas and development of sulfate-reducing bacteria permit preservation of the organic material.

Some Pennsylvanian black fissile shales of the midcontinent definitely appear to have been formed under such restricted conditions. The fossils are much flattened, suggesting compaction of the colloidal mud with development of paper-thin laminae in the shale.

Calcium carbonate may be a common accompaniment of sediments formed in partially stagnant conditions. The limestone is commonly dense and dark

TABLE 6-4. THE RESTRICTED HUMID (EUXINIC) ENVIRONMENT
[Adapted from Table 2, Krumbein and Garrels, 1952.]

ITEM	AVERAGE VALUE	REMARKS
Temperature	Surface: 16° C. Bottom: 6° C.	Values apply to Norwegian fiords; higher values in tropical basins
Pressure	Surface: 1 atm	Pressure increases 1 atm for each 30 feet of depth
Salinity	Surface: 19 parts per thousand Bottom: 30 parts per thousand	Probably a wide variation from near-fresh water at surface to normal salinity at depth
Ions in Solution	Relative proportions may remain as in normal sea water, except that phosphate ion is unusually high (0.3 mg/liter in fiords); and there may be conversion of sulfate to sulfide	
Dissolved gases	Oxygen: surface, 6 ml/l; bottom, nil	
	Carbon dioxide: surface, 46 ml/l	Some increase in CO_2 toward bottom
	Hydrogen sulfide: surface, nil; bottom, 9.14 ml/l	Maximum H_2S observed in fiords is 40 ml/l
Hydrogen-ion concentration	Surface: 8.0 Bottom: ±7.0	When the pH exceeds 7.8, as it may in some instances, calcareous deposits can form.
Oxidation-reduction potential, Eh	Surface: +0.1 Bottom: −0.3	

colored, with bituminous matter or phosphate present in variable amount. Associations of black shale and dark limestone, as in the Bone Spring (Permian) of west Texas, are called **pontic sediments** (Lloyd, 1929), or **euxinic sediments,** and imply stagnation of the waters during deposition.

As with evaporation in arid climates, many interruptions and changes may occur in the degree of stagnation under humid conditions. Recurrent freshening of the water may occur, depending upon the magnitude of the barrier and the depth of the restricted sea. As a result, euxinic associations may occur interbedded with normal marine deposits. Under some conditions black shale may be associated with evaporites, as in the Paradox formation (Pennsylvanian) of eastern Utah.

Formation of Phosphatic Sediments. The Phosphoria formation (Permian) of western Wyoming and eastern Idaho has numerous characteristics which relate it to restricted conditions of deposition. The limestone is phosphatic and is associated with black phosphatic shale and dark chert. The phosphate is believed to have been derived, in part, from resorbed shells or other hard parts of organisms, and occurs as coatings on fossil teeth, in oolites, and as earthy phosphorite. Common association of pyrite with the sediments also implies deposition of ferrous sulfide, later modified to pyrite.

Starved Basins. The concept of a starved basin was introduced by Adams and co-workers (1951) to account for thin euxinic deposits within subsiding basins surrounded by abundant reefs. Pennsylvanian strata in the Midland Basin of Texas show an abrupt thinning basinward with change from dominant limestone to dominant dark shale. The implication is that within the barrier of reefs the water in the subsiding basin stagnated, and without abundant inflow of detrital materials, developed only thin black shales in water that deepened as subsidence progressed.

Summary of Ions Extracted. The principal attributes of sediments formed in humid restricted areas are their dark color, their high organic content of bituminous material, the common association of pyrite, and their generally depauperate faunas. Practically all nonclastic sedimentation is the result of biological or biochemical processes, with preservation of soft organic material by the anaerobic conditions.

In terms of the principal ions extracted from sea water in these depositional processes, it is evident that the precipitation of calcium, ferrous iron, and sulfide, carbonate, and phosphate is favored.

Brackish and Fresh-water Conditions. In estuaries and on deltas, as well as in lagoons behind barrier beaches, the influx of fresh water from streams may dilute normal sea water to varying degrees. Such intermediate stages of salinity are called **brackish.**

Brackish conditions may be associated with partial stagnation in isolated areas where influx of fresh water exceeds or attains a balance with inflow of marine water. Partial stagnation is common in some tidal lagoons behind barrier beaches, but the association of brackishness with partial stagnation is not invariable.

In brackish conditions without stagnation, the organisms are adjusted to the lower salinity by the inhibition of less tolerant forms, and by a marked expansion in brachiopods, annelid worms, crabs, and other tolerant types. These are also able to withstand the higher turbidity associated with mud carried to the brackish areas by streams in flood. With restricted circulation, the forms are further reduced to a depauperate fauna, adjusted both to low salinity and stagnation.

The deposits formed under brackish conditions include mainly poorly sorted sands, dark humic or bituminous shale, and fossiliferous limestone with high argillaceous matrix. The recognition of brackish deposits among ancient sediments depends largely upon fossil content and associated rocks. The nonclastic end members include calcium, ferrous and ferric iron, carbonate, sulfide, and organic matter.

Nonclastic, fresh-water deposits are confined to lakes, ponds, swamps, and bogs. Marl, ranging in composition from relatively pure calcium carbonate to mixtures with mud and organic matter, are formed by biochemical processes. Iron oxide, mainly limonite, is formed in some fresh-water lakes, perhaps, in part, through bacterial action. Organic matter preserved in lakes may be humic or bituminous. Organic matter in swamps is most commonly humic, giving rise to peat and coal.

The ions favored in fresh-water, nonclastic deposition are calcium, ferric iron, and carbonate. The most important organic end member is coal (peat).

Summary of Nonclastic Deposition

Optimum conditions for the formation of nonclastic end-member sediments fall into two main groups. The first includes those conditions in which organisms may make their maximum contributions to the accumulating sediments. These conditions in general, include shallow marine water, open circulation, and an absence of land-derived detritus. In terms of Eh and *p*H, the conditions include **abundant oxygenation** and **mild alkalinity.**

The second set of optimum conditions for the formation of chemical end-member sediments includes the restrictions on circulation that give rise, in the main, to chemically controlled processes of deposition. In terms of Eh and *p*H, these conditions include varying degrees of stagnation due to **lack of oxygen,** and may include **mild to strong acidity.** The two main kinds of sediments formed under restricted conditions are evaporites and euxinic sediments. For such dominantly chemical processes of sedimentation, the influx of coarse detrital material acts mainly as a diluent, without affecting the nature of the chemically formed deposits. Influx of fine material, such as clay, may result in some modifications, owing to the adsoptive and other surface properties of the clay minerals.

PROCESS AND RESPONSE IN SEDIMENTARY TRANSPORTATION AND DEPOSITION

The discussion of transportation and deposition of clastic sediments, and of the formation of nonclastic sediments, has centered mainly around present-day processes that can be studied in the field and laboratory. In these circumstances it is possible to relate the properties of the sediment to the specific operative agents. That is, the sedimentary **responses** can be functionally related to the geological **processes** that control them. In stratigraphic studies of ancient rocks the formative agents have long since vanished, and only the response elements are left. Emphasis must thus be placed on studies of rock texture, structure, and areal distribution of properties (the **dispersal patterns**) as a guide to identification of the particular process elements responsible for the observed rock attributes.

Though some stratigraphic units consist of a single rock type formed under essentially fixed conditions, more commonly the units represent a composite response to a number of controls. The study of this complex of interacting elements—the environment of sedimentation—forms the material of the next chapter.

SUPPLEMENTARY READINGS

The description of sedimentary processes of transportation and deposition has moved increasingly toward explicit application of physical and geochemical principles in their analysis. Much of this material has not yet been assembled and integrated into text or reference works. Garrels's book, cited below, is an excellent example of the application of geochemical theory to interpreting the conditions of formation of chemical sediments.

1. Pettijohn, F. J., 1957, Sedimentary rocks: New York, Harper & Brothers.

   Dispersal of sediments: Chapter 12.

2. Twenhofel, W. H., 1950, Principles of sedimentation: New York, McGraw-Hill Book Co., Inc.

   Origin of inorganic sediments: Chapter 4.
   Organisms and sediments: Chapter 5.
   Transportation and deposition of sediments: Chapter 6.

3. Weller, J. M., 1960, Stratigraphic principles and practice: New York, Harper & Brothers.

   Physiography of sediments: Chapter 6.

4. Dunbar, C. O. and Rodgers, J., 1957, Principles of stratigraphy: New York, John Wiley & Sons, Inc.

   Sedimentary processes: Chapter 1.

5. Sverdrup, H. U., Johnson, M. W., and Fleming, R. H., 1942, The oceans: New York, Prentice-Hall, Inc.

   Chemistry of sea water: Chapter 6.
   Marine sedimentation: Chapter 20.

6. Garrels, R. M., 1960, Mineral equilibria: New York, Harper & Brothers.

   Carbonate equilibria: Chapter 3.
   Eh-pH Diagrams, Chapter 6.
   Some geological applications of Eh-pH diagrams: Chapter 7.

7. Grim, R. E., 1953, Clay mineralogy: New York, McGraw-Hill Book Company, Inc. This important reference work provides basic information on this group of sedimentary minerals.

   Old and new clay-mineral concepts: Chapter 2.
   Classification and nomenclature of the clay minerals: Chapter 3.

8. Keller, W. D., 1955, The principles of chemical weathering: Lucas Brothers, Columbia, Missouri. A readable introduction to those principles of chemistry that are important in understanding geochemical aspects of geology.

9. Reiche, P., 1950, A survey of weathering processes and products: University of New Mexico Publications in Geology, No. 3, Albuquerque. An excellent summary of some aspects of weathering and soils important in geology.

10. Scheidegger, A. E., 1961, Theoretical geomorphology: Englewood Cliffs, Prentice-Hall, Inc. An advanced reference book on gradational processes treated from a mathematical point of view. Stream, wind, and shore processes are discussed in detail in terms of the relations between processes and land forms.

CHAPTER 7

Sedimentary Environments

INTRODUCTION

THE **sedimentary environment** is the complex of physical, chemical, and biological conditions under which a sediment accumulates. This complex largely determines the properties of sediments deposited within the environment.

The general processes which control sedimentation were described in the preceding chapter. These processes operate within a framework controlled by the physiographic setting of the environment, by relations of land and sea, and by the action of dominant geologic agents, such as streams, wind, waves, or currents.

Sedimentary environments vary widely in their persistence through time, in the size of the area occupied by them, and in the uniformity or variability of their conditions. A shallowly submerged continental shelf may be of wide extent and display relatively uniform conditions of sedimentation for long intervals of time. An ox-bow lake on a floodplain, on the other hand, may be small and ephemeral, changing to a bog within the span of a few years.

Geographic variation in an environment is illustrated by a sea coast with waves breaking on the beach, currents in the shallow water, and quiet conditions offshore. There is a systematic decrease in mechanical energy seaward, shown by a seaward decrease in turbulence and rate of sediment movement. The high degree of turbulence in the zone of breaking waves exerts a marked selective action on particles. Fine material is winnowed out, leaving predominantly coarse deposits behind. The finer material accumulates on a bottom occupied by organisms living under quieter offshore conditions, forming calcareous mud or argillaceous lime mud with abundant organic remains.

In some instances, a single factor may dominate the environment, but more commonly a combination of factors determines its gross characteristics. Breaking waves may control physical conditions of sedimentation in the beach zone, but in quiet water, temperature, salinity, and the nature of the bottom organisms may be the controlling factors.

234

IMPORTANCE OF SEDIMENTARY ENVIRONMENTS IN STRATIGRAPHY

The sedimentary environment sets the pattern of sediment deposition. In the study of ancient sedimentary rocks, the environment must be inferred from the rocks themselves. An important part of stratigraphic analysis is the reconstruction of ancient environments.

Understanding of the sedimentary environment bears strongly on problems of correlation. As later chapters will show, the fossil assemblages in rocks have climatic and environmental implications. A given stratigraphic unit, when followed from terrestrial desert deposits through restricted lagoonal evaporite sequences to normal marine deposits, may show marked changes in the fossil fauna. To demonstrate the equivalency of the several deposits requires close analysis of the environmental significance of the rocks.

The study of stratigraphic units for oil exploration is facilitated by an understanding of the sedimentary environment. Suitable environmental conditions for the occurrence of source and reservoir beds, and the inter-tonguing or gradational relations of the deposits, may be very important in control of migration and localization of oil. Abrupt lateral changes from sand to shale develop sharp changes in permeability that may trap oil on suitable structures, whereas a gradual lateral change from sand to shale carries with it a gradual permeability change much less effective for strati-graphic trapping of oil.

SEDIMENTARY PROCESSES AND THEIR PRODUCTS

Although the stratigrapher is concerned with the reconstruction of ancient environments, he must be familiar with sedimentary processes and their associated deposits as they occur in present day environments, in order to make reliable interpretations regarding the environments of ancient sedimentary deposits.

The study of present-day sedimentary environments includes consideration of at least two major topics. The first concerns the physical, chemical, and biological **processes** that take place in the environment, and the second is related to the kinds of sedimentary **deposits** being formed. The sedimentary deposits, in turn, have two main attributes. The first of these is concerned with the volume, shape, and areal extent of the resulting body of sediment, and the second with the composition, texture, and structure of the sedimentry deposit, including areal variations in these attributes.

In many studies of present-day environments, the emphasis has been placed on the texture and composition of the sediments being formed, rather than on the processes that form them. Although textural and mineralogical analysis of the sediments sheds much light on the specific kinds of deposits associated with given environments, such analyses may yield only a qualitative understanding of the relations between the sediments and the physical, chemical, or biological processes that shape the deposits and control their attributes. It has long been recognized by many geologists that the environmental processes and their products must be studied simultaneously in order to understand the relations between specific sedimentary properties and the processes that control them.

Only within the relatively recent past, however, has it been possible to measure accurately the many physical and chemical factors operating within environments. Because of the great variety of processes and deposits that occur in nature, it is desirable to organize their systematic study into a framework of reference that contains their essential features. The concept of a **sedimentary environment model** provides such a framework.

In this chapter, sedimentary environments are discussed in terms of a generalized model based on geological processes operative in the environment and on the sedimentary products that arise from these processes. In later chapters, the model concept will be extended to tectonic factors and to other controls on the overall attributes of sedimentary rock masses.

ELEMENTS AND FACTORS OF THE ENVIRONMENT

In any sedimentary environment, the sediment is derived from some source, it is carried from the source to the point of deposition by some agent, and the agent is energized in some manner. During the process, erosional land forms are developed in the source area, and depositional land forms and sedimentary deposits are formed in the sedimentary environment. Under suitable conditions, organisms in the environment may greatly affect the accumulating sediments.

The Sedimentary Environment Model

The environmental concept as expressed above can be formalized into a generalized sedimentary environmental model in any of several ways. In terms of the closing remarks in Chapter 6, a **process-response model** can be set up that shows the relations between the attributes of the environment and the corresponding attributes of the sediments being formed. Table 7-1 is a schematic arrangement of such a model. On the left are the **geometry** of the environment (its shape), the **materials** available (nature of the materials being transported), the **energy** sources (for example, breaking waves), and any **biological elements** that may be present (such as bottom-dwelling fauna). On the right are the **geometry** of the resulting deposits (sheet, lens), their **composition** (texture, mineralogy), and the **areal variations** in the deposits formed within the environment. Under each of these headings on both sides are entered the processes and responses appropriate to any particular environment. A specific illustration, and discussion of alternative ways of expressing the model, are given later in this chapter.

The process side of the model in Table 7-1 implies that the study of any sedimentary environment includes consideration of the four basic **environmental elements** listed. Of these, the geometry also represents the **boundary conditions** of the environment, in the sense that the geometry may influence the distribution of energy over the environment, as in shallow water, where wave-generated currents may be active, as against deeper water, where such currents are of less importance. As used throughout this chapter, the boundary conditions may be thought of as being essentially synonymous with the geometry. The term **environmental factor** as used here refers to any specific aspect of an environmental element. For later reference the elements and factors are summarized below.

Boundary Conditions. The boundary conditions of the environment include the geometrical features of the environment, such as depth of water, shape of a bay, configuration of the depositional surface, and others. The boundary conditions set the geologic or physiographic framework of the environment.

Material. The materials of the environment include the medium of sedimentation (air, fresh water, sea water, glacial ice) and the texture and composition of material in transit or being deposited. Sea water contains dissolved salts and gases, which are included among environmental factors. As stated above, the term geometry of the environment is essentially synonymous with the boundary conditions.

Energy. The energy of the system includes such diverse factors as the kinetic energy of wind, the turbulent energy of waves and currents, or the thermal energy in a body of sea water. Part of the available energy may not be utilized, such as the energy of waves passing over a deep-water environ-

TABLE 7-1. A GENERALIZED SEDIMENTARY ENVIRONMENT PROCESS-RESPONSE MODEL

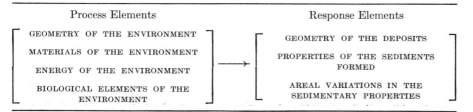

Process Elements	Response Elements
GEOMETRY OF THE ENVIRONMENT MATERIALS OF THE ENVIRONMENT ENERGY OF THE ENVIRONMENT BIOLOGICAL ELEMENTS OF THE ENVIRONMENT	GEOMETRY OF THE DEPOSITS PROPERTIES OF THE SEDIMENTS FORMED AREAL VARIATIONS IN THE SEDIMENTARY PROPERTIES

ment. If the bottom is not disturbed, the net effect of the wave energy on the sediment may be negligible. It is the energy which acts upon the material, or is dissipated in the environment by friction or other factors, that is important in sedimentation.

Biological Features. The fourth element of the sedimentary environment is the biological complex. In some environments, organisms are the principal agents of sediment accumulation. Coal, coquina, and crinoidal limestone are examples. In clastic sedimentation, the biological agents have a varying effect by their addition of nonclastic end members. Humic materials are contributed to clastic sediments by woody plants, and bituminous matter may be contributed by animals of algae.

Organisms also affect sediments in other ways. Burrowing animals and scavengers rework the deposited material and may destroy bedding or other depositional features.

Relations Among Elements and Factors

The relative influence of environmental elements varies with the nature of the environment. Similarly, the factors in any element vary in their importance within different environments.

In discussing the general relations of elements and factors, emphasis is placed on marine environments in which the bulk of ancient sedimentary rocks was deposited.

Material Factors in the Environment. The medium of deposition in marine environments is sea water, characterized by a concentration of dissolved salts and gases, the temperature of the medium, and suspended solids. The material factors include the medium, the salts and gases, and the solids.

Each of the material factors may have some effect on sediments being deposited, but the importance of the effect is controlled, in part, by factors of other elements. In the zone of breaking waves, where the dominant sediment is sand or gravel, such factors as dissolved salts and gases are of little importance. In quiet water, relatively remote from shore, on the other hand, they become of great importance in controlling organisms, and hence play a part in the deposition of calcium carbonate.

The composition of the depositional surface (bottom mud or sand) and the nature of the material in transit are important material factors. Abundant fine clastics in suspension cause turbidity, which may inhibit organisms. Movement of sand across the bottom also limits prolific life, and partly controls contributions of organisms to the depositing sediments.

Boundary and Energy Factors. Boundary condition factors in the marine environment include water depth, distance from shore, topography of the bottom, and, in a general way, the geography of the depositional area.

Water depth is normally related to distance from shore, although shoals may be interspersed among deeper zones in areas of irregular bottom topography. Surface roughness, superimposed on bottom topography, is a frictional factor that influences the rate of detrital movement across the bottom.

In a general way, distance from shore influences the amount and coarseness of detrital material available for sedimentation. This simple relation is complicated by relative nearshore and offshore depths, and by directions of prevailing currents.

Boundary conditions are important in controlling the distribution of energy over the environment. Several kinds of energy may be present, including thermal and mechanical. Thermal energy is related to temperature, and mechanical energy is expressed in the laminar or turbulent motion of the medium.

Water depth and configuration of the shore line control the distribution of wave energy on the shore and influence the prevailing paths of currents. Wave refraction occurs in shallow water, with the wave fronts bent into curves controlled by depth changes and shore configuration. As a result of refraction, some parts of the shore receive more energy per unit length than others, and are subject to more turbulent conditions as the waves break.

The interplay between boundary conditions and environmental energy is shown by the flow of energy over the environment, and localization in areas of highest energy dissipation. Areas of high energy application include zones in which turbulence is generated, where currents are strongest, where lifting forces on particles are strongest, and where the greatest degree of sorting takes place. Finer material is transferred to quieter zones, to produce a segregation of clastic material into textural groups.

As sediments accumulate in given parts of the environment, they may exert an influence on the process elements. Thus development of bars or other features may change the bottom conditions sufficiently to modify the subsequent pattern of wave refraction and of energy distribution. This sort of interlocked relation between process and response is called **feedback,** in the sense that the results of a given process may themselves modify later stages of that process. Thus a dashed arrow could be added to the model of Table 7-1 as follows:

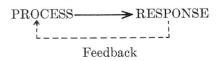

Factors in the Biologic Complex. Organisms that live within the sedimentary environment are controlled by many of the same factors that control the sediments. In clear warm seas, well oxygenated and mildly alkaline, organisms may thrive and produce abundant carbonate sediment. If fine grained mineral detritus is washed in, increased turbidity may restrict living conditions for some forms, such as corals. The concurrent accumulation of mud on the bottom may improve conditions for other forms, such as pelecypods.

As detrital inwash continues, the accumulating sediment may change from predominantly carbonate to detrital mud, with a resultant faunal change from clear-water to muddy-water inhabitants. The indurated sediment changes vertically from limestone to shale. The same kind of change may occur geographically, leading to a lateral variation from one rock type to another within the same stratigraphic unit.

EXAMPLE OF A COMPLEX ENVIRONMENT

Figure 7-1 shows a portion of Barataria Bay, along the Mississippi delta. The elongate islands that stretch northeast-southwest across the map represent a barrier beach with a tidal inlet cutting through the barrier. Southeast of the barrier beach lies the open water of the Gulf of Mexico, and northwest of the barrier, the relatively quiet water of Barataria Bay, a tidal lagoon.

The map thus presents portions of several sedimentary environments. One of these is the shallow nearshore water of the Gulf of Mexico, representing well oxygenated conditions of open circulation. The barrier islands represent a beach environment, with wave action along the gulfward edge, and with some reworking of the beach sand by wind action. Relatively quiet water exists behind the barrier except during times of ebb and flood tide, when moderate currents are present in the principal tidal channels. Behind the barrier beach, there are several low lying, marshy islands, in contrast to the sandy composition of the barrier beach.

Although Barataria Bay represents only a small part of the Mississippi delta complex, it is convenient in terms of the sedimentary environment model to consider the area shown in Figure 7-1 as representing separate but contiguous environments. Thus the **boundary conditions** of the several environments are partly held in common. That is, the shoreward limit of the shallow water Gulf environment is bounded by the shoreward edge of the barrier beach environment. Similarly, the inner edge of the barrier beach represents the boundary between the beach environment and the tidal lagoon environment. Water depth, another boundary condition, is commonly six feet or less within the main part of the tidal lagoon, but it extends to depths exceeding twelve feet on the Gulf of Mexico side; within Barataria

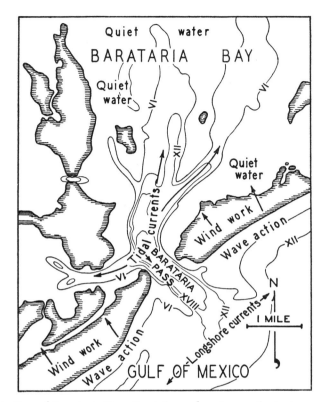

Fig. 7-1. Portion of Barataria Bay, Louisiana, showing geological processes. [After Krumbein (1941).]

Pass, as well as in the tidal channels, depths of twelve or eighteen feet are relatively common.

In regard to the **materials** of the environment, the Gulf of Mexico portion includes sands in the vicinity of the barrier beaches, grading seaward to fine sands and silt. The barrier beaches have the coarsest deposits in this environmental complex, consisting of relatively well sorted, moderate to coarse grained sand. Except for the tidal channels, where silt is relatively abundant, most of the bottom of the quieter parts of Barataria Bay contains relatively fine grained clay or silty clay. The content of dissolved salts in the waters ranges from essentially normal marine concentrations in the Gulf to brackish water concentrations in the inner part of the lagoon.

The **energy** element in these environments also shows some striking contrasts. The energy of breaking waves is almost wholly expended along the gulfward edge of the barrier beaches. Thus, a narrow band of intense energy dissipation exists along the zone of breaking waves (that is, along the boundary between barrier and Gulf), part of which is utilized in the movement and sorting of sand, and part of which develops long shore currents parallel to the boundary. These energy factors are mainly mechanical energy, and are also present in the prism of tidal waters that move into and out of the bay through Barataria Pass. The flood currents encounter frictional resistance from the quiet water in the bay, and dissipate their energy in part by the shifting of bottom materials and by frictional loss. In the quieter lagoonal waters, away from the tidal channels, the energy is largely thermal, with the temperature controlled by seasonal changes.

The **biologic element** also plays a different role in the three environments. Within the tidal lagoon, especially near the edges of the tidal channels, oyster reefs are locally prominent, representing the adjustment of organisms to localized areas in which oxygen and abundant food supplies are available. The relatively high organic content of the muds in the quieter parts of the lagoon also represents the contribution of organic remains, either plant or animal, to the accumulating sediment. The role of organisms is less prominent in the accumulating sediments along the gulfward edge of the barrier beaches and in the shallow offshore waters of the Gulf. This is due, in part, to the higher mechanical energy levels, which tend to favor only relatively thick-shelled organisms.

This illustration, though mainly qualitative, shows how any single environment or complex of environments may be analyzed within the framework of the several elements in the environmental model. Evidently, a rational approach would involve an examination of the principal factors that make up each element of the model, including the measurement of physical and chemical factors, as well as the attributes of both the sedimentary deposits and their associated organic remains.

Perhaps the most comprehensive study embracing both environmental and sedimentary features is the American Petroleum Institute Project 51, organized and conducted largely under the supervision of F. P. Shepard of the Scripps Institute of Oceanography, and more recently by T. H. van Andel. This project includes investigation of the oceanographic, physical, chemical, and biological factors, as well as the movement and distribution of sediments in the northwest Gulf of Mexico, including the Mississippi delta area. This work has been summarized in a symposium edited by Shepard, Phleger, and Van Andel (1960), cited in the annotated bibliography at the end of this chapter. Fisk (1944) conducted a thoroughgoing study of the alluvial valley of the Lower Mississippi valley. In 1954 Fisk and coworkers published a definitive paper on the Mississippi delta, and more recently Fisk (1961) described the geometry of the bar-finger sands of the delta. This material is discussed in more detail in Chapter 13.

A second excellent example of a comprehensive environmental study is that of Van Andel and Postma (1954) made in the Gulf of Paria along the northern coast of South America, just west of Trinidad. This study was conducted under the auspices of the Institute for Marine Geology of the University of Groningen. As in the API study, detailed consideration was given to oceanographic factors (temperature and salinity), distribution of sedimentary types, and occurrence of organisms. A large number of contour-type maps is included in the report, summarizing the areal variations in environmental factors and sediment properties.

ENVIRONMENTAL PATTERNS

The areal variation of sedimentary properties within an environment is called the **environmental pattern** of the deposit. A natural extension of the term includes the areal variation of environmental factors and the distribution of organisms as well as the associated deposits. Environmental patterns are most effectively shown on contour-type maps, provided quantitative data are available. But many features of environments are effectively displayed qualitatively on maps in which areas to be distinguished are shown by cross-hatching or by dot patterns.

Figure 7-2 shows the distribution of bottom-water salinity in the area east of the Mississippi delta (Lankeford, 1959). The salinity contour lines, drawn through a field of measured values, show how the salinity is influenced by the outflow of fresh water, resulting in a salinity gradient outward from the delta edge. This variation in salinity is a factor in the materials-element of the environment, and may have effects on both the deposits and the organisms. The degree to which clay particles are flocculated by waters of varying salinity may control some of the attributes of the finer bottom deposits. Similarly, the distribution of living organisms on the sea bottom is influenced by their tolerance to various concentrations of dissolved salts.

Figure 7-3 shows four examples of environmental maps taken from Van Andel and Postma (1954). These maps show some of the relations among environmental factors and sediment properties. The upper left map shows the distribution of pH in the upper layers of sediments that are located immediately below an oxidized layer. The upper right map shows the distribution of Eh in the same layers. These two maps reflect some of the geochemical conditions in the environment a short distance below the depositional interface. The two lower maps in Figure 7-3 show the distribution of carbonate (as percentage of $CaCO_3$) in the finer fractions of the bottom sediments, and the distribution of colors of the freshly-collected wet samples. Comparison of these four maps shows some interesting relations between

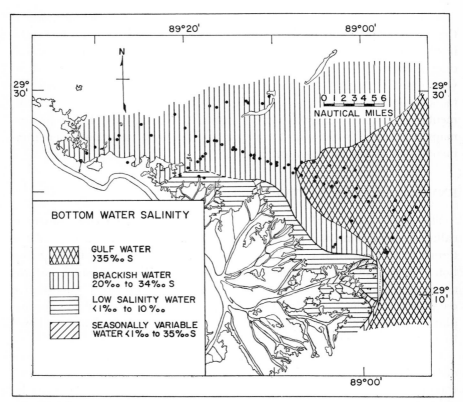

Fig. 7-2. Generalized distribution of bottom-water salinity east of the Mississippi delta. This map gives an example of a property of the depositional medium that exerts an influence on the sediments and fauna of the environment (see text). [After Lankford (1959).]

relative carbonate content and pH, and between sediment color and Eh. The reader will find it worth while to examine these maps in terms of the Eh-pH diagram of Figure 6-12.

The maps in Figure 7-4 show the distribution of sediment types (Shepard, 1956) and the distribution of organisms (Phleger, 1954) in the Mississippi delta area. Shepard's map is divided into areas on the basis of his textural triangle mentioned in Chapter 5. This quantitative pattern map emphasizes the classes of sediments present, and gives an over-all view of areal variation in textural properties. Phleger's map shows the observed data directly, without superimposed contours. Use of the observed values, instead of contours or patterned areas, is particularly effective when the data vary widely within small areas.

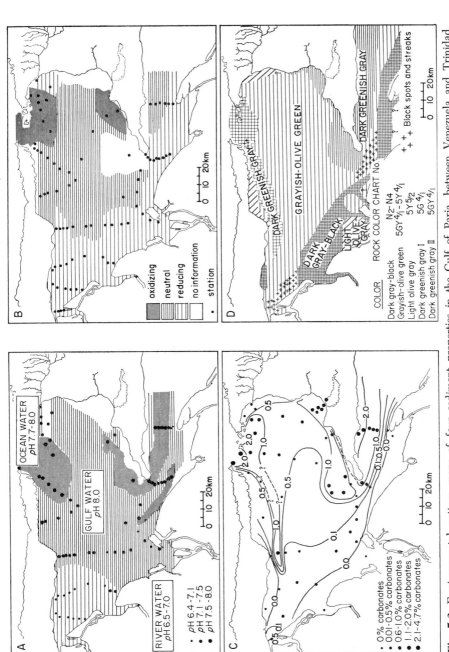

Fig. 7-3. Environmental pattern maps of four sediment properties in the Gulf of Paria, between Venezuela and Trinidad, South America. Maps A and B show the pH and Eh of the bottom muds, and maps C and D illustrate their carbonate content and color. See the text for details. [After Van Andel and Postma (1954).]

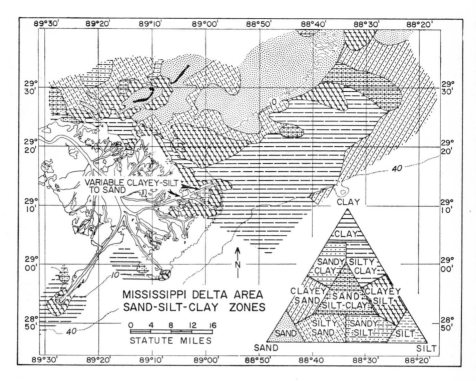

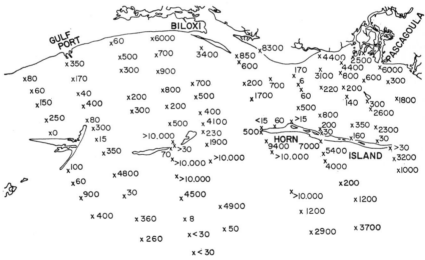

Fig. 7-4. (*Top*) Distribution of sediment textures in an area east of the Mississippi delta. The triangular legend divides the sand-silt-clay components into ten well-defined classes. (*Bottom*) A portion of the Gulf of Mexico east of the Mississippi delta, showing the areal variations in the total number of foraminifera observed in samples of uniform size. Note the extreme variation from more than 10,000 to almost none. Total east-west length of map about 35 miles. [Top map after Shepard (1956); bottom map after Phleger (1954).]

APPLICATIONS OF ENVIRONMENTAL PATTERNS
IN STRATIGRAPHY

The study of environmental patterns yields important information about simultaneous areal variations among the elements and factors that control deposition, as well as about the corresponding patterns of the accumulating deposits. Comparison of these patterns, supported by statistical analysis of the data, makes it possible to relate attributes of the sediments and organisms to particular physical and chemical aspects of the environment. In addition, a set of pattern maps of a given present-day environment provides an example of a specific sedimentary environment model and becomes of importance in the interpretation of ancient environments by the stratigrapher.

When sufficient outcrop or subsurface data are available, the stratigrapher can prepare stratigraphic maps showing selected attributes of ancient sedimentary rocks that bear some relation to environmental factors. Such maps aid in the interpretation of the conditions of deposition of stratigraphic rock bodies as they relate to historical geology or to economic evaluation. The use of selected end members in the preparation of stratigraphic maps for the reconstruction of ancient environments is discussed more fully in Chapter 12.

Where data are available for stratigraphic analysis of ancient environments, it is sometimes possible to infer localization of high energy areas, prevailing directions of ancient currents, average depths of water, and other features of importance in environmental interpretation. It is highly important that fossil organisms associated with the rocks be included in such studies, inasmuch as the organisms often yield information about specific features characteristic of the environment.

The environmental patterns reconstructed from observation of ancient sediments may permit segregation of closely related environments, such as beaches and dunes which usually cannot be distinguished by examining only individual samples of sandstone from two such environments. In this reconstruction, vector properties such as grain orientation, as well as scalar properties, such as the degree of sorting, may be highly diagnostic.

Although information may be available for making stratigraphic environmental maps, it may not always be possible to reconstruct the exact nature of the ancient environment. Complexities due to gradations among environmental elements and factors may be present, and postdepositional changes may alter some of the original sedimentary properties, as discussed later in this chapter.

Many contributions from the study of present-day environments have direct application in stratigraphic analysis. Among these are studies made in the northwest Gulf of Mexico, a number of which are included in Shepard.

Phleger, and Van Andel (1960). In these comprehensive investigations much light has been shed on sedimentary environmental patterns as well as on patterns of distribution of bottom-dwelling organisms. To a large extent these and similar studies have as one objective the development of criteria by which one environment may be distinguished from another. For example, Shepard and Moore (1954) used coarse-fraction studies of bottom sediments as environmental criteria. Several authors, cited under the discussion of particle frequency distributions in Chapter 4, use textural and other attributes to distinguish beach and dune environments. A comprehensive study by Biederman (1962), on shoreline environments in New Jersey, applies statistical design to the problem of distinguishing among beach, dune, lagoon, and marsh deposits.

Miller and Olson (1955) discuss in terms of ancient environments the problem of those attributes of sediments that pass through the postdepositional phase without alteration. It is these attributes that most clearly define the original conditions of sedimentation. Rich (1951) used the framework of shallow water, sloping bottom, and deep-water conditions (**undaform, clinoform,** and **fondoform**) to discriminate sediments formed under different environmental conditions. This leads to **undathem, clinothem,** and **fondothem** as terms applied to lithosomes (see Chapter 9) formed under the corresponding conditions.

GRADATIONS AMONG SEDIMENTARY ENVIRONMENTS

In addition to variations in environmental factors and elements within a given environment, as evidenced by pattern maps, it is sometimes found that sedimentary environments show all degrees of gradation from one to another. As a result of variations in processes and deposits within any one environment, the same environment may produce a variety of sediments related to the range of dynamic conditions within it. Similarly, if the range of conditions in two environments overlap, both of them may form the same kind of sediment, at least locally. It is not unusual to find that individual samples of sediment from one environment cannot be distinguished from those of another environment.

Because of these gradations within and among sedimentary environments, the analysis of present-day environments and the reconstruction of ancient environments require that a number of attributes be examined simultaneously. It is largely from the convergence of several lines of evidence that it becomes possible to make distinctions between different, though similar, environments in terms of their broad overall characteristics.

When a set of environmental maps based on several attributes of the processes or deposits is available, it is commonly found that some show a parallel or subparallel pattern of contours, such as when systematic changes in sediment texture occur seaward from a straight, sandy shore. Some patterns may be dendritic, such as those showing the distribution of sedimentary properties along channels in tidal lagoons. Some environmental patterns are seemingly haphazard, with a "spotty" distribution of contours over the mapped area. These may occur in shallow marine environments, where clusters or colonies of organisms locally develop shell mounds on a muddy bottom.

When the data of environmental analysis are presented in numerical form (as in contour-type maps) it is sometimes possible to separate by statistical methods the local "spotty" patches from the underlying broader pattern that characterizes the environment. In some stratigraphic studies, the broad pattern may be of major interest, in which case the spottiness of the observed data may obscure underlying diagnostic patterns. In detailed studies, on the other hand, the nature of the local patches and their distribution over the environment may be of major concern. This separation of map data into two components, one broad and one local, is an aspect of **trend surface analysis,** treated more fully in Chapter 12.

Miller and Zeigler (1958) provide an illustration of the use of trend analysis in the study of beach phenomena, based upon the concept of a dynamic beach model. The design of the model included assumptions regarding the particle size pattern on the foreshore just after a wave has passed over it, the velocity required to move a grain down slope during wave backwash, and the velocity distribution in the surge zone on the foreshore. The theoretical contours of particle size and sorting on the foreshore could then be constructed in accordance with the model.

To test the model, measurements were made of wave characteristics, of the foreshore slope, the average velocity of wave backwash, and the median diameter and degree of sorting of the sand grains. From these and related observations, it was possible to develop the observed patterns of variation from the nearshore zone of shoaling waves through the zone of breaking waves, and up on the foreshore slope. Figure 7-5 shows the map for median grain size as a three-dimensional surface. The height of the surface is proportional to the average size of the sand grains, and it indicates that the coarsest sediments occur in the zone of breaking waves, with a decrease in average grain size both seaward and toward the foreshore. The lower diagram shows that sorting is best for the coarsest sediments in the breaker zone B. Such changes are in accord with the implications of the model.

Miller and Zeigler's analysis emphasizes the importance of relating sediment properties to the dynamics of environmental processes. Such studies

(a) TREND MAP FOR MEDIAN SEDIMENT SIZE

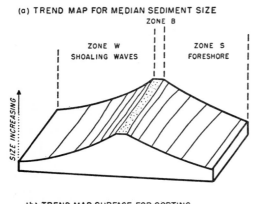

(b) TREND MAP SURFACE FOR SORTING

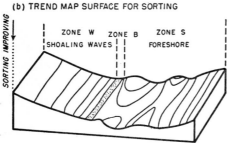

Fig. 7-5

Block diagrams illustrating the distribution of particle size and sorting across a beach from shallow water to the foreshore. These surfaces are responses to the energy conditions along the shore. [Copyright by the University of Chicago.]

differ from conventional environmental analyses in that they first set up a theoretical model for predicting or inferring what should occur as a result of the interaction between environmental agents and deposits, and then use observational data to test the soundness of the inference. In terms of earlier remarks, Miller and Ziegler's study illustrates the use of a specific process-response model.

CLASSIFICATION OF SEDIMENTARY ENVIRONMENTS

Preceeding sections of this chapter have shown that sedimentary environments may be described in terms of elements and factors. It was emphasized that most sedimentary environments show variations in their dynamic conditions, in their deposits, and in associated organisms. Even though different environments may overlap in terms of environmental factors, it is useful to group environments into classes based on certain similarities in order to provide a convenient frame of reference for describing them.

Sedimentary environments may be classified on any of several bases, depending upon the features to be emphasized. A physicochemical classification may be based on the dominance of certain environmental factors or elements. The nature of the depositional medium, such as air, water, or glacial ice, may be used as a basis. A classification may depend upon the principal geological agent responsible for the deposit, such as streams, waves, or currents. A common basis for classifying marine environments is water depth. Environmental models may also be used as a basis, in which the presence and magnitude of the operative agents, as well as patterns of sediment distribution, are used to set up the classification. Miller and Zeigler's beach model is an example of this approach.

Though it may be predicted that environmental classification will ultimately be based on models, there is some advantage to retaining the classical descriptive grouping laid down by Grabau and extended and amplified by Twenhofel. The high point of this approach is developed by Twenhofel in his now classical *Principles of Sedimentation* (1950). Table 7-2 shows this classification. Among the continental environments (i.e., non-marine), four are emphasized to indicate their relatively greater importance in stratigraphic analysis. Numerous examples of ancient wind, stream, lake, and swamp deposits occur in the geologic column. Glacial and cave deposits are less commonly encountered in stratigraphic practice.

The transitional environments are all of major importance in stratigraphy, and an important problem in many studies is the location of ancient strand lines, now represented mainly by transitional beds.

Perhaps the most important environments in stratigraphic analysis are marine. It is believed that the bulk of sedimentary rocks in the geologic column were deposited under marine conditions. This is a reflection, in part, of the better preservation of sediments formed in epicontinental seas than of those deposited on land areas subject to further erosion.

The classification shown in Table 7-2 has the advantage that it includes several composite environments (such as the deltaic environment), which are more conveniently analyzed as an interlocked complex than as a series of separate environments. This sort of complex was illustrated above in the discussion of Barataria Bay. In terms of quantitative environmental models,

TABLE 7-2. CLASSIFICATION OF SEDIMENTARY ENVIRONMENTS [After Twenhofel.]

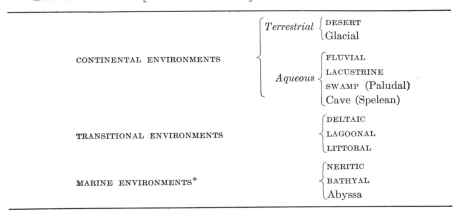

CONTINENTAL ENVIRONMENTS	*Terrestrial*	DESERT / Glacial
	Aqueous	FLUVIAL / LACUSTRINE / SWAMP (Paludal) / Cave (Spelean)
TRANSITIONAL ENVIRONMENTS		DELTAIC / LAGOONAL / LITTORAL
MARINE ENVIRONMENTS*		NERITIC / BATHYAL / Abyssa

* The classical subdivision is used in this table, but these environments are subdivided differently in the discussion of marine environments.

however, it is probably more convenient to analyze the individual environments that make up the complex—such as the barrier beach, the tidal lagoon, the distributary channels, and so on—in terms of the process and response elements that occur in each.

As environmental models become more common in sedimentary and stratigraphic studies, the relatively simple form of model illustrated in Table 7-1 can be expressed in other ways. For example, an alternative arrangement of the process and response elements is shown in Table 7-3. Here the model consists of three parts. The first includes the boundary conditions and the materials of the environment, the second has the energy and biological elements, and the third is the same as in Table 7-1. In this alternative form the model takes cognizance of the boundary conditions and materials of the environment as being the framework in which specified environmental processes take place. Thus the energy and the biological elements that modify the materials within the given boundary conditions are placed in a separate array, to take cognizance of the different ways in which specific environmental agents may modify a given "initial state" of the materials present in the environment. The same principle of feedback from response to process that was mentioned earlier also plays a part in this form of the model.

The concept of three blocks making up an environmental model can be illustrated by reference to Figure 6-9. In that figure the materials operated on by the wind (sand, silt, clay) are arranged along a main linear source, represented by the floodplain of the Illinois River. This material is picked up by the wind and arranged into dunes near the bluff line, and as a blanket of loess downwind. Thus the materials and geometry of the general environment, acted upon by wind as the operative agent, produce a particular kind and pattern of sediments. If this same framework of geometry and material were operated upon by a shallow sea encroaching from the south, the reworking of the wind deposits by the advancing strandline would produce a series of responses different from that produced by the present wind

TABLE 7-3. MATERIAL PROCESS AND RESPONSE MODEL FOR SEDIMENTARY ENVIRONMENTS. (Compare with Table 7-1.)

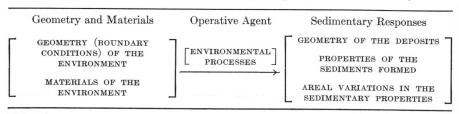

Geometry and Materials	Operative Agent	Sedimentary Responses
GEOMETRY (BOUNDARY CONDITIONS) OF THE ENVIRONMENT	ENVIRONMENTAL PROCESSES	GEOMETRY OF THE DEPOSITS
		PROPERTIES OF THE SEDIMENTS FORMED
MATERIALS OF THE ENVIRONMENT		AREAL VARIATIONS IN THE SEDIMENTARY PROPERTIES

work, even if the geometrical setting and the available materials were the same.[*]

SUMMARY DESCRIPTIONS OF SELECTED SEDIMENTARY ENVIRONMENTS

The brief environmental sketches that follow, like the descriptions of specific sedimentary rocks in Chapter 5, are intended primarily as a check list on a variety of depositional conditions. The reader is referred to Twenhofel (1950) for the main reference book on this subject. More recently, Dunbar and Rodgers (1957, pp. 3–96) have presented an excellent up to date treatment of this subject. Weller (1960, Chapter 6) also treats the subject of sedimentary environments.

In ancient sedimentary deposits, one may commonly observe a variety of individual beds or lenses making up the rock body. Hence, the specific kinds of deposits that occur within a sedimentary environment through time can be effectively treated for stratigraphic purposes by considering the associations of rock types that normally occur within stratigraphic units. These associations are influenced not only by the sedimentary environment, but also by the nature of the source area and by the rate of subsidence in the basin of deposition. Thus, the detailed discussion of stream channel deposits, for example, is not included under stream environments in this chapter, but is developed as part of the larger subject of **lithologic associations** covered in Chapter 13, after discussion of sedimentary tectonics in Chapter 11.

In each of the environmental "thumb-nail" sketches that follows, emphasis is placed on the combination of environmental elements and specific environmental factors present. In a broad sense, these may be considered as qualitative models of the environments, with main emphasis on the process portion of the models. The reader is urged to summarize these sketches into specific models of the types shown either in Table 7-1 or 7-3.

---

[*] An advantage of the form of model shown in Table 7-3 lies in the ease with which it can be converted to a fully quantitative counterpart. The blocks in this case become numerical arrays called matrices (with rows and columns of entries) that can be treated by conventional matrix-algebra procedures with high-speed computers. Griffiths (1962) developed this theme for a "generalized petrogenetic model,"

$$A \xrightarrow{(t)} B,$$

in which (A) is a matrix representing the attributes of the source material, (t) is a transformation matrix representing the processes that operate on the material, and (B) is the end-product or response matrix. Although the mathematics is advanced and not treated here, it is thought appropriate to call the reader's attention to what appears to be a definite trend in the analysis of sedimentary data.

Continental Environments

The continental environments as a class are nonmarine. That is, the surface of deposition normally lies above sea level, although in some enclosed basins, such as Death Valley, continental deposits may actually be laid below sea level.

The distinction between **terrestrial** and **aqueous** environments depends upon whether the deposit is formed in water (streams, lakes, swamps) or formed either by wind or glacial ice. The glacial environment is classified as terrestrial rather than aqueous. Continental aqueous environments need not have fresh water. The deposits of Great Salt Lake are considered continental aqueous.

The Glacial Environment. The glacial environment is generally considered to include the environment of the glacier itself and the associated fringing meltwater environment. Meltwater deposits, formed in water escaping from the ice, may be classified as continental aqueous, but their intimate association with ice deposits renders a single grouping more convenient.

The glacial environment, as a whole, is characterized by low temperatures, which limit plant growth and restrict the fauna to more hardy species. In terms of elements and factors, the **energy** is almost wholly that of moving ice and flowing meltwater. The **boundary conditions** include the size and thickness of the glacier and the surface configuration of the glaciated terrain. **Materials** of the environment are wholly clastic, ranging from huge blocks to the finest clay. **Biological factors** are negligible in their contribution to the sediments.

Deposits laid directly by the ice are unsorted and unstratified till, which may be interbedded with outwash deposits of gravel, sand, or silt. The outwash deposits, formed by meltwater, have most of the characteristics of alluvial deposits. The till may occur in terminal moraines, ground moraines (till plains), or in such special features as drumlins. Outwash features include pitted plains, kames, eskers, and valley trains. Ice-dammed or moraine-dammed glacial lakes accumulate lacustrine sediments, commonly varved.

Glacial deposits form a very minor part of the geologic column, except in the Pleistocene. Several episodes of glaciation occurred in Precambrian time, and a classic example of late Paleozoic glaciation is found in the Permian deposits of South Africa, where both the indurated glacial till and the striated bedrock surfaces are preserved. Pettijohn (1957) describes the characteristics of till and tillite in some detail.

The Desert Environment. The desert environment is not strictly eolian, inasmuch as temporary streams and playa lakes may be relatively important in the environment. During dry seasons, such deposited material is subject to wind work, superimposing eolian characteristics on the material. As with the glacial environment, a combination of specific environmental types is accordingly included in the desert environment.

The analysis of existing deserts in the western United States, in terms of principal elements and factors, indicates that the main **energy factors** are the kinetic energy of wind and temporary streams, and the thermal energy involved in evaporation of playa lakes. **Boundary conditions** include steep slopes surrounding undrained basins, in which the playa lakes temporarily form. The **materials** of the desert environment are cobbles and pebbles in the fanglomerates at the base of steep slopes, wind-blown sand in dunes, and fine grained deposits, sometimes with evaporites, in the basin centers. **Biological factors** play only a small part in the formation of desert deposits.

Desert sediments show wide variability. The deposits are commonly lenticular and may show rapid alternations of fine and coarse material. Many pebbles in deserts contain "desert varnish," considered to be a combination of dust polish and deposition of salts on surface fragments. Ventifacts, pebbles with beveled faces, may also be common.

Eolian cross bedding is common in wind-deposited sands, and ripple marks and mud cracks are common in playa deposits. Evaporites may form as the lakes evaporate, and it is not uncommon to find sodium chloride or sodium sulphate in some modern desert sediments.

Sediment colors in the desert show a wide range from white and gray through shades of yellow, brown, and red, to black. The high incidence of oxidizing conditions in the environment tends to promote the development of browns and reds, but the finer sediments may have less such coloring matter in them, with locally enough humic material to acquire a dark color.

The Alluvial Environment. Alluvial deposits are formed in stream channels and associated floodplains of individual streams, or as broad alluvial fans or plains where stream braiding dominates an appreciable area.

In terms of elements and factors, the **energy** of the alluvial environment lies mainly in the kinetic energy of the stream, and **boundary conditions** include the stream gradient, linear shape of the channel, and limiting valley walls. The **materials** range from boulders to clay, with the coarser sediments commonly associated with headward portion of the stream. **Biological factors** play a variable part in stream deposition, with major contributions of humic material in the finer sediments formed on wide floodplains in the lower reaches of the stream.

In any single stream, the deposits develop as elongate lenses, generally oriented downstream. On alluvial fans and plains, the master streams may braid into numerous channels which form intertonguing lenses or small sheets of sediment, characterized by cut-and-fill structures and abrupt changes in particle size. From bed to bed, the textural gradations appear to be irregular, but systematic sampling shows a progressive change from coarse material at the apex to increasingly finer material downslope along the apron.

The Swamp (Paludal) Environment. Swamps and marshes are bodies of shallow standing water or low, wet ground occupied by relatively abundant plant life. Swamp water may be marine, brackish, or fresh. Temperate marine and brackish swamps support reeds and grasses. In the tropics, mangrove or cypress is characteristic. Fresh-water swamps have reeds, grasses, alders, or tamarack.

Swamp **boundary conditions** include their oval or linear shape and shallow depths. **Energy** is chemical or thermal rather than mechanical. The **materials** of the environment include silt and mud which may be washed into the swamp, and dissolved salts and gases that develop anaerobic conditions in the water. The **biological complex** is a dominant element in sedimentation, inasmuch as the deposits may be entirely or mainly accumulated plant debris.

Swamp deposits may range from relatively pure organic end members (such as peat), through mixtures of organic and detrital materials, to detrital clays and silts. The geometric form of the deposits tends to be sheet-like, within the restraints imposed by the boundary conditions of the area of sedimentation.

The Lacustrine Environment. The lacustrine environment shows a wide range of conditions, characterized by shallower depths, smaller waves and weaker currents, and shorter life histories as compared with the oceans. Lakes do not have tides, and changes in level are seasonal rather than diurnal.

The **boundary conditions** of lakes include their size, shape, and water depth. Large lakes may have sufficient wave energy to develop well marked shore features. Thermal and chemical **energy** are important in influencing biological processes. The detrital **materials** of the lake environment may range from coarse to fine, and in some lakes, the content of dissolved salts and gases strongly influences sedimentation. **Biological factors** vary in importance and may locally dominate lake deposition in shallow, restricted parts of the environment.

To a large extent, the characteristics of lake deposits are determined by the size of the lake. Small lakes along stream courses may show gradations from alluvial to swamp conditions. In most small lakes, the sediments are essentially fine grained, quiet-water deposits, except for a narrow shore zone of sand and coarser particles. The shore deposits, where dominantly sandy, have linear lens-like forms, and the offshore deposits tend to be more sheet-like. In relatively large lakes with detrital sediments (such as the glacial lakes in the Great Lakes region), the lacustrine silts and clays appear mainly to be relatively thin lenses or sheet-like deposits that are moderately well sorted.

In lake areas less affected by detrital accumulation, marl may accumulate through biological or chemical agencies. The marl is either relatively pure calcium carbonate or mixtures with varying amounts of clay and organic matter. Iron hydroxide, mainly limonite, is formed in some lakes.

Transitional Environments

Three environmental conditions, deltaic, lagoonal, and littoral, are commonly classified as transitional, although numerous subdivisions are possible. Estuaries may range from fresh through brackish to normal sea water. Coastal swamps may be true transitional environments in that they may alternate between fresh and salt water.

The Delta Environment. A delta is a transitional sedimentary deposit fed by a stream, and distributed by waves and currents of lake or sea. The growth of a delta depends upon a rate of supply greater than waves and currents can completely disperse. Essential equilibrium may be reached when rate of detrital inflow equals the rate of distribution by shore agents, provided tectonic subsidence also proceeds at a constant rate.

The deltaic environment is a composite of several, including alluvial, lacustrine, eolian, lagoonal, swamp, and beach environments. As with other composite environments, the intimate association of deposits favors treatment under a unified heading.

Boundary conditions of the deltaic environment include the size and shape of the deposit, the pattern of stream channels, general topographic expression, and barriers or other fringing features on the seaward side. **Energy** is mainly mechanical, including the kinetic energy of streams, wind, waves, and currents. **Materials** of the environment include coarse and fine detritus, as well as such nonclastics as marl and organic matter. Dissolved salts in the seaward part of the delta are materials in the environment that influence sedimentation. **Biological factors** may be very important locally, as in the formation of oyster reefs in lagoons, and swamp vegetation in abandoned stream channels and shallow lagoonal areas. Deltaic processes and deposits have received detailed and comprehensive analysis within recent years, as mentioned earlier. As a result, a much more comprehensive deltaic model can be constructed now than was possible even a decade ago. Since deltaic deposits are of major importance in stratigraphic analysis, this topic is treated in an integrated manner in Chapter 13.

For purposes of the present discussion, and in terms of the relatively simple models of Tables 7-1 and 7-3, some remarks are included here on deltaic deposits. Characteristically they are a complex of deposits formed in distributary stream channels, floodplains with their associated lakes and swamps, plus beach and lagoon deposits formed along the marine margin.

The Lagoonal Environment. A lagoon is a body of relatively quiet shallow water, separated from the sea by a barrier beach, spit, or bar, which prevents wave energy from entering the lagoon. The lagoon receives fresh water and sediments from streams, and salt water from the sea through tidal inlets. These conditions develop a gradation from normal sea water at the inlets to brackish water in the body of the lagoon and fresh water near the stream mouths.

Boundary conditions of the lagoonal environment include the shape, water depth, and limiting barriers of the lagoon. **Materials** of the environment include detritus brought in by streams and the dissolved salts in the water. **Energy** is mainly thermal, except near stream mouths and along tidal channels, where current action is important in controlling sediment texture. The **biological complex** includes aquatic plants, bottom-dwelling organisms, and floating forms, which contribute significant amounts of organic matter and carbonate to the accumulating sediments, especially in quiet water away from tidal channels.

The bottom sediments normally show a pattern of textural gradation from fine sand and silt in the channels to organic-rich silt and clay in the quiet areas. Fine sand, silt, and clay brought in by streams, supplemented by wind-blown sand from the barrier, and organic material and carbonate from organisms, yield a wide variety of sedimentary types in the lagoon. Locally, where circulation is poor, sulfate-reducing bacteria may become abundant on the bottom, developing dark, euxinic muds.

The lagoon environment passes through a cycle of development that involves a gradual silting of the lagoonal area. Low, scattered islands develop, with progressive invasion by swamp flora. Ultimately, the lagoon may become filled with organic-rich sediment except for narrow, winding, shallow tidal channels in an otherwise moist or swampy environment.

The Littoral Environment. The littoral environment is the shore environment, extending from the region of high tide to that of low tide. An important characteristic of the littoral environment is its alternate submergence and subaerial exposure during the tidal cycle.

The typical expression of the littoral environment is the beach, formed by breaking waves along the coast. Most beaches are composed of sand, brought by streams or from sea cliffs by wave work. Where the littoral environment is protected from wave action, as in estuaries, it may be a wide tidal flat, composed mainly of mud.

Boundary conditions of the littoral environment include the configuration of the coast, the beach slope, width of tidal flat, and other geometrical features. Material of the environment includes mainly clastic particles, ranging from cobbles or pebbles to mud. The energy is mainly mechanical, represented by breaking waves and longshore currents. Biological factors are relatively minor in controlling beach sedimentation, because the strongly agitated waters inhibit most life forms. On tidal flats, however, annelid worms, crabs, and some brachiopods may flourish, and contribute organic material to sediments.

Tidal flat deposits resemble those of lagoons, except that the incidence of oxidation is greater because of the intermittent subaerial exposure. Tidal flat deposits are mainly fine grained gray or dark mud, with lenses or stringers of sand or gravel associated with the shallow tidal channels on the flat.

The development of linear beach deposits depends upon a supply of detritus and a stillstand of the sea sufficiently long to produce a well marked shore line. Shallow epeiric seas, continuously advancing on a slowly submerging land, bring the littoral environment with them. Material won by the waves is progressively submerged, developing a sheet sand which represents the sorting action of the littoral zone, without producing typical linear beach deposits.

Marine Environments

General Introduction. The classical subdivision of marine environments, as sketched in Table 7-2, has been modified in recent years to provide a more realistic classification based in part on the organisms present, as well as on a better understanding of the physical features of the ocean bottom.

The neritic zone of the classical grouping is now referred to as the sublittoral zone. This extends from low tide level to a depth of 600 feet, and is divided into two subzones. The infralittoral subzone extends from low tide level to a depth of 150 feet, and the circalittoral subzone extends from 150 feet to 600 feet. The depth boundaries of the sublittoral zone are accordingly the same as those in the classical neritic zone.

The bathyal environment, which classically extended from depths of 600 to 6,000 feet, has been modified to extend to depths of 13,500 feet, representative of the deeper portions of the main ocean basins. The bathyal environment is divided into two zones, the epibathyal, extending from 600 feet to 3,600 feet, and the mesobathyal, extending from 3,600 feet to 13,500 feet. The abyssal environment, which classically included all depths greater than 6,000 feet, now covers the depth range from 13,500 feet to 21,000 feet. The trenches in the ocean basins are referred to as the hadal environment and include all depths greater than 21,000 feet.

Although these oceanic environments are considered in greater detail in Chapter 8 in connection with the marine organisms that occupy these zones, the following sections are included here in order to complete the present survey of sedimentary environments.

The Sublittoral Environment. As mentioned, the sublittoral environment extends from low tide to a depth of 600 feet. The infralittoral depth limit of 150 feet represents the approximate depth to which sunlight penetrates oceanic waters. Below this depth, the waters of the ocean are universally dark.

The sublittoral environment may be visualized as a broad band paralleling the coast. Clastic material, poured in from the landward side by streams, is spread over the bottom in response to the effective mechanical energy in the environment. Currents and wave action during storms may be prominent in parts of the infralittoral zone, and although wave ripple marks are found at greater depths, the proportion of wave energy available for agitation of the bottom deposits diminishes markedly with depth.

Irregularities along the bottom play an important part in the distribution of land derived clastic material. Where the bottom gradually deepens, a fairly regular decrease in average particle size may occur seaward, but where the bottom is irregular, with deeper basins and higher shoal areas, the pattern of sediment distribution may be very irregular. Steep slopes along parts of the coast, as well as submarine canyons, provide localities where turbidity currents may be generated, carrying clastic materials to deeper environments and developing typical turbidite deposits.

The influence of chemical and biological factors increases seaward, while that of the corresponding physical energy factors diminishes. The environmental elements and factors are largely dependent upon water depth and supply of clastic materials, and they vary in importance accordingly. In much of the infralittoral zone, the **boundary conditions** include shallow water and nearness to shore. The **material** of the environment may be largely clastic, and the **energy** of the environment may be dominantly mechanical and related to waves and currents. The **biological factor** may be of relatively minor importance in shallow zones that are strongly agitated by mechanical energy.

Farther from shore, in the circalittoral zone, the **boundary conditions** include increased water depths, the **energy** is mainly thermal, the **materials** of the environment may be considerably finer, with less clastic content than near shore, and the **biological complex** may become increasingly important in sedimentation. The dissolved salts and gases in the sea water, and the degree of penetration of sun light are controlling factors in the nature and distribution of organisms.

Taken as a whole, the sublittoral environment is perhaps the most important from the viewpoint of stratigraphic analysis. Twenhofel (1950) estimated that about 80 percent of the sediments in the geologic column were deposited in water less than 600 feet deep. Moore (1929) in his analysis of Pennsylvanian environments, concluded that most of the sediments, including the limestone, were formed in water that did not exceed 200 feet in depth. Elias (1937) also concluded that the limestone in the Big Blue Series (Permian) of Kansas was deposited in water 200 feet or less in depth.

The Bathyal Environment. The bathyal environment includes water depths between 600 and 13,500 feet. The epibathyal zone, extending to 3,600 feet, includes much of the outer slopes of the continental shelves, and the mesobathyal environment includes the major part of the floor of the ocean basins.

Bathyal sediments include very fine sand, mud, and calcareous, glauconitic, and siliceous sediments. The deposits grade into those of the deep neritic environment, with perhaps an emphasis on the formation of siliceous deposits in bathyal depths.

Bottom conditions in the bathyal environment are relatively quiet. **Mechanical energy** is essentially negligible, except as density currents or slumping phenomena may affect parts of the bottom. The **boundary conditions** include the limiting water depths and local steep slopes in parts of the environment. **Materials** of the environment include the salts dissolved in the sea water, the fine detrital material which settles from suspension, and, more rarely, coarser debris which may slump from shallower depths.

The **biological complex** is mainly important in the contributions to sedimentation made by the tests of floating organisms. Bottom-dwelling forms are more limited in number and variety than on neritic bottoms, and consist mainly of scavengers. Light penetration is limited in bathyal depths, and marine plants are sparse or absent.

The Abyssal and Hadal Environments. These environments, as mentioned, include all oceanic depths greater than 13,500 feet, with the hadal environment comprising oceanic trenches at depths greater than 21,000 feet.

Light does not penetrate to abyssal depths, the hydrostatic pressure exceeds 2,000 pounds per square inch, and the temperature is generally less than 5 degrees Centigrade. These conditions seriously impede life development. Marine plants are absent, and such animals as live on the bottom depend for their food on the remains of floating organisms that settle to the bottom.

Boundary conditions of the environment include mainly the factor of depth. **Mechanical energy**, as represented by current action, is at a minimum. The **materials** of the environment include dissolved salts and such fine detrital material as may settle from suspension, plus the siliceous and calcareous tests of floating forms. The tests form an important part of the accumulating sediments, thus **biological contributions** to the deposits are important, though they are not added by bottom-dwelling organisms.

Although present deep-sea deposits formed under open circulation conditions consist of oozes and red or blue mud, increased exploration of the sea bottom during the past decade has revealed clastic materials extending to considerable depths as a result of deposition by turbidity currents, as described in Chapter 6.

There is disagreement about the occurrence of abyssal deposits in the sedimentary rocks now exposed on the continents. Chalk and certain black shales were formerly assigned to abyssal depths, but detailed petrographic and faunal studies, plus greater knowledge of field relations support the inference that all or most of such deposits were formed at sublittoral depths.

Some associations of siliceous shale and bedded chert with thin dark siliceous limestone, found in geosynclinal deposits, have been interpreted as abyssal in origin. It is not unlikely that the rate of subsidence in linear geosynclines may at times develop abyssal or near-abyssal depths. It seems doubtful, however, that epicontinental seas on the interior continental platforms have ever attained such depths.

POSTDEPOSITIONAL CHANGES IN SEDIMENTS

The Diagenetic Environment

At the instant of deposition, a sediment may consist of loose, detrital particles, crystals, organic fragments, colloidal mud, or mixtures of such substances. As a given lamina of sediment is formed, it becomes the **interface** between the previously deposited material and the medium of sedimentation.

The **diagenetic environment** is the environment of postdepositional change. It extends an indefinite distance downward from the depositional interface. The nature of the diagenetic environment and the rapidity of the postdepositional changes depend upon the medium of deposition and the kind of sediment being deposited.

The **depositional interface** represents an important boundary condition that separates two different physicochemical regions. As a simple illustration, clay and silt settle through sea water as a group of particles in a liquid medium. When the particles come to rest on the bottom, they form a solid matrix with water-saturated pores. The water has the same composition as the medium above, but marked changes occur once it is sealed from free circulation by confinement in the pores.

As deposition continues, the lamina of sediment passes from the interface to successively lower positions and enters a realm of greater pressure, higher temperature, and of changed chemical and biological conditions. These new conditions promote the consolidation or lithification of the sediment into a sedimentary rock.

The geologic literature affords many examples of diagenetic studies, and many writers have introduced special terms for specific post depositional changes. Some 30 such terms were briefly reviewed and consolidated into several major processes by Krumbein (1942). During the past decade especially, important advances in recognition of geochemical and biological controls on diagenetic processes have permitted a more critical examination of present-day diagenetic environments and have improved interpretation of diagenetic changes in ancient sediments.

Marine Diagenetic Environment

ZoBell (1946) gave considerable impetus to the study of conditions in present-day postdepositional environments by his examination of geochemical and biological phenomena in marine bottom muds. Figure 7-6 illustrates some of ZoBell's findings. The number of bacteria per gram of mud changes

Fig. 7-6. Diagram of changes in characteristics of marine bottom mud below the depositional interface. The Eh scale is in units of 0.1. [Data from ZoBell (1946).]

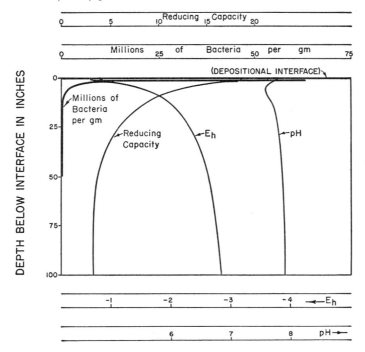

from 63,000,000 in the first two inches below the interface, to less than 1,000 per gram at depths of about 60 inches. The Eh becomes increasingly negative from the interface downward, from a value of -0.07 near the interface to -0.28 at a depth of 96 inches. The pH changes irregularly from 7.8 to 7.9, as shown in the figure. The oxygen content, though not included in the graph, is essentially depleted within a short distance below the interface.

The Eh (**oxidation reduction potential**), as will be recalled from Chapter 6, is a measure of the state of oxidation or reduction of the ions present. In general, positive values indicate that most ions are in their higher oxidation states, and negative values indicate that they are in lower valence states. The pH (**hydrogen ion concentration**), also previously mentioned, represents the alkaline or acidic nature of the medium or bottom mud. Neutrality is 7.0 on the scale; smaller numbers indicate increasing acidity, and larger numbers indicate increasing alkalinity.

Although the Eh represents the general oxidizing or reducing nature of the environment, the **reducing capacity** of the mud, expressed in terms of milliequivalents of methylene blue reduced by the mud, indicates the degree to which reduction actually occurs. The curve for reducing capacity in Figure 7-6 shows a decrease, below the interface, from 18 to 4. The significance of this is that, although the Eh indicates the general prevalence of reducing conditions, the decrease in reducing capacity with depth indicates that the largest degree of reduction occurs close to the interface. The mere fact that an environment has negative Eh does not mean that all ferric ions, for example, are necessarily reduced to the ferrous state. The actual reaction depends on the reducing capacity, and as Figure 7-6 shows, this capacity tends to lessen downward. Hence if some materials escape being reduced while they are shallowly buried, they may retain their state of oxidation indefinitely, even though surrounded by reducing influences of low capacity.

It is apparent, from an examination of Figure 7-6, that even under conditions of open circulation in relatively shallow marine water, a number of important changes may occur in the transition from sediment freshly deposited, to sediment buried a few inches or feet beneath the depositional interface. Evidently the number and kind of changes depend largely upon the nature of the sedimentary material. In nearshore areas of dominant sand deposition, the changes may be essentially negligible, since quartz is relatively stable, biological agents may be relatively unimportant, and waves or currents may periodically disturb the interface. Sand bottoms in well aerated waters near the coast have Eh positive, and pH from 8.0 to 8.3.

In 1952, Emery and Rittenberg published a comprehensive paper on the early diagenesis of sediments in the offshore basins along the California coast. A number of sediment cores were collected from the basins and subjected to detailed observation to note what changes occur with depth below the depositional interface. Some cores were 5 to 6 feet long. Among the properties measured were the mean size, the percentage of moisture, the percentage of carbonate ion, the percentage of nitrogen, and the observed pH and Eh values of the core material.

Among the most important of the changes noted was the downward decrease of water content in the cores. This decrease is related to compaction of the sediment as the overburden increases. The pH of the sediments generally increased with depth, and their organic content decreased with depth.

Emery and Rittenberg's study showed the importance of an integrated set of detailed physical and chemical observations on sediments from the depositional interface downward. It is interesting to note in this connection that in addition to the twenty-odd general conclusions about diagenetic changes that Emery and Rittenberg were able to derive from their detailed study, they listed a dozen lines of future investigation that were shown to be feasible and important by their investigation.

It may be anticipated that, as in the case of fine grained detrital sediments, carbonate muds should also reveal changes below the depositional interface. Ginsburg (1957) made a detailed study of early diagenesis and lithification of the shallow-water carbonate sediments in southern Florida. He recognized three dominant processes of early diagenesis, which he classified as organic, physicochemical, and physical. As in the case of clastic sediments, Ginsburg observed that some changes are very marked within the first few feet of burial. Organic processes include the aggregation of the forming sediment and the intermixing which goes on during the formation of mounds, tubes, and burrows by organisms. These organic processes exert some control on the pH and Eh values observed beneath the interface.

The physicochemical processes in carbonate diagenesis include solution, precipitation, and transformation of the carbonates, as well as the formation of associated glauconite, sulfide, and chert. Dominantly physical processes of diagenesis include compaction, shrinkage on desiccation, and penecontemporaneous deformation within the soft sediments.

Ginsburg observed a marked reduction in the moisture content beneath the interface, just as Emery and Rittenberg (1952) did with clastic sediments. In one core, the moisture (expressed as a percentage of the dry weight) decreased from about 250 to 100 in the first foot below the interface. No marked evidence of magnesium enrichment or any marked tendency toward silicification was observed. Seemingly, these changes occur mainly during the later stages of diagenesis.

Nonmarine Diagenetic Environments

Conditions in nonmarine diagenetic environments are different from their marine analogues in several ways. Fresh-water environments lack the content of dissolved salts that are found in sea water, thus the chemical changes involving these ions are less apparent beneath the interface. The downward decrease in dissolved oxygen produces reducing conditions, however, and apparently lacustrine mud is reducing and alkaline like its marine counterpart.

In similar manner to restricted marine environments, restricted freshwaters, as in swamps, tend to develop reducing acidic conditions in the bottom deposits. Some open-circulation or partly restricted fresh-water diagenetic environments develop oxidizing conditions, however, as shown by the occurrence of ferric iron in some bottom muds.

Some terrestrial diagenetic environments, such as in deserts or alluvial plains, are continuously or periodically exposed to subaerial agencies. Atmospheric drying causes marked shrinkage of mud, and produces mud cracks and related postdepositional sedimentary structures. Atmospheric oxygen tends to eliminate organic matter from the sediments, and to maintain iron in its ferric state.

Summary of Diagenetic Environments

The general prevalence of reducing conditions in the diagenetic environment, and of alkaline conditions below the depositional interface do not hold without qualification. In fact, the basic relation seems to depend upon the position of the zero-value Eh surface with respect to the depositional interface. Figure 7-7 shows three positions of the zero-value Eh surface. When the sedimentary medium is normal marine water with open circulation conditions, the surface of zero-value Eh coincides with the depositional interface as shown in diagram B of the figure. Under these conditions, the sediments accumulating mechanically, or by chemical or biological agencies in the oxygenated waters, become subjected by burial to the kinds of diagenetic changes discussed in the preceding sections of the chapter. On the other hand, in some nonmarine environments the zero-value Eh surface may lie some distance below the depositional surface, as shown in Figure 7-7C. This implies that postdepositional changes of a reducing nature do not occur until the sediment has been buried to a depth sufficient to bring it below the zero-value Eh surface. A sandy river bed may be an illustration of this relationship.

The zero-value Eh surface may lie above the depositional interface, as it does in environments that are characterized by stagnant deoxygenated conditions, as were described in Chapter 6, and shown in Figure 7-7A. Sediments accumulating on such an interface, especially chemical deposits that form in reducing (and sometimes acid) conditions, may pass through the depositional interface to the burial stage without marked chemical change. Compaction occurs as burial continues, with resultant decrease in water content, but the abrupt physicochemical changes observed in more normal marine environments with open circulation are either absent or less conspicuous.

The relations between the chemical state of the depositional medium and that of the diagenetic environment, as illustrated by Figure 7-7, imply that early diagenesis is most prominent where the zero Eh surface coincides with the depositional interface. At the other extreme, those sediments that are mainly chemical in origin and which are adjusted to reducing conditions during their formation, may thus pass through the depositional interface without substantial chemical change.

This and preceding sections have emphasized the present-day diagenetic environment associated with the first few inches or feet of sedi-

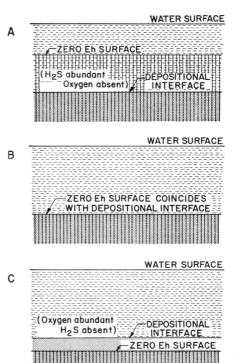

Fig. 7-7

Diagrams of relations between zero Eh surface and depositional interface for three conditions. Diagram *A* represents stagnant bottom-water conditions, *B* shows coincidence of the two surfaces, and *C* shows conditions when oxidizing conditions penetrate below the depositional interface. [After Krumbein and Garrels (1952). Copyright by the University of Chicago.]

ment below the depositional interface. The relatively strong changes observed with depth may imply that most diagenesis occurs during the early stages of burial. Depending in part upon whether deposition is rapid or slow, these changes may be relatively rapid or they may continue indefinitely after burial. Secondary dolomitization, for example, appears to range over a time span from early to late diagenesis (Pettijohn, 1957, pp. 421–425).

Diagenetic Changes in Sediments

As mentioned previously in this chapter, early writers on the subject of diagenetic changes tended to ascribe each effect to its own unique process.

As knowledge increased, it became apparent that several dominating processes are operative rather than a score or more. In a recent review of the diagenetic environment, Dapples (1959) suggested further simplification by considering three aspects or phases of the diagenetic process. The first involves changes in the sediment that occur during the course of its burial. The second includes the changes that occur in the early stages of moderate burial. The third phase is deep burial, sometimes associated with a long time span.

The first stage of diagenesis is thus, in essence, the passage of the sedimentary grains from the depositional interface to a position immediately below it as deposition continues, and the second stage is essentially that disclosed in cores of shallow depth, such as are reported by Emery and Rittenberg (1952). The stage of shallow burial is transitional to the conditions of lithification that occur more typically as deeper burial continues and as the process initiated in the early phases of diagenesis come into full effect.

An important integrative paper on diagenesis is that of Packham and Crook (1960), in which the concept of **diagenetic facies** is developed in some detail. Each diagenetic facies is defined as including all sedimentary rocks which, during diagenesis, have developed a mineral assemblage related to a particular diagenetic environment, expressed in terms of such environmental controls as pH, Eh, pressure, temperature, and materials present. Packham and Crook subdivide diagenesis into alterations that may occur before or during deposition; immediately after burial; and under deep-seated conditions. An interesting feature of the paper is the series of parallels drawn between diagenetic and metamorphic facies.

Diagenetic Models. Progress in geochemistry and biogeochemistry, combined with studies of sediment cores from present-day environments, permit more critical examination of diagenetic processes in terms of their controlling factors and with regard to their sequence as burial removes the sediment farther from the depositional interface. From this integrated viewpoint, it becomes apparent that diagenetic processes and the sequence of diagenetic changes that occur with continued burial exhibit many intergradations and interrelationships. Although it is appropriate and convenient to classify changes into categories, such as compaction, cementation, recrystallization, and others to be mentioned later, it is probably more rewarding to define a formal framework in which the study of diagenesis may be placed. Such a framework would start with the nature of the buried sediment and its interstitial fluids in terms of their initial chemical and physical states as they become buried; the Eh, pH, and other controls present; and the tendencies toward equilibrium that arise from interactions developed by these associations. An example of a cementation model is given below.

Such an approach would involve setting up models of diagenetic environments, similar to those used to study depositional environments. The authors of this book are not aware that formal model analysis has been applied, although some writers (Krauskopf, 1959 and Dapples, 1959) have approached certain phases of diagenesis from this integrated point of view.

Classification of Diagenetic Processes. Although the concept of a generalized diagenetic model appears to offer a rational approach to the subject as a whole, there still is need for thorough analysis of specific diagenetic processes. Numerous writers have set up classifications of these processes, and Table 7-4 is a check-list with some examples. Each process may dominate in some conditions, although, as stated, many of them may operate essentially simultaneously.

Two Examples of Diagenetic Processes. As a supplement to Table 7-4, the following sections describe two common processes of diagenesis. The first furnishes an example of a dominantly physical process, illustrated by compaction; the second describes a physicochemical process, illustrated by cementation. These treatments expand the material in Table 7-4 and suggest some of the interrelationships that have been emphasized here.

Compaction of Sediments. Compaction is a reduction in bulk volume of the sediment, caused mainly by the vertical forces exerted by an increasing overburden. Compaction is conveniently expressed as a change in porosity brought about by the tighter packing of the grains.

Fine grained detrital sediments, such as some marine muds, may have as much as 80 percent of pore space filled with trapped water. The compaction of these fine grained sediments proceeds in several stages, the first of which involves forcing the interstitial water out until the particles are brought into contact with each other. As compaction proceeds, there may be some rearrangement of grains with a resultant development of closer packing. The fine clay minerals may be forced into interstices between more rigid silt particles, resulting in the virtual elimination of porosity by the time the sediment is consolidated into shale. Weller (1959) discusses these processes in his comprehensive article on the subject.

Sand shows relatively little compaction in comparison with mud, for at least two reasons. First, the porosity of sand, at the time of deposition is lower than that of fine grained sediments. In addition, the absence of abundant matrix material in well sorted sand allows the pores to remain relatively open as the rigid quartz grains assume tighter packing.

The consolidation of calcareous sediments due to compaction is apparently more complicated than for detrital sediments. Fine grained calcareous sediments have a higher initial porosity than sand, but evidences of any marked degree of compaction during consolidation are not clear. Such consolidation

TABLE 7-4. CLASSIFICATION OF DIAGENETIC PROCESSES

PROCESS	DEFINITION	REMARKS
Authigenesis	Development of new minerals or overgrowths within a sediment.	Secondary growth of quartz a common example. Authigenic feldspar may develop in sandstone or limestone.
Cementation	Deposition of minerals in interstices among the grains of a sediment.	May be simple physical addition of cementing material.
Compaction	Reduction in bulk volume of sediment produced by increasing weight of overburden as sediment is buried.	Strongest effects noted in fine grained sediments. Sand shows little compaction.
Diagenetic Differentiation*	Redistribution of material within sediment by solution and diffusion toward centers or nuclei where reprecipitation occurs.	Chert nodules in limestone, concretions in shale are examples.
Differential Solution	Selective solution processes within sediment, as of particular constituents or along bedding planes.	Intergranular penetration; stylolites along beds are examples.
Recrystallization	Changes in sediment texture and structure by growth of small crystals or fragments into an aggregate of coarser crystals.	Development of coarse limestone without change in composition is an example.
Replacement	Development of new minerals by reactions between original constituents of sediments and materials brought in from external sources. New mineral develops in space occupied by original, without volume change.	New mineral may assume form of replaced mineral (pseudomorph). Alteration of mica to chlorite is an example.

* Adapted from Pettijohn (1957, p. 672).

as occurs appears to be due mainly to the introduction of cementing material at a fairly early stage of diagenesis, seemingly before the sediment has been buried to a depth sufficient to produce marked compaction.

In addition to the recent paper by Weller (1959), compaction is treated by Emery and Rittenberg (1952), and by Ginsburg (1957) with respect to calcareous sediments.

Cementation. Cementation is the deposition of minerals in the interstices of a sediment. It is one of the commonest diagenetic changes, and produces rigidity of a sediment by binding the particles together. Cementation may occur essentially simultaneously with sedimentation, or the cement may be introduced at any later time.

The most common cementing materials are calcite, dolomite, siderite, and silica. The cementing material may be derived from the sediment or its entrapped water, or it may be brought in by solution from extraneous sources.

When only one cement is present in a sandstone, for example, it is most commonly silica. If two or more cements are present, the first to be introduced is silica, and the second is most commonly calcite or dolomite (Waldschmidt, 1941).

A recent study by Siever (1959) on cementation in Pennsylvanian sandstones illustrates some of these relationships. Figure 7-8, adapted from Siever, shows the sequence of cementation and de-cementation in some quartzose sandstones. The initial sand may contain a very weak solution of silica in its pores. During shallow burial, this silica will develop overgrowths on the original quartz grains, producing small euhedral faces. With deeper burial carbonate cement may be introduced into the remaining pores of the sandstone, but as the process continues, the carbonate tends, in part, to replace the original silica or the secondary overgrowths. If, in its later history, the rock is brought near the surface by erosive agents, the carbonate may be dissolved, leaving behind a partially de-cemented rock.

The introduction of carbonate cement into sandstone subsequent to the partial development of quartz overgrowth is illustrated in Figure 7-9, also adapted from Siever. As indicated, the carbonate cement may simply fill the pores not already occupied by the quartz grain overgrowths. With somewhat deeper burial carbonate tends to replace quartz as previously mentioned,

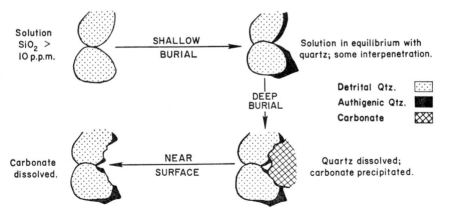

Fig. 7-8. Sequence of cementation and decementation in quartzose sandstone, from initial shallow burial, through deep burial, to subsequent near-surface conditions. [After Siever (1959).]

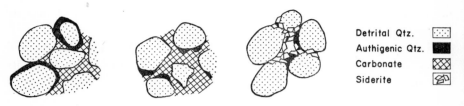

Detrital Qtz.	⬚
Authigenic Qtz.	■
Carbonate	⬚
Siderite	⬚

Pore filling   Replacement   Siderite rhombs

Fig. 7-9. Three aspects of sandstone cementation, involving pore-filling, replacement, and introduction of siderite rhombs. See the text for details. [After Siever (1959).]

producing a sandstone in which the quartz grains seem to be separated by patches of carbonate as indicated in the figure. A somewhat different pattern results when the carbonate cement is siderite. This cementing material is introduced as small rhombs that form as attachments to the original detrital grains or their overgrowths. Some of them actually replace the quartz as indicated in Figure 7-9.

The development of overgrowths on quartz, as illustrated in the upper part of Figure 7-8, can be used to illustrate a simple process-response model in diagenesis that is similar to the environmental model of Table 7-1. This is shown in Table 7-5, with the process elements in the left array and the response element on the right. The depth of burial could be expressed as pressure and temperature, and the biologic controls are included mainly as a reminder that in some diagenetic processes these cannot be ignored. The arrow represents the physicochemical reactions required to move from control to response, and hence in a quantitative model the energy terms would form an intermediate block as in the model of Table 7-3.

TABLE 7-5. EXAMPLE OF A DIAGENETIC MODEL (Shallow-burial Silica-cementation of Quartz Arenite)

Process Elements (Controlling Factors)	Response Element
NATURE OF DEPOSITIONAL INTERFACE Sharp PRESENT DEPTH OF BURIAL Shallow NATURE OF BURIED SEDIMENT Quartz Arenite INTERSTITIAL FLUID Weak silica concentration $pH = 8+$, variable Eh may be positive BIOLOGIC CONTROLS None necessary	⟶ Development of quartz overgrowths on quartz grains

RECONSTRUCTION OF ANCIENT ENVIRONMENTS

It was mentioned in the section on applications of environmental patterns to stratigraphy that diagenetic changes may complicate the task of reconstructing ancient environments by modifying the observable properties of sedimentary rocks. In many instances diagenetic changes are relatively minor, although in some nonclastic rocks, it may be especially difficult to discern original environmental textures and structures. Even when diagenetic changes are not prominent, the more subtle evidences of postdepositional change may afford clues to the history of the rock body during its burial in the subsurface.

In addition to his need for evaluating diagenetic changes for environmental interpretation of sedimentary rocks, the stratigrapher must take account of the rate of subsidence of the depositional area during accumulation. Because of the need for including the tectonic setting of the environment in sedimentary interpretation, the problem of reconstructing the depositional history of sedimentary rocks is deferred to Chapter 11, which brings the tectonic factors into the analysis.

SUPPLEMENTARY READINGS

1. Bradley, W. H., 1948, Limnology and the Eocene lakes of the Rocky Mountain region: Geol. Soc. America Bull., v. 59, p. 635–648. A very readable reconstruction of environmental conditions during deposition of the Green River formation.
2. Dunbar, C. O. and Rodgers, J., 1957, Principles of stratigraphy: New York, John Wiley & Sons, Inc.

   Environments of deposition: Chapters 2, 3, 4.

3. Emery, K. O. and Rittenberg, S. C., 1952, Early diagenesis of California basin sediments in relation to origin of oil: Am. Assoc. Petrol. Geologists Bull., v. 36, p. 735–806. A well designed study, supported by abundant data, of diagenetic changes during shallow burial.
4. Ireland, H. A. (editor), 1959, Silica in sediments, a symposium: Soc. Econ. Paleontologists and Mineralogists, Spec. Pub. No. 7, Tulsa, Oklahoma. This publication is invaluable as a source of information on the latest advances in this broad field. In particular, the reader is referred to the following papers for their bearing on the topics in this chapter:

   The geochemistry of silica in sedimentary environments, by K. B. Krauskopf.
   The behavior of silica in diagenesis, by E. C. Dapples.
   Petrology and geochemistry of silica cementation in some Pennsylvanian sandstones, by R. Siever.

5. Le Blanc, R. J. and Breeding, J. G. (editors), 1957, Regional aspects of carbonate deposition, a symposium: Soc. Econ. Paleontologists and Mineralogists, Spec. Pub. No. 5, Tulsa, Oklahoma. This symposium contains papers of basic importance in the deposition and diagenesis of carbonate sediments. The reader is referred especially to the following papers in connection with the present chapter:

The distribution of marine carbonate sediments; a review, by J. Rodgers.
Geological studies on the Great Bahama Bank, by N. D. Newell and J. Keith Rigby.
Early diagenesis and lithification of shallow-water carbonate sediments in South Florida, by R. N. Ginsburg.

6. Shepard, F. P., Phleger, F. B., and Van Andel, T. H. (editors), 1960, Recent sediments, northwest Gulf of Mexico: Am. Assoc. Petroleum Geologists, Tulsa, Okla.

7. Pettijohn, F. J., 1957, Sedimentary rocks: New York, Harper & Brothers.

Depositional environments: p. 588–605.
Lithification and diagenesis: Chapter 14.

8. Peterson, J. A., and Osmond, J. C. (editors), 1961, Geometry of sandstone bodies: Am. Assoc. Petroleum Geologists, Tulsa, Okla.

9. Twenhofel, W. H., 1950, Principles of sedimentation: New York, McGraw-Hill Book Co., Inc.

Environmental factors: Chapter 2.
Classification and description of environments: Chapter 3.

10. Weller, J. M., 1960, Stratigraphic principles and practice: New York, Harper & Brothers.

Deposition of sediments: p. 161–189.
Diagenesis: p. 292–318.

11. Weller, J. M., 1959, Compaction of sediments: Am. Assoc. Petrol. Geologists Bull., v. 43, p. 735–806. A comprehensive and analytical re-examination of this important phase of diagenesis.

12. ZoBell, C. E., 1946, Studies on redox potential of marine sediments: Am. Assoc. Petrol. Geologists Bull., v. 30, p. 477–513. A comprehensive paper on oxidation-reduction potential and pH of sediments. This is one of the basic papers on diagenesis.

CHAPTER 8

Stratigraphic Paleontology

INTRODUCTION

PALEONTOLOGY, the study of ancient life, in common with the other sciences, has become so complex that no single worker can gain proficiency in all its branches. The result has been the subdivision of the paleontologic field into a number of specialized areas: paleobotany and paleozoology; vertebrate paleontology and invertebrate paleontology; palynology and micropaleontology. Within each of these, further fragmentation is evident. We have specialists in Tertiary mollusks and specialists in Paleozoic brachiopods, specialists in Permian reptiles and specialists in Cenozoic foraminifera.

In addition to this inevitable specialization, the stratigrapher is being made aware of the results of studies of modern organisms (neontologic studies) which are exerting increasing pressures tending to modify paleontologic concepts. Advances in such fields as genetics, ecology, and biometrics generate principles that carry over to paleontology and, unavoidably, to stratigraphy. The average stratigrapher is not necessarily prepared by training or experience to apply advanced biologic principles to the interpretation of extinct organisms. Nevertheless, these principles bear heavily on stratigraphic concepts and must be taken into account. The stratigrapher should be capable of applying biologic knowledge without being a biologist, just as he need not be a physicist to use electric logs.

A collection of fossils is not a group of "figured stones." Each fossil represents what was once a living organism, whose remains in the rocks are testimony to the coincidence of a number of factors operating in the dimensions of both space and time. Like other stratigraphic materials, paleontologic data require organization and classification in order to become useful. A system of nomenclature is a necessary prelude to the recording and dissemination of the data. It is no exaggeration to state that the manner in which fossils are classified and named has as great an influence on stratigraphic concepts and interpretations as any other similar organization of materials.

In this chapter, the distribution patterns of organisms in space and time are reviewed, as are the problems of classification and nomenclature which are important to the stratigrapher.

DISTRIBUTION OF ORGANISMS IN SPACE

The Biosphere

Present-day animal and plant life extends over the whole surface of the earth, including all lands and seas. Life also penetrates deep into the earth, is represented in the abyssal depths of the ocean, and is borne aloft in the form of flying animals, spores, and pollens. The entire space occupied by living organisms is called the **biosphere.** In contrast to the lithosphere, the dimensions of which were established relatively early in earth history, the biosphere has expanded with geologic time as animals and plants adapted themselves to an increasing variety of habitats.

Like the lithosphere, the biosphere is not uniform in character throughout its extent, but it is subject to subdivision according to the horizontal and vertical distribution of organisms. The nature of the horizontal distribution is the basis for **geographic subdivision,** while vertical distribution is the basis for **bathymetric subdivision** of the biosphere. The pattern of the distribution of animals and plants in the three dimensions of space is an important factor in the analysis of the fossil record, and geologists are further concerned with distribution in a fourth dimension, time. Therefore, biostratigraphy requires an understanding of the ever-changing patterns of geographic and bathymetric distribution, and the effects of perpetual organic evolution on the character of the biosphere.

Ecology and Paleoecology

The organic population of any area, whether sea floor or mountain top, is composed of indigenous animals and plants descended from established residents, plus immigrants from adjoining areas. In either case, the organic assemblage contains only those elements that are adapted to the complex of physical and biological relations that constitute the environment. Migrating animals unsuited to any area because of the character of the food supply, the temperature range, the humidity or aridity, the presence of predators, or for one or more of many other reasons, would quickly be eliminated. Therefore, the distribution of organisms, geographically and bathymetrically, is largely controlled by the distribution of environments. The study of the relationships between organisms and their environment is the science of **ecology.** The 1300 pages of the first volume, *Ecology,* edited by J. W. Hedgpeth (1957), of the *Treatise on Marine Ecology and Paleoecology* is a measure the amount of ecologic data now available for geologic interpretation.

Biocoenosis and Biotope. Ecologists term an assemblage of organisms that live together as an interrelated community, a **biocoenosis.** An area inhabited by a uniform community adapted to its environment is a **biotope.** The sea floor is divided into many areal units (biotopes), each inhabited by a particular biocoenosis whose animal and plant elements are confined, by ecologic factors, within the limits of their biotopes. A trained ecologist, given an accounting of the biocoenosis, can recognize the environmentally significant elements and reconstruct the environmental pattern.

This sort of reconstruction is, of course, of little value in dealing with modern organisms and present environments, but it is of great potential value in stratigraphy. If it were possible to reconstruct the details of ancient environments and to trace the changing patterns of various environments with time, we should be able to understand many of the now obscure phases of earth history.

Paleoecology. The science which attempts to reconstruct the relationship between ancient animals and plants and their physical and organic environment is **paleoecology.** In its elementary form, paleoecology is simple, direct, and obvious. Marine shells indicate a marine environment, bones of terrestrial vertebrates a continental environment. However, in attempting refinement of ecologic detail, two major stumbling blocks are encountered. The biocoenosis, the living community, is only partly preserved and is confused by extraneous admixtures, whereas the physical elements of environment are not buried with the fossils. The latter deficiency is so obvious that its mention seems unnecessary, but it should be clear that ecology is a sufficiently complex subject when all environmental conditions are available for study.

Thanatocoenosis. The term **thanatocoenosis** has been suggested for a group of organisms brought together after death. This seems an unusually unwieldy term, but it is worth the effort of pronunciation if it serves to distinguish between the biocoenosis of any site of deposition and the remains actually preserved. The fossil biocoenosis disappeared with the mastication of soft-bodied remains by scavengers and the bacterial decay of whatever may have been overlooked.

Furthermore, sedimentation in any depositional environment buries not only the hard remains of local inhabitants, but also the preservable parts of swimmers and floaters that are carried by currents, perhaps from tens or hundreds of miles away. Not uncommonly, fossils are swept into a depositional site in the same manner as are sedimentary fragments, thus mingling the records of one part of geological history with those of another. Thanatocoenoses, the assemblages of fossils upon which paleoecology must be based, are obviously complex and should be treated with the respect and caution due them.

Ancient Biotopes. Fortunately, it is often possible to eliminate from consideration those elements of a thanatocoenosis which were not indigenous to the site of deposition. Obviously exotic fossils, such as Paleozoic brachiopod fragments in Tertiary strata, are easily detected, as are those fossils which bear evidences of transportation, such as abrasion or inclusion in masses of foreign lithology. Further narrowing of the field is accomplished by the elimination of floating types, such as graptolites and some of the smaller foraminifera, which may be suspected of drifting in from distant areas. Finally, by this process of elimination, the worker is able to focus attention on those organic remains which may be judged to have lived at the site of deposition of the rocks in which they are entombed.

If the geographic distribution of these critical and significant forms is studied and defined, it must be assumed that the defined distribution pattern, where not affected by such postdepositional agencies as erosion, is limited by environmental factors. Therefore, the geographic pattern of distribution of assemblages of environmentally significant fossils outlines the distribution and geographic limits of ancient biotopes.

The vertical distribution of such critical assemblages can be established in any locality by tracing the occurrence of the fossils through successive layers of strata. Once established, the vertical range of a fossil assemblage marks the duration in time of a specific organic environment or biotope at that locality.

Thus, an ancient biotope may be recognized by study of the fossil record, and, like a modern biotope, its geographic distribution may be traced and charted. Moreover, the distribution of ancient biotopes in time can also be determined, making possible the study and analysis of ancient organic environments in terms of distribution in both time and space.

This concept of biotopes may be clarified by considering conditions in a hypothetical ancient seaway. At any moment in geologic time during the existence of this sea, it is partitioned by a variety of environmental factors into a number of biotopes, each populated by a community of organisms, a biocoenosis, which contributes hard parts to the sedimentary record. The resulting sheet of sediments therefore contains the record of a number of biotopes and their pattern of distribution about the sea floor. Now, if it were possible to observe the course of events at one spot on the sea floor over, say, one hundred thousand years, a succession of biotopes would appear at the point of observation. Some of these might appear but once, but more likely, others would reappear, perhaps in cyclical succession. This appearance of successive and recurrent biotopes is the result of a nearly continuous shifting of environments and their organic communities under the influence of such factors as climate, depth of water, position of shore, and a host of others. Therefore, it may be seen that, at any moment in its depositional history, the

Fig. 8-1. Marine biotopes of Todos Santos Bay, Lower California. Living foraminifera characteristics of each biotope are listed in Table 8-1. [After Walton (1955).]

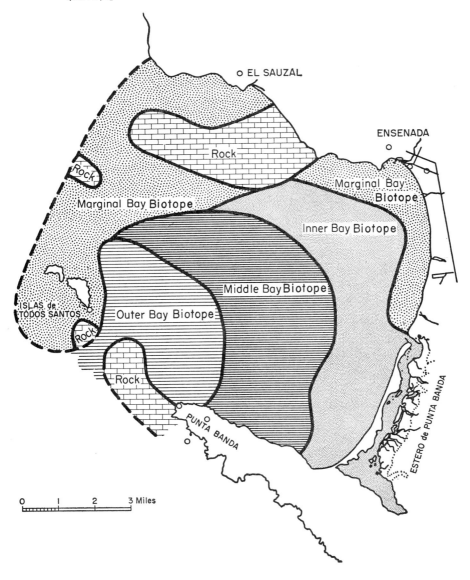

area covered by a sea includes a variety of biotopes, while any point on the sea floor may lie in a succession of biotopes as time advances.

Figure 8-1 illustrates the distribution of biotopes in an area of marine deposition. Walton (1955) has analyzed the living, bottom-dwelling foraminifera in 215 samples taken from the floor of Todos Santos Bay, Lower California. He found that the foraminifera fall naturally into four biocoenoses, each occupying a distinct area of biotope. The *outer bay* and *middle bay biotopes* are restricted to the deeper portions of the bay, generally at depths greater than 15 fathoms. The distributions of these two biotopes appear to reflect depth and attendant temperature conditions. The *inner bay biotope* is characteristic of shallow off-shore areas subject to a wide latitude of environmental conditions. The *marginal bay biotope* coincides with areas of accumulation of coarser sediment and Walton suggests that the distribution reflects conditions of bottom character, food supply, and other factors apart from depth and temperature. The species characteristic of each biotope are listed in Table 8-1.

A comparison of the distribution patterns of the living foraminifera and of the tests (shells) of dead specimens shows that the areal distributions,

TABLE 8-1. FORAMINIFERAL BIOCOENOSES OF TODOS SANTOS BAY. [Adapted from Walton (1955).]

OUTER BAY BIOTOPE	MIDDLE BAY BIOTOPE
Reophax gracilis	*Goesella flintii*
Uvigerina peregrina	*Reophax curtus*
Recurvoides spp.	*Proteonina* sp.
Chilostomella ovoidea	*Ammotium planissimum*
Bolivina acuminata	*Labrospira* cf. *L. advena*
Bolivina pacifica	*Reophax scorpiurus*
Bulimina denudata	
Globobulimina spp.	

INNER BAY BIOTOPE	MARGINAL BAY BIOTOPE
Nonionella miocenica stella	*Angulogerina angulosa*
Proteonina atlantica	*Cassidulina subglobosa*
Nonionella basispinata	*Cibicides fletcheri*
Discorbis spp.	*Cibicidina nitidula*
Labrospira cf. *L. columbiensis*	*Elphidium tumidum*
Trochammina pacifica	"*Rotalia*" spp.
Eggerella advena	*Bolivina striatella*
Quinqueloculina sp.	*Textularia* cf. *T. schencki*
Elphidium translucens	*Gaudryina* cf. *G. subglabrata*
Buliminella elegantissima	*Bolivina vaughani*
	Bifarina hancocki
	Planulina exorna

species for species, are roughly the same. Even though the frequency distribution of dead specimens differs from that of the live population, the general character of the biocoenoses and the position of each biotope can be defined by study of the dead tests alone. Thus, the distribution and qualitative composition of the several thanatocoenoses, or burial assemblages, can be used to outline the geographic distribution and characteristics of the biotopes.

If water depths and other environmental factors were to remain constant at Todos Santos Bay for a significant length of time, the volume of sediment accumulating on the floor of the bay would eventually be represented by a thickness of sedimentary rock deposited in each biotope. The study of these strata and their fossil assemblages at some future time would make possible the reconstruction of the character and distribution of the several biotopes. A shift in the geographic positions of the biotopes, under the influence of sea level changes, for example, would be reflected in the vertical succession of fossil assemblages. Figure 8-2 shows such a vertical succession and the environmental interpretations made by Natland (1957) in his analysis of Cenozoic foraminiferal assemblages from the Los Angeles Basin.

Bathymetric Distribution of Organisms

The vertical distribution of animals and plants is termed *altitude range* above sea level and *bathymetric range* below sea level. Sedimentary environments may exist thousands of feet above or below the sea-level datum, and each such environment has a particular distribution of energy, materials, and boundary conditions that define and limit the distribution of organic communities. In terms of the available stratigraphic rceord, the most important depositional and organic realms are those whose altitude and bathymetric ranges fall within a few tens or hundreds of feet of sea level. These are the transitional realms (littoral, estuarine, lagoonal, and others) described in the preceding chapter and the shallow marine realms, which require further discussion here.

In considering the depth distribution of marine animals and plants it is necessary to differentiate between organic communities (benthonic) related to the sea floor and quite different communities (pelagic) inhabiting the overlying volume of water. Geologists have tended to ignore this differentiation, and a confusion of terms is apparent in stratigraphic literature. Ecologists and oceanographers have not reached agreement on the terms and their defining limits, but figure 8-3 (adapted from Hedgpeth, 1957) illustrates a provisional system of classification.

Bathymetric Subdivisions of the Sea Floor. Seaward from the intertidal *littoral zone* the shallow bottom realm is termed the *sublittoral zone*. As is

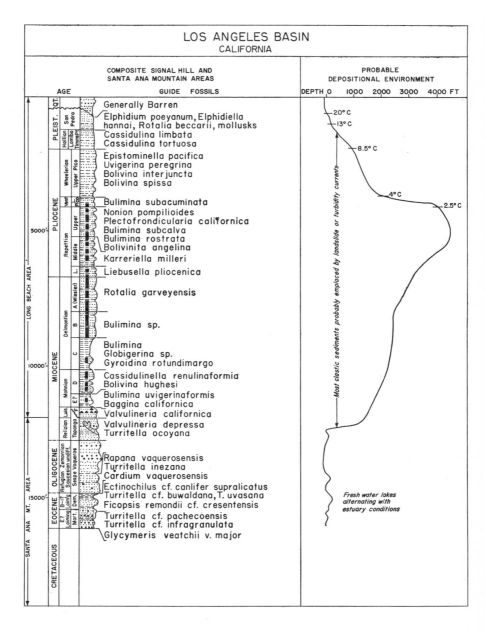

Fig. 8-2. Vertical succession of molluscan (Eocene-Oligocene) and foraminiferal (Miocene-Pleistocene) local-range zones in a southern California area. (*Left*) A generalized lithologic column, with subdivisions into series and stages. (*Right*) An environmental interpretation presented in terms of water depth and temperature. [After Natland (1957).]

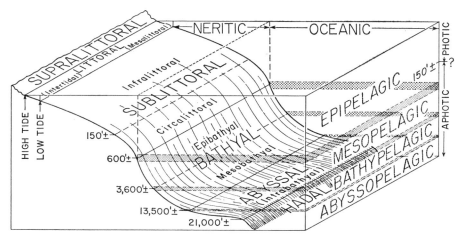

Fig. 8-3. Bathymetric subdivision of the sea floor and of the overlying water mass. [Modified after Hedgpeth (1957).]

true with the limits of other bathymetric zones, recognition of the lower limit of the sublittoral zone is determined as much by light penetration, temperature, and other factors dependent on latitude and geographic position, as it is on precise depth. However, a lower limit of 600 feet is suggested as an average. In general, the sublittoral zone covers the floor of the continental shelves and is the zone in which the great majority of marine sediments were deposited in the epicontinental seas of the past. Geologists and paleontologists have commonly applied the term "neritic" to this bottom environment, but a more precise usage confines this term to the water above the sublittoral zone.

Ecologists also recognize a shallower subdivision of the sublittoral zone, which is drawn to include those bottoms bathed with sufficient sunlight to promote photosynthesis and a consequent abundant growth of marine algae. This subzone, sometimes termed *infralittoral*, has an average depth limit of approximately 150 feet. Infralittoral sea floors, with their abundance of food provided by the algae, sustain the greatest density and variety of animal populations and seem to be responsible for many of the highly fossiliferous epicontinental deposits in the stratigraphic record.

Deeper marine floors are divided into the *bathyal zone* (from about 600 to about 13,500 feet in depth) which, in general, coincides with the continental slope, and the *abyssal zone*, which covers the floors of the deep ocean basins. Oceanographers apply an additional term, *hadal zone*, to the bottoms of the oceanic trenches, which form linear depressions in the abyssal plains, typically below a depth of 21,000 feet. With increasing depth, the deposits of these zones are less and less commonly recognized in the observed stratigraphic record on the continents except in the rocks of upheaved island-arc belts discussed in a later chapter.

Subdivisions of Marine Water Masses. The volume of water overlying the bottom zones of the seas and oceans is also a complex of organic environments. The organic populations are divided between *plankton,* the animals and plants floating at the surface, and *nekton,* the active swimmers, which can control their own movements. These biotic communities have contributed hard parts to the accumulating sediments of the sea floors, where the burial assemblages contain a mixture of the remains of both bottom dwellers and inhabitants of the water mass. The interpretation of such mixed assemblages is aided by consideration of the ecologic classification of the mass of marine waters.

The water mass above the sea floor is divisible according to several schemes of classification. The thin layer of water penetrated by sufficient sunlight to sustain photosynthesis and algal growth is called the *photic zone.* This layer varies with latitude and turbidity but averages about 150 feet and is an extension of the water mass overlying the infralittoral subzone. Deeper waters, below the depth of penetration of useful solar energy, are referred to the *aphotic zone.* The water above the sublittoral zone is termed the *neritic realm* and is contrasted with the waters of the deeper open ocean, which constitute the *oceanic* or *pelagic realm.* This huge water mass is subdivided bathymetrically into the four zones, from *epipelagic* to *abyssopelagic,* as indicated in figure 8-3.

The pelagic realm is by far the most extensive, areally, of all the organic realms. Fossils derived from the pelagic realm may be represented in the thanatocoenoses of all marine and transitional environments. However, since pelagic forms are dominantly minute and soft-bodied, or are equipped with delicate shells and skeletons, pelagic fossils are not prominent in paleontologic assemblages, rising in importance only where benthonic types are few. Wherever bottom conditions promote the development of a strong benthonic fauna, the remains of these forms are likely to obscure the pelagic fossils or at least draw attention away from them. Therefore, the thanatocoenosis dominated by pelagic fossils may be indicative of conditions inimical to life at the sea floor, a possible result of any combination of depth, material, or energy factors. Radiolarian cherts and graptolite shales are probable examples, and others would be found if bathyal and abyssal sediments were more common in the stratigraphic record. Occasionally, pelagic forms may be so abundant as to predominate in the thanatocoenosis despite the presence of benthonic species. Certain foraminiferal chalks of the Cretaceous and diatomites of the Tertiary are examples,

Geographic Distribution of Organisms

In the preceding paragraphs, great emphasis has been placed on the environmental control of the distribution of organisms, and it is difficult to overstate the importance of this control. However, the corollary thesis that identity of environment produces identity of fauna and flora does not necessarily follow.

As has been stated, the organic population of any area is composed of indigenous animals and plants descended from established residents plus immigrants from adjoining areas. Most organisms inhabiting any locality, even those considered indigenous, have descended from migrant forms. Throughout the course of organic evolution, new types, superior to pre-existent species, have continuously developed, spreading out from their points of origin to supplant older types wherever proper habitat conditions could be reached. If migration routes were uniformly available so that all possible habitats could be reached by a new species, it would quickly be represented in appropriate biotopes all over the world. Because of barriers to migration, however, the geographic range of any form is usually limited and no single species ever reaches all the biotopes it could theoretically inhabit.

It follows, then, that the easier the intermigration is between two areas, the more similar the organic communities in similar environments. Conversely, the more effective the barriers between two areas, the greater the difference in fauna and flora of essentially parallel environments.

The causes of isolation of land animals are relatively obvious, and the effects may be spectacular, as in the case of the post-Cretaceous fauna of Australia or the early Tertiary of South America. Since all seas and oceans are interconnecting parts of one great body of water, the reasons for the geographic differentiation of marine animals and plants is less easily understood. Perhaps a brief review of factors in the dispersal of marine organisms will help clarify the situation.

Means of Dispersal. The migration and dispersal of the marine invertebrates with which we are chiefly concerned are more difficult to visualize than is the movement of such mobile land animals as the lemming or the caribou. Many of the shell-bearing marine forms are attached to some fixed position, while others are able to move but slowly and spend their entire adult lives within narrowly circumscribed areas. It is obvious that these animals have very limited capacities for migration in the adult state, even considering the scope of time available to them. Some, like the bryozoa, barnacles, and certain corals and pelecypods, may be attached to floating vegetation and be dispersed in the form of **pseudoplankton.** Under more exceptional circumstances, rafting can bring about the transportation of many elements of a marine community over long distances. However, none of these more or less accidental means seems sufficiently dependable to account for the widespread distribution of common invertebrate types.

All members of the invertebrate groups important as fossils pass through a mobile larval stage. These larval forms (**meroplankton**) are commonly minute in size and most are equipped with some sort of locomotor apparatus. They are therefore capable of floating or swimming, and thus of entering the pelagic realm where they may be widely dispersed by marine currents. During such dispersal, they may pass, unaffected, above areas in which bottom conditions provide impassable barriers to adult migration and settle in favorable areas beyond.

There should be no suggestion here of active selection by the individual larva of the point at which it settles down for life. Many—in fact, all but a very few—come to rest in unsuitable areas and are quickly eliminated. However, the larvae are produced in such numbers as to permit the laws of chance to operate and make possible the establishment of a few individuals in a new area, thus extending the geographic range of their kind.

Transportation of mobile larvae by marine currents must be considered the chief agent of dispersal of the marine invertebrates and an important factor in geographic distribution. The currents are affected by the distribution of land and seas, by prevailing winds, and submarine topography. The changing paleogeographic pattern—sometimes dominated by emergent continents, as at present, sometimes by broad epicontinental seas—has resulted in a variety of degrees of provincialism and cosmopolitanism in organic communities of the past.

Barriers to Dispersal. Separation of marine bodies by land masses, which are obvious barriers to marine dispersal, results in differences between faunas like those on opposite sides of the Isthmus of Panama. The distance between suitable habitats may act as a barrier. Larvae of certain sublittoral forms, for instance, cannot traverse the bathyal and abyssal depths of the Pacific within the course of the mobile stage. Therefore, unless they can proceed by way of successive "island hopping" generations, they cannot make the crossing.

Although meroplanktonic larvae may migrate independently of bottom conditions, they are affected by temperature, salinity, and a number of other factors which may effectively limit their dispersal. Of these, temperature is probably the most important, not only in limiting the spread of larvae but also as a controlling factor in deciding the suitability of any potential habitat for a migrating species. As a result of temperature controls, marine faunas of any bathymetric level are roughly zoned according to latitude, modified, of course, by the disposition of warm and cold currents. It is interesting to note that arctic and temperate species are capable of extending their range toward the equator by slipping down the bathymetric gradient, thus maintaining a constant temperature environment while moving into lower latitudes. Tropical forms, however, cannot take similar advantage of the bathymetric temperature gradient.

The marine temperature zones which limit the geographic distribution of many animals and plants are not fixed in position, but shift with respect to latitude as do other climatic zones. Any given site of deposition may be the successive habitat of subarctic to warm temperate communities as marine isotherms shift within a relatively short fragment of geologic time. Studies of the latitude ranges of late Tertiary and Pleistocene mollusks of the Pacific Coast, for instance, in comparison with present ranges of the same species, clearly demonstrate shifting temperature zones.

Aside from the purely physical barriers to the dispersion of marine organisms, there are a number of biological factors involved. The most important among these is due to the fact that, under normal conditions, any area is populated by very nearly the maximum number of animals and plants it can support. In other words, most areas are saturated with organisms. Each type, under the spur of prodigal overproduction of offspring, is continually attempting to expand its distribution in all directions, thus exerting a constant outward-directed **biotic pressure.** Therefore, any exotic species attempting to invade an area must be able to overcome this biotic pressure in order to gain a foothold. This it can accomplish only by more perfect adaptation to the prevailing environment than that of the species it attempts to displace.

Effects of Barriers. The major effect of geographic isolation on organisms is a result of the absence of interbreeding between separated communities. Within any single community, genetic modification of a species, whether by way of mutation or minute variation, is transmitted by interbreeding throughout the biotope. By migration of larval stages, such genetic modifications may be further transmitted to other areas, and evolutionary advances in one community can affect the character of a given species over a large area. However, if barriers to intercommunication between communities are formed, genetic changes are limited in the scope of their influence, and populations of separated areas develop along separate paths. Thus, the difference in aspect of the biologic community of one area as compared with another of similar ecologic constitution is a function of the degree of separation and duration of separation of the areas.

An important and fundamental problem facing biostratigraphers is the distinction between differences caused by separation in space (geographic separation) and those caused by separation in time (temporal separation).

Separation of organic communities inevitably results in the development of differences in equivalent biological elements, but these differences arise whether separation is caused by a physical barrier, like the Isthmus of Panama, or by a time barrier. There is no interbreeding between contemporaneous communities separated by a physical barrier, and no interbreeding is possible between communities that occupy different positions in geologic time.

DISTRIBUTION OF ORGANISMS IN TIME

If we examine the fossil content of a succession of strata that includes several systems and in which the relative ages of successive units can be established by superposition alone, it may be demonstrated that the older strata bear organic remains that differ markedly from the younger strata, and various less marked distinctions appear in the rocks between extremes. Such observations, repeatedly checked and substantiated, lead to the almost universal acceptance of three basic biostratigraphic concepts: (1) Organisms have changed with advancing geologic time; (2) these changes are progressive; and (3) the geologic age of strata representing major portions of geologic time may be determined by their fossil content.

Application of these principles has made possible the enormous strides made during the past 150 years in the compilation and analysis of earth history. Without concerning ourselves with interpretation or analysis of these concepts, they are still capable of yielding vast amounts of useful data to the present generation of stratigraphers. In other words, the nature of the distribution of animals and plants in time is a useful phenomenon which can be applied scientifically and economically without raising questions as to the mechanisms of the distribution pattern.

These questions have, of course, repeatedly been raised and a variety of answers proposed. It cannot be said that the final solution has been found or that it is even close at hand, but, since certain stratigraphic interpretations are based on one view or another, it is worth while reviewing the past and current status of the problem.

The Catastrophist Concept

In the early decades of the nineteenth century, the stratigraphic significance of fossils, demonstrated by William Smith and others, was an accepted part of geologic philosophy. The majority of opinion on the explanation of the time distribution of organisms was strongly influenced by the teachings of the French vertebrate paleontologist, Cuvier, and his adherents. According to Cuvier, each major period of geologic time was terminated by world-wide catastrophe, which extinguished all life. Animals and plants were then re-established in modified form by an act of Creation at the beginning of the succeeding period. Within each period of time, the various animals and plants were thought to remain practically unchanged, new forms being introduced only at the widely separated times of re-creation.

This concept of repeated catastrophe was a popular and useful hypothesis. It offered no conflict with theology and permitted the concise classification of fossiliferous strata. Inevitably, however, as the gaps in the western European section were filled by more extensive studies, the inconsistencies in Cuvier's rigid chronological divisions became obvious.

The Concept of Organic Evolution

While the Catastrophist philosophy was dominant during the formative years of stratigraphic science, there were a number of workers, Bronn and Lamarck among others, who were impressed with evidence of gradual change, or evolution, of organisms throughout time, and who attempted various explanations. With the publication of Charles Darwin's epochal works in the mid-nineteenth century, **organic evolution,** based upon **variation, heredity,** and **natural selection,** became the accepted concept, and, with modifications, remains so today.

There are a number of important stratigraphic implications in the concept of evolution. Perhaps the most basic of these is the realization that a species arises from a combination of genetic characters at one place and time. The geologic range of a species, its pattern of distribution in time, depends upon the speed with which it evolves into something recognizably different, or is replaced by another species of greater adaptive characteristics. In either case, each animal and plant species lives for a finite fraction of geologic time, and once eliminated, a species never recurs.

It may be demonstrated that some forms have very long time ranges extending through several periods, while others have very brief ranges. The long-range forms show little evidence of adaptation to restricted environmental conditions. These so called **generalized types** are tolerant of a wide variety of environments and therefore survive over long periods of time. At the other extreme, are highly **specialized types** adapted to a narrow range of environmental conditions, and therefore subject to speedy elimination by physical or biological changes in their surroundings. Obviously, the species of short geologic range are the most significant in a time-stratigraphic sense.

The rate of evolution, so important in determining the range of an animal or plant, is not, in all cases, simply explained by degrees of specialization. Many biologists and vertebrate paleontologists are impressed with evidences of environmental control of evolution, suggesting that a stable environment results in a relatively slow evolutionary tempo, while rapidly changing environments promote relatively rapid evolution. The apparent coincidence between major epochs of crustal instability and major changes in the characteristics of the land vertebrates, as at the close of the Permian and Cretaceous, is often cited in support of this view.

While it is certainly true that some phases of vertebrate evolution were, indeed, fast moving, it is difficult, in many cases, to prove the coordination with complementary physical events. Thus, the elimination of dominant reptiles and their replacement by a varied mammalian fauna at the Cretaceous-Tertiary boundary appear to have been remarkably simultaneous on all continents, although perhaps not so sudden and abrupt as the interrupted record of some areas would indicate.

To attribute this event to the influence of the Laramide and related orogenies, however, is overstating the case. In the American Cordillera, profound mountain-making movements and attendant changes in environment began at least as early as Jurassic and continued several million years into the Tertiary. Yet, apparently simultaneous evolutionary developments in the vertebrates appeared over wide areas, including those, such as the Gulf Coast, not affected by the diastrophic events.

Invertebrate paleontologists can also find evidences of synchronized physical and biological events, but to many workers, such evidences are outweighed by examples of continued evolution of marine forms under seemingly highly stable conditions. Perhaps the most critical data are derived from the planktonic smaller foraminifera which evolved rapidly, though they were shielded from environmental changes by the stable nature of the pelagic realm. Should we therefore conclude that evolution proceeds at tempos quite unaffected by environments?

Space limitations prohibit further elaboration of this interesting topic. It is introduced in the hope that it will demonstrate the complexity of factors governing the distribution of organisms in time. Recognition of these complex factors and an understanding of their influence aid materially in making biostratigraphy a rational key to earth history.

CLASSIFICATION OF ORGANISMS

The vast amount of data accumulated in biology and paleontology requires organization for study and application. This self-evident need has motivated a number of systems of classification by which organisms can be pigeonholed into a variety of categories based upon a variety of attributes. Certain of these systems of classification are directly involved in biostratigraphic studies and some comprehension of their framework is necessary to an understanding of problems of classification of ancient organisms. The most pertinent systems of classification are those based on genetic relationships (**taxonomic, zoologic,** or **botanic classification**), mode of life (**bionomic classification**), environment, geographic distribution, and **distribution in time.**

Taxonomic Classification

The genetic or taxonomic classification attempts to group organisms according to their blood relationships. If it is assumed that life arose from a single combination of inorganic materials in one time and place in the remote geologic past, then all organisms are blood relatives of one another. This relationship is more apparent among animals on one hand and plants on the other, establishing the primary breakdown into the plant and animal kingdoms. Within each kingdom, various categories of decreasing relative rank, such as phyla, classes, orders, families, and genera, are recognized.

The fundamental unit of taxonomic classification, and basic to all the other categories, is the **species** and it is this fundamental unit with which stratigraphers are primarily concerned. The characteristics of biostratigraphic assemblage zones are commonly expressed in terms of species; thus, if these are not defined, the zones are indefinable. The geologic age of fossiliferous strata is determined by comparison of the species composition of their fossil assemblages with assemblages of known age. Such determinations are supported by lists of species showing the similarity, or difference, between the assemblages of fossils in question. In the great majority of cases the listed *names* are compared, rather than the fossils themselves. As a result, the age assignments of strata are strongly subject to the individual worker's concept of the definition of a species. Variations in the application of the species concept can bring about wide differences in apparent age, even where actual collections of fossils are compared directly.

The Species Concept. There is no unanimity of opinion on just what constitutes a species. To many paleontologists, the "splitters," it is the finest subdivision that can be established on morphologic grounds and recognized as different, in one attribute or another, from other subdivisions—thus confusing individual variations with species. Faunal lists prepared under this concept show little relationship to one another, and all collections appear to have come from strata of differing age, regardless of their demonstrable equivalency according to other lines of evidence. To other paleontologists, the "lumpers," a species is an open wastebasket into which are tossed quite unrelated forms unified by common stratigraphic or geographic occurrence. Indiscriminate lumping has led to assumptions regarding the chronologic or biostratigraphic equivalency of strata that may be widely separated in terms of both geologic time and position in the biostratigraphic column. Fortunately, these extremes of behavior are rare and rapidly disappearing, but their imprint is encountered in the stratigraphic literature upon which much current work must rely.

In recent years, there has been a growing awareness of the inadequacies of the species concept as applied by paleontologists, and a number of attempts have been made to reconcile paleontologic and neontologic principles. Part of the difficulty is caused by the inability of neontologists to agree among themselves on a definition of species, and this problem is compounded by the essential difference between the materials available to neontologists and paleontologists.

Biological Species. Most biologists consider a species as an interbreeding community of organisms. The interbreeding community has in common a complex of hereditary characteristics, but these characteristics may be expressed in various combinations by different individuals or **varieties.** Therefore, a range of variation in size, shape, color, behavior, and many other characteristics is possible within the species. However, in the same manner as grain sizes of sandstones (Chapter 4), the measurable characteristics of species can be expressed as frequency distributions having a mean and a standard deviation. Moreover, when measurements on one characteristic are compared to another characteristic for the same species, they are seen to be statistically correlated. The community of organisms that constitutes the species may consist of a number of geographically separate populations, as long as actual or potential communication in terms of interbreeding is maintained. Groups of organisms which meet this rather general definition are called **biological species,** or **biospecies.**

Geographic Species and Subspecies. Where the area occupied by a species community is subdivided by partial barriers of a geographic or ecologic nature, complete intercommunication and interbreeding are inhibited. The resulting subpopulations develop minor intergrading differences that permit the recognition of **geographic subspecies.** When the barriers between interbreeding groups in the same species community become absolute and impenetrable, two or more separate communities are formed, and each develops independently as a **geographic species,** without necessary intergradation of marginal variants.

Morphologic Species. Paleontologists cannot demonstrate either the genetic unity of fossil assemblages or the genetic isolation between fossil species. It might be assumed that individuals of the same apparent type, collected at the same locality from the same stratigraphic horizon, were members of a single interbreeding community, but no such assumption is valid in terms of geographically or stratigraphically separated assemblages.

Therefore, the concept of the biospecies is something of an abstraction to the paleontologist who must work with the observable characteristics of fossil forms—the preserved hard parts of plants and animals. Species described solely on the basis of morphology are **morphologic species**, or **morphospecies**; all paleontologic species are included in this category.

In practice, those fossil specimens which resemble each other in most visible characteristics, growth stage for growth stage, are placed in the same morphologic species. Ideally, the closer the approach between a morphologic species and a true biospecies, the greater is the usefulness of the species to the stratigrapher in terms of chronologic and ecologic interpretation. As has been noted, a wide range of variations in individual characteristics is common among organisms belonging to the same biospecies. The same inherent variability is present among fossil organisms, but in the absence of knowledge regarding the limits of the interbreeding community, the latitude of variation considered to represent a single species is a matter of judgement and personal opinion. Paleontologic "lumpers" will establish "species" with extremes of variability, while "splitters" will describe many "species" from a study of the same collections.

Investigations of the morphologic characteristics of living biospecies by statistical methods have shown that these methods are applicable to fossil morphologic species and can remove much of the subjective interpretation from the definition of such species. At a given growth stage, the measurable characteristics (hinge-length or number of plications on a brachiopod, for example) of individuals of the same biospecies are grouped about definable mean values with definite standard deviations. The characteristics of subspecies within the same community have slightly different but intergrading mean values and overlapping standard deviations. Thus, most modern biospecies could be recognized by statistical analysis of their morphologic features (including preservable hard parts) alone.

This statistical approach promises to provide the stratigrapher with well defined morphologic species that come close to representing biospecies, although much of the descriptive paleontology the past 150 years will have to be repeated. An early example of statistical differentiation among related species is provided by the work of Davies and Trueman (1927) on Carboniferous non-marine pelecypods. Burma (1948, 1949) has described methods whereby a number of individual characteristics can be treated simultaneously by multivariate analysis to define the group characteristics of fossil forms. More recent workers (Imbrie, 1957, and Sylvester-Bradley, 1956, illustrate a number of examples) have relied on simpler treatments of single characteristics or ratios between two characteristics in order to obtain values that are more easily visualized in terms of the morphologies involved.

Chronologic Species and Subspecies. The progress of geologic time introduces yet another complication into the definition of paleontologic species
that is not involved in the consideration of neontologic biospecies. Separation in time produces the same isolation of interbreeding communities as
does separation in space. Vertically successive strata may contain fossils
representing the same hereditary complex, with the range of variation present at one stratigraphic position overlapping the range of variation in the
succeeding beds. A series of collections taken from successive stratigraphic
levels would fall into an intergrading series of forms. The characteristics of
contiguous pairs of assemblages would exhibit the separate statistical means
and overlapping standard deviations that are commonly associated with
geographic subspecies. Assemblages more widely separated in a stratigraphic and chronologic sense would not necessarily show an overlap of
characters and would be clearly recognizable as separate species (**transient
species** of Imbrie, 1957) until the "missing links" were discovered.

In certain, relatively uncommon, surface exposures, fossils of a single
evolving genetic lineage can be traced from bed to bed without significant
gaps in the record. In such circumstances a continuum of variations in observable attributes may be found and definition of individual species can not
be made without recourse to arbitrary limits which are best established by
statistical methods. More or less arbitrary species of this type have been
called **paleospecies** by some workers (Cain, 1954), **chronospecies** by others
(Thomas, 1956), and **successional species** by Imbrie (1957). Chronospecies
have been applied successfully to the solution of stratigraphic problems for
many years, especially by workers dealing with Late Paleozoic and Mesozoic
ammonoids. A classic early example is provided by the biostratigraphic
column devised by Rowe (1899) on the basis of vertically successive heart-
urchin faunas in the Cretaceous of the south of England. Further attention
to the relatively unbroken micropaleontologic successions available to the
subsurface stratigrapher will certainly increase the importance of chronospecies in stratigraphic research. The application of chronospecies to problems of correlation of biostratigraphic and time-stratigraphic units is discussed in Chapter 10.

Higher Taxonomic Categories. A **genus** is theoretically a group of ge-
netically related species evolved from a common ancestral lineage. Since
these relationships are often obscure in paleontology, many genera are convenient groupings of species with superficial resemblances. In many cases,
it is necessary to identify the species before assignment of a fossil to a genus
can be made, thereby stripping the genus category of its value as a useful
level of identification and classification. Nevertheless, there are many genera
of stratigraphic value, since their geologic, geographic, or environmental

ranges are restricted, and their recognition permits a degree of stratigraphic analysis without the necessity of specific identification.

The higher taxonomic categories are even less firmly based than genera. Characteristics considered sufficiently distinctive to differentiate families in one phylum may be of the same order of magnitude as those used to differentiate classes of another phylum.

In spite of these difficulties, some of the major categories are useful, as, for example, the fusulinids, and the graptolites. The first of these is considered a family, the second generally a subclass; recognition of either one suggests involvement with a specific portion of the Paleozoic without further refinement of classification.

It is clear, however, that as increasingly detailed biostratigraphic work is done, more and more effort and thought are to be applied at the species level.

Stratigraphic Implications of Taxonomic Classification. The emphasis placed in this chapter on the species concept and taxonomic classification may appear as overemphasis to students of stratigraphy. It is quite true that a large amount of biostratigraphic work can be done without recourse to any formal classification. One need only review the contributions by William Smith to the Mesozoic stratigraphy of England a century and a half ago to see how much can be accomplished by accurate observations alone.

Today, however, results of a stratigraphic study are subject to interpretation not only by the individual worker but also by other workers involved in other problems, hundreds or thousands of miles distant. To make this possible, the data must be recorded in a form that is intelligible to all. Taxonomy provides the framework for classifying such data and the international language by which they may be transmitted.

A real understanding of modern concepts of the origin and distribution of species is basic to a comprehension of biostratigraphic problems. These concepts point out the fact that related organisms differ from one another in a manner that can be studied systematically, and that the differences are related to space factors, or time factors, or both. Determination of which factor is responsible for the occurrence or absence of a given species is a constant challenge to the stratigraphic paleontologist. This is a challenge which can be met by continuing efforts toward the recognition and definition of species of real stratigraphic significance and the exposure and elimination of spurious "species" which serve only to cloud the issue.

Bionomic Classification

Bionomic classification is based on the mode of life followed by various organisms. Accordingly, animals and plants may be divided into groups by the character of their mutual interrelationships. Thus, there are **free-living** forms which have no fixed or permanent association with other organisms, and there are **parasitic, commensal,** and **symbiotic** types which exhibit various degrees of detrimental and beneficial relationships with their hosts. This classification has many useful connotations, particularly in paleoecology, but it is not as significant to the stratigrapher as a bionomic classification based on relationships between organisms and their physical environment. In the case of the marine forms with which we are most concerned, this classification is most easily established in terms of the organism's relationship to the sea floor and in terms of its locomotor ability, if any.

Plankton. Planktonic types are floating forms that have little or no ability to direct their own movements. Their distribution is therefore wholly the result of wave and current action. The majority are microscopic to submicroscopic and most lack preservable hard parts. However, important contributions to the paleontologic record are made by such planktonic forms as pteropods, radiolaria, diatoms, and certain graptolites and smaller foraminifera.

The planktonic larval stages of bottom-dwelling types are important, as has been discussed, in the distribution of organisms. Such floating larva are termed **meroplankton.**

Some organisms normally living in a fixed position become attached to floating seaweeds or driftwood and float about like plankton. These, including barnacles, bryozoa, and many others, are termed **pseudoplankton.** Still others may be nonplanktonic during life but contribute floating shells to planktonic assemblages after death. The distribution of ammonoid and nautiloid tests is attributed by some workers to this pseudoplanktonic behavior.

The truly planktonic organisms reflect the environment of the pelagic realm; therefore, they are of small value in the interpretation of depositional environments. Their remains, however, may be deposited with those of almost any marine biotope, thereby forming the key to the correlation of faunas which may have no other species in common.

Nekton. Nektonic forms are swimming animals which can direct their own movements against the action of marine currents. If those bottom-dwellers which can swim short distances but which remain within relatively confined areas are excluded, nektonic forms are rather scarce in the fossil record. Invertebrate examples are belemnites and other mobile cephalopods. There are, of course, great numbers of vertebrate types, but the latter are insufficiently common as fossils to be of more than occasional value.

Like the plankton, nektonic animals are of limited environmental significance, although they are at least capable of restricting their movements to favorable parts of the pelagic realm.

Benthos. Benthonic types are the bottom-dwellers and are either attached to the substratum (**sessile benthos**) or capable of crawling, burrowing, or swimming on, in, or above the substratum (**vagrant benthos**). Benthonic forms, because of their characteristic hard parts, make up the great bulk of the materials of paleontology of each post-Precambrian period of earth history from Cambrian trilobites to Quaternary pelecypods.

These are the forms which are directly related to conditions at the depositional interface and which are subject to reliable interpretations of environments. Because of this environmental relationship, these are the animals and plants which may exhibit great diversity from community to community at any instant of geologic time, thereby taxing the interpretive powers of the stratigrapher concerned with problems of correlation.

Other Classifications

Identification of the environment inhabited by assemblages of organisms makes possible an environmental classification into such categories as littoral, neritic, biohermal, and others. The geographic distribution patterns of animals and plants are the bases for classification according to geographic provinces: Boreal, Pacific, Caribbean, and the like.

The patterns formed by distribution of animals and plants in geologic time establish the framework for a classification into such chronologic categories as Paleozoic assemblages, Silurian assemblages, or Niagaran assemblages. This is the classification most essential to time-correlation problems in stratigraphy.

SUPPLEMENTARY READINGS

The fields of ecology and paleoecology, lightly touched on in the present chapter, are treated exhaustively in the following references:

1. Allee, W. C., Emerson, A. E., Park, O., Park, T., and Schmidt, K. P., 1951, Principles of animal ecology: Philadelphia, W. B. Saunders Co.
2. Hedgpeth, J. W. (editor) 1957, Treatise on marine ecology and paleoecology: v. 1, Ecology, Geol. Soc. Am., Memoir 67. A collection of 29 papers on the distribution of organisms in the sea and in related transitional realms, and on the physical, chemical, and oceanographic factors affecting their distribution.
3. Ladd, H. S. (editor) 1957, Treatise on marine ecology and paleoecology: v. 2, Paleoecology, Geol. Soc. Am., Memoir 67. The first six papers are concerned with paleoecologic principles. These are followed by 15 papers on the paleoecology of selected stratigraphic units from Precambrian to Pleistocene and

two papers on the paleoecologic implications of modern depositional environments.

Further exploration of the factors influencing the distribution of organisms in geologic time may be gained from the following:

4. Henbest, L. G. (editor) 1952, Symposium on distribution of evolutionary explosions in geologic time: Jour. Paleontology, v. 26, p. 297–394.
5. Simpson, G. G., 1944, Tempo and mode in evolution: Columbia Univ. Press, New York. A discussion of evolutionary rates, their measurement and significance.

Varying points of view on the species concept are discussed in these works:

6. Cain, A. J., 1954, Animal species and their evolution: London, Hutchinson's University Library.
7. Sylvester-Bradley, P. C. (editor) 1956, The species concept in paleontology: Systematics Association, Publ. 2. A symposium of 13 significant papers.
8. Mayr, E. (editor) 1957, The species problem: Am. Assoc. Adv. Science, Publ. 50. Another valuable symposium, comprising nine contributions.

CHAPTER 9

Stratigraphic Relationships

INTRODUCTION

IN the preceding chapters the materials with which the science of stratigraphy is concerned have been discussed, and at least a part of the body of fact and concept dealing with the modes of origin of sedimentary rocks and their mineralogic and paleontologic content has been reviewed. Many avenues of fruitful exploration have been opened by further consideration of these topics; among potential subjects for more intensive treatment, the investigation of the complex interrelationships between masses of sedimentary rock is of particular interest.

These interrelationships tend to be confusing unless an accounting is made of the dimensions and scale of sedimentary rock bodies. The complete sedimentary record of all preserved deposits, from late Precambrian to present, rarely exceeds five or six miles in thickness and is commonly much thinner. Even such great accumulations as those filling the Michigan Basin, which constitute a much thicker stratigraphic section than those found in neighboring areas, are not thick enough to depress the surface of the Precambrian crystalline rocks into a concave form. Instead, the floors of such basins depart only very slightly from the normal convexity of the earth's curvature. Within the relatively thin veneer of sediments, the shifting environments and source areas and the successive episodes of deposition and erosion are recorded in the succession of lithologic types. No single mass of rock, such as a body of limestone or sandstone, is likely to exceed a mile in thickness, and the vast majority of such homogenous layers have thicknesses measured in fractions of miles—commonly in very small factions.

Consider the contrast between the paper-like vertical dimensions of individual rock masses and the enormity of their lateral extent, commonly involving tens and hundreds of miles, and in some instances approaching a thousand miles. In exposures, the significant and obvious vertical lithologic changes define units of rock, which succeed one another at right angles to the bedding. Parallel to the bedding, the degree of lithologic change is infinitely less, and individual units seem to extend endlessly.

This impression, reinforced by the linear nature of most outcrop belts, helps explain the emphasis placed on stratigraphic description and interpretation of vertically successive sedimentary rock bodies. Indeed, an influential school of stratigraphic thought in America, led by E. O. Ulrich in the early decades of this century, was based on the concept that most bodies of strata extend, virtually unchanged, until their depositional limits are reached or until they are truncated by erosion. Well over a hundred years ago, stratigraphic studies, particularly certain European investigations, had revealed quite contrary conditions, as will be noted later, but most North American stratigraphic work continued to stress the vertical differentiation of the rock column and underestimate the importance of lateral relationships.

With the advent of the practice of mapping smaller areas in greater detail and the initiation of many intensive stratigraphic studies based on closely spaced points of observation, it became apparent to most stratigraphers that bodies of sedimentary rock must be studied in terms of a three-dimensional solid geometry, an approach not adequately considered by subdivision into groups, formations, and members. Even more influential in this regard is the flood of data produced by drilling. These data, unconfined by linear outcrop trends and supported by the wealth of detail furnished by sample studies, cores, and, especially, mechanical logs, make possible the visualization of the complex solid geometry of sedimentary masses. It is toward the unravelling of these complexities that much petroleum exploration effort is expended, and stratigraphers can anticipate continuing advances in the gathering and analysis of critical sedimentary data.

A rational approach to the resolution and understanding of an intricate stratigraphic pattern demands a framework of classification within which description, analysis, and interpretation can be oriented. No such framework has been established and accepted with any degree of unanimity, and it seems unlikely that concepts and terminology will become stabilized for some time. Nevertheless, the present chapter attempts to examine the fundamentals governing the relationships among sedimentary bodies and seeks for a usable language by which the relationships may be expressed.

LITHOSOMES

Readers will have noted, in the introductory paragraphs, the repeated use of somewhat awkward and not overly meaningful combinations of terms— "body of limestone," "sedimentary bodies," "units of rock," and so forth. These constructions have been employed in order to avoid any implication that the units of formal rock-stratigraphic classification (groups, formations, or members) are necessarily involved. Such units are established and defined on the basis of utility and practicality in mapping and are of primary importance as *vertically successive* subdivisions of the stratigraphic column. In this chapter, the primary concern is with bodies of rock which would emerge if it were possible to preserve one rock type, say sandstone, and dissolve away all others. Each sandstone body would then be seen as a roughly tabular mass with intricately shaped boundaries representing its surfaces of contact with erosion surfaces and with other rock masses of differing constitution above, below, and to the sides.

Wheeler and Mallory (1956) have proposed the term **lithosome** for these masses of essentially uniform lithologic character which have intertonguing relationships with adjacent masses of different lithology.* The term is adopted in this book as a useful measure of word economy and to avoid confusion with other types of rock units. The relationship between lithosomes and the units of formal rock stratigraphy is clarified by reference to Figure 9-1. Note that the Rutledge, Maryville, and Honaker Limestones form distinct mappable units in various parts of the area of the cross section, but that all three limestones are parts of a single lithosome, which extends into adjacent areas where it is represented by still different mappable formations.

By extension, the lithosome concept is equally applicable to three-dimensional rock masses of uniform paleontologic content, termed **biosomes** by Wheeler (1958). The discussion which follows is based on the consideration of lithosomes and other rock units, but much is directly translatable in terms of biosomes and other biostratigraphic units. In addition, part of the discussion can be applied to time-stratigraphic units.

SHAPES OF LITHOSOMES

The shape of sedimentary bodies was discussed briefly in Chapter 4, as an important sedimentary structure. Since the shape of a particular lithosome is

---

* In the first edition of this text, the term *lithotope*, following Sloss, Krumbein, and Dapples (1949), was applied both to an area of uniform sedimentation (paralleling the usage of *biotope* discussed in the chapter on Stratigraphic Paleontology) and to the *body* of uniform sediments formed by persistence of the depositional environment. This was believed to be close to the meaning of the term as originally defined by Wells (1947), but subsequent experience suggests that neither Wells's definition nor the writers' restatement was sufficiently explicit. Wheeler and Mallory (1956) have noted this deficiency and have proposed that the application of *lithotope* be restricted to *areas* of uniform deposition, a restriction that is etymologically sound and geologically useful but which complicates the picture further by coupling the redefinition with the introduction of the term *lithostrome*, which they define as "a stratigraphic layer consisting of one or more beds of essentially uniform or uniformly heterogeneous character." For present purposes, the usage of *lithotope for areas and lithosome for volumes* provides sufficient terminology for clarity in description and discussion. For still another view see Teichert (1958).

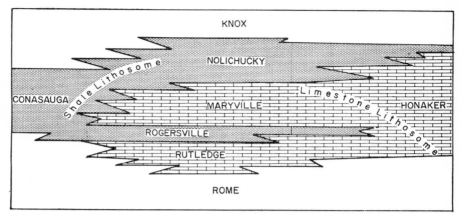

Fig. 9-1. Formations and lithosomes in the Cambrian of the southern Appalachian area. Between the Rome Formation below and the Knox Formation above, intertonguing shale and limestone lithosomes are subdivided into four vertical successive rock units at the center of the diagram, whereas only two mappable units are recognized at the right and only one such unit at the left. [After Wheeler and Mallory (1958).]

largely controlled by its relationship to adjacent lithosomes, a more complete discussion is included in this chapter.

Effect of Scale

As noted, the thicknesses of most lithosomes are so small in comparison to their geographic distributions that significant differences in shape are not readily observable without recourse to techniques designed to make the distinctions apparent. One such technique is the use of geologic cross sections and diagrams drawn with a greatly exaggerated vertical scale; another is the three-dimensional stratigraphic map, which requires no scale distortion. A more detailed treatment of stratigraphic maps is deferred to a later chapter, but the present discussion requires some generalized integration of lithosome geometry from both map and cross-sectional views.

Classification of Shapes

As a result of the attempts to classify the shapes of sedimentary bodies, a number of descriptive terms, most of which are based on the geometry of vertically distorted cross sections and some of which involve genetic implications, appear in the geologic literature. Examples are found in such terms as "sheet," "blanket," "lens," "shoestring," "wedge," "prism," which are purely geometric; and "reef," "bar," "bank," "channel," and many others, which carry connotations as to the mode of origin. Krynine (1948) has used the width-to-thickness ratios of lithosomes to establish a strictly geometric classification into blanket (greater than 1000:1), tabular (50:1 to 1000:1), prism (5:1 to 50:1) and shoestring (less than 5:1) shapes diagrammatically illustrated by Figure 9-2.

VERTICAL RELATIONSHIPS AMONG LITHOSOMES

The vertical relationships between successive sedimentary bodies are the most easily visualized, since they can be studied at a single point of observation, either in outcrop or in the subsurface, without involvement with the problems of lateral changes in character. Since the geologist is familiar with these relationships, through his routine subdivision of the local stratigraphic column into vertically successive groups, formations, and members, they do not demand an exhaustive examination here, and the following paragraphs are presented more in the nature of a synoptic review.

Conformable Relationships

Surfaces of contact between vertically successive lithosomes are considered conformable if there is no significant evidence of interruption of deposition between adjacent units. Conformable contacts may be abrupt, gradational, or intercalated. In each case, the change in lithologic character reflects a shift in the conditions of deposition or in the materials brought to the site of deposition.

Abrupt Contacts. Abrupt, yet strictly conformable, contacts between vertically successive lithosomes are relatively rare. Where such contacts can be observed, they do not persist over large areas but commonly pass laterally into unconformable relationships. Abrupt conformable contacts resulting from primary causes are most frequently encountered in areas of very slow

Fig. 9-2. Shapes of lithosomes. [Adapted from Krynine (1948).]

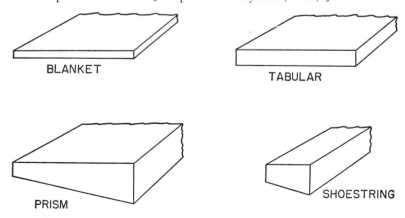

deposition, in which changes taking place over spans of thousands of years are represented by accumulations measured in fractions of inches.

Secondary postdepositional effects can result in sharply defined lithosomes. Dolomitization, for example, may selectively affect certain elements of a previously uniform limestone lithosome, producing abrupt distinctions in color, grain size, and resistance to weathering.

Gradational Contacts. Normally, the changes in material and conditions that differentiate successive sedimentary bodies are gradual throughout a variable thickness of stratigraphic section. The resulting gradational contacts are of two types, mixed and continuous. **Mixed gradation** occurs where two distinct sediment types grade from one to the other. A sandstone, for example, may grade upward into shale by gradual admixture of clay. Starting with a clay matrix in the voids between sand grains, the composition may change to sand grains enclosed in clay laminae, then to "floating" sand grains in a mass of clay, and finally to pure, sand-free, clay shale. **Continuous gradation** involves the progressive change in a single sedimentary parameter, without mixing of end members. Examples are found in sand-to-shale gradations in which there is a progressive reduction in grain size from sand to silt to clay.

Intercalated Contacts. The majority of intercalated lithosome contacts are problems of formation and member definition rather than questions of lithosome differentiation. When—as, for example, in a sand body that becomes interbedded with shale before giving way to an overlying shale body—a three-dimensional picture is assembled, the interbeds are seen to be tongues (lithostromes of Wheeler and Mallory, 1956) extending from the main bodies of shale and sandstone, each of which exhibits abrupt or gradational contacts with lithosomal tongues above and below. Such complex three-dimensional patterns are more easily understood after discussion of the lateral relationships among lithosomes.

Unconformable Relationships

Relationships between lithosomes separated by a surface of nondeposition or erosion are unconformable, and the separating surface is an **unconformity.** A number of attempts have been made to classify such surfaces. A modern example of such a classification is presented by Sanders (1957), who distinguishes between types formed by subaerial, subaqueous, and unknown processes, and between concordant, discordant, and non-evident discontinuities. The resulting terminology illustrates the complexity of the relationships, but the terms, like those with genetic implications proposed by Twenhofel (1926) or those based on geometric relationships (Heim, 1908; Crosby, 1912), are unlikely to find wide application.

The following three terms are most universally used and commonly understood by North American stratigraphers.

Angular unconformity: a surface separating tilted or folded strata from overlying undisturbed strata (the strata covering the surface of unconformity are essentially horizontal except for the effects of a younger episode of deformation).

Disconformity (Grabau, 1905): a surface of unconformity separating essentially parallel strata.

Nonconformity: an erosion surface cut into plutonic igneous or massive metamorphic rocks and covered by sediments. Less commonly the term has been used as a synonym for angular unconformity (Pirsson and Schuchert, 1920; Twenhofel, 1926).

Barrell (1917) introduced the term **diastem** to refer to the slight discontinuities in marine sediments that indicate minor interruptions in deposition. It was Barrell's intention to distinguish between major breaks in the sedimentary record (unconformities) and minor interruptions of brief duration (diastems). In order to make this distinction, diastems were defined as breaks in the record involving a "bed or series of beds" but not an entire formation. The implication that a formation has a definite time value is no longer acceptable, but the differentiation between major and minor discontinuities remains valid and useful.

Not all unconformities are equally recognizable, although a number of criteria have been developed for their recognition, as noted below. In some cases, recognition of the precise surface is very difficult, if not impossible, even though the disparity in the ages of the strata make it clear that an unconformity exists. Such phenomena occur when a deep residual soil is developed on an erosion surface and is subsequently partially reworked and redeposited with the basal beds of the succeeding unit. An obscure unconformity of this sort is typified by the contact between the Cambrian and Devonian throughout much of Northwestern Montana and adjoining areas of Alberta (Sloss and Laird, 1947). Other examples are found where limestones lie disconformably on other limestones without the development of a basal clastic zone. Dunbar and Rodgers (1957) have proposed that these obscure relationships be identified by the term **paraconformity**—not to be confused with the terms **para-unconformity** or **parunconformity** introduced by Crosby (1912) as synonyms for disconformity.

The growing availability of subsurface data and the opportunity to study many unconformities over wide areas rather than in a single linear direction along their outcrops, has reduced the significance of a complex classification of unconformities. From a regional point of view, all major disconformities can be shown to exhibit angular relationships, which may range from near parallelism to marked discordance. Similarly, within sedimentary basins, major discontinuities commonly diminish down dip to diastemic levels or completely disappear.

Regional Versus Local Unconformities. More significant than the distinctions raised by geometric classification is the recognition that some unconformities are strictly limited in geographic extent while others are nearly continent-wide in extent. **Local unconformities** are typically developed around the margins of sedimentary basins and along the axes of structural trends that rose intermittently while continuous deposition took place in adjacent areas. Numerous obvious unconformities in the Cambro-Ordovician of the Ozark Dome and Wisconsin Arch areas, for instance, cannot be found in the adjacent Illinois and Forest City Basins. Even more extreme examples typify areas in which marked tectonic activity was concurrent with sedimentation, such as in the Pennsylvanian of Oklahoma, where marked angular unconformities occur on anticlinal axes but disappear within a few miles in neighboring synclinal basins.

Certain unconformities, on the other hand, can be traced for hundreds of miles through the thick deposits of sedimentary basins, as well as around their margins and across uplifted trends. These, the **regional unconformities**, are identifiable only by the magnitude of the areas involved; there is no necessary relationship between areal extent and the degree of angular discordance or thickness of strata eliminated. In fact, many local unconformities may be readily identifiable at a single point of observation and yet be regionally insignificant, while important regional discontinuities may be obscure and difficult to identify locally. Yet these are the surfaces which provide an important approach to subdivision of the stratigraphic column, as discussed in a later chapter.

Nature of Unconformable Surfaces. Most unconformities represent surfaces of erosion; as such they may exhibit many of the topographic forms evident in modern erosional land forms. Typically, surfaces of unconformity are relatively flat and indicate an advanced stage of peneplanation. Some, however, have a rolling, mature topography that greatly influences the shape of overlying lithosomes. Bridge (1930) illustrates a classic example exposed at the base of the Cambrian in the Ozarks, and Walters (1946) has discussed the effects of Precambrian topography in the subsurface of Kansas. Elsewhere, buried topography can be shown to include sink holes, dendritic channel patterns, hogbacks, mesas, and many other erosional features. Siever (1951) presents an excellent description and documentation of the channelled pre-Pennsylvanian unconformity in southern Illinois, illustrating the importance of the regional view in analysis and interpretation of buried erosion surfaces.

In addition to the surfaces of erosional unconformity resulting from sub-aerial exposure and the action of nonmarine degradational agencies, there are also **marine unconformities,** established without benefit of uplift above sea level. Marine wave and current energies are capable of stripping minor thicknesses of sediment from limited areas. On return to a depositional regime, local unconformities are formed, which are commonly of no greater than diastemic significance.

Marine erosional unconformities of greater than diastemic magnitude are characteristic of depositional basins of relatively high mobility, such as certain of the Tertiary basins of California. Sediment, which may accumulate to considerable thickness on the flanks of such basins, is made gravitationally unstable by deep subsidence of the basin axis and consequent oversteepening of unconsolidated flank deposits. When the slope thus produced reaches a critical angle, huge masses of sediment move by submarine slump and turbidity current toward deeper portions of the basin, leaving a "scar" on the flank of the basin. The "scar" becomes a surface of unconformity through continued sedimentation which tends to fill and bury the effects of slump.

Although the majority of recognized unconformities represent a greater or lesser degree of erosion and stripping of older rocks, a true surface of unconformity can be formed by a pause in deposition alone. The conditions for unconformity without significant erosion are met in areas that have reached an equilibrium state, in which neither deposition nor erosion takes place. In this state, the area is said to have achieved **depositional base level,** a condition which persists until the equilibrium is upset by uplift (resulting in erosion) or by subsidence (initiating renewed sedimentation and the establishment of a surface of unconformity without erosion). While equilibrium prevails, the materials that reach the area affected are transported by the available agencies to adjacent areas where depositional interfaces are below depositional base level and are thus capable of accommodating and retaining additional sediment. The phenomenon of sedimentary transport across areas of nondeposition is known as **sedimentary by-passing** and is a fundamental process in the formation of numerous, obscure marine unconformities.

Non-erosional marine unconformities are relatively common in highly mobile depositional basins in which the sedimentary fill is dominated by turbidity current deposits. Each successive turbidity current represents a time of rapid sedimentation followed by a time of virtual nondeposition. The resulting sedimentary succession is therefore broken by numerous, minor local unconformities, each marking a nondepositional episode between sedimentational pulses.

Recognition of Unconformities. Although a number of obscure unconformities (paraconformities of Dunbar and Rodgers, 1957) defy precise location, there are many criteria available for the recognition of unconformable surfaces, both in outcrop and in the subsurface. These criteria fall into three classes: sedimentary, paleontologic, and structural. The following treatment lists several of each. A more complete discussion may be found in Krumbein (1942), Shrock (1948), and Lahee (1961).

Sedimentary Criteria. More than twenty sedimentary criteria have been proposed. The more important ones include the presence of a basal conglomerate, residual (weathered) chert, buried soil profiles, and zones of glauconite, phosphatized pebbles, or manganiferous zones.

The first three criteria are generally accepted as evidences of subaerial disconformities. The latter three, especially in combination, are taken to represent submarine disconformities or diastems, indicative of solution or nondeposition.

Paleontologic Criteria. More than a half dozen paleontologic criteria are known, among which three are most significant. Abrupt changes in faunal assemblages, gaps in evolutionary development, and the occurrence of bone and tooth conglomerates represent generally accepted criteria.

Perhaps the most decisive criterion of an unconformity is an abrupt change from one fossil assemblage to another in vertical succession of the rocks. If the beds below a stratigraphic surface contain Lower Silurian fossils and the beds above contain Pennsylvanian forms, a subaerial unconformity of major proportions is established.

Less marked faunal changes indicate unconformities of lesser magnitude. An abrupt change of biosome from marine to continental is significant. A gap in the orderly evolution of a single organism through a vertical series of beds is indicative of a hiatus. Bone and tooth conglomerates, commonly associated with phosphatized pellets, and which show some evidence of reworking, indicate at least a submarine diastem, if not subaerial exposure.

Structural Criteria. Four structural criteria are recognized. Discordance of dip above and below a contact is a definitive criterion of an angular unconformity. An undulatory surface of contact which cuts across bedding planes of the underlying formation marks a disconformity caused by emergence and erosion.

Truncation of dikes at a surface of contact, with no evidence of thermal alteration of the overlying beds, marks subaerial unconformities caused by erosion. Similarly, relative complexity of faults above and below a surface of contact may indicate an erosional disconformity. If the lower formation is more complexly faulted, with abrupt cessation of fault planes at the contact, an unconformity is established.

Stratigraphic-map Criteria. A number of useful criteria of unconformities are not observable at any single point of observation but, instead, require the integration of many observations, preferably by means of stratigraphic maps of various types, as is developed in Chapter 12. Some of the evidences of unconformable relationships that emerge from interpretations of stratigraphic maps are listed in Table 12-7.

LATERAL RELATIONSHIPS AMONG LITHOSOMES

All sedimentary bodies, large and small, widespread and local, have laterally bounding peripheries. In many instances, the lateral boundary is the result of erosion and the edge of the lithosome no longer represents its original depositional limits. Or, a particular lithosome may be bounded by lateral passage into beds of a different lithology. Such lateral termination of a lithosome may involve pinch-out, intertonguing, or lateral gradation.

Pinch-out

The term **pinch-out** is applied to the termination of a lithosome, a sandstone for example, that thins progressively to extinction. Pinch-out may be accompanied by an increase in the thickness of an adjacent body (a shale, for instance) which may lie above, below, or both above and below; or, pinch-out may involve thinning or **convergence** of the stratigraphic section. In a typical pinch-out, the lithologic character of the lithosome is maintained right to the feather-edge of the body. Commonly, the angle formed by the converging upper and lower surfaces of the lithosome is very small —one degree or less. However, in some bodies such as reefs and channels, significant thicknesses may be reduced to nothing in a few hundred feet.

Pinch-outs are among the most eagerly sought after sedimentary relationships, since many stratigraphic-trap oil and gas fields have been discovered along the pinch-out zones of porous and permeable lithosomes.

Intertonguing

Some bodies of sediment disappear and are lost in laterally adjacent masses owing to splitting into many thin units, each of which reaches an independent pinch-out termination. The resulting intertonguing zone has many vertically successive intercalations of thin representatives of two lithosomes. The numbers of tongues increases with the distance from the main mass of either sedimentary body, reaching a maximum as tongues split and split again and falling as individual tongues pinch out.

Lateral Gradation

In lateral gradation, there is no necessary thinning of rock units. Instead, lithosomes are commonly terminated by gradual replacement of their lithologic characteristics by those of another type. Lateral gradation may be either **mixed** or **continuous**, similar in nature to the vertical gradational relationships described earlier, except that the lateral rate of change is normally very low, and distances of hundreds of feet, or even miles, must be traversed in order to observe the same magnitude of change exhibited within a few beds in vertical succession.

Mixed lateral gradation of sandstone to shale is typical of the "shale-out" of petroleum geologists and is responsible for oil and gas trapping where the zone of gradation is relatively narrow. Similar relationships are common between carbonate rocks and shale and between carbonates and sandstone. Continuous gradation is exemplified by many sand-to-shale patterns and is also common among carbonates, as in the gradual change of a coarse biogenic limestone to a micrite lithosome.

COMBINED LATERAL AND VERTICAL RELATIONSHIPS

For the sake of simplicity, it is useful to separate stratigraphic relationships into their vertical and lateral components. However, some such relationships cannot be so neatly pigeon-holed, since they reflect the operation of both vertical and horizontal vectors. Among the most complex interrelationships are those brought about by the geographic shifting of the agencies responsible for the deposition of various sedimentary masses during a particular span of geologic time. At each instant of time, the distribution of depositional agencies governs the geographic pattern of sedimentation, and with passage of time, the shift in sedimentational pattern is reflected in the sizes, shapes, and interrelationships of the resulting three-dimensional lithosomes. The time-imposed interrelationships typically form systematic patterns that are readily subject to investigation, classification, and interpretation.

Instability of Sedimentary Environments

The most significant relationships are those discernible at or near the margins of sedimentary basins, where minor changes in sea level or base level cause marked displacements of sedimentary environments and the deposits formed within them. Consider the environmental pattern at the border of a modern depositional basin—the Gulf Coast, for example. A few miles offshore, normal shallow marine environments prevail, and calcareous muds are forming under relatively quiet conditions. The strand line is marked by barrier beaches formed by the action of breaking waves. Behind the barrier beaches, black muds accumulate in the poorly aerated bottoms of brackish lagoons. Farther landward, the lagoons give way to vast swamps choked with vegetable matter, living and dead. The swamps are bordered by featureless plains lying virtually at base level, undergoing neither erosion nor deposition to significant degrees. At some distance inland, the land surface rises above base level, and streams are actively engaged in eroding older sediments exposed on this higher ground.

The Gulf coastline marks a position of equilibrium among a number of opposed factors: the rate at which sediment is supplied, tending to fill in the shallow sea and extend the land area; the rate of shore erosion, which tends to cut into the land; and the rate of subsidence of the depositional area, which tends to sink as sediments accumulate. That all these factors will remain long in equilibrium and maintain a stillstand of the shoreline is unlikely. In addition, more or less independent factors, such as changes in the elevation of the continental margin through subcrustal movements or changes in sea level caused by shrinkage or enlargement of continental ice caps, may grossly affect relationships between erosional and depositional regimes. Any shift in equilibrium, from whatever cause, will shift the entire complex of subparallel depositional belts related to the basin margin, either bringing conditions of deposition to areas formerly subject to erosion, or exposing areas of previous accumulation to erosion. Thus, the stratigraphic record may be expected to reflect displacements of sedimentary environments and the interplay between erosional and depositional regimes.

Stratigraphers have long recognized the processes involved and their effects on the distribution of sediments and erosion surfaces. However, there has not been much uniformity of terminology applied either to the processes or their sedimentary record. The following paragraphs include suggestions for a satisfactory and usable terminology, but it must be admitted that a number of areas of potential disagreement remain.

Transgression and Regression. Conditions at the margin of a marine basin provide the most easily discernible patterns of shifting depositional and erosional equilibria. Furthermore, these basin margin conditions are among the most frequently evidenced in the stratigraphic record. Therefore it seems appropriate to use these conditions as a basis for terminology and classification.

Using the center of the marine basin (Figure 9-3) as the point of reference, any change that shifts the boundary between marine and nonmarine deposition, or the boundary between deposition and erosion, outward from the basin center is a process of **transgression**. The converse is **regression**.

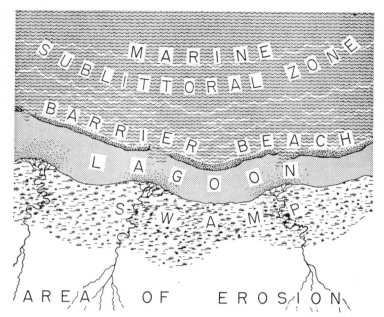

Fig. 9-3. Marine and transitional depositional environments. Any environmental
shift away from the marine point of reference (top of diagram) involves
transgression; conversely, a shift of environments toward the marine
point of reference involves regression.

Extension of this concept dictates that any change that brings offshore
(typically deeper-water) environments to areas formerly occupied by nearshore (typically shallow-water) conditions is also transgression, the converse
constituting regression.

Major sedimentary basins can seldom be characterized as transgressive or
regressive in their entirety, since at a given time, particular sectors of the
basin periphery may be transgressive simultaneously with regression of
other sectors.

Continental Transgression. Whereas the establishment of a satisfactory
point of reference for the identification of marine transgression and regression is obvious, this degree of clarity is not necessarily present in treatment
of shifting nonmarine patterns. Some offer no serious problems. Lake deposits, such as the complex of Green River shales and Wasatch sands in the
Eocene of the Rocky Mountain States (Bradley, 1948), can be described in
terms precisely parallel to those applied to marine conditions. Swamp and
other basin margin environments studied in relation to adjoining conditions
are easily categorized, as long as their positions relative to marine depositional realms are clear. Thus, if the lagoonal conditions illustrated by Figure
9-3 shift and displace the swamp areas, transgression is evident.

Where no marine point of reference can be established, the differentiation between transgression and regression must be more or less arbitrary; this need not generate confusion as long as the establishment of a point of reference is clear. In general, any enlargement of a depositional area may be considered a transgressive tendency. An area of continental deposition, such as a piedmont plain (Figure 9-4), may enlarge and cover previously erosional or neutral areas or may even spread into areas of previous marine deposition. Any such enlargement of the area of deposition is **continental transgression.**

If the transgressive piedmont deposits of Figure 9-4 crossed the intervening area of erosion and reached the margin of the marine basin, an opportunity for confusion in interpretation could arise. From the point of reference of the piedmont environment, the extension of alluvial environments into the areas of marine deposition would be transgressive. From the point of reference of the marine basin, the same extension, accompanied by retreat of the sea, would properly be considered regressive. Similar circumstances

Fig. 9-4. Continental erosional, depositional, and equilibrium realms and their relationship to an area of marine deposition. Spread of the area of piedmont deposition over the equilibrium area would constitute continental transgression; a concurrent enlargement of the area of deltaic deposition toward the marine point of reference (bottom of figure) would involve marine regression. Both processes may be active simultaneously and are differentiated by means of the point of reference adopted.

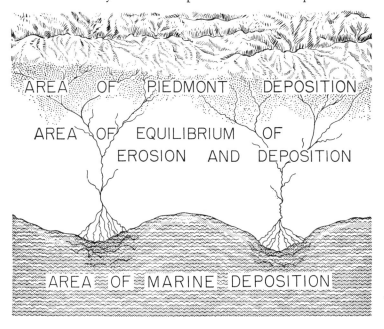

(the Cretaceous of the Rocky Mountain states exhibits many examples) have led to disputes that could have been avoided by recognition of the fact that two valid points of reference are involved.

Overlap and Offlap

The effects of transgression and regression affect both the vertical and lateral relationships of sedimentary bodies. The accompanying diagrammatic cross section (Figure 9-5) illustrates typical relationships. Units A–I are time-stratigraphic units identified by well established biostratigraphic zones. Sandstone, shale, and limestone lithosomes, representing strand-line, near-shore, and offshore environments, are indicated by standard symbols. The lack of parallelism or coincidence of time-stratigraphic and lithosome boundaries is typical. The marine basin reference point is to the left of the cross section.

Units A–E reflect **regression** and resulting **offlap** relationships; units **F–I** represent **transgression** and **overlap** relationships. Note the contrasting criteria for these opposed processes and their resulting stratigraphic relationships, as listed in Table 9-1.

The criteria and relationships given in the table are easily discerned if a cross sectional view such as that shown in Figure 9-5 can be assembled from outcrop and well data. More commonly, however, observations are limited to isolated exposures or wells, yet an interpretation of the stratigraphic relationships is possible. At point 1 of the accompanying figure, for instance, the relationships are fairly obvious. The regressive strata are truncated and the overlapping transgressive beds rest upon them with angular unconformity.

Fig. 9-5. Offlap and overlap relationships. Units A to E illustrate regression and offlap; units F to I represent transgression and overlap; unit H onlaps unit G, but both overstep units A to E.

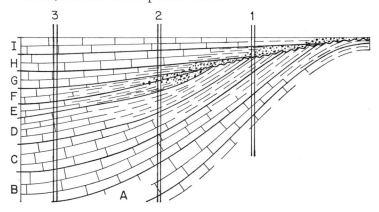

TABLE 9-1.   CRITERIA OF OVERLAP AND OFFLAP

	OVERLAP	OFFLAP
1. Lithosomes typical of near-shore environments progressively displaced in relation to marine point of reference.	Displacement away from marine point of reference.	Displacement toward marine point of reference.
2. Vertical relationship among lithosomes.	Offshore lithosomes overlie near-shore (fine-grained above coarse).	Near-shore lithosomes overlie offshore (coarse-grained above fine).
3. Relationship of lithosomes to time-stratigraphic markers.	Lithosomes become younger away from marine point of reference.	Lithosomes become younger toward marine point of reference.
4. Depositional extent of time-stratigraphic units.	Depositional limits successively more distant from marine point of reference.	Depositional limits successively closer to marine point of reference.
5. Depositional limits of strata.	Covered and protected from erosion by younger units.	Exposed to erosion; not commonly preserved.
6. Lateral termination of individual lithosomes and beds.	Pinchout common.	Truncation common.

Furthermore, strand-line sands lie with abrupt contacts on nearshore shales and are in turn succeeded by nearshore sediments.

At point 2, no evidence of unconformity exists between the regressive and transgressive phases, and it is apparent that the regressive strata were not exposed to erosion, even at the time of maximum retreat of the sea. Nevertheless, the offlap—overlap relationship is clearly expressed by the upward shift from offshore sediments to strand-line deposits and back to offshore conditions.

At point 3, all physical criteria of regression and transgression are lacking. However, by application of paleontologic data, an interpretation would be possible. Relatively deep-water faunas should be present in units A and I and an increase in shallow-water species would be anticipated as units E and F are approached. Since changes in water depth are almost inevitably related to advances and retreats of the sea, this information alone is sufficient for the detection of regression and offlap from A to E; transgression and overlap from F to I.

Onlap and Overstep. Offlap relations pose few questions of terminology and classification. By its very nature, regression tends to obliterate its own record as the depositional medium withdraws and exposes the newly formed sediments to erosion. The most common expression of offlap is an unconformity developed on truncated strata.

Transgression, on the other hand, covers and preserves its record, thus introducing terminological problems. The term **overlap** has been applied indiscriminately to both the burial of the truncated edges of underlying units (as units A–D of Figure 9-5 are covered by units G–I) and to the progressive pinching out of strata in a transgressing succession (as in units F–I of the cross section). Thus, overlap may refer to the progressive burial of an unconformity and to the mutual relationships of transgressive strata above an unconformity.

A number of geologists have objected to this ambiguity (Melton, 1947; Lovely, 1948; Swain, 1949) and have suggested clarification. There is no strong consensus of opinion, and usage will no doubt continue to vary, but there is some justification for distinguishing between the two relationships in cases where the meaning is not implicit. The following definitions (modified from Swain, 1949) are offered to clarify the distinction between the two component relationships of overlap.

Onlap: the relationships *within* an overlapping succession, in which each unit of strata reaches a depositional pinch-out and is transgressed by the next overlying unit; each in turn terminates farther from the point of reference. Unit G (Figure 9-5) *onlaps* unit F and is onlapped by unit H.

Overstep: the relationships *between* an overlapping succession and the truncated strata below the surface of unconformity. Unit G (Figure 9-5) *oversteps* unit D.

SEDIMENTARY FACIES

From the early decades of the nineteenth century to the present, all geologists who rejected the rigid and formalized strictures of Werner's Neptunism and accepted Hutton's uniformitarian concepts have recognized the role of environment in the accumulation of sediments. Further, it has long been apparent that the variety of depositional environments influencing present-day sedimentation was equally effective in controlling the character of ancient sediments. In the 1830's, for example, Sedgwick and Murchison recognized that environmental differences were responsible for the lithologic and paleontologic contrasts between the Old Red Sandstone of South Wales and equivalent marine beds in Devonshire. The French geologist Constant Prevost published a paper in 1838 in which he discusses the effect of environment on accumulating sediments and their contained fossils and points out that similar rocks and fossil assemblages may indicate equivalency in environment rather than equivalency in age. Concurrently, many other British and Continental workers were encountering complex stratigraphic relationships of the types discussed earlier in this chapter. However, their terminology did not differentiate between vertically successive units of strata (formations, assemblage zones, and stages of modern nomenclature), representing changing conditions with the passage of time, and lateral changes, representing differences in depositional conditions at the same geologic time.

Gressly and the Definition of "Facies."

A perceptive Swiss geologist, Amanz Gressly (1838) attacked the Mesozoic stratigraphy of the Jura Mountain Canton of Solothurn and studied these well-exposed and abundantly fossiliferous strata in detail. He recognized the Triassic and Jurassic Systems ("formations" in his usage) in the Solothurnian Jura and differentiated each into vertically successive "groupes" and "terrains" which are clearly rock-stratigraphic units (modern geologists would call them groups and formations, or formations and members). Gressly was not satisfied with studying the rock succession at a number of separate points represented by isolated measured sections. Instead, he traced each unit "in the horizontal dimension" along its strike and immediately encountered marked lateral changes in lithology and paleontology of the sort noted elsewhere by his contemporaries.

The Jura Mountain area is a classic one for the study of such laterally developed shifts in the character of deposition, and it is certain that Gressly had a more nearly perfect documentation of the relationships than workers in other areas. In any case, he found he could not adequately describe the stratigraphy of the area in terms of a vertical succession of "groupes" and "terrains." To designate the lateral changes in the lithologic and paleontologic aspect or appearance of each unit, he proposed the term **facies** (generally pronounced with a long "ā" in North America, a short "ă" elsewhere) and used the word in the description and analysis of each rock-stratigraphic unit.

Nonstratigraphic Facies

Although stratigraphers may properly claim to be the first geologists to use the term "facies" systematically, petrologists and biologists have also adopted the term. The concept and usage of "metamorphic facies" has been made familiar to most geologists by Eskola (1915). Usages such as "facies" of igneous rocks and "mineral facies" (Eskola, 1922) are less commonly encountered in the literature, but remain in the petrologic vocabulary. There has been some complaint by stratigraphers regarding the usurpation of a stratigraphic term, but in the context of the petrologic usage there is little opportunity for confusion.

Ecologists concerned with modern faunas and floras have also used "facies." Application of "facies" to the differentiation of a sea floor ("sand-bottom facies," "oyster-bank facies," etc.) raises the possibility of confusion with stratigraphic facies for which similar words may be used in reference to the character of the sediment formed rather than the surface of deposition. Where there is a chance of confusion, as in paleoecologic studies, geologists should avoid the use of "facies" in a biologic sense and use "lithotope," "biotope," or "depositional surface" when speaking of areas—"lithosome," "biosome," and "facies" are thus reserved to denote volumes of sediment.

Varied Usages of "Facies" in Stratigraphy

Gressly's applications of the term "facies," particularly in his descriptions of Jurassic units, make it quite clear that he intended to confine usage to lateral changes within a stratigraphic unit. However, in discussing the recurrence of similar facies, representing similar environments, in the deposits of successive portions of Jurassic time, he writes of facies "in the vertical direction." Gressly was trying to point out that rocks of the same lithologic and paleontologic aspect appear in vertical succession without regard to stratigraphic boundaries, but this has been widely, and, the present writers believe, mistakenly interpreted to mean that facies and facies changes refer to vertical as well as lateral differences in character.

Gressly states: ". . . the sum of [lateral] changes (*ensemble de modifications*) which I call facies." He then goes on to describe "sandy," "muddy," "littoral," "pelagic," and other facies, designating them in terms of both sediment type and inferred environment. This, along with the confusion between vertical and lateral relationships, has led to widely varying usages and definitions of "facies" that have been reviewed by Moore (1949, 1957), Teichert (1958), and Weller (1958).

Stratigraphically Unconfined Facies. Continental stratigraphers tend to designate "facies" without stratigraphic limitations and in both vertical and lateral dimensions. Johannes Walther (1893–1894), for example, enunciated the *Law of Correlation of Facies*, which essentially states that within a given sedimentary cycle, the same succession of facies that occurs laterally is also present in vertical succession. Walther's "Law" appears to have been anticipated many years earlier in a paper by the Russian geologist, Golovkinsky (according to Lombard, 1956). In any case, the concept is as old as Gressly and Prevost and remains a ruling principle and practice in much European stratigraphic synthesis.

The influential French textbook, "Traité de Géologie," by E. Haug (1907), defines facies as "the sum of the lithologic and paleontologic characteristics of a [sedimentary] deposit at a given place." This is perhaps the most generally accepted and vigorously defended definition among Continental stratigraphers (see comments by C. P. M. Frijlinck and J. Cuvillier following paper by Sloss (1956). In European practice, the term "facies," defined in this manner, has been usefully applied to sedimentary masses (lithosomes) in environmental interpretation. It is also implicit in European usage that a facies does not stand by itself, but is instead an indication of change in character relative to adjacent facies. This preserves Gressly's essential principle and makes such applications significant and valuable.

A number of workers have utilized the facies concept in a stratigraphically unconfined sense to devise facies classifications related to specific environmental interpretations. Nalivkin (1955–1956, reviewed by Teichert, 1958) has proposed a complex facies treatment in which he introduces a hierarchical facies classification in environmental terms, which is comparable to biologic classification. Others have seen value in identifying sedimentary masses deposited in specific tectonic settings as "geosynclinal facies," "shelf facies," and so forth. Still other usages employ a geographic or paleogeographic differentiation into "western facies," "boreal facies," and the like, particularly where an analysis of fossil assemblages is involved.

If the term facies were used only to convey a sense of change, or of contrast between differing conditions of deposition, there is no question that the descriptions rendered would be more meaningful. No such claim can be made for the indiscriminate application of the term to all bodies of rock of similar appearance, as in referring to all evaporites as "evaporite facies," or all red beds as "red-bed facies." If employed in this manner, the term is reduced to stratigraphic jargon, and its use contributes nothing to description or analysis.

Facies of Specific Stratigraphic Units. While European geologists concentrated on the useful employment of "facies" in a stratigraphically unconfined sense, they were not unaware of the distinction between vertically and laterally successive bodies of rock of differing character. Mojsisovics (1879) made a clear distinction between *isopic facies* (similar facies), which are repeated in vertical succession, and *heteropic facies* (differing facies), which replace one another laterally in deposits of the same age. For many years, North American stratigraphers lagged behind their European colleagues in formal application of the facies concept. However, in the past two or three decades, the concept has been utilized with increased interest and emphasis has been placed on applying it to the identification and description of lithologic and paleontologic changes within defined stratigraphic boundaries. Facies differentiated in time-stratigraphic units are the heteropic facies of Mojsisovics; other applications have extended the usage to facies confined within rock-stratigraphic limits without necessary regard for time equivalence.

Caster (1934) proposed a type of facies classification involving both rock- and time-stratigraphic units. Basing his concepts on the regressive Upper Devonian strata of Pennsylvania (Figure 9-6), Caster proposed that each lithologic assemblage, representative of a distinct depositional environment, be termed a *magnafacies*, and be identified by an appropriate geographic name, whereas each portion of a magnafacies between traceable time-strati- graphic boundaries should be termed a *parvafacies* and also geographically identified. Except for the fact that the concept of magnafacies is tied to regressive and diachronous relationships, the term is very nearly synonymous with lithosome and precedes the latter by twenty-two years. Parvafacies are the heteropic facies of European usage.

Other examples of American applications of the facies concept demon- strate that, although there is general agreement regarding the restriction of the term to the differentiation of a defined stratigraphic unit, there are at least two kinds of facies recognized. In one concept, facies are intertongued rock masses of differing characteristics, which, in any given vertical section, may occur singly or repeatedly. Figure 9-7, from Cooper and Cooper (1946), is a northeast to southwest cross section of certain Middle Ordovician formations in northern Virginia. In this example, two facies are recognized in the Edinburg Formation: (1) Liberty Hall facies of black limestone and

Fig. 9-6. Diagrammatic cross section of part of the Upper Devonian of Pennsyl- vania, showing regressive lithosomes, identified as magnafacies; each magnafacies is subdivided into parvafacies by time-stratigraphic surfaces. [Modified from Moore (1949), after Caster (1934).]

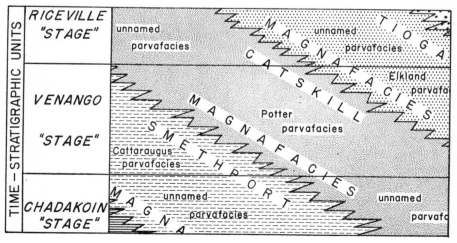

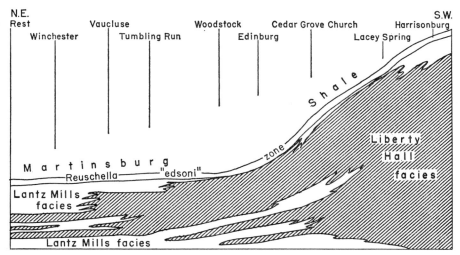

Fig. 9-7. Cross section of part of the Middle Ordovician of northern Virginia. A black limestone and black shale lithosome, the "Liberty Fall facies," is shown intertonguing with a light colored limestone lithosome, the "Lantz Mills facies." [After Cooper and Cooper (1946).]

black shale, and (2) Lantz Mills facies of "cobbly to nodular, buff-weathering limestone." Note that although the Liberty Hall facies is dominant in the southwest and the Lantz Mills in the northeast, the two facies intertongue and are intercalated at intermediate points of observation.

Other workers have handled similar intertonguing relationships without recourse to facies terminology. An example is given by Pike's (1947) treatment of intertonguing Upper Cretaceous sandstones and shales of the Colorado Plateau, as shown on Figure 9-8. Note that the application of individual names to mappable members makes the interrelationships apparent and that the introduction of facies would add no further clarification. It should also be noted that the carbonate and shale bodies of the Ordovician example and the sandstone and shale bodies of the Cretaceous example are lithosomes in the sense that the term is used in this text.

A few investigators have mapped the areal distribution of facies of the intertongued type. Figure 9-9 shows the distribution in Illinois of three facies (lithosomes) of one member of the Upper Ordovician Maquoketa Formation, as mapped by Du Bois (1945). Distinct patterns are used in the figure to indicate the areas of intertonguing. In other cases of this type, the same differentiation is made through recognition of separate rock-stratigraphic units (and lithosomes), as in the Cretaceous example cited.

Another concept applied in North America treats facies as mutually exclusive areal subdivisions of a defined stratigraphic unit. Defined in this

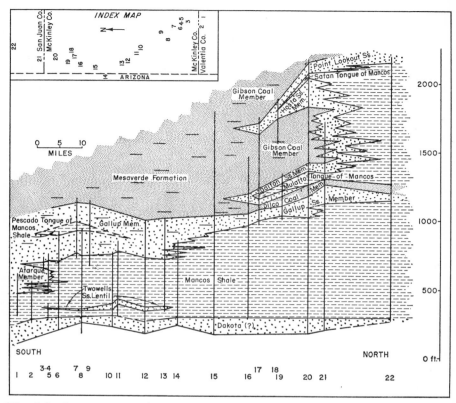

Fig. 9-8. Cross section of Upper Cretaceous strata in New Mexico, illustrating the treatment of intertonguing relationships by the identification of individual tongues and members. [Modified from Pike (1947).]

manner, facies do not intertongue with one another nor is more than a single facies recognized in a given stratigraphic unit at any one spot. Areal differentiation of this sort has long been applied in rock-stratigraphic nomenclature to distinguish among lateral variants within the regional distribution of a major stratigraphic unit. The Pennsylvanian and Lower Permian strata of the Northern Rocky Mountain states, for example, constitute an easily recognizable and mappable rock unit dominated by sandstone. Areal variation in the character of the sandstone has led to identification of a number of separate formations, each representing a lithologic variant, and each occupying an exclusive area. As an illustration, the arkosic sands of Colorado are termed the Fountain Formation; in Wyoming, interbedded arkose and quartzose sands are placed in the Casper Formation whereas pure quartzose sandstone is mapped as Tensleep. Each may be considered a facies of the major regional unit, but each also forms a mappable rock unit throughout a significant area and is more properly defined in rock-stratigraphic terms.

Other lateral variations of stratigraphic units may be more subtle than the example given and may not depart sufficiently from the characteristics at their type localities to justify the application of different names. Or, the units involved may have biostratigraphic or time-stratigraphic boundaries and thus be outside of the realm of rock-unit nomenclature. An example of the first category is provided by the Permian Kaibab Formation of the Grand Canyon area (Figure 9-10). McKee (1938) has mapped the distribution of a unit designated as the β member of the Kaibab Formation and indicates the distribution pattern of five facies, each characterized by a distinctive lithology and fossil assemblage. Note that the distributions of the facies are mutually exclusive and are therefore separated from one another

Fig. 9-9. Facies of the middle member of the Maquoketa Formation (Ordovician) in Illinois. The distribution of three lithosomes is shown, intertonguing relationships being indicated by superimposition of the patterns. [After DuBois (1945).]

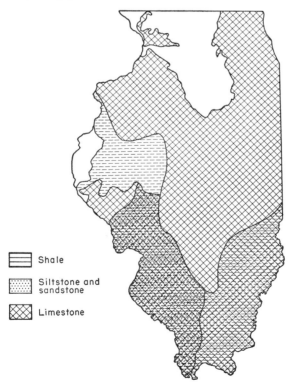

Shale

Siltstone and sandstone

Limestone

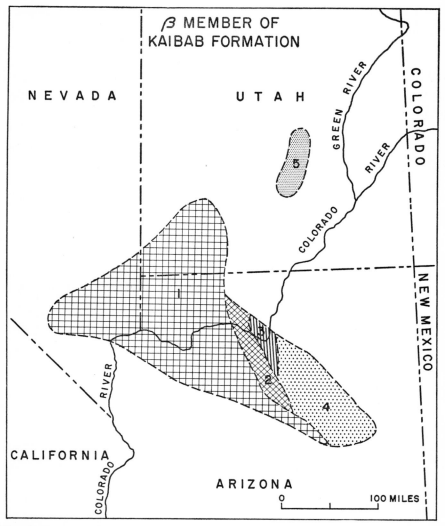

Fig. 9-10. Facies of a member of the Kaibab Formation (Permian) in Arizona and adjoining states. Mutually exclusive areal subdivisions of a defined stratigraphic unit are shown. [After McKee (1938).]

by vertical partitions or bounding surfaces erected normal to the bedding planes.

Kay (1948) has provided an example of similar treatment of a time-stratigraphic unit. Figure 9-11 shows the distribution of "lithologic belts" in a Middle Ordovician subseries located in the Appalachian area. Here again the "belts," or facies, are mutually exclusive and must be imagined as separated by vertical surfaces passed through the thickness of the unit.

In both of the examples cited, facies were differentiated on the basis of distinctions in the gross appearance of the strata and the fossils they contain. No attempt was made to map individual tongues or lithosomes. Rather, the emphasis was placed on recognition and mapping of differences in the *aspect* of the stratigraphic unit involved; each aspect being the summation or "flavor" resulting from contributions by one, few, or many lithosomes and biosomes. Such a facies concept is very similar to that envisaged by Gressly in 1838.

Abstract Facies. Among the many debatable points in any facies discussion the question remains whether a facies is a tangible body of rocks or an abstraction—"something a rock has" (Teichert, 1958). Walther (1893, 1894) defined facies as "the sum of all the *primary* characteristics of a sedimentary rock" (present authors' italics). Walther's intent, and the intent of many European workers who have followed him, was to include in the description

Fig. 9-11. Facies of part of the Middle Ordovician of the Appalachian area. Mutually exclusive areal subdivisions of a defined time-stratigraphic unit are shown in combination with paleogeographic interpretation. [After Kay (1948).]

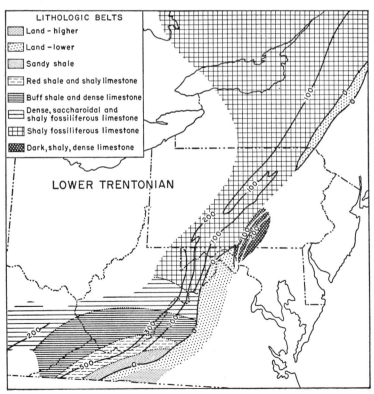

LITHOLOGIC BELTS

Land - higher

Land - lower

Sandy shale

Red shale and shaly limestone

Buff shale and dense limestone

Dense, saccharoidal and shaly fossiliferous limestone

Shaly fossiliferous limestone

Dark, shaly, dense limestone

LOWER TRENTONIAN

of a facies all the characteristics that make an environmental interpretation possible. In this view there is no such thing as a "lagoonal facies," only a summation of characteristics, an appearance or aspect, that can be interpreted to indicate lagoonal deposition. Further, if identification of facies is restricted to primary characteristics, it is not admissible to speak of "dolomitic facies" or "quartzitic facies," since both may be considered to represent diagenetic or secondary effects that may not be related to environment.

The validity of this classical concept rests upon its clear differentiation between facies studies and paleogeographic synthesis, which is the *product* of facies studies. North American stratigraphers, in general, have tended to preserve the spirit of this concept without strict observance of either the limitation to primary characteristics or the abstract quality of facies.

OPERATIONAL CONCEPT OF FACIES

Influence of North American Stratigraphy on Facies Concepts

Stratigraphers on the North American continent face a number of problems and opportunities that are not encountered elsewhere to the same degree. The essential stability of broad areas of the continental interior for hundreds of millions of years of geologic time is reflected in the relative ease with which individual rock-stratigraphic units can be identified and traced over large areas of regional and even interregional scope. This factor, plus the proved practicability and economic importance of mapping on the basis of tangible rock units, as contrasted to inferential units based on geologic time, has placed great emphasis on rock-unit stratigraphy and on the discrimination between rock-stratigraphic and time-stratigraphic units —an emphasis that seems almost an obsession to European geologists.

Regardless of the variety of opinion which may be expressed regarding the issue, North American stratigraphers are inclined to investigate facies relationships within rock-stratigraphic units as well as within time-stratigraphic units. Although many of the units analyzed are enclosed by synchronous surfaces, this is not necessarily typical, and the studies may be considered departures from the classical approach, which stresses the analysis of isochronous facies. It is a departure, however, that is imposed by the practical necessities of American geology.

Influence of Subsurface Data

Of even greater impact on North American concepts is the influence of the data from tens of thousands of bore holes drilled each year in the exploration for oil and gas. The contribution to thoughts on facies is at least three fold, as outlined below.

Emphasis on Lithologic Data. The information from subsurface sources is overwhelmingly weighted toward the physical data of lithostratigraphy rather than toward the paleontologic data of bio- and time-stratigraphy. Although it is true that micropaleontology is an important tool in many subsurface studies, it is overshadowed in most areas by lithologic data gained from sample and core analysis and, particularly, from mechanical logging devices. As a result, subsurface stratigraphy tends to emphasize tangible units of strata based on lithology. Facies concepts developed under this emphasis stress observable lithologic variations rather than the more subjective and abstract interpretations of environment.

Discrete Nature of Subsurface Data. Subsurface information consists of a number of separate observations at individual points, in contrast to the continuous observations which a surface stratigrapher can make along the outcrop of a well exposed stratigraphic unit. Whereas the environmental significance of lateral changes seen in outcrop may be clarified, or even made self evident, by the interrelationships among the bodies of strata involved, these same relationships are almost never apparent in subsurface studies. Instead, the data from each bore hole require separate analysis, and no interpretation can be made until several subsurface records have been examined. The results of the independent examination of data from separate wells must then be expressed in some integrated form from which a logical interpretation can be made. Interpretation is thus necessarily preceded by objective expression of the characteristics of the rocks involved at each control point. These characteristics comprise the concrete observable parameters of the strata and their properties as measured by logging devices, rather than the more abstract and sophisticated aspects analyzed in classical facies studies.

Volume of Data to be Utilized. The continued expansion of subsurface exploration to new areas, the deeper penetration of areas previously considered to be well understood, and the refinement of techniques in sample study and mechanical logging combine to produce an avalanche of new information which the stratigrapher is required to absorb and interpret. Such masses of data are not susceptible to integration and analysis by strictly traditional methods, and as a result, North American stratigraphers have eagerly sought new solutions to the problem of handling great volumes of data. Of the potential solutions, it is natural that facies studies would represent a possible breakthrough. It is no less natural that facies concepts would be modified to meet these special needs.

The Operational Concept of Facies

The resultant of these three major factors is an essentially pragmatic approach to the complex stratigraphic patterns called facies relationships. The pragmatic approach requires a language for communication with clearly delineated terms objectively defined and subject to more or less formalized procedures or operations. To set this approach apart from classical facies concepts, it will be called an **operational facies concept,** which leads to the following definition.

Operational Definition of Facies. Facies are lateral variations in the aspects of a defined stratigraphic unit. A number of corollaries are implicit in this definition:

1. Facies occupy mutually exclusive areas bounded by arbitrarily, or preferably, quantitatively determined limits.
2. A single facies may comprise one or several lithosomes and biosomes that occur in vertical succession or are intertongued. The facies of a given stratigraphic unit, however, exclusively occupy the complete thickness of the unit and are neither vertically successive nor intertongued within the unit. The relationship between stratigraphic units, lithosomes, and facies is clarified by reference to Figure 9-12.
3. Facies boundaries are surfaces passed through the thickness of the unit involved, perpendicular to its contact with the next overlying unit. Such boundaries are essentially vertical surfaces in areas of low dip.
4. Where the stratigraphic units approach horizontality, or where the effects of dip are corrected in stratigraphic studies, the projection of a facies boundary to a horizontal plane is a line. Therefore, the distribution of facies is ideally represented on a map.

Aspect and Facies. The delineation of the facies of a stratigraphic unit and the construction of a facies map involve three operations: (1) determining the aspects of a stratigraphic unit at several points of observation; (2) plotting these qualitative or numerically expressed aspects on a suitable map base; and (3) constructing lines that connect points of equal aspect. Thus, the determination and expression of aspect are the fundamental procedures in operational facies mapping. This subject is treated in detail in Chapter 12.

Operational Aspect. Classical facies studies are almost entirely directed toward an understanding of the character and distribution of sedimentary environments. In this view, the aspect of a stratigraphic unit at a point of observation is the summation of all the environmentally significant characteristics of the strata and their fossil content. Under the operational concept,

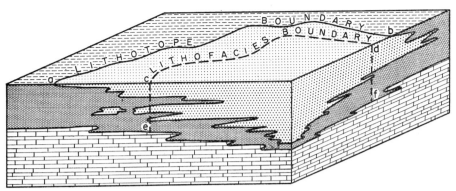

Fig. 9-12. Lithotopes, lithofacies, and rock-stratigraphic units. Two mappable rock units are shown (a limestone formation below and a clastic formation above) on a block diagram whose top represents a synchronous time-stratigraphic surface. At a moment in time (represented by the top surface of the block) two depositional environments, one accumulating shale and the other sand, are present; thus, two areal subdivisions of the depositional surface—lithotopes—are identified as shown by the defining boundary a–b. Lateral shifts of environment during accumulation of the clastic unit are responsible for the intertonguing, three-dimensional lithosomes identified by the shale and sand patterns of the figure. The clastic unit is divided by a vertical partition (as at c–e and d–f) into two lithofacies, one more than half sandstone, the other more than half shale. Projected to a horizontal plane, or map view, the lithofacies boundary is shown by a line (c–d) that divides the unit into two areally distinct facies of differing lithologic aspect. [Adapted from Wheeler and Mallory (1956).]

no such limitation is recognized, and facies studies may have as their goal the interpretation of many characteristics of the rocks, in addition to their environmental significance. Facies studies may be directed toward the evaluation of the mineral content of sedimentary rocks, their engineering properties as foundation materials, their response to seismic waves, or toward the understanding of an almost endless list of other properties. In this broader sense, each stratigraphic unit, at each point of observation, has many aspects which may be determined and mapped.

Specific Aspects. In some cases a unit under investigation presents at each exposure, or in the records of each well that penetrates it, an aspect that is clearly defined in terms of the goal of the investigation. If environmental analysis is the objective, for example, a unit may be shown to present two differing aspects in adjoining areas. In one area all points of observation, for instance, may indicate red beds, bearing impressions of land plants. The same time-stratigraphic unit, penetrated in adjacent wells, may yield samples composed of limestone and shale, with abundant brachiopods and bryozoa.

It is not difficult, in this over-simplified case, to distinguish two aspects, non-marine and marine. These are **specific aspects;** their mapping leads to the delineation of **specific facies.**

Nonspecific Aspects. In the overwhelming majority of facies studies, whether they be devoted to paleogeographic reconstruction or to the location of mineral deposits, the observable characteristics of the rocks investigated defy unequivocal assignment to specific environments, economically significant conditions, or other directly interpretable aspects. It is necessary under these circumstances to define and map a variety of **nonspecific aspects** and construct **nonspecific, or operational, facies** maps. These, at a higher level of analysis, make the desired interpretations possible.

Lithofacies and Biofacies. As will be seen in Chapter 12, there is virtually no limit to the number of nonspecific aspects that can be determined, nor to the kinds of facies maps that can be produced. Because of this multiplicity of aspects and facies, it is convenient to distinguish two major classes of aspects and of the facies they characterize. The physical, mineralogic, and petrographic characteristics of sedimentary rocks are expressed in terms of **lithologic aspects,** which result in the delineation of **lithofacies.** The biologic, or, more properly, paleontologic character of the strata is represented by **paleontologic aspects** and **biofacies.**

Concluding Remarks. These are the broad outlines of the operational facies concept. Inasmuch as application of the concept is dependent on the identification and traceability of the boundaries of stratigraphic units, it is necessary to consider the problems of correlation before proceeding further with a discussion of facies. The consideration of facies is resumed in Chapter 12, following an exploration of the principles of stratigraphic correlation and the discussion of the response of sedimentation and sedimentary environments to the behavior of the earth's crust.

SUPPLEMENTARY READINGS

Many of the principles and concepts discussed in this chapter are covered in the indicated pages of the following texts, which present variations in emphasis and interpretation from the point of view adopted in this book:

1. Dunbar, C. O. and Rodgers, J., 1957, Principles of stratigraphy: New York, John Wiley & Sons, Inc., p. 116–156.
2. Weller, J. M., 1960, Stratigraphic principles and practice: New York, Harper & Brothers, p. 383–412, 503–524.

Further analysis of the complex interrelationships among rock units and among biostratigraphic units is provided in the following two papers:

3. Wheeler, H. E. and Mallory, V. S., 1956, Factors in lithostratigraphy: Am. Assoc. Petrol. Geologists Bull., v. 40, p. 2711–2723.
4. Wheeler, H. E., 1958, Primary factors in biostratigraphy: Am. Assoc. Petrol. Geologists Bull., v. 42, p. 640–655.

An excellent discussion of facies concepts, reaching conclusions that are notably different from those of the present text, is given by the following:

5. Teichert, C., 1958, Concepts of facies: Am. Assoc. Petrol. Geologists Bull., v. 42, p. 2718–2744.

CHAPTER 10

Principles of Correlation

INTRODUCTION

STRATIGRAPHIC correlation is the demonstration of equivalency of stratigraphic units. To an earlier generation of geologists, trained to think of rock units and paleontologic assemblages as bounded by essentially synchronous surfaces, equivalency was invariably stated in terms of geologic age. This usage prevails today among a segment of American stratigraphers (see Dunbar and Rodgers, 1957; Rodgers, 1959). However, recognition of the distinctions that separate rock-stratigraphic, biostratigraphic, and time-stratigraphic units makes it apparent that "equivalency" may be expressed in lithologic, paleontologic, or chronologic terms. Therefore, most stratigraphers apply the noun "correlation," the verb "correlate," and the adjective "correlative" to lithostratigraphic equivalency as well as to time-stratigraphic equivalency. In each situation, it is necessary to identify the nature of the equivalency, the kind of correlation involved (such as lithologic correlation, biostratigraphic correlation, and so on) unless, as is commonly the case, the context of the usage makes this clear. Under any circumstances, it is vitally important that there be no confusion among the classes of stratigraphic units being treated or the kind of equivalency and correlation implied.

Correlation is an essential element of most stratigraphic investigations and typically occupies a major portion of a stratigrapher's time. Without correlation, the facies relationships, and others discussed in the preceding chapter, would be meaningless and the rational treatment of the analytical aspects of stratigraphy would be impossible.

CORRELATION OF LITHOSTRATIGRAPHIC UNITS

Review of Definitions and Classification

Lithostratigraphic units, more commonly called rock units, are bodies of strata identified by objective lithologic criteria and are delineated in vertical succession by surfaces representing changes in lithologic character or breaks in the depositional continuity or, less commonly, by "key" or "marker" beds.

Continuing advances in technology have greatly broadened the scope of the "objective lithologic criteria" available to the stratigrapher for the discrimination of rock units. Nineteenth-century workers subdivided the stratigraphic column into usable rock units on the basis of the gross characteristics (color, bedding, dominant lithology, and so on) readily observable in the field but without fastidious distinctions among rock, biostratigraphic, and time units. The present generation recognizes the distinctions among the three major classes of units, but other problems of definition and classification have arisen with the development of new techniques for measuring and recording lithologic attributes in the laboratory, in bore holes, and in the field. In some cases, these newer techniques serve to more sharply delineate the units established by the methods of an older generation. More commonly, the bounding surfaces of natural units, defined by the newer techniques, do not coincide with the boundaries based on gross lithologic criteria, and there may be marked discordance in geometry and attitude.

Parastratigraphic Units

In an attempt to avoid confusion, the following discussion of lithologic correlation draws a distinction between formal or conventional rock units and parastratigraphic units. **Formal rock units** are the groups, formations, members, and other units of strata treated in the *Stratigraphic Code* and identified by geographic names. Their formal status is indicated by capitalization of the unit term (Viola Limestone, Wedington Sandstone Member, Madison Group). These are the practical mapping units that the field geologist uses to delineate the structure of an area, the lithologic character of rocks cropping out at the surface, and the distribution of economic deposits associated with the recognized units. Formal rock units that are established by work in outcrop can commonly be traced into the subsurface and may be usefully applied in subsurface stratigraphy; or certain formal units may be recognized only in the subsurface.

In general, it may be said that there are two chief requisites of formal rock-stratigraphic units: **mappability,** as defined in Chapter 2, and **lithologic constancy.** The latter may be expressed by a single dominant rock type or by a distinctive intercalation of several lithologies, but in either case, there is lateral continuity of lithologic character.

Parastratigraphic rock units include a variety of groupings of strata, identified by objective lithologic criteria but lacking in either mappability or, most commonly, in lithologic homogeneity and constancy.

Attribute-defined Units. The criteria applied to the recognition and tracing of parastratigraphic units are of two types. One class of units is based upon special attributes of the component strata—attributes other than those

conventionally considered in the establishment of formal rock units. The
attributes involved may include heavy-mineral composition, insoluble residues, trace-element content, or indirect measures of lithology such as the
velocity of transmission of seismic or sonic energy. The application of these
criteria does not necessarily remove the unit defined from the realm of
formal stratigraphy. However, it is common to find that bodies of strata
identified by these characteristics have boundaries that do not coincide with
or are discordant with those conventionally established as the limiting surfaces of formal units. Further, the defining characteristics may be traceable
far beyond the lateral extent of recognition of a formal unit as limited by its
lithologic continuity. An insoluble residue zone (Figure 10-1, for example)
may be confined to a particular formal unit in one area and yet be traceable
into an adjacent area where it is associated with quite different carbonate
rock types that make up dissimilar formations and members with boundaries
at other stratigraphic positions. Such residue zones do not constitute formal

Fig. 10-1. Formal rock-stratigraphic units and parastratigraphic units. Insoluble
residue zones and formations have the same limits in the column at
left; only one of the formations is recognizable as a formal rock-stratigraphic unit at the right, but all insoluble residue zones may be correlated across the intervening area, although their contacts have no
necessary relationship to the formation contacts at the right side of the
diagram.

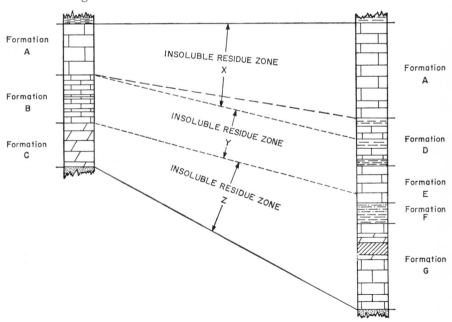

units, inasmuch as they extend beyond the limits of recognition of stratal grouping based on gross lithology or other traditional criteria.

The units utilized by geophysicists in seismic surveying are a more extreme example of parastratigraphy. Seismic surveys find their greatest stratigraphic application in areas where there is little or no significant information from outcrops or drill holes and consequently where the structure, thickness, and facies variations of formal units recognized in adjacent areas are poorly understood. In such an area, vertically successive stratal units distinguished by variations in the apparent velocity of transmission of seismic energy can in some cases be traced for many miles, yet little may be known regarding the relationship of these parastratigraphic units to what may emerge as the formal stratigraphy of the area after years of intensive drilling. Even after the subsurface stratigraphy is well understood, it may be found that there is little coincidence and concordance between the formal units and the seismically defined parastratigraphic units. Nevertheless, these attribute-defined stratal units are extraordinarily important clues to an understanding of the regional stratigraphy and structure.

Marker-defined Units. It has long been the practice in areas of monotonously homogeneous or excessively heterogeneous stratigraphy to delimit stratigraphic units by easily recognizable and traceable beds of distinctive lithology called "key beds" or "marker horizons." The Pennsylvanian Carbondale Group of Illinois, for instance, is defined as extending from the base of the Colchester, or number 2, coal bed upward to the top of the Herrin, or number 6, coal bed. In other instances, units may be bounded by thin limestones, bentonite beds, sandstones in a dominant shale succession, or any of a number of examples of key beds. In each case the marker-defined unit is a part of the body of formal stratigraphy insofar as it maintains a proper degree of constancy of lithologic character.

In subsurface stratigraphy, the variety of mechanical logging techniques described in Chapter 3 provides means for the identification of many key beds, some of which can be traced over very wide areas. The relative ease with which individual key beds and markers can be recognized on mechanical logs has led to great reliance on these features for the establishment of rock units in subsurface stratigraphy. Furthermore, the relative difficulty of identifying certain lithologic contacts without laborious and time-consuming sample studies has intensified the emphasis on marker-defined units—in some cases to the extent that quite different limits are applied, in outcrop and in the adjacent subsurface, to what is ostensibly the same unit, with the attendant generation of much confusion.

The electronically recorded reflections obtained by modern seismic surveying techniques, when processed by special automatic computing equipment, make available a constantly growing number of stratigraphically valuable key-bed horizons and marker-defined units of the type illustrated by Figure 10-2A. The key beds represent the stratigraphic positions at which seismic energy is reflected to a marked degree. Where there is no direct subsurface information from drilling, the relationship between the formal rock units of the area and the units outlined by reflecting horizons is unknown or, at best, subject to conjecture and approximation. Note that in Figure 10-2A the vertical axis of the cross section indicates travel time rather than feet, and the depth and thickness of the units represented can not be estimated without velocity data. Under these circumstances, the marker-defined units are clearly in the parastratigraphic category. Where velocity data from drill holes are available, and particularly where sonic (CVL) logs have been run, the seismic records can be corrected in terms of actual depths or sea-level elevations, as in Figure 10-2B, and the reflecting interfaces can sometimes be related directly to formal rock units. An even clearer portrayal of the parastratigraphic units picked up by the reflection seismograph is made possible by **variable-density cross sections** in which the deflections of the seismometer are translated into variations in the intensity of light striking a photographic film. Cross sections prepared in this manner present a striking pattern of alternating dark and light bands, which are readily interpreted in terms of stratigraphy and structure. An example is given by Hollister and Hasbrouck, in Haun and LeRoy (1958). In some cases, even when all these supporting data are available, the reflecting horizons exhibit no apparent relationship to the obvious physical character of the strata, and the units delineated, although of great utility, remain in the limbo of extreme parastratigraphy.

It seems obvious that the parastratigraphic units defined by reflecting horizons, as well as those defined by the velocity of transmission of seismic or sonic energy, require attention from stratigraphers and should be integrated into the body of stratigraphic knowledge.

Other problems of definition and classification are created where the strata between key beds change markedly in character. A marker-defined unit may, for example, be dominated by shale in one area, by carbonates in an adjacent area, and by evaporite elsewhere. It has been common practice to treat such a unit as a formal member or formation, applying the same geographic name to all three facies variants. This usage violates the principle of the lithologic constancy of a formal rock unit and destroys the significance of the unit as an indicator of a specific lithology or group of lithologies. Some stratigraphers have held, therefore, that such units are invalid where marked facies

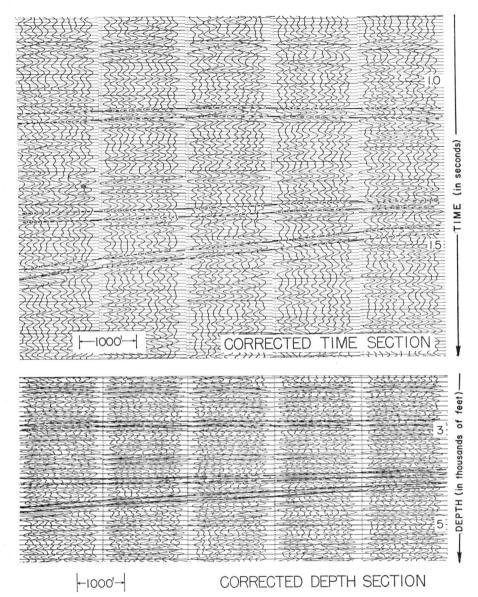

Fig. 10-2. Parastratigraphic units defined by seismic reflecting horizons. In the upper figure the vertical dimension is travel time; in the lower figure travel time is recomputed as depth in thousands of feet by use of velocity data. [From Dunlap (1956).]

changes are involved, and that separate units, individually named and defined, are required on either side of facies boundaries.

This is the correct view in terms of the *Stratigraphic Code* and the definition of formal rock units. Nevertheless, the key beds and the bodies of strata
they enclose are among the most useful of stratigraphic horizons and units
available for subsurface studies of structure, thickness variations, and facies,
and (as discussed in a later paragraph) are applicable to time-stratigraphic
correlation.

By recognizing a distinction between formal, marker-defined units of relative lithologic constancy and parastratigraphic units of laterally varying
lithology, the purposes of the *Stratigraphic Code* may be achieved without
sacrificing the great utility of marker-defined units of strata. Forgotson
(1957) has proposed that the distinction be observed by establishing a new
class of rock units called **formats**, which would include the marker-defined
units that lack lithologic constancy. Moore (1958) has objected to the term
on etymologic grounds and suggests "lithozone" or "assise" as possible sub-
stitutes. Of these, the latter is the more appropriate because of its previous
application to units of the same type, and it may be that this word will find
acceptance among stratigraphers. In the meantime, the important distinction
is that between formal rock units (groups, formations, members, and others)
and parastratigraphic rock units, whatever their names.

In this book, the term **operational unit** is used to designate parastratigraphic rock units, in recognition of the objective and non-inferential criteria
applied in their identification and because of their applicability to the operations and techniques of stratigraphic mapping, discussed in a later chapter.

Methods of Rock-unit Correlation

There are many methods and techniques applicable to the correlation of
rock units. The choice of methods rests with the nature of the problem, the
character of the formal or parastratigraphic units involved, and the nature
and distribution of the outcrops or subsurface control points available.
Normally, two or more methods are integrated in the solution of any individual correlation problem. In the following discussion, the correlation of
formal rock units is emphasized, except where the problems of parastratigraphic rock units require special attention.

Since correlation is the *demonstration* of equivalency, it is not established
by a simple statement or a single stratigraphic cross section unless the relationships are uncomplicated and self-evident. In most cases, the demonstration of equivalency requires the establishment of **closed correlation traverses**
and **correlation networks** comparable to those used in stadia surveying,
levelling, and triangulation in plane surveying. Figure 10-3 is a fence dia-

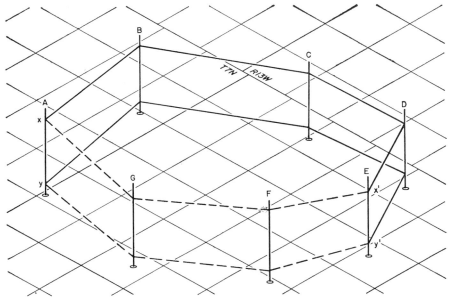

Fig. 10-3. Closed correlation traverse. Stratigraphic horizons *x* and *y* are correlated with *x′* and *y′* by point-to-point correlation from *a* to *e* (solid
lines). If the horizons can be traced back to point *A* through *F* and *G*
the traverse is closed, and correlation can be considered to be demonstrated.

gram illustrating a correlation traverse. At point A, stratigraphic horizons x
and y are the upper and lower contacts of a given rock unit. Points B–G are
other points of observation. The tentative correlation of the unit from A to
E by way of points B, C, and D is as indicated by the solid lines, which
suggest that the upper and lower contacts of the unit at point E are at stratigraphic positions x′ and y′. If continuation of the traverse to close on the
starting point A by way of F and G (dashed lines) indicates coincidence
with the original contacts (x and y) the traverse is closed and the correlation of the unit at all seven points may be considered established. A correlation network is built up by a series of linked and closed correlation
traverses.

Tracing Lateral Continuity. Perhaps the simplest method of rock-unit
correlation is by tracing stratigraphic units from place to place along continuous outcrops. This method, known as "walking out" the unit, may involve
the actual tracing of contacts between rock units where such contacts are
well defined, or may involve the tracing of key beds that are lithologically
distinctive or tend to form distinctive outcrop expressions. "Walking out" of
strata finds its maximum applicability in areas of abundant surface exposure,
unhampered by vegetational or soil cover.

The lateral continuity of strata may be traced, even where a minor amount of soil cover or vegetation is present, by the use of aerial photographs, which, by changes in soil pattern and character of vegetation, make possible the tracing of units of varying lithology over very broad areas. In some cases, particularly where aerial photographs are lacking, plane-table mapping is a useful method of demonstrating the lateral continuity of rock units from one place to another.

A modified version of lateral tracing of rock units is employed in subsurface stratigraphy. In areas of closely spaced wells, individual units can be traced from well to well by application of sample studies, electric logs, and other data, much as a formation can be traced laterally from outcrop to outcrop. Where abundant subsurface data from closely spaced wells are available in areas of low rates of lithofacies change, correlations can be carried from well to well in an expanding network over hundreds of square miles, and farther in some instances. Areas of rapid lithofacies change obviously require a greater density of control points, and the distance to which correlation can be established by tracing lateral continuity is more limited.

The behavior of the fluids in strata that produce gas, oil, or water is also a means of establishing lateral continuity. If withdrawal of oil from a producing well affects the bottom-hole pressures and gas-oil ratios in other wells, an interconnection is indicated and the correlation of the productive unit throughout the affected area may be considered established. The correlation of aquifers can be established by similar engineering data on piezometric and drawdown effects, indicating a common water reservoir. It is also possible to demonstrate the lateral continuity of aquifers by introducing dyes and chemical or radioactive tracers into the water.

In both surface and subsurface problems, as the density of stratigraphic control points falls, or the rate of lithofacies change rises, the accuracy of correlations is open to question and recourse must be made to other methods.

Lithologic Identity. Many lithologic units have characteristics which serve as identifying hallmarks, permitting correlation between widely spaced exposures or wells, and even across areas where the unit in question may be missing or deeply buried. Among the lithologic characteristics useful in correlation, color is perhaps the most obvious. The flaming red color of the Chugwater Formation of Wyoming, for instance, makes possible its identification and correlation from uplift to uplift across the state. Any criterion, or combination of criteria that serves to identify a unit may be useful. Those gross features likely to be important include weathering characteristics, bedding, thickness, general mineralogic constitution, and such primary structures as cross lamination, ripple marks, and the like.

In the absence of identifying gross features, a number of finer details of lithology find application in the correlation of rock units in outcrop and in the subsurface. The Fire Clay coal of the Appalachian Basin, for example, can be identified over a large area of Eastern Kentucky and adjoining parts of Virginia and Tennessee (Wanless, 1952) by means of an enclosed thin parting of flint clay, a partially silicified kaolin, which is unique in the Pennsylvanian stratigraphy of the region. Heavy mineral and insoluble residue studies provide useful criteria for the recognition and correlation of rock units, although, as pointed out earlier, the units traceable by these means commonly fall into the parastratigraphic category.

In short, any observable or measurable characteristics that distinguish specific rock units may be applied to the solution of correlation problems. Many of the gross features applicable to the correlation of rock units in outcrop are not observable in subsurface samples and records. Here, however, they are replaced by other attributes measurable in samples or cores or on mechanical logs and seismic records. Weaver (1958) has shown that the clay mineralogy of shales can be used as a correlation attribute over broad areas. Electrical properties, gamma-ray emission, drilling time, travel time, and other indirect measures of lithology contribute to the correlation of attribute-defined rock units of both formal and parastratigraphic types. In addition, the physics and chemistry of the contained fluids constitute a kind of lithologic attribute that is useful in correlation. An aquifer sand, for example, may be correlated on the basis of the salinity, or other properties, of the water it yields.

Although fossils are chiefly applied to the delineation and correlation of biostratigraphic and time-stratigraphic units, they may also be viewed as contributors to the lithologic identity of rock units. This is particularly true in the case of those rock units which may be composed in very large part of fossil fragments. Thus, a particular limestone may be identified by the large number of crinoid columnals of which it is composed. In this case, the fossil crinoid fragments are primary features of the lithology and aid in correlation without reference to the biologic or temporal significance of the fragments. Within limited areas, the relationship between rock and biostratigraphic units may be so well established that formations and members may be identified by the assemblage zones with which they are associated. It must be emphasized that correlation of rock units on this basis is valid only where the rock unit–biostratigraphic unit interrelationship is thoroughly determined and beyond question. The extrapolation of such correlations to less well known areas and units is hazardous and often misleading.

In some instances, the age of the strata, as indicated by the contained fossils, is an aid in lithologic correlation. In parts of Wyoming, for example, the Madison Limestone (Mississippian) rests with obscure unconformity on the Bighorn Dolomite (Ordovician), and it is not easy to separate the units in isolated exposures on purely lithologic grounds. However, the occurrence of either Mississippian or Ordovician fossils immediately clarifies the identity and correlation of the enclosing rock units. Unless there is a significant difference in the ages of the units involved, as in the example cited, this too is an untrustworthy criterion of correlation.

Position in Sequence. Under normal circumstances, each lithologic unit possesses a unique position with reference to other units above and below. Once the stratigraphic succession is established in any area under study, the succession itself becomes a primary tool in correlation. Where the lithology of a unit is not sufficiently distinctive to permit correlation from place to place, the position of the unit in the local stratigraphic succession may be the only satisfactory method.

In any area under study, there may well occur three limestone units with such similarity of lithology as to prevent their correlation in isolated exposures. The chances are remote, however, that each limestone bears the same relation to other lithologies in the sequence. Thus, one limestone may rest upon a shale and be succeeded by a sandstone, a second limestone may rest upon a dolomite and be succeeded by red beds. In each case, it is not the lithology of the individual limestone unit which makes correlation possible, but the position of that unit with reference to the determined sequence of units in the area.

Where cyclical successions are encountered, as in the case of the Pennsylvanian cyclothems, correlation by position in sequence is rendered more difficult. In the cyclothems, successive cyclical sequences display similar successions of lithology, and errors may be introduced if two separate cycles are encountered with similar sequences developed. In these cases, it is first necessary to correlate the cyclical unit, or cyclothem, before attempting correlation of individual formations or members of the cycles.

Mechanical logs of subsurface sections are produced as measuring sondes pass successive stratal units, recording electrical, radioactive, or other variations in the responses of the beds as curves representing continuous functions of depth. Therefore, the study of mechanical logs to establish lithologic correlations between two wells, is in effect, a study of the stratigraphic position in sequence of the units encountered. It is the position of each unit in a succession of lithologies as represented by the logs that is important, rather than the character of any individual unit reflected in the curves.

Figure 10-4 illustrates a correlated stratigraphic cross section utilizing a measured outcrop section and electric logs of wells in southern Oklahoma.

The relative ease with which the several units of the Simpson Group can be traced from their outcrops in the Arbuckle Mountains to a nearby well and thence to more distant wells is a function of the lateral persistence of the succession, rather than expression of the unique lithological character of any of the component units. Inasmuch as the subdivisions of the Simpson Group in this area maintain a high degree of lithologic constancy, they are formations of the conventional or formal type.

Position in sequence is a widely applied approach to the correlation of parastratigraphic rock units defined by marker horizons. Figure 10-5 is a modified version of one of several cross sections of the Lower Cretaceous Trinity Group of the Gulf Coast area presented by Forgotson (1957). The section illustrates the correlation of marker-defined units through a series of facies changes that occur between the Lower Cretaceous outcrop area of North Texas and the deeper portions of the Gulf Coast Basin. The Glen Rose Subgroup is differentiated into three units by the Ferry Lake Anhydrite, which is identified by prominent displacements of the resistivity curves. The overlying unit is named the Rusk Formation. Its type section is in well number 6 of the cross section, where the formation is characterized by alternating beds of limestone and dark shale in nearly equal proportions. To the north, the unit is largely sandstone and shale but remains identifiable because of its position with reference to traceable electric log markers. To the south, the same unit is recognizable, although it is almost entirely limestone in the southernmost well. The Rusk is a marker-defined operational unit in those areas in which its lithology departs significantly from that of the type area. However, the fact that it remains as a well defined stratigraphic interval, identified by its position between marker horizons, has led to the use of the term **interval correlation** for operations of this type.

The Ferry Lake Anhydrite also changes facies, occurring as a shale and limestone unit in the three southern wells of the cross section. However, as an operational unit, it is identifiable by its position in sequence and by the continuity of its characteristic resistivity-curve expression for very considerable distances beyond the area in which the Ferry Lake Anhydrite is formally recognized as a formation. The underlying Rodessa and Pearsall units exhibit facies changes much like those of the Rusk and are classed as operational units throughout much of the area because of their lithologic inconstancy. In spite of marked changes in lithology, the intervals occupied by these units can be correlated widely on the basis of electric-log character and position in sequence among marker beds. For a demonstration of the distances over which such correlations can be made, as well as of the many criteria that are integrated to make the correlations possible, the reader is

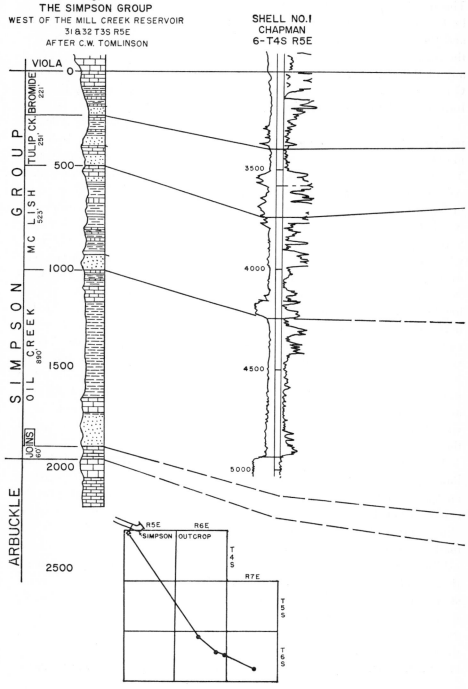

SURFACE SECTION
OF
THE SIMPSON GROUP
WEST OF THE MILL CREEK RESERVOIR
31 & 32 T3S R5E
AFTER C.W. TOMLINSON

SHELL NO.1
CHAPMAN
6-T4S R5E

344

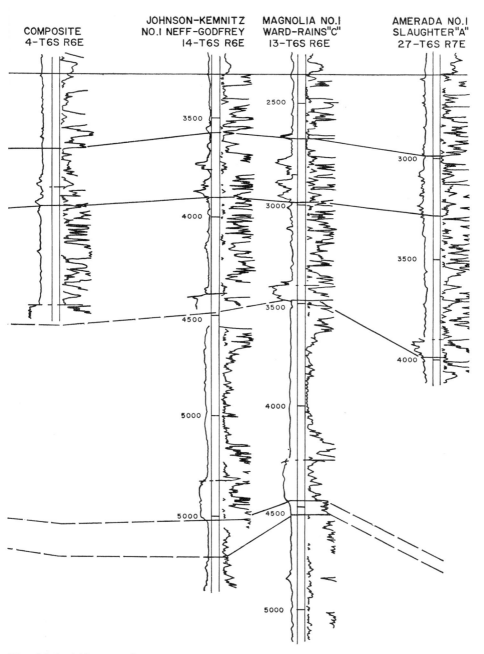

Fig. 10-4. (*Above and on facing page.*) Surface to subsurface correlation of lithologic units. The lithologic identity and position in sequence of the several formations of the Simpson Group make the correlation between the outcrop section and the adjacent well obvious, as is the extension of correlation to other wells at a greater distance. [After Womack (1956).]

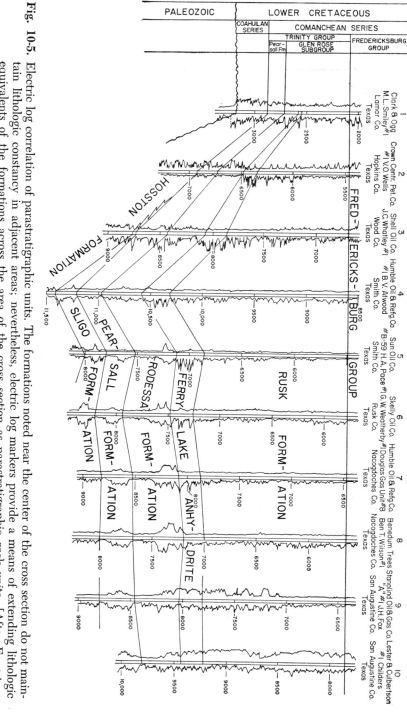

Fig. 10-5. Electric log correlation of parastratigraphic units. The formations noted near the center of the cross section do not maintain lithologic constancy in adjacent areas; nevertheless, electric log markers provide a means of extending lithologic equivalents of the formations across the area of the cross section as parastratigraphic rock units. [After Forgotson (1957).]

referred to Forgotson's (1957) original paper. Many other examples, but commonly lacking the differentiation between formal and parastratigraphic units, are available in the literature of subsurface stratigraphy.

Interval correlation of operational units is not confined to subsurface stratigraphy and to data from mechanical logs. Similar units are commonly applied in outcrop investigations, where markers such as coal beds, bentonite beds, and concretion zones are invaluable in the delineation of both stratigraphy and structure.

Structural Relationships. In addition to their relationships to overlying and underlying strata, rock units have a definite sequential position in relation to such features as unconformities, folds, faults, igneous activity, and metamorphic effects. The relationship of individual units to such features may be of considerable value in establishing the correlation of a unit over a limited area, but such features cannot be expected to be of value over broad areas or beyond the confines of a depositional basin.

Problems of Rock-unit Nomenclature and Correlation

Effect of Terminology. Regardless of the implied rigor of the rules established by the *Stratigraphic Code* for the definition and identification of rock units, a number of terminological problems remain regarding rock-unit correlation. Inasmuch as these problems are at least in part semantic, there is a tendency to dismiss them as geologically unimportant. However, since correlation is expressed through the application of names to rock units, their misapplication may lead to the assumption of correlations that are incorrect or may obscure relatively simple relationships. Geologists are familiar with the multiplicity of local names attached to single, widespread rock units in different physiographic or political subdivisions. These cases of synonymy are more annoying than serious and are usually resolvable by applying the rule of priority, as far as is consistent with practical usage.

A more damaging confusion arises from extension of a formation name to a noncorrelative unit. This is a situation which is more often encountered where correlation of subsurface and surface units is concerned. For many years, the term "Frio" has been applied to a subsurface unit in the Gulf Coast Oligocene, but the strata involved are not correlative with the type Frio Clay of the Texas outcrop. Before this condition was remedied by redefinition of the unit, much confusion was generated by the implied correlation, and this confusion remains in many quarters as the heritage of misapplied nomenclature. Similar instances could be cited for nearly all depositional provinces.

A fundamental source of correlation difficulties is produced by differences in the designation of rock units. Figure 10-6 illustrates how two opposed

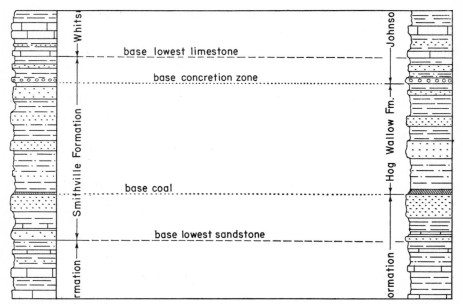

Fig. 10-6. The two columnar sections represent the same stratigraphic succession mapped by different geologists in adjoining quadrangles. The formations on the left are differentiated by their gross lithology, whereas the limits of those to the right are defined by key beds. Although obscured by the differences in limits and terminology, the actual correlation between the two columns is clear.

concepts of the limits of a rock unit serve to obscure correlation. The unit involved has been described in two adjoining areas with a different name. Essentially, it is composed of interbedded sandstones and shales with gradational contacts and includes mixed limestone and shale units above and below. In one instance, the lower contact has been placed at the base of the lowest significant sandstone bed, and the upper contact at the base of the lowest succeeding limestone. In this case, the unit has contacts which separate the major lithologic differences and are yet mappable on the basis of the specific beds picked. The second column represents a closely parallel section, but the formational limits are based on key beds—in this instance, a coal bed and a prominent concretionary layer. These beds are readily traced and are therefore excellent mapping horizons, but they do not differentiate the section into units of homogeneous lithology. Correlation between the two areas is quite obvious but is obscured by the difference in treatment accorded by different workers.

Effect of Lithofacies Change. The terminological problems noted above are largely an expression of the subjective approaches taken by different workers. Of more fundamental importance are the questions of nomenclature that arise where units involved in correlation exhibit lateral changes in lithologic character. Consider, for example, the Niobrara Formation of the Upper Cretaceous in the Great Plains area (Fig. 10-7A). The unit was named for exposures in northeastern Nebraska where it consists of chalky limestone and marl. The same distinctive lithology persists south into Kansas, where it is variously treated as a formation and a group, and where the prominent chalk members make it a unique and useful stratigraphic unit. The term Niobrara has also been applied in Wyoming to shales occupying the same stratigraphic position, but which lack the lithologic characteristics of the type area. It is clear that the term Niobrara Formation is a misnomer in Wyoming; it is, rather, an operational parastratigraphic unit and requires another designation in formal stratigraphy. What geographic and lithologic criteria should be used to limit the usage of Niobrara as a formal unit in accordance with the principle of lithologic constancy? Other areas and other parts of the stratigraphic column pose similar problems of nomenclature.

Effect of Change in Sequence. As has been discussed, many formal rock units owe their identity and correlation to their characteristic position in a fixed succession of other units. If a succession changes laterally, such that the defining limits of certain units become unrecognizable, the correlation of formal rock-stratigraphic units is circumscribed, even though the lithologic equivalents can be traced farther as operational units.

A classic and long recognized example is provided by Upper Cretaceous strata in Montana (Figure 10-7B). In the central part of the state, the Montana Group falls naturally into five mappable formations; two dark shale units separate three light-colored sandstone or sandy units. To the east the middle sandy unit, the Judith River Formation, pinches out, and no distinction can be drawn between the similar Claggett and Bearpaw Shales. For this reason, a single major shale unit, the Pierre Shale, is recognized in Eastern Montana and the Black Hills area. To the northwest, the Claggett Shale pinches out, making it impossible to separate the Eagle and Judith River Formations. The lithologic equivalents are the Two Medecine Formation and a basal unit, the Virgelle Sandstone. Because of these lateral changes in the sequence of mappable units, at least three sets of formation names, each applicable in a distinct area, are required for subdivision of the Montana Group. If the group is traced north into Canada or south into Wyoming, other systems of nomenclature are necessary, in addition to those imposed by geographic separation and political boundaries.

Stratigraphic Cut-off. The majority of problems of correlation and nomenclature that involve the termination of stratigraphic units through changes in facies or sequence are relatively clear-cut. However, the literature of stratigraphy records many examples of confusion and misunderstanding caused by differences in treatment and interpretation. Wheeler and Mallory (1953) have proposed that greater uniformity might be achieved by the systematic application of **arbitrary cut-offs** where the identity of stratigraphic units is lost. Cut-offs are, in effect, specialized facies boundaries. As such, they are surfaces erected normal to bedding planes and mark the areal limits of specific stratigraphic units where these are not defined by erosion, pinch-out, faulting, or other obvious means. Cut-offs are applicable to map, cross sectional, and three-dimensional views. Several cases are discussed by Wheeler and Mallory, and two examples are illustrated by Figure 10-7.

The Niobrara cut-off (Figure 10-7A) is purely arbitrary, since it is chosen at the line along which the unit changes from a dominant carbonate to a dominant shale lithology. Application of the cut-off obviates the possibility

Fig. 10-7. Facies change and stratigraphic cutoff. (*Top*) The chalk and limestone of the Niobrara Formation of Kansas are shown to pass, through intertonguing and gradation, into a shale in Wyoming, where application of the same formation is in clear violation of the *Stratigraphic Code*. Application of an arbitrary cut-off along the line at which the unit loses its dominant carbonate lithology marks a limit beyond which the term Niobrara should not be applied as a formal rock-unit name. (*Bottom*) The terminations of the Claggett Shale and the Judith River Formation mark the positions at which stratigraphic cutoff is applied to the terminology of the Montana Group in the northern Great Plains.

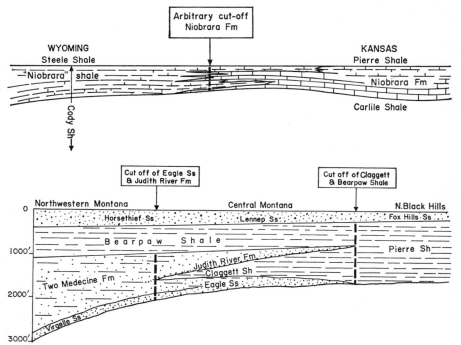

of intertongued relationships between the Niobrara Formation and the Cody Shale. This is a descriptive device sometimes used, but one which leads to confusion in mapping and in the differentiation of stratigraphic sections in outcrop and subsurface by violating the systematic superposition of formal units. The cut-off applies only to the usage of the *formal* units and does not affect the recognition and mappability of the shale and limestone lithosomes or the extension of the Niobrara as an operational unit.

The cut-offs within the Montana Group (Figure 10-7B) are examples of what may be considered non-arbitrary cut-offs, inasmuch as they are placed at the finite limits of defining units in the sequence. The positions of other cut-offs placed at pinch-outs of defining units are less easily chosen, since there may be a number of possible choices among tongues. The complex Mancos-Mesaverde relationships of the Colorado Plateau as illustrated by Figure 9-8 are an example of the problems commonly encountered. Application of the principle enunciated by Wheeler and Mallory (1953) would suggest that a cut-off be placed near the San Juan—McKinley County line to avoid vertical intercalation of Mesaverde and Mancos units. If this were done, the sandstone tongues and members (Gallup, Dilco, Dalton, Hosta, Point Lookout) would be treated as members of the Mancos Formation north of the county line and as members of the Mesaverde Formation to the south. Conversely, the shale tongues (Mulatto and Satan) would be regarded as Mesaverde members south of a position approximating the county line. It must again be pointed out that the purpose of such an arbitrary treatment is to create a unified and simple system of formal stratigraphic units that can be applied to mapping and description; no limitation is thereby placed on the handling of lithosomes and operational units.

CORRELATION OF BIOSTRATIGRAPHIC UNITS

Review of Definitions and Classification

Biostratigraphic units are vertically successive bodies of strata characterized by their contained fossils. The fundamental unit, commonly termed a **zone,** is based on the assemblage of fossils present and is designated by the name of a characteristic animal or plant, although the limits of a given zone need not necessarily coincide with the vertical range of the designating taxon. The term **assemblage zone** is applied to biostratigraphic units of· this type where there is a possibility of confusion with other kinds of units such as range zones.

A **local-range zone** is the stratigraphic interval encompassing the vertical range of a single fossil taxon at one locality, or within a limited area. Within a local-range zone, the stratal thickness characterized by the maximum representation of the taxon involved may be identified as a **peak zone.** The body of strata enclosed between surfaces marking the upper and lower limits of the known local-range zones of a single taxon is a **range zone.** Individual range zones vary in lateral extent from extreme provincial to intercontinental status.

Concurrent-range zones are defined by overlapping range zones, some with ranges having a lower stratigraphic limit and others having an upper stratigraphic limit.

By application of paleontology to the definition of biostratigraphic units, the biostratigraphic column of any area can be subdivided into vertically successive assemblage zones. These are analogous to other observable units of strata (formations, heavy-mineral zones, operational units, and so forth) defined by other properties of the strata. However, inasmuch as all strata are not fossiliferous, it is commonly necessary to recognize **barren zones** as a type of quasi-biostratigraphic unit in the differentiation of the biostratigraphic column of most areas. Assemblage zones, like rock units, are of limited areal extent, and cannot, in general, be correlated beyond the confines of a single depositional basin or province. Therefore, each province bears its own biostratigraphic column, in which zones may vary in sequence and character from those of adjacent areas.

Theoretically, a sequence of strata in any area should be divisible into but one series of vertically successive zones. In practice, however, workers concerned with different taxonomic groups are prone to recognize parallel, but not equivalent, zones based on separate groups of organisms. Table 10-1 illustrates the time-stratigraphic and biostratigraphic subdivisions of a portion of the Upper Cretaceous of Europe, with zones based on ammonites, other megafossils, and foraminifera.

An assemblage zone, like a rock unit, has objectively determined contacts with other contiguous zones above and below. Just as a sandstone unit may grade upward into a shale unit, the fossil components of one zone commonly intermingle with the fossils of the succeeding zone and the operational contact must then be chosen somewhat arbitrarily.

Relation of Biostratigraphic Zones to Rock Units

Biostratigraphic zones bear no necessary relationship to rock units. In stratigraphic sections interrupted by numerous hiatuses, rock and biostratigraphic boundaries are likely to exhibit a high degree of coincidence. Even in sections reflecting fairly continuous deposition, environmental factors commonly affect lithotopes and biotopes simultaneously, and rock units and biostratigraphic zones may thus coincide over broad areas. In some cases, this relationship is so well established that, through usage, a rock unit may

TABLE 10-1. TIME-STRATIGRAPHIC AND BIOSTRATIGRAPHIC UNITS RECOGNIZED IN THE UPPER CRETACEOUS OF EUROPE. [Modified from Muller and Schenck, 1943.]

SERIES	STAGES	AMMONITE ZONES	ZONES BASED ON FOSSILS OTHER THAN AMMONITES		
			OTHER MOLLUSKS	ECHINODERMS	FORAMINIFERA
UPPER CRETACEOUS	Danian	(Hercoglossa danica)			
	Maestrichtian	Discoscaphites constrictus	Belemnitella lanceolata	Echinocorys sulcatus	Globotruncana conica
		Bostrychoceras polyplocum			
	Campanian	Kossmaticeras theobaldianum	Belemnitella mucronata	Hemipneustes striatoradiatus	Globotruncana arca
		Hoplitoplacenticeras coesfeldiense			
		Submortoniceras delawarense	Actinocamax quadratus ?	Offaster pilula	
		Diplacmoceras bidorsatum			
	Santonian	Stantonoceras guadalupae	?	Marsupites testudinarius	
		Texanites texanus	Actinocamax granulatus	Micraster coranguinum	
		Texanites emscheris			
	Coniacian	Barroisiceras haberfellneri	Actinocamax vestfalicus	Micraster cortestudinarium	Globotruncana linneiana
	Turonian	Pseudojacobites farmeryi		Holaster planus	
		Prionotropis woollgari		Terebratula lata	
		Mammites nodosoides	?	Rhynchonella cuvieri	
		Fagesia superstes			
	Cenomanian	Metoicoceras pontieri	Actinocamax plenus ?	Holaster subglobosus	Globotruncana aff. appenninica
		Acanthoceras rhotomagense			
		Schloenbachia varians		Holaster nodulosus	
		Mantelliceras martimpreyi	Neohibolites ultimus	Cardiaster fossarius	

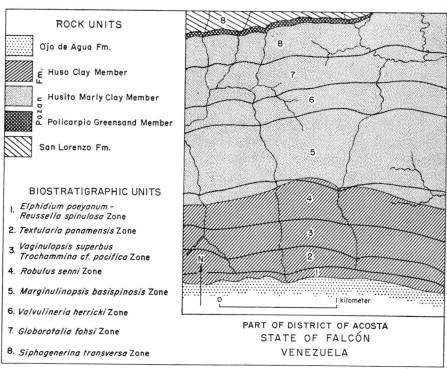

ROCK UNITS

▦ O'jo de Agua Fm.

▨ Huso Clay Member

▦ Husito Marly Clay Member

▦ Policarpio Greensand Member

▨ San Lorenzo Fm.

(Pozan Fm.)

BIOSTRATIGRAPHIC UNITS

1. *Elphidium poeyanum - Reussella spinulosa* Zone

2. *Textularia panamensis* Zone

3. *Vaginulopsis superbus Trochammina cf. pacifica* Zone

4. *Robulus senni* Zone

5. *Marginulinopsis basispinosis* Zone

6. *Valvulineria herricki* Zone

7. *Globorotalia fohsi* Zone

8. *Siphogenerina transversa* Zone

PART OF DISTRICT OF ACOSTA
STATE OF FALCÓN
VENEZUELA

Fig. 10-8. An area in Venezuela in which both rock and biostratigraphic units of Oligocene and Miocene age have been mapped. Note that the boundaries of the foraminiferal zones are generally parallel to the rock units, except in the central portion of the map, where the lower boundary of the *Robulus senni* Zone transgresses the boundary between two members of the Pozan Formation. [Adapted from Renz (1948).]

become identified with the associated biostratigraphic zone. The *Heterostegina* Zone of the Gulf Coast Oligocene, for instance, is often distinguished on electric logs without reference to foraminiferal data. The relative ease with which certain assemblage zones are recognized and traced has led to the designation of such zones as though they were rock units, with attendant generation of confusion between the two categories. Most of the Upper Ordovician "formations" and "members" of the classic Cincinnati Arch area, for example, have purely biostratigraphic boundaries. The proper treatment of these units as assemblage zones would in no way impair their validity and usefulness and would make it possible to establish and utilize genuine rock units based on lithologic criteria.

Where fossils are moderately abundant, assemblage zones may be mapped with great utility in both surface and subsurface, particularly where traceable rock units are few and far between. Figure 10-8 illustrates an area in

Venezuela where both rock units and assemblage zones have been mapped areally. Note that, although there is a minor discordance near the center of the map area and the boundaries of the two classes of units do not coincide, the same general attitude and structure of the strata is indicated by rock and biostratigraphic units. This degree of concordance is fairly typical of the patterns found in outcrops around the rims of sedimentary basins in which structural strike and biofacies and lithofacies strike tend to be parallel.

If the relationships between rock units and biostratigraphic units are studied across the structural and facies strike and into the depths of sedimentary basins, a more marked divergence is commonly revealed. Figure 10-9 is a generalized downdip cross section of part of the Oligocene in the Texas portion of the Gulf Coast Basin. The biostratigraphic horizons shown are the upper surfaces of two kinds of units: the *Heterostegina* and *Mar-*

Fig. 10-9. Generalized dip cross section of part of the Oligocene in Texas, showing rock and biostratigraphic units. Note the marked discordance of certain of the foraminiferal zones with respect to rock boundaries and the discordances evident among the biostratigraphic horizons themselves. [Modified from Reedy (1949).]

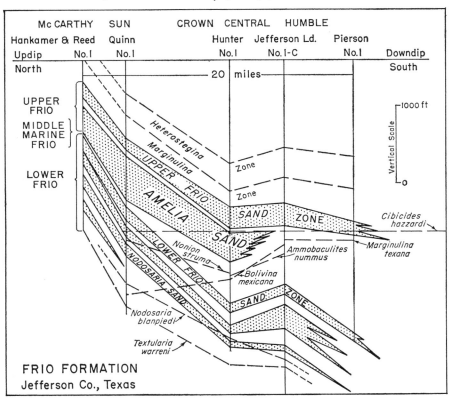

ginulina Zones are assemblage zones; the others are range zones of individual species, drawn by connecting the "tops," or first appearances in samples, of particular species. The discordance between the range zone tops and the sand tongues, and among the range zones themselves, is clear.

It may be remarked parenthetically, that the stratigraphic discordances of the type noted above, as well as those between formal rock units and parastratigraphic units, do not necessarily indicate that one class of units gives "true" or "correct" relationships while the patterns suggested by the other units are "false" or "incorrect." It is more appropriate, since the units in question are directly observable (tangible and non-inferential), to consider that a choice is available to the geologist regarding the class of units to use. The petroleum geologist is concerned with the distribution of fluids in permeable rocks. In the Oligocene example (Figure 10-9) he would be more likely to choose the sand tongues and the parallel foraminiferal zones (*Heterostegina, Marginulina,* and *Textularia warreni*). Other workers interested in chronologic or environmental relationships might well select other units with equal cause.

Methods of Biostratigraphic Correlation

The following discussion is limited to the consideration of assemblage zones, the fundamental biostratigraphic units. Range zones and concurrent-range zones have a more direct application to the problems of time-stratigraphic correlation and, for this reason, are treated later in this chapter. Assemblage zones are observable units of strata, and as such they may be correlated by many of the same methods applied to the correlation of formations and members. Similarly, work with biostratigraphic units is subject to parallel difficulties of nomenclature, facies change, and the necessity of recognizing arbitrary cut-offs.

If it were possible, by use of some hypothetical selective optical filter, to see only the fossils in sedimentary rocks without the interference of inorganic grains, cement, and matrix, then the successions of assemblage zones, intervening barren zones, and their complex interrelationships would be as apparent as rock-unit patterns in well exposed terrains. In the absence of metaphysical aids, biostratigraphic correlation requires painstaking observation, most often supplemented by careful collecting and detailed laboratory analysis. The field biostratigrapher cannot, in the average case, observe, correlate, and map assemblage zones by an integration of gross features such as those available to the physical stratigrapher. Nor, in the subsurface, has the biostratigrapher any recourse to devices similar to mechanical logs that can be used to obtain indirect measures of paleontologic attributes (except where, as in organic reefs, fossils may dominate the lithologic aspect). In view of these difficulties, the present degree of biostratigraphic knowledge is a tribute to generations of patient work.

Zonal Guide Fossils. Fossil assemblages are usually mixtures of long-ranging nondiagnostic forms and others of known limited stratigraphic range in the local succession. With experience, the biostratigrapher can recognize **zonal guide fossils** among the latter types, making the identification of specific assemblage zones possible, just as lithologic identity is applied to the correlation of rock units. Many rock units can not be identified by any single lithologic attribute; similarly, it is the association of several guide fossils in an assemblage that characterizes a zone. Subsurface stratigraphers, particularly those engaged in work with the Tertiary, have long recognized the value of determining the relative abundance of species in an assemblage as a means of distinguishing between zones which bear the same fauna. The large numbers of forms available in micropaleontologic investigations make possible the precise quantification of the characteristics of foraminiferal zones in some areas.

Emphasis has been placed on rapid recognition of biostratigraphic horizons in the routine micropaleontologic analysis of subsurface samples. The resulting data are of great practical importance in determining structural position and in detecting changes in thickness of stratigraphic intervals from well to well. For these purposes, the first appearances of zonal guide fossils in the samples are used to establish the position of the "tops" of successive zones penetrated during drilling. The so called "tops" are correlated from well to well like key beds in a lithologic section.

Position in Biostratigraphic Sequence. For any area of fossiliferous strata, the **biostratigraphic column** can be constructed to record the relative positions of various biostratigraphic zones. The sequence established may then be used as a correlation tool in much the same manner as a rock column.

The application of the biostratigraphic column is particularly valid where the identification of guide fossils is an insufficient basis for correlation. Just as lithologic identity cannot be used alone in sections characterized by repetition of similar lithologies, guide fossils are inadequate in sequences containing recurrent faunas of similar aspect. In such cases, two similar zones may be correlated or differentiated only by reference to position in sequence.

Before a biostratigraphic column can be established and divided into appropriate assemblage zones, it is necessary to construct a **range chart**. A range chart normally records the local-range zone of each significant fossil taxon encountered in terms of genera and species. Where possible, it is useful to refine a range chart by graphically indicating the stratigraphic position (peak-zone) at which each significant faunal element is particularly prominent.

The biostratigraphic column is easily differentiated into obviously distinct units within those sections that exhibit numerous hiatuses or abrupt shifts in biotopes. However, zones are commonly established that do not coincide with the local-range zones of any of the component taxons, but which are defined on the basis of assemblages and the positions in which predominant forms occur. Figure 10-10 illustrates a range chart and the assemblage zones established from it.

TIME-STRATIGRAPHIC CORRELATION

Review of Definitions and Principles

The preceding portions of the present chapter have dealt with the correlation of observable stratigraphic units. Although there are many problems in correlation of rock and biostratigraphic units, the majority of these could be solved if more data were available in the form of nearly complete exposures, a greater density of drilling, and a more complete paleontologic record.

Time-stratigraphic correlation involves the same questions of incomplete information, and in addition, is greatly complicated by the necessary application of concept, inference, and interpretation. Thus, a somewhat more intensive review is required before attacking the specific problems of correlation.

Geologic Time as a Continuum. In the past, under the influence of the catastrophist philosophy, it was considered that geologic time could be neatly segmented into eras and periods by worldwide upheavals of universal extent and influence. Today we recognize that uplift, erosion, and partial destruction of the geologic record in one area is accompanied by transportation, deposition, and the accumulation of a stratigraphic record in other areas. It is therefore necessary to consider geologic time as a complete continuum, only partially represented by a rock record in any one area. Thus, at any geographic point, geologic history is divided, quite unequally, into times of deposition of sedimentary rocks or implacement of igneous bodies, time of erosion of previously accumulated materials, and times during which the locality remained in equilibrium without appreciable deposition or erosion.

Geologic Time as a Dimension. The relationships among observable stratigraphic units at a single geographic point may be shown by a columnar section or well log in which the vertical dimension is stratigraphic thickness, expressed in the dimensions of length, usually in feet or meters. If a stratigraphic cross section is constructed, another length dimension, feet, miles, or

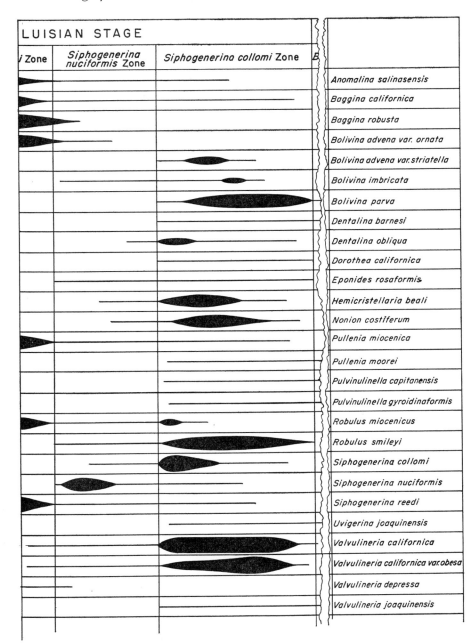

Fig. 10-10. Part of a generalized range chart for the Miocene of California, showing assemblage zones, range zones, and peak zones of component foraminiferal species. [Data from Kleinpell (1938).]

kilometers, is added to the diagram. Similarly, a block diagram or panel diagram is a three dimensional representation in which there are two horizontal or geographic coordinates and one vertical or stratigraphic coordinate, all of which are measured in the dimensions of length. In time-stratigraphy, however, the vertical axis of any graphic representation is always *time* rather than *length*. Thus, the horizontal axis of a time-stratigraphic correlation chart has the length dimensions of geographic coordinates, whereas the vertical axis is geologic time. Carrying the discussion one step further, it is possible to consider a block in which the two horizontal dimensions are length (in terms of geographic coordinates) and the vertical dimension is time. The "volume" defined by these three axes (termed "space-time" by Wheeler 1958) is more precisely called **area-time,** and it is within this conceptual framework that the problems of time-stratigraphy must be set.

Figure 10-11A is a block diagram, in which all three axes have the length dimensions of space. Note that the volume enclosed by the block is totally occupied by material bodies of rock divided by unconformities and lithologic changes into a number of rock-stratigraphic units. Part B is an area-time representation of the same situation. The vertical axis is time, replacing the length dimension of thickness, or depth below a given datum, used in the preceding diagram. Note that the area-time "volume" is only partially occupied by material bodies of rock and that these are separated by gaps or **lacunas,** indicated by closely spaced vertical lines, which represent area-time "volume" without physical or material substance. The lacunas represent the greatest amount of time on the axis of the anticline indicated in Figure 10-11A. Here the amount of time represented in the stratigraphic record is reduced by both nondeposition (shown by the overlap pattern above the unconformities) and by erosion (indicated by the truncation of the rocks below the unconformities). Wheeler (1958) has proposed that that part of the area-time lacuna, resulting from the removal of previously deposited rocks, be termed an **erosional vacuity,** whereas he suggests application of the term **hiatus** to the results of nondeposition. Hiatus, in a similar sense, had been applied earlier by Grabau (1906).

In addition, the area-time block differs in another respect from the tangible mass illustrated in Figure 10-11A. In the latter, the vertical dimension is a length (stratigraphic thickness or depth below a datum plane), which can be measured and expressed with precision. Therefore, given sufficient information, the geometry and relationships between observable stratigraphic units may be fixed with a high degree of accuracy. In area-time, however, the precision of measurement in the vertical dimension, time, is very low and geologists are unable to define the height of the area-time block or to divide the time represented into equal intervals.

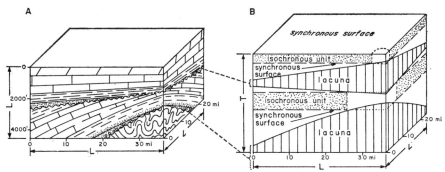

Fig. 10-11. (*A*) Standard block diagram showing two unconformity-bounded successions of strata overlying crystalline basement rocks. All dimensions of the block are expressed as lengths (L × L × L). (*B*) The same relationships are shown in an area-time diagram in which two geographic coordinates expressed as lengths are combined with a vertical dimension of geologic time (L × L × T). The vertically ruled portions represent nondeposition and erosion at the positions of the unconformities of *A*. The blank portions between the lacunas represent the areas and times of deposition of the preserved sedimentary successions. The area-time values of these preserved successions is divisible into isochronous units by time-parallel synchronous surfaces.

Placement in the dimension of geologic time may be likened to the imprecision of geographic placement before the development of accurate length measurement by geodetic surveying. The ancient Greeks, for example, were fully aware that the distance from Athens to Sicily was less than the distance to the Pillars of Hercules, but they had no means of precise measurement of either distance. So it is with measurement in geologic time; it can be demonstrated that the lacunas on the anticlinal axis of Figure 10-11 have a greater time value than at the left margin of the block, but it is not possible to determine and express these time dimensions in any but the most approximate terms. Similarly, the horizontal strata at the top of the block are known to be younger than the units underlying the unconformity but no accurate quantitative measure of this difference in age can be made.

In any assemblage of stratified rocks that is not hopelessly confused by structural complexity and metamorphism, it is possible to recognize the temporal order and succession of the units by applying the principle of superposition in all its ramifications. Each unit of strata may be assigned to a *relative* positive position in geologic time, as "older than" or "younger than" other units. Fossiliferous strata can commonly be assigned to their correct position in succession without necessary consideration of the physical relationships among the units involved. However, by whichever method is applied, superposition or paleontology, only the order and succession of the units in time and their relative ages are established.

Ordinal Time and Ordinal Age. Mathematicians use the term "ordinal scale" in reference to a scale of measurement in which the things measured are of a definite rank or order but without equality of intervals or differences between the several ranks. Familiar examples in geology are Moh's Scale of hardness of minerals and the Rossi-Forel Scale of earthquake intensity. The geologic time scale is another prime example, and it is useful to keep in mind that most discussions of geologic time are couched in terms of an **ordinal time scale** and most assignments of geologic age may be considered as references to **ordinal age.**

As pointed out in the discussion of the stratigraphic column (Chapter 2), early in the history of stratigraphy, the rocks of the earth's crust were assigned to three ranks of decreasing geologic age—Primary, Secondary, and Tertiary—a purely ordinal scale. With further work and increasing maturity of stratigraphic concepts these major groupings were subdivided into the several systems of rocks recognized today, and a clear differentiation was made between these material bodies of strata (time-stratigraphic units) and the periods (time units) represented by their deposition. In this long accepted sense, a time-stratigraphic unit (Cambrian System, for example) is defined at a type locality (a specific section in North Wales in this example). The time unit (Cambrian Period) was considered to include that span of time between the initiation and close of deposition of the Cambrian System at its type locality. In view of the unconformities and resulting lacunas that exist at the boundaries of the classical systems, it is desirable that this concept be modified slightly to avoid attributing too much significance to a single type section, since this would inevitably lead to "orphaned" spans of time, representing the lacunas between the systems at their classically designated localities. Instead, there is now a tendency to designate **type boundaries** for systems and other time-stratigraphic units at positions within unbroken successions in which it is unlikely that appreciable amounts of geologic time are unrepresented by rocks. When this problem has been resolved by the redesignation of type boundary localities, a period will represent, in both concept and practice, the span of time between the initiation of deposition of one system and the initiation of deposition of the next succeeding system and will exclude unassigned gaps from the time continuum. The same concept and practice is to be accorded the lesser time-stratigraphic units and their parallel units of geologic time—series and epochs, stages and ages.

Chronologic Time and Chronologic Age. Chronology is defined as the science of measuring or computing time by regular divisions or periods, and which assigns to events their proper dates. If chronology were strictly applicable to geologic time, the vertical dimension of the block in Figure 10-11B would be subdivisible into units representing equal spans of geologic time. If this were possible, the ordinal time scale could be replaced by an **interval scale,** permitting the precise determination of the time values of the time-stratigraphic units and lacunas and their definition in terms of **chronologic time** and **chronologic age.**

Generations of geologists have sought a "geologic clock" which would permit precise measurement of chronologic time and precise determinations of the chronologic age of rocks. Geologists and archeologists working with the younger Quaternary strata have been able to use varves and tree rings to attain a fair degree of precision in limited areas within limited stratigraphic successions. In addition, the radio-carbon dating method offers promise, as yet unfulfilled, of providing reasonable approximations of chronologic dates in the recent geologic past.

A number of approaches have been made toward establishing chronology among the more ancient rocks, utilizing thickness of accumulated sediment, the salt content of the seas, the amount of erosion, the changes in the orientation of the earth's magnetic field, and other physical phenomena and processes as measures of geologic time. These approaches, for a variety of reasons, yield markedly discordant "measures" which aid in appreciation of the magnitude of geologic time but do not provide an accurate chronologic scale.

In the last few decades, and at an accelerated pace today, efforts have been made to arrive at accurate chronologic dates based on the isotope ratios of radiogenic minerals. It is accepted as a fact that these ratios vary directly with the time elapsed since crystallization of the minerals, and, theoretically, they should yield precise dates in terms of chronologic time. However, this potentially important method has not yet been refined to the degree necessary to provide the accuracy desired. Different ratios measured within the same samples commonly give highly discordant estimates of age, and there is no sound means of determining which of the dates is most accurate. Age determinations of igneous rocks, even where there is apparent agreement among separate analyses, do not often establish the chronologic age of the associated sedimentary rocks, except within rather broad limits. A similar lack of agreement is found when isotope-ratio measurements are made on authigenic minerals in sediments, although the method is of great possible utility in the direct dating of stratigraphic units. The disagreement between measurements of different minerals and different ratios presumably reflects the instability of the sedimentary minerals and the effects of post-depositional changes.

Table 10-2 presents estimates of the limiting ages of the Paleozoic and younger periods from two sources and illustrates the disparity which exists among these estimates. It is apparent that geologists' hopes for a strictly

TABLE 10-2. COMPARISON OF TWO ISOTOPE-RATIO DETERMINATIONS OF THE AGES OF PERIOD BOUNDARIES*

* From Mayne, K. I., Lambert, R. St. J., and York, D., 1959, The geological time scale: Nature, v. 183, p. 212–214, and Kulp, J. L., 1961, Geological time scale: Science, v. 133, p. 1105–1114.

chronologic time scale and for the application of chronologic ages have not yet been attained, and that time-stratigraphy must be discussed in terms of an ordinal time scale.

Synchrony, Time-parallelism, and Isochronism. In dealing with problems of time-stratigraphy, three terms are commonly misapplied or misconstrued. Conceptually, boundaries between time-stratigraphic units in continuous and unbroken succession are **synchronous surfaces** on which every point has the same geologic age. There are other surfaces that are not necessarily synchronous, but which are parallel to or which closely approximate unobservable surfaces of simultaneous time. An example would be the surface of a rapidly transgressed unconformity, involving a geologically insignificant amount of time in the overstep. Such a surface would not be synchronous, inasmuch as it involves strata of varying age below the unconformity, but it would be time-parallel in terms of the area-time geometry of overlying strata.

Figure 10-11B shows two synchronous surfaces. The area-time "volume" between the two surfaces is everywhere equal; that is, it is an **isochronous interval**. That portion of the interval represented by a complete rock record (indicated by shading) is an **isochronous unit** of rock.

To the practical stratigrapher, synchrony, time-parallelism, and isochronism are among the intangibles, in that they are not directly visible in the rocks. There are, however, certain relationships which can be clearly seen between observable rocks and biostratigraphic units on one hand, and time-stratigraphic units and their associated synchronous boundaries on the other.

It is obvious, for example, that within stratigraphic successions that are interrupted by numerous unconformities and breaks in deposition, it is highly probable that the bounding surfaces of time-stratigraphic units and the contacts of rock or biostratigraphic units may coincide. In the area-time framework, such a succession contains many lacunas, which may indeed occupy more time than the preserved sediments. It is therefore likely that one or more time unit boundaries will pass through a lacuna and exhibit distinct lithologic and paleontologic differences in the preserved rock record above and below. Conversely, the record in areas of long continued deposition is characterized by the occurrence of time-stratigraphic boundaries in the midst of unbroken successions of strata that bear no relationship to unconformities or to the contacts of rock and biostratigraphic units.

As is developed in greater detail on later pages, some rock and biostratigraphic units give every evidence of simultaneous deposition over wide areas and can be considered to mark synchronous surfaces. Ash falls and the resulting bentonite beds are examples. Other units are just as obviously related to narrow depositional environments, which may be expected to shift laterally with advancing time, thus differing widely in age within different areas of their deposition. These are known as **time-transgressive** or **diachronous** units. Examples are found in strand-line deposits of advancing seas and among deltaic sediments. Figure 10-12 illustrates a classical case of diachronism long recognized in Jurassic strata of the south of England. Here the vertically successive ammonite zones give every evidence of time-parallelism (for reasons discussed in succeeding paragraphs of this section). A sandstone unit is seen to be markedly younger as it is traced from the Cotswold Hills to the Dorset Coast. In this case, the lithic unit is considered time-transgressive, whereas in the earlier example cited (Figure 10-9), the interpretation indicates that the range zones are the transgressive units.

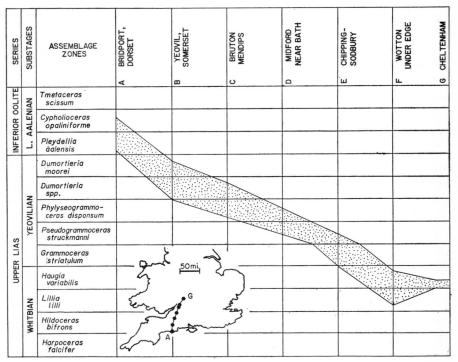

Fig. 10-12. Time-length (T × L) cross section showing the diachronic relationship of time-parallel Jurassic ammonite zones in the south of England
to a rock-stratigraphic unit (variously termed Bridport, Yeovil, Mid-
ford, and Cotswold Sandstone). [Modified from Wills (1929).]

Methods of Interregional Time Stratigraphic Correlation

The aims and methods of time-stratigraphic correlation applied to interprovincial, interregional, or intercontinental problems differ from those of
local scope which apply to a single basin of deposition or a part thereof.
Interregional correlation is the mechanism whereby the sequence of geologic events in one area is related to the universal geologic time scale and to
the record of historical geology. Local time-stratigraphic correlation demonstrates the synchroneity or lack of synchroneity of events over a limited area
of immediate interest, without necessary reference to the world-wide geologic calendar.

Paleontologic Correlation. Although the mechanisms of organic evolution
remain somewhat obscure and subject to debate, few thinking individuals
will deny that progressive changes have altered the character of the earth's
fauna and flora with the advance of geologic time. These progressive changes
provide the stratigrapher with his most useful tool in interregional correla-

tion and are the basis for integrating the geologic events of widely separated areas.

The products of organic evolution must be applied to problems of time-stratigraphic correlation with a certain degree of restraint and caution. Fossils typical of the Ordovician are quite obviously different from those found in Cretaceous strata, but the distinction between the faunas of adjacent series is hard to define. In other words, evolution serves, almost universally, to resolve the differences between the larger time-stratigraphic units, but this resolving power is commonly insufficient for the sure differentiation of units at the stage or series level. A comparison may be drawn with the hour hand of the clock which may be read to distinguish 2:30 from 3:30 but is valueless in determining individual minutes or seconds.

In Chapters 8 and 9, emphasis was laid on the influence of environment on the character of faunas and floras. Figure 10-13 attempts to illustrate the rising influence of environment in evaluation of the significance of an assemblage as consideration narrows from eras and systems to series and stages. Minor variations in faunal aspects controlled by environment will not obscure the assignment of a Middle Mississippian marine fauna to the Paleozoic, and, in all probability, to the proper system, but determination of precise placement, as Late Osagian or Early Meramecian, may well be difficult. Two Osagian faunas from dissimilar biosomes of equivalent age may appear radically different, while either one may closely resemble the fauna of similar biosomes from the Kinderhookian or Meramecian.

Range Zones and Index Fossils. A range zone is the body of rock enclosed between the vertical and lateral limits of occurrence of a particular genus, species, or other fossil taxon. Every range zone occupies a span of geologic time, referred to as its **biozone** by some workers, but not all taxons and their range zones are equally applicable to

Fig. 10-13

The character of a fossil assemblage is a reflection of the environment of the original biocoenosis and of the stage in evolution attained by component species. The paleontologic identification of major time intervals, such as eras, is little influenced by environment. At approximately the epoch-series level, however, environment and evolution are of approximately equal influence. Biostratigraphic zonation of shorter time intervals tends toward discrimination of units that are more a reflection of changes in environment than of evolution and the passage of geologic time.

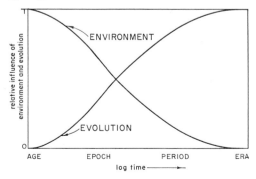

problems of time-stratigraphy. Some, like certain phosphatic brachiopods, are so long-ranging in time as to be almost meaningless in a time-stratigraphic sense. Others are too rare to be useful or too closely confined geographically to be of interregional significance. The range zones of many organisms, particularly benthonic types, inhabiting a specific bottom environment, have marked time-transgressive limits, which preclude their application to inter-regional time-stratigraphy. Nektonic and planktonic organisms, inhabiting the very widespread and stable environments of the open sea, are commonly characterized by range zones having boundaries that closely approach synchronism. For this reason, graptolites, the planktonic foraminifera, and microscopic spores are of maximum utility in time-stratigraphic correlation.

The evolution of certain organisms is clearly demonstrated by morphologic changes and abundantly documented by the fossil record. Among the Mezozoic ammonoids, for example, the variety of morphologic detail available for analysis makes it possible to define and recognize a great many morphospecies. In certain groups of ammonoids, within the limits imposed by geographic speciation, the same morphospecies appear in the same order wherever encountered. Moreover, progressive trends of development are commonly noted in the details of ornamentation or in the suture lines. The combination of an unvarying relative position and of progressive morphologic development identifies a **phylogenetic** series made up of vertically successive **chronospecies.**

The accompanying diagram (Figure 10-14) illustrates a phylogenetic series among scaphitoid ammonites in the Cretaceous of the Western Interior, ranging in age from Late Turonian to Early Coniacian, in terms of the European time scale. Although there is a progressive change in the degree of coiling and in ornamentation, the most significant clues are found in the details of the suture patterns. Note, for example, the modifications of the first lateral lobe, shown enlarged in the right hand side of the diagram. In this rapidly-evolving stock, each step in the development toward the ultimate trident-like lobe of *Clioscaphites novimexicanus* is indicative of a specific and brief span of Cretaceous time. The forms illustrated are chronospecies whose successive and vertically contiguous range zones may be considered to be separated by virtually synchronous surfaces which subdivide this portion of Cretaceous time in the Western Interior area into a series of isochronous intervals. The identification of any one of the chronospecies in this phylogenetic series establishes the time-stratigraphic correlation of the enclosing strata with a high degree of accuracy.

Because of the geographic variation within and among species, it is unlikely that the finely discriminated species of the example can be traced far beyond the limits of interconnected depositional provinces. However,

SCAPHITOID CEPHALOPODS OF THE COLORADO GROUP

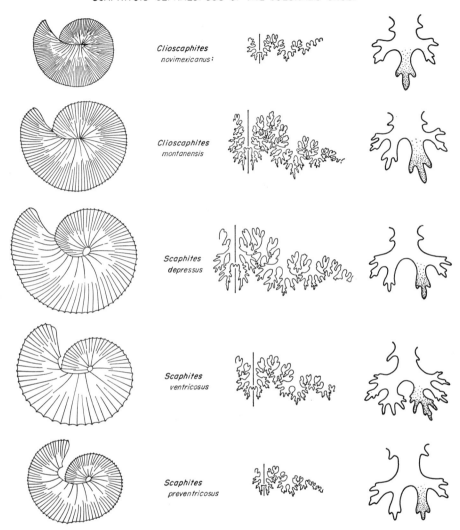

Clioscaphites novimexicanus

Clioscaphites montanensis

Scaphites depressus

Scaphites ventricosus

Scaphites preventricosus

Fig. 10-14. Phylogenetic series among Cretaceous ammonites of the Western Interior region. Note the progressive modification of the first lateral lobe (enlarged at right) from *Scaphites preventricosus* (Turonian) to *Clioscaphites novimexicanus* (Coniacian). [Modified after Cobban (1951).]

other phylogenetic series, involving larger segments of geologic time and commonly expressed in terms of the range zones of genera, rather than of species, make possible the recognition of isochronous intervals of interregional and even intercontinental scope. A fossil taxon that is characterized by a broad geographic range and by a range zone that may be demonstrated to approach isochroneity, and which, in addition, combines morphologic distinctiveness with relatively common occurrence, is an **index fossil.** That is, the occurrence of such a fossil is an index to a specific portion of geologic time and makes possible the accurate time-stratigraphic correlation of the strata in which it is found.

Chronospecies and "chronogenera" include the most obvious index fossils, since the synchronism of their range zones may be established without serious doubt. It is the large number of phylogenetic series and time-parallel range zones which can be identified among cephalopod faunas that makes possible the accurate correlation of the nautiloid and ammonoid bearing strata of Late Paleozoic and Mesozoic time. The same is true of continental Tertiary deposits bearing the bones and teeth of mammals of established evolutionary position.

Excellent index fossils are also known among groups in which no clear phylogenetic succession is apparent. Cambrian trilobites, Ordovician and Silurian graptolites, and late Paleozoic fusulinids are examples of fossil types that exhibit range zones which appear in approximately the same vertical succession wherever encountered, thus indicating a degree of time-parallelism of the biostratigraphic boundaries between successive zones. Index fossils of this type include the most numerous examples, but since their ranges may be controlled as much or more by the distribution of environments than by replacement in an evolutionary sequence, such range zones are subject to change as new extensions of range are found. The genus *Monograptus*, for example, had been considered an index to the Silurian Period. In recent years, the genus has been found to extend into the Early Devonian. The apparent ranges of other index fossils are also subject to modification, and it is apparent that supposed index fossils of unknown evolutionary position cannot yield the precise age placements possible with members of a phylogenetic series.

The range zones of index fossils available in the deposits of certain parts of geologic time or of certain environmental settings may involve rather long spans of geologic time; thus they cannot be directly applied in precise time-stratigraphic correlation. However, by consideration of the coincidence of occurrence of two or more fossils representing overlapping range zones, it is possible to define relatively brief portions of ordinal time through recognition of concurrent-range zones. Consider, for example, a collection which includes two index fossils. Species A is known to range through Middle and Upper Ordovician. The time range of species B is from Late Upper Ordovician to Middle Silurian. The coincident occurrence of the two index fossils indicates an age of Late Upper Ordovician—the unique time span indicated by the overlap or concurrence of the two ranges.

The utility of the application of multiple fossil indices to time-stratigraphic correlation is obvious. However, it does not necessarily follow that the mere application of large numbers of fossils of uncertain time-stratigraphic value is a valid means of establishing geologic age with precision. Nevertheless, the "percentage method" is commonly used in interregional time-stratigraphic correlation. The method involves calculating the percentages of species in a given collection that are also found in units of known time-stratigraphic position in a given reference area. The age of the collection is then assumed to be the same as that of the reference unit having the greatest similarity, in terms of the percentage of species in common. Such age assignments are commonly made without consideration of the true range zones of the component species, without quantitative evaluation of the numbers of individuals represented, and, too often, in terms of faunal lists, without regard for the vagaries of identification of morphospecies discussed in Chapter 8. An example of this type of "correlation" is found in the treatment of Ordovician strata of northwestern North America, discussed later in this chapter under another topic.

It should be noted that correlation problems in time-stratigraphy are more likely to be solved on the basis of established index fossils, recognized by their position in a phylogenetic series or established through interregional occurrence in a known biostratigraphic sequence, rather than by weight of numbers of taxons of undefined time values. The range zones of fossil taxons, including index fossils, appear to occur in characteristic stratigraphic positions, some of which represent specific portions of geologic time, in which the number of individuals per unit volume of rock, or in which the relative number of a given taxon present is particularly high. Quantitative measures of this tendency offer promise of the possible refinement of interregional correlation, but the method has not been commonly applied, except on a local scale.

Correlation by Quantitative Physical Measures. There have been many attempts made to discover age-related attributes of sedimentary rocks, other than their contained fossils, that could be used in correlation. Mention has already been made of chronologic age determinations based on the isotope ratios of radiogenic minerals found in sediments and in the igneous rocks with which they are associated. If this approach were perfected, it would permit highly accurate time-stratigraphic correlation on both chronologic and ordinal time scales. Unfortunately, this state of perfection has not been attained and in dealing with Paleozoic and younger strata, age determinations and correlations based on paleontology continue to be less conflicting and more accurate than those derived from radiogenic isotope measures.

There are other apparent age-related physical or physiocochemical attributes of sedimentary rocks, and it is possible that one or more of these will provide the breakthrough to more accurate measurements of ordinal or chronologic time. A number of carbonate minerals give off light upon heating and the intensity of this **thermoluminescent effect** is thought to result from damage to the crystal-lattice structure by naturally occurring high energy radiation (Zeller, 1954; Zeller, Wray, and Daniels, 1957). This radiation damage, in turn, is believed to vary in proportion to the rate and duration of the radiation. Therefore, if the natural radioactivity of a given carbonate sample can be determined, the instrumentally measured intensity of thermoluminescence can be expressed in terms of geologic time. Geothermal heat and the heat generated by igneous activity or movements of the earth's crust have the effect of draining the thermoluminescent energy and starting the "clock" over again. The effects of these phenomena on thermoluminescence have not thus far been eliminated from the calculations employed in this method, but the field of investigation remains a promising one.

The velocity of transmission of sonic waves in shale increases with depth of burial and with geologic age. Since the development of the CVL, or sonic log, measurements of these velocities in the subsurface have become quite common. Furthermore, the effects of depth of burial can be calculated, and the velocity measurements can be expressed in terms of geologic time, at least on the ordinal scale. Table 10-3 presents data from Faust (1951), showing average velocities measured in strata of different geologic ages, corrected for the effects of burial. The values followed by question marks indicate those velocities based on less reliable data.

Correlation by Eustatic Changes. Marked eustatic changes in sea level can be shown to have accompanied Pleistocene glacial episodes as water was withdrawn from the oceans and trapped in continental ice sheets. The effects

TABLE 10-3. SEISMIC VELOCITY AS A FUNCTION OF GEOLOGIC TIME. Surface-equivalent velocities (corrected for effect of depth) given in feet per second. [Data from Faust, 1951.]

GEOLOGIC AGE	VELOCITY
Tertiary (post-Eocene)	2,190
Eocene	2,332
Cretaceous	2,607
Jurassic–Triassic	2,823(?)
Permian	2,866
Pennsylvanian	3,047
Mississippian	3,235(?)
Devonian	3,380(?)
Ordovician	3,439(?)

are seen in elevated and submerged terraces and reefs and in the displacement of bathymetrically controlled environments. These visible effects of universal change in sea level make possible a highly accurate time-stratigraphic correlation of Pleistocene littoral and sublittoral deposits.

In general, it is very difficult to separate the local or regional effects of epeirogenic movements from the widespread effects of eustatic change, and this difficulty effectively inhibits the application of eustatic changes to interregional correlation of the older rocks.

Correlation by Interregional Unconformities. Certain unconformities of interprovincial and interregional scope have been so thoroughly documented and established by the methods of lithologic correlation that they can serve as limiting surfaces in establishing the minimum age of rocks below, and the maximum age of overlying strata. It is well known, for example, that the first Paleozoic transgression of much of the continental interior of North America took place in Middle and Late Cambrian time. Therefore, within this broad area, strata resting on the Precambrian basement can confidently be considered as Middle Cambrian or younger in age. A second major interregional unconformity represents exposure of almost the entire continental interior area at the approximate close of Early Ordovician time. Rocks below this unconformity can be no younger than Early Ordovician, whereas the overlying strata must be Middle Ordovician or younger. Four other interregional unconformities of Paleozoic, Mesozoic, and Cenozoic age can be employed in a like manner, and although this correlation method seldom makes possible a precise definition of the age of a given stratigraphic unit, it is of great utility in the absence of significant paleontologic data.

Correlation by Gross Lithologic Character. Experienced stratigraphers, whose work has extended over several stratigraphic provinces, recognize that certain time-stratigraphic units exhibit similar characters in widely separated areas. This has led to informal descriptions of rock units as having a "Mississippian look" or a "Cretaceous appearance." Precambrian stratigraphers have long applied lithologic character, as determined by the degree of metamorphism and structural complexity, to attempts at long-range time-stratigraphic correlation. It has been general practice to assign highly metamorphosed and intricately deformed rocks to the Archeozoic or Archean and less altered strata to the younger Proterozoic, Algonkian, or Beltian. In many cases though, further investigation has proven these derived correlations to be in error by a wide margin. Nevertheless, this approach has provided at least a tentative basis for the time-stratigraphic correlation of strata in the absence of fossils or other confirmatory data.

If lithologic character or gross appearance is of doubtful value in correlation of Precambrian rocks, has it any proper application to correlation of

Paleozoic and younger strata? Any answer to this question must be made with a number of reservations. In some cases, the time-stratigraphic "look" of strata is a reflection of composite organic influences which are, in turn, controlled by evolution and thus by time. That is, the appearance of the strata is governed by dominant fossil components and correlation by "look" is actually based on gross paleontology. Examples are found in the tabulate coral biostromes of the Silurian and Devonian, the crinoidal limestones of the Middle Mississippian, the Carboniferous coals, the oyster-rich limestones of the Jurassic, and the foraminiferal chalks of the Cretaceous.

Each of these types is intercontinental in distribution and each is typical of a specific portion of the time-stratigraphic column. On the other hand, none of the lithologic types is actually confined to so narrow a range and may be duplicated, at least in gross appearance, in widely separated positions of the stratigraphic column.

Other lithologic characteristics, without apparent organic controls, appear to have time-stratigraphic significance over areas of interregional or intercontinental scope. Cases in point include the green, micaceous shales and edgewise conglomerates of the Cambrian and Lower Ordovician; the dolomitized limestones of the later Ordovician, Silurian, and Devonian; the red beds of the Permo-Triassic; and the glauconitic sandstones and oolites of the Jurassic. These attributes may also occur in almost any part of the stratigraphic column. Their presence is suggestive of certain time-stratigraphic units but can scarcely be considered a reliable criterion without support from other lines of evidence.

In addition to these gross characteristics, it has been shown (Fairbridge 1954) that the intimate details of the sedimentary petrography of rock units can also yield suggestions on time-stratigraphic correlation. Whether by gross character or by "microfacies" the lithologic approach to correlation is often a useful method in rapid stratigraphic reconnaisance. It furnishes a starting point in time-stratigraphic evaluation, but it requires substantial verification by other data before the suggested correlations can be accepted.

Correlation Based upon Time-parallel Rock Units. Within the continental interior of North America, many rock units exhibit so extraordinarily low a rate of facies change that they may be traced, in outcrop and especially in the subsurface, over distances of hundreds of miles and across several sedimentary provinces. Furthermore, even where the physical continuity is interrupted by erosion, the correlation across areas of nonpreservation and into adjoining provinces is possible by means of the lithologic identity and position in sequence of successive formations, members, and parastratigraphic units. Such correlations are commonly apparent in spite of the confusion introduced by a multiplicity of locally applied rock unit names.

Some of these interregionally traced units are obviously time-transgressive and are of no time-stratigraphic significance, except in a purely negative sense. Others, especially the widespread carbonate–evaporite units, maintain the same aspects and details of sequence and the same relationship to parastratigraphic markers to a degree that defies any explanation other than approximate isochronism over the entire area considered.

The Ordovician of the Southern Midcontinent, Upper Mississippi Valley, and Northern Great Plains areas is diagrammatically illustrated by Figure 10-15. Above the second interregional unconformity mentioned on a previous page, the Oklahoma succession is characterized by the sandstones, green shales, and limestones of the Simpson Group. Above the Simpson, the Viola Limestone is succeeded by the Sylvan Shale. When this succession is traced to the north, it is seen that the lower units of the Simpson are successively onlapped by the younger, thus the basal sandstone, identified as the St. Peter Sandstone in the Upper Mississippi Valley area, is significantly younger than the Oil Creek Formation of Oklahoma. The carbonates and shales of the Bromide Formation, however, can be shown to be the rock equivalents of the Glenwood, Platteville, and Decorah Formations, whereas the Viola–Sylvan and Galena–Maquoketa successions are demonstrable lithic equivalents. The continuity of marker beds in these units and the lithologic constancy of carbonate members from south to north, strongly suggest isochronous relationships in which time-stratigraphic correlations are virtually parallel to the pattern of rock-unit correlation, a parallelism that is largely confirmed by the paleontologic evidence (see accompanying time-stratigraphic correlation chart, Figure 10-15).

On the western flank of the Sioux (or Transcontinental) Arch, from which Ordovician strata have been stripped, and in the Williston Basin of the Dakotas, Manitoba, Saskatchewan, and Montana the same basal unconformity can be identified, overlapped by the Winnipeg sandstones and shales. These are remarkably similar in lithology and sequence to the Simpson Group of Oklahoma and to the St. Peter–Glenwood–Platteville–Decorah succession of the Upper Mississippi Valley. The overlying Red River Group, Stony Mountain Shale, Stonewall Formation, and Interlake carbonates duplicate, in convincing detail, the lithologic assemblages and sequences of parastratigraphic units observable in the Galena, Maquoketa, and Edgewood Formations of the Upper Mississippi Valley, and the Viola, Sylvan, and Hunton units of the Southern Midcontinent. Thus, the detailed rock unit correlation, established between central Oklahoma and northwestern Iowa, can be extended across a relatively short gap into South Dakota and the remainder of the Williston Basin area. It is difficult to interpret the widespread distribution of many of the units and the extraordinary

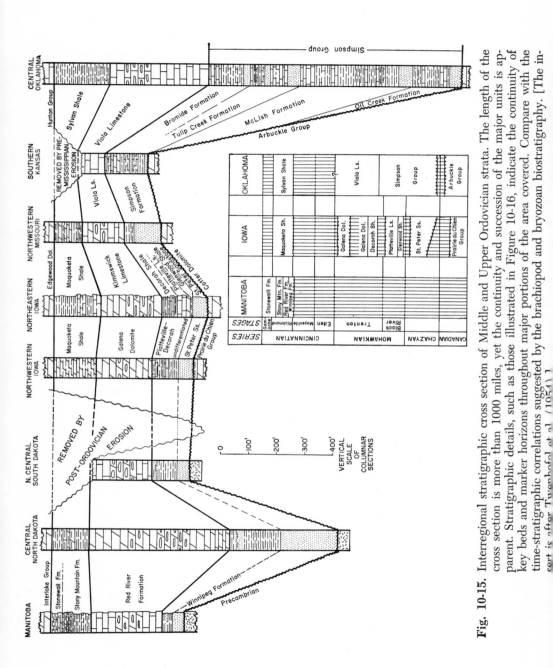

Fig. 10-15. Interregional stratigraphic cross section of Middle and Upper Ordovician strata. The length of the cross section is more than 1000 miles, yet the continuity and succession of the major units is apparent. Stratigraphic details, such as those illustrated in Figure 10-16, indicate the continuity of key beds and marker horizons throughout major portions of the area covered. Compare with the time-stratigraphic correlations suggested by the brachiopod and bryozoan biostratigraphy. [The insert is after Twenhofel et al. (1954).]

lateral constancy of lithologic detail and sequence, except as reflections of essentially synchronous events.

In view of these compelling evidences of time-stratigraphic equivalency, it is interesting to review the correlations suggested by the Ordovician Subcommittee of the Committee on Correlations of the National Research Council (Twenhofel, et al., 1954). Pertinent columns of the Ordovician Correlation Chart, based entirely on paleontologic interpretations, are reproduced in Figure 10-15. Note that the entire Ordovician section of the Williston Basin area is considered to be no older than the basal beds of the Maquoketa and Sylvan Formations. As in a number of similar conflicts between the physical and paleontologic criteria of time-stratigraphic correlation, it would appear, in this case, that the more reasonable correlations are those based on the interregional tracing of apparently time-parallel rock units. Indeed, recent re-evaluations of the paleontologic data involved indicate that the correlations shown on the chart reflect inaccuracies in the assumed range zones of many of the fossil taxons applied. Further, it can be shown (Flower, 1956) that those critical faunal elements that approach chronospecies and true index fossil status largely confirm the correlations suggested by the rock unit relationships.

A similar apparent stratigraphic paradox is found in Ordovician–Silurian relationships in the Williston Basin area. Here the Interlake Group is classified on paleontologic evidence as being no older than Middle Silurian, implying the existence of a lacuna embracing all of Early Silurian time between the Stonewall Formation and the Interlake. Yet the thin Stonewall, including finely discriminated marker horizons (see Figure 10-16) can be traced over an area of nearly a quarter of a million square miles without appreciable thickness change (Porter and Fuller, 1959). In a like manner, markers low in the Interlake strata maintain a remarkable parallelism with the lower contact of the Group. Therefore, it seems erroneous to invoke either post-Ordovician erosion or pre-Middle Silurian nondeposition in the area. Rather, the physical evidence strongly suggests almost continuous deposition from Late Ordovician through Middle Silurian, and time-stratigraphic placement of at least part of the lower Interlake strata in the Early Silurian is indicated.

It has also been shown (Gutstadt, 1958) that the strata of the Eden and Maysville Stages can be traced in the subsurface from their type area on the Cincinnati Arch to Iowa. This continuity suggests that the lacuna between the Galena and Maquoketa Formations indicated on the correlation chart. as in the case discussed above, does not exist. Extension of this line of reasoning to the cross section of Figure 10-15 would imply a relatively complete and unbroken succession of strata, in the Williston Basin, from Early Middle Ordovician to Mid-Silurian—an implication that is strongly supported by the vertically transitional character of the strata and the lack of physical evidence of hiatus or erosion.

There is no inference in the example presented that interregional time-stratigraphic correlation based on traceability of apparently isochronous rock units is to be preferred in every case to correlation by paleontologic methods. Rather, this example, as well as others, indicates the utility of physical approaches to time-stratigraphic correlation in certain geographic areas and parts of the stratigraphic column in which valid interregional index fossils of known range have not been isolated.

Methods of Local Time-stratigraphic Correlation

Within the limits of a sedimentary basin or depositional province, the correlation of time-equivalent strata may often be carried to a degree of refinement not obtainable in interregional correlation. Differentiation of time-stratigraphic units less than series and stage rank is commonly possible, providing a finely calibrated time scale by which local geologic events may be dated with reference to a locally applicable geologic calendar. Even where such events cannot be correlated accurately with other areas, their demonstrated sequences and relative age relationships are of value in establishing details of the local historical geology.

Locally defined and named stages and substages are useful time-stratigraphic units, although their relation to equivalent subdivisions applied in other areas may be obscure. In the Tertiary, for example, interregional correlation is difficult to establish, yet provincial stages are successfully applied within the marine Tertiary of the Gulf Coast area (Murray and Wilbert, 1950; Murray, 1952, 1955), within the Pacific Coast province (Kleinpell, 1938; Mallory, 1959), and within the nonmarine, mammal-bearing strata of the Rocky Mountain basins and adjacent Great Plains (Wood, et al., 1941). Significant application of the stages recognized in these areas is not dependent upon their correlation from province to province and remains a valuable aid in the classification, description, and analysis of the stratigraphy and historical geology of the areas concerned.

Paleontologic Correlation. All of the methods and principles of paleontologic, time-stratigraphic correlation discussed earlier in terms of interregional problems are applicable to local correlations as well. In most cases, the methods may be locally applied with even greater assurance of accuracy and pursued in finer detail. Factors such as barriers to migration and the influences of geographic speciation have little significance within depositional provinces and the lack of precise definition of the total range zone of individual taxons need not be a problem. In intraprovincial investigations, the local time-stratigraphic range of fossils can commonly be established and applied without necessary reference to specific ranges in other provinces.

In essence, local time-stratigraphic paleontologic correlations require the recognition of biostratigraphic zones that approach time-parallelism and which may be used to divide the local stratigraphic column into stages, sub-stages, and smaller units, applying the guide fossils of such zones as local index fossils to time-stratigraphic units. Range zones based on phylo-genetic series, such as the ammonite zones illustrated by Figure 10-14, are, of course, of great value in intraprovincial correlations. The boundaries be-tween many vertically successive assemblage zones may be locally consid-ered to represent shifts in the depositional environments that affected major parts of a sedimentary province relatively simultaneously. Hendrix (1959) has plotted the occurrence of individual foraminiferal species in wells pene-trating the Tertiary of the Los Angeles Basin and has shown that the pat-terns of occurrence and non-occurrence delineate systematic and traceable zones. These zones appear to represent simultaneous environmental changes which are applicable to basin-wide, time-stratigraphic correlation. The ma-jority of assemblage zones, which are of doubtful value in establishing inter-regional correlation, may be used in the solution of local problems with greater confidence. A significant refinement of this application is achieved by the use of concise quantitative methods in the definition and differentiation of the biostratigraphic zones.

Correlation by Time-parallel Strata. Certain rock units may be shown to be closely time-parallel. Lithologic correlation of rock units of this type is used to establish datum planes that can be used for very accurate time-stratigraphic correlation within limited areas. Bentonite beds, for instance, result from volcanic ash falls that blanket whole depositional provinces simultaneously, providing provincial time-stratigraphic markers of greater precision than those based on index fossils. Bentonites have proved valuable in correlation of Cretaceous beds in the Great Plains and in Middle Ordo-vician strata of the Appalachian and Upper Mississippi Valley areas.

Individual limestone units in dominantly shale successions represent con-ditions which presumably were essentially simultaneous in effect over much of a sedimentary province. An example is found in the Triassic deposits of Wyoming. Here, the unfossiliferous Chugwater red beds offer no possibility of precise time-stratigraphic correlation and, in themselves, give no indica-tion of the degree of time-transgression involved in deposition. In the midst of the red beds, however, the thin but persistent Alcova Limestone Member is a time-stratigraphic datum that establishes the temporal relationships within the red bed sequence.

A bed or series of beds of anhydrite, gypsum, or salt in a marine succession indicates a significant and necessarily widespread change in the chemistry of the sea water. Such a change reflects restriction and concurrent excess of evaporation with simultaneous effects on sedimentation throughout much of a province or basin. More subtle shifts in marine environments may also represent change in sea water composition that accompanied synchronous effects over broad areas. These changes may be indicated by gross characteristics, by significant insoluble residue or heavy mineral suites, or by spectrochemically-determined trace-element composition.

Thin beds characterized by sand, silt, or clay content can commonly be traced for great distances within thick carbonate–evaporite successions. Such thin and widespread units are thought to represent brief pulses of deposition, during which land-derived debris was spread over a marine basin by dust storms or turbidity currents, resulting in virtually synchronous deposition over the entire area. Where turbidity-current deposits are common, individual units with marked graded bedding are time-parallel markers that can be applied to local time-stratigraphic correlation problems with great confidence. Sutton (1959) has investigated flute casts and related structures on the bottom of siltstones of assumed turbidity-current origin in the Devonian of New York. A unique orientation of the markings below each of several units is considered a measure of current direction and is applicable to the identification of individual units and to their correlation over a significant area.

The formation of coal deposits requires the coincidence of favorable topographic, tectonic, and climatic conditions. Many authorities hold that these conditions are satisfied for only relatively short intervals of time and that individual coal beds are essentially time-parallel throughout their extent.

Para-time-stratigraphic Units. The abundance of subsurface information now available in many areas and the development and refinement of mechanical logging devices make possible the recognition and tracing of thin key beds and marker horizons throughout the major portion of a given sedimentary province. Many distinctive key beds, of the types discussed in the preceding paragraphs, may be considered truly synchronous units. However, not all marker positions can be directly related to observable shifts in lithology. Some appear to represent minor fluctuations in sedimentary attributes that are made apparent only through the instrumentation of the mechanical logging devices. Such markers do not, of themselves, provide any evidence of synchrony or time-parallelism. However, the common parallelism between mechanical-log marker beds and key beds of known synchronism implies that many of the markers are also time-parallel throughout their traceable extent. The parastratigraphic rock units defined by such key beds and marker horizons may be considered to have great local time-stratigraphic significance and the term **para-time-stratigraphic** has been applied to them. Regardless of the utility of the term, the recognition of synchronous or time-parallel key beds and marker horizons makes it possible to differentiate the stratal units of many depositional provinces into successive isochronous units, which may be used to describe and interpret the local depositional and tectonic history.

Figure 10-16 illustrates the application of key beds to the establishment and tracing of isochronous units within a basin of deposition. The section runs approximately 150 miles north-to-south in the Williston Basin area of eastern Montana and represents but a fraction of the area over which the key beds can be traced. The stratigraphic succession is very nearly the same as that at the western end of the preceding interregional cross section (Figure 10-15), but in this more westerly area, the Stony Mountain and Stonewall Formations are not identifiable as distinctive rock units. As a result, the Wyoming rock unit terminology (Bighorn) is applied to the strata between the Winnipeg Formation and the Interlake Group. Numerous key beds can be traced across the area by their distinctive character and position in sequence, as revealed by the gamma–neutron curves. A few of the key beds are shown on the cross section. At the scale represented, it is not possible to present sufficient lithologic detail of the individual key beds, but their distinctive radioactive attributes are clear. A number of cyclical evaporites are present, each cycle characteristically carrying thin shaly beds immediately above and below the anhydrite member. Beds p and q and the horizon marked "datum" are key beds of this type and can be traced for great distances beyond the areas of distribution of the evaporite beds with which they are associated. Beds t, u, v, and the top of the Bighorn Group are argillaceous, sandy interruptions of the monotonous dolomite succession. These beds are of the type discussed earlier, and have been termed "non-sequential beds" by Porter and Fuller (1959). The several key beds differentiate the Ordovician–Silurian section into a number of parastratigraphic units identified as "beds" to indicate their informal status in rock-stratigraphic terminology. These are operational units, without lithologic constancy but of extreme significance in time-stratigraphic correlation within the Williston Basin.

The Lower Cretaceous cross section of Figure 10-5 illustrates a number of marker-defined operational units with obvious parallelism among the defining markers. The Ferry Lake Anhydrite may be assumed to be essentially time-parallel; therefore, it is reasonably safe to assume that other markers parallel to the Ferry Lake Anhydrite also approach time-parallelism. Proceeding on this assumption, operational units such as the Pearsall, Rodessa, and Ferry Lake have been widely applied in a para-time-stratigraphic sense to Early Cretaceous correlations in the Gulf Coast area.

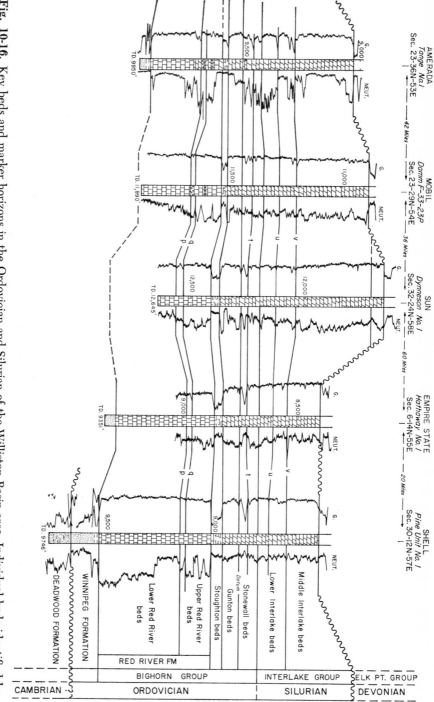

Fig. 10-16. Key beds and marker horizons in the Ordovician and Silurian of the Williston Basin area. Individual beds identified by sample studies and gamma-neutron responses can be traced over an area of a quarter of a million square miles. [Modified after Porter and Fuller (1959).]

There are many other examples of formal rock units and parastratigraphic units with time-stratigraphic significance, with all degrees of dependability. Some, though valid in one area, lead to erroneous correlations elsewhere. In each case, as in the examples cited above, the resulting time-stratigraphic correlation cannot be more accurate than the lithologic correlation on which it is based.

Correlation by Position in Bathymetric Cycle. Earlier in this chapter, the application of eustatic sea-level changes to time-stratigraphic correlation was discussed. Changes in sea level and shifts in the strand line are also significant at the intraprovincial level of correlation. Moreover, the distinction between eustatic and epeirogenic control is not important, since either produces effects that may influence sedimentation within a single province.

Figure 10-17 is a cross section which illustrates certain relationships in the Upper Cretaceous of the San Juan Basin area of northwestern New Mexico. The cross section extends for about thirty-five miles in a northeasterly direction and is a more detailed view of part of the pattern of intertonguing sandstones and shales shown in Figure 9-8. The Mulatto and Satan Shale Tongues are extensions of the marine Mancos shale lithosome, which is represented by an unbroken succession of shale in areas to the northeast. The Dalton and Hosta Sandstones are beach deposits, formed at the margin of

Fig. 10-17. Regressive-transgressive tongues in the Cretaceous of New Mexico. Both the regressive Dalton Sandstone and the transgressive Hosta Sandstone are present in the upper tongue; a time-parallel surface is approximated by the line A–A'. In the lower tongue, only the regressive Gallup Sandstone member is present, and the time-parallel surface is indicated by the line B–B'. [After Sears, Hunt, and Henricks (1941).]

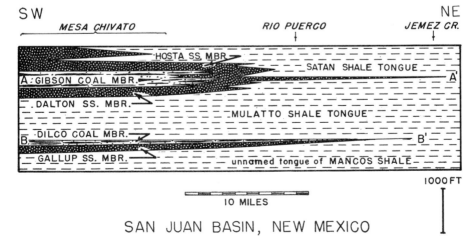

the Mancos sea. The Gibson Coal Member is a lagoonal and swamp deposit, formed behind the barrier beach. It is clear that the Dalton Sandstone is a regressive deposit, formed as the beaches marking the strand line retreated northeasterly until, at the time of maximum regression, the beach and strand line lay in the area represented by the right margin of the diagram. In the following transgressive episode, a relative rise in sea level caused the strand line to migrate back to the southwest, spreading the Hosta Sandstone as a series of beaches at the margin of the transgressive sea. As has been noted by Sears, Hunt, and Hendricks (1941) and by Spieker (1949), the regressive and transgressive sandstones cannot be time-parallel; hence, at any point the sandstones represent a beach separating a marine seaway to the northeast from lagoons and swamps on the southwest. However, the tongue formed by the two sandstones and the enclosed coal-bearing member must involve a kind of isochroneity, inasmuch as the entire body of rock was formed between the time of transgression, marked by the Mulatto Tongue, and the next transgressive climax, represented by the Satan Tongue. Where apparently symmetrical regressive–transgressive cycles, such as the Dalton–Gibson–Hosta cycle, are encountered, it may be assumed that approximately equal amounts of time were involved in the regressive and transgressive phases. If this assumption can be made, a synchronous surface (A-A′) would extend from the northeastern tip of the sandstone through the center of the tongue and would represent the time of maximum regression. Note that, in the example cited, the validity of the assumed synchronous surface is strengthened by its close agreement with the maximum northeastern extension of the nonmarine swamp and lagoonal deposits.

Lower on the same cross section (Figure 10-17) the Gallup Sandstone and Dilco Coal Member form an asymmetrical tongue between an unnamed member of the underlying Mancos Shale and the overlying Mulatto Shale Tongue. In this example, only the regressive sandstone and succeeding nonmarine beds are preserved; the transgressive off-shore marine shales rest directly on the Dilco Coal Member. It seems evident that the transgressive phase was very rapid; the strand line evidently advanced quickly to the southwest, minimizing the accumulation of beach sands. Here, the closest approximation to a time-parallel surface is probably coincident with the contact between the nonmarine beds and the overlying marine shale, rather than along the center of the Gallup–Dilco tongue.

Regressive-transgressive cycles of the type illustrated can commonly be traced for great distances within a depositional province and used for the establishment of intraprovincial time-stratigraphic correlations. The Gallup–Dilco cycle, for example, is the earliest of four Upper Cretaceous cycles that can be recognized from New Mexico to Montana, according to Weimer

(1960). Other deposits of regressive-transgressive cycles commonly provide recognizable, if approximate, time-parallel surfaces applicable to problems of local time-stratigraphic correlation. If the cyclic tongues are relatively thin, no excessive errors of correlation are introduced, even where the precise synchronous surface is difficult to identify.

Many cyclic phenomena, related to fluctuations in sea level but not necessarily involving strand line deposits, are represented by sedimentary successions that can be interpreted in terms of time stratigraphy. Evaporite cycles are in this category, as are many coal cyclothems, including those which are entirely nonmarine in character, but which are apparently controlled by base level shifts related to changes in sea level. Israelsky (1949) has shown that consideration of the depth significance of foraminiferal assemblages in wells penetrating the Tertiary of Louisiana permits the recognition of bathymetric cycles that range from shallow to deep and back to shallow conditions. If the stratigraphic position of the deepest part of a given cycle is determined, that stratigraphic position may be considered to be time equivalent at each well studied. As illustrated by Figure 10-18, a time-stratigraphic horizon established in this manner may encompass faunas of widely differing aspects, but each horizon marks the deepest bathymetric zone reached during the cycle studied at the datum point analyzed. Presumably, other cyclical successions, controlled by bathymetry and recorded by sequences of assemblage zones, could be similarly treated.

Correlation by Position in Climatic Cycle. Evidence of climatic variation may be read from variation in the physical and biological attributes of the sediments. These variations are typically cyclical in character, and individual cycles can, in some cases, be identified by their longevity and amplitude of variation and by their position in a known sequence of cycles. Climatic cycles interpreted from varved clays and tree rings have been applied with considerable success as a finely definitive tool in the correlation of certain Late Quaternary deposits. Hough (1953) has shown that Pleistocene glacial cycles are represented in deep oceanic sediments by rhythmic variations in sediment type and that correlation on the basis of these cyclic deposits is possible between widely spaced deep-sea cores.

The vegetation of land areas is very sensitive to climatic changes. These changes are reflected in the types and quantities of spores and pollens carried by the winds and buried in the sediments of adjoining marine basins. The relatively new application of palynology, the study of pollens and spores, as an extension of micropaleontology, aids in the recognition and analysis of climatic cycles and permits their employment in accurate time-stratigraphic correlation of Quarternary sediments. Marine faunas also respond to variations in water temperatures and can be used in the identifica-

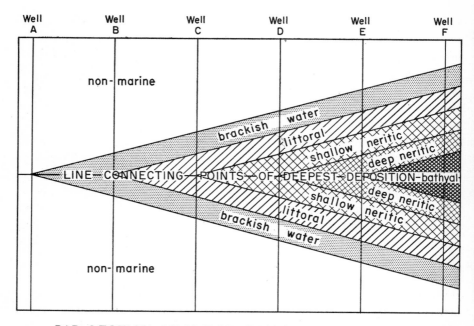

DIP SECTION OF HYPOTHETICAL MARINE CYCLE

Fig. 10-18. In this simplified example, foraminiferal samples from six wells have been analyzed to determine the relative positions of assemblage zones (indicative of bathymetrically controlled biosomes) penetrated by each well. The wells are plotted as a cross section, and biostratigraphic correlations from well to well are shown. The pattern indicates deepening and shallowing phases of a bathymetric cycle (for "shallow" and "deep neritic," read infralittoral and circalittoral, respectively). A line connecting the points of deepest deposition in each well may be considered as essentially time-parallel. In such cases similarity of faunas suggests lack of time equivalency, whereas systematic diversity of faunas suggests time-stratigraphic correlation. [Adapted from Israelsky (1949).]

tion of climatic cycles. Schenck (1945) has shown that analysis of Late Pliocene and Early Pleistocene faunas of California, in terms of their indicated climatologic position, clarifies the time-stratigraphic correlation of the strata involved. This approach has not been generally used in problems concerning older strata, but it offers possibilities for fine scale, intraprovincial, time-stratigraphic correlation, even in strata of Paleozoic age. The effects of climatic cycles may be seen in variations in the thickness of shell laminae and in other structures observable in the tests of many organisms. Compilation and comparison of data on such variations would be useful as a key to local correlation in many areas. It can be demonstrated (Wiseman 1959) that the rate of accumulation of calcium carbonate in marine sediments is related to water temperature. Therefore, the thickness of calcite and aragonite laminae in carbonate accumulations may aid in defining specific climatic cycles and permit their application to correlation problems.

Oxygen isotope ratios in the hard parts of organisms have been found to be indicative of the water temperatures in which the organisms lived (Lowenstam and Epstein, 1954). Paleotemperature measurements, by the isotope ratio method, give promise of establishing accurately defined climatic cycles, with a consequent increase in the precision with which these cycles may be utilized for the purposes of time-stratigraphic correlation.

Evaporites and organic deposits, such as coals and oil shales, accumulate in response to the phases of climatic cycles, as well as to the periodic changes in sea level and other environmental factors. The apparently unique combination of humid climate and lowered sea level, required for the widespread coals of the Pennsylvanian, have suggested to many workers that there is a relationship between coal cyclothems and periodic continental glaciation. Wheeler and Murray (1957) have explored this hypothesis in the light of newer concepts regarding the causes and effects of glacial episodes. If the glacial-control hypothesis could be established, it would fortify the significance of coals and other cyclothem members in time-stratigraphic correlation.

Cyclic variations in the thicknesses of interlaminations of oil shale and marl in the Eocene of southwestern Wyoming can be interpreted in terms of major climatic cycles, possibly related to precession, sunspot maxima and minima, and other periodic phenomena (Bradley, 1929). Similar varve-like laminations among evaporites and related sediments (Anderson and Kirkland, 1960) are also believed to reveal the influence of climatic cycles. Where such cycles can be traced over a significant area, they are the basis for precise time-stratigraphic correlation, analogous to that provided by glacial varves and tree rings in Quaternary chronology.

SUPPLEMENTARY READINGS

1. Dunbar, C. O., and Rodgers, R. (1957), Principles of Stratigraphy, John Wiley and Sons, Inc., New York. Chapter 16 is devoted to the principles of correlation.
2. Milner, H. B., 1962, Sedimentary petrography, vol. 2, Principles and applications, New York, The Macmillan Co. Chapters 4 and 5 present a modern treatment of mineralogic and petrographic methods, with emphasis on heavy minerals, applied to problems of stratigraphic correlation.
3. Weller, J. M., 1960, Stratigraphic principles and practice: New York, Harper & Brothers. Chapter 15.
4. Research Committee, Soc. Econ. Paleontologists and Mineralogists, 1959, Symposium on concepts of stratigraphic classification and correlation, Am. Jour. Sci.,

v. 257, p. 673–778. A collection of eight papers, presenting a variety of points of view on the subject matter of this chapter. A ninth paper of the symposium, of particular importance because of its treatment of the special problems of the Precambrian (James, 1960), is printed in another issue of the same journal, v. 258A, p. 104–114.

CORRELATION CHARTS

The Committee on Stratigraphy of the National Research Council has, from time to time, published time-stratigraphic correlation charts representing the systems, their subdivisions, and their rock and biostratigraphic components in North America. The following list includes the charts published and announced prior to 1962. All references are to the *Bulletin of the Geological Society of America*; the names indicated are those of the chairmen of the subcommittees responsible for each chart.

Cenozoic

1. Wood, H. E., 1941, North American continental Tertiary, v. 52, p. 1–48.
2. Cooke, C. W., 1943, Atlantic and Gulf coastal plain and Caribbean region, v. 54, p. 1713–1723.
3. Weaver, C. E., 1944, Marine formations of western North America, v. 55, p. 569–598.

Mesozoic

CRETACEOUS

4. Stephenson, L. W., 1942, Outcropping formations of the Atlantic and Gulf coastal plain and trans–Pecos Texas, v. 53, p. 435–448.
5. Imlay, R. W., 1944, Greater Antilles, Central America, and Mexico, v. 55, p. 1005–1045.
6. Cobban, W. A. and Reeside, J. B., 1952, Western Interior of the United States, v. 63, p. 1011–1044.
7. Imlay, R. W. and Reeside, J. B., 1954, Greenland and Alaska, v. 65, p. 223–246.
8. Popenoe, W. P., 1960, Pacific Coast of United States and Northwestern Mexico, v. 71, p. 1491–1540.
9. McLearn, F. H., Canada, in preparation.

JURASSIC

10. Imlay, R. W., 1952, North America exclusive of Canada, v. 63, p. 953–992.
11. Frebold, H., 1953, Canada, v. 64, p. 1229–1246.

TRIASSIC

12. McLearn, F. H., 1953, Canada, v. 64, p. 1205–1228.
13. Reeside, J. B., 1957, North America exclusive of Canada, v. 68, p. 1451–1513.

Paleozoic

PERMIAN

14. Dunbar, C. O., 1960, North America, v. 71, p. 1763–1806.

PENNSYLVANIAN

15. Moore, R. C., 1944, North America, v. 55, p. 657–706.

MISSISSIPPIAN

16. Weller, J. M., 1948, North America, v. 59, p. 91–196.

DEVONIAN

17. Cooper, G. A., 1942, North America, v. 53, p. 1729–1794.

SILURIAN

18. Swartz, C. K., 1942, North America, v. 53, p. 533–538.

ORDOVICIAN

19. Twenhofel, W. H., 1954, North America, v. 65, p. 247–298.

CAMBRIAN

20. Howell, B. F., 1944, v. 55, p. 993–1004.

CHAPTER 11

Sedimentary Tectonics

INTRODUCTION

Sedimentary tectonics is the study of relations between tectonism and sedimentation. Two aspects of the subject are important in stratigraphy. One is the tectonic framework of sedimentation, and the other is the degree of tectonism to which each tectonic element is subjected during accumulation of a sedimentary rock body.

The **tectonic framework of sedimentation** is defined as the combination of subsiding, stable, and rising tectonic elements in sedimentary source and depositional areas. The term **tectonics** refers to earth movements and rock structures in general. In the sense used here, **tectonism** is the structural behavior of an element of the earth's crust during, or between, major cycles of sedimentation. The combination of elements present, their relative geographic distribution, and the degree of tectonism in each, all play a part in controlling the nature and thickness of accumulating sediments.

Sedimentary environments produce the detailed patterns of sediment distribution within the larger tectonic framework. The relative interplay of tectonism and environment is a balance between broad framework elements and specific sedimentary processes. Stratigraphic analysis must take account of tectonism in its reconstruction of the history of sedimentary rocks.

As long as a century ago, James Hall of the New York State Museum recognized that the thick accumulation of Paleozoic sediments in the Appalachian region required that subsidence of the area took place at about the same rate as that of accumulation. He concluded that the weight of the accumulating sediments caused the subsidence. J. D. Dana of Yale University, on the other hand, argued that the contemporaneous subsidence of the earth's crust was the phenomenon responsible for accumulation.

In 1873 Dana published his classic paper on the origin of mountains and the nature of the earth's interior. In this paper he defined a **geosynclinal** as "a long-continued subsidence," thus laying the foundations for study of the tectonic framework of sedimentation. The leader in the classical development of geosynclinal theory was Charles Schuchert, who published a definitive paper

390

on North American geosynclines in 1923. His work, and that of others, is described in a later section.

Sedimentary tectonics itself, representing the detailed study of relations between tectonism and the characteristics of the accumulating sediments, is a much newer branch of geology. Several early writers observed that geosynclinal sediments differ in their lithologic characteristics from those formed in more stable areas, but the sedimentary-tectonic implications of these differences were not clearly understood until the 1930's. Bailey (1930), Fischer (1933), and Jones (1938) were leaders in exploring this subject in Europe.

BARRELL'S CONCEPT OF SEDIMENTATION AND SUBSIDENCE

One of the most important principles relating sedimentation to subsidence was introduced by Joseph Barrell in 1917. Although Hall recognized that subsidence accompanies sedimentation in geosynclines, it remained for Barrell to extend the concept to all sedimentation. Barrell established the principle that the critical plane of erosion and deposition is that of base level, represented by river-flood level on continents and by wave or current base in the sea.

Barrell used the term "base level" in a broader sense than was common among physiographers. He defined base level as that surface toward which external forces strive, at which neither erosion nor deposition takes place. It is, accordingly, a surface of equilibrium.

In this view, erosion and deposition are both dependent upon changes in base level. Depression of the surface below base level allows sediments to accumulate until the level is reached, and elevation above the critical level produces erosion or scour. Barrell emphasized that the rate of sedimentation is controlled by the rate of subsidence of the surface of deposition, rather than by the rate of supply of detritus.

If subsidence is slow, any excess detritus beyond that required to bring the depositional surface to the level of base level is carried farther, and comes to rest only when it encounters an area in which the surface is below the critical level. If subsidence and rate of supply are equal, the balanced conditions may establish a depositional surface essentially at base level.

Barrell emphasized that subsidence is discontinuous, interrupted by numerous oscillations, permitting the removal of part or all of the material deposited during the previous submergence. These oscillations produce a corresponding number of disconformities or diastems in the stratigraphic column. The important point was made that the deposits in a stratigraphic section may represent only a small part of the total elapsed time.

The inference of discontinuous subsidence was based largely on the many lacunas observable in most outcrop sections. As subsurface data accumulated from literally thousands of wells, it became apparent that many of the lacunas disappear or become less significant as stratigraphic intervals are followed into the subsurface. These observations paved the way for the concept that subsidence may be continuous during sedimentation in areas where conformable sequences are found.

The great mass of factual data supplied by modern sample logs, electric logs, and detailed faunal studies show that a wide range of conditions may occur. In neutral parts of the continent, where only thin deposits normally accumulate, oscillations are demonstrated by numerous lacunas. In sedimentary basins, such as the Illinois and Michigan basins, thicker deposits with fewer stratigraphic breaks imply more nearly continuous sedimentation, and presumably, therefore, more nearly continuous subsidence.

These newer data support Barrell's fundamental principle that sedimentation is controlled by subsidence, with the slight modification that the subsidence may range from discontinuous to continuous.

SEDIMENTATION AND RATE OF SUBSIDENCE

Four general sets of conditions are recognized regarding the relations between sedimentation and subsidence below base level. They include combinations of rapid or slow subsidence with rapid or slow deposition.

The terms **degree of tectonism** and **tectonic intensity** apply equally to subsiding and rising tectonic elements. Inasmuch as sediments are preserved mainly in subsiding areas, the term **rate of subsidence** may be taken as essentially synonymous with tectonism, when applied to depositional areas.

The rate of subsidence and the degree to which it may be interrupted during a major sedimentary cycle depend, in part, upon the behavior of the main elements in the tectonic framework. In geosynclines, the rate of subsidence may range from rapid to slow with interruptions numerous at some times, and essentially absent at others. The rate of subsidence may be very slow in more stable areas, and may be interrupted by numerous oscillations that persist long enough to develop stratigraphic breaks in the rock column.

Rapid Subsidence and Rapid Deposition

When the rate of subsidence and the rate of detrital supply are both large, thick accumulations of rapidly buried sediments are formed. Such conditions are typical of some phases of geosynclinal sedimentation, during which sediments are literally poured into the subsiding trough.

Rapid filling of rapidly subsiding areas implies strong uplift in the source area to compensate the rapid subsidence in the receiving site. An example is furnished by the Fountain Arkose (Pennsylvanian) along the Front Range in Colorado. The rapid uplift of a faulted granite block shed arkosic debris into a subsiding basin on the east, developing a wedge of arkose more than 2,000 feet thick.

Rapid accumulation of sediment also means that the deposited material quickly passes through the depositional interface and is buried before the environmental agents can operate on it for long periods of time. As a result, poorly sorted deposits, containing abundant unstable minerals, are formed. Because of the rapid influx of detrital material, limestone and other non-clastic rocks are absent or are present in very minor amount relative to the volume of clastic sediments.

Rapid Subsidence and Slow Deposition

When the rate of subsidence exceeds that of accumulation, the depositional interface may sink to bathyal or abyssal depths. The detrital sediments are commonly fine grained, and deposition may be dominated by nonclastic components.

Slow deposition implies relatively little uplift in the source area, although the position of sea level is a factor in the rate of erosion. Rapidly subsiding troughs in linear geosynclines may provide conditions for rapid subsidence and slow deposition if corresponding positive areas are not active enough to fill the trough as it subsides.

The Michigan Basin, during part of its history, was a subsiding basin without complementary uplift in nearby cratonic areas. There is no evidence in the sediments that bathyal or abyssal depths were attained, but the presence of thick, nonclastic sequences attests to the lack of appreciable land-derived debris.

The terms "rapid" and "slow," as used in this discussion, are purely relative. In ancient sedimentary deposits a slow rate of deposition may be inferred from the occurrence of relatively thin stratigraphic units in areas that by other evidence appear to have been subsiding at such rate that the deposits should be thicker if deposition had kept pace with subsidence. A case in point is the "starved basin" concept of Adams and co-workers (1951). According to this concept, the thin, euxinic Pennsylvanian deposits of the Midland Basin suggest that deep-water conditions developed in a subsiding area into which the flow of detrital materials was very limited. Within the context of the present heading, this is an example of relatively rapid subsidence.

Slow Subsidence and Rapid Deposition

Deposition may occur more rapidly than subsidence, with the result that sediments accumulate above base level. A rapidly growing delta may accumulate debris more quickly than waves and currents can distribute it along the shore, thereby raising the depositional surface above wave or current base.

This condition appears to contradict Barrell's general principle that sedimentation is controlled by base level. However, Barrell did show that such a lack of balance is temporary, because, when the supply of debris decreases again, waves and currents shift the material along the shore and into deeper water.

Preservation of deposits formed above the controlling surface requires renewed subsidence of the depositional area to carry the sediments below base level and permit their burial by subsequent deposition.

Sediments formed when deposition exceeds subsidence are mainly clastic and may represent mixtures of shallow-marine, brackish, and continental deposits. Marine conditions are not necessarily involved, inasmuch as continental sediments may temporarily accumulate above base level as alluvial fans or other rapidly accumulated deposits.

Slow Subsidence and Slow Deposition

When the rate of subsidence and rate of sediment supply are both low, detritus may be shifted about by waves and currents for long intervals before it comes to final rest. Accumulation represents a slow passage of the material through the depositional interface and a correspondingly slow rate of burial.

Under these conditions, the environmental agents impress their characteristics fully on the sediment. Unstable minerals are removed, detrital sand grains become well rounded, and the final sediment is well sorted and mature.

Slow subsidence and deposition imply slow erosion of the source area, but this is not necessarily true. A relatively active source may supply detritus to a slowly subsiding area slightly faster than it can be assimilated in terms of a profile of equilibrium. In such instances, the excess sediment may be by-passed to other depositional sites farther removed from the source.

The problem of sedimentary by-passing is only partly understood, as was pointed out in Chapter 6, but there is evidence from subsurface data that sediments may be carried across a neutral area to a depositional basin where more rapid subsidence provides conditions for rapid trappings of the sediment.

Turbidity currents (see Chapter 6) may play a varying role in the interplay between subsidence and deposition. Sediments poured in from the margins of linear troughs may accumulate temporarily on the depositional slope; occasional disturbances (due either to depositional instability or tectonic shocks) trigger the development of turbidity currents. These currents move the sediment down the sides of the trough and even axially along the bottom (Kuenen, 1958). This sporadic movement of debris may give rise to complex relations between the sedimentary bodies that accumulate in the trough.

EPEIROGENY AND OROGENY

Although the tectonic intensity in areas of accumulating sediment or in complementary uplifted source areas may vary widely, the diastrophic movements involved may be grouped into two broad classes. Relatively slow or slight diastrophic movements producing broad uplifts or downwarps affecting large portions of a continent are **epeirogenic,** whereas more intense diastrophic movements producing faults or folds, and generally, mountainous topography, are **orogenic.**

Epeirogenic movements disturb the attitude of the sedimentary rocks only slightly. Orogenic movements are more intense, and greatly modify the structural attitude of the rocks during mountain building, or in the development of normal and thrust faults.

Epeirogeny and orogeny show distinctly different effects in their influence on sedimentation. Slow submergence of low-lying land under an advancing shallow sea produces widespread sheet deposits, commonly including a basal quartzose sandstone. Intense uplift in the source area, accompanied by correspondingly strong subsidence in the depositional area, results in rapid accumulation of thick, wedge-shaped clastic bodies, with graywacke or arkose prominent.

In a general way, tectonism during sedimentation on the interior continental platforms is epeirogenic, with mild uplift of positive areas, mild subsidence in negative areas, and essential stability of neutral areas. In the major geosynclines, on the other hand, the tectonism may range from epeirogenic to orogenic depending on whether the geosyncline subsided slowly or rapidly. Similarly, positive movements of the source areas associated with the geosyncline may range from moderate to strong.

DEVELOPMENT OF GEOSYNCLINAL THEORY

The most prominent feature of the tectonic framework is the folded geosyncline, the first element that was studied in detail. Hall's geosynclinal theory, re-expressed and amplified by Dana, gained wide acceptance in

America, and the concept was absorbed into European thought. By the end of the nineteenth century, the Appalachian Geosyncline was recognized in America as the type geosyncline. It was visualized as a linear belt of subsidence along a continental border, separated from the ocean basin by a positive borderland, and deriving its sediment from the borderland. At the end of its activity as a geosyncline, it was folded into the Appalachian Mountains.

In 1900, Haug, in France, departed from this classic concept by defining geosynclines as the mobile belts between rigid continental masses. He included the great oceanic depressions (such as the East Indian Trough and the Japan Trough) with geosynclines. He called these features **foredeeps** and considered their bathyal sediments typical geosynclinal deposits.

Haug's concept, derived in part from Bertrand in 1897, was influenced by his study of the Eurasian mountain systems and their relation to the great geosynclinal belt that stretched from Spain to the Himalayas. In 1912, Deecke, in Germany, pointed out that the Mediterranean-Alpine region had been a highly mobile zone since the Carboniferous, full of archipelagoes, shallow seas, deep basins, and long troughs. The sediments were not all bathyal; on the contrary, abundant clastics and some limestone show clear evidence of shallow-water deposition.

In America, the Appalachian Geosyncline remained pre-eminent as the type, and other Paleozoic geosynclines, such as the Cordilleran and Franklinian, were found to have similar characteristics in their location near continental margins and in their association with adjacent borderlands. The relation of the major geosynclines to other elements in the continent was discerned and defined. The leader in this development was Schuchert, who published a definitive paper on North American geosynclines in 1923.

SCHUCHERT'S CLASSIFICATION OF GEOSYNCLINES

Schuchert set up a classification of geosynclines in which Haug's definition was included as a special case. The classification included positive and neutral elements, which, together with the geosynclines, comprise the tectonic framework. Table 11-1 summarizes the classification.

Monogeosynclines, as represented by the Appalachian, are the type example. Polygeosynclines, represented by the Paleozoic Cordilleran Geosyncline are derived from monogeosynclines by the elevation of a central geanticline, which separates the subsiding area into two parallel monogeosynclines. Mesogeosynclines and parageosynclines include Haug's Mediterranean example, and such "foredeeps" as the Japan Sea. Embayments are

TABLE 11-1. SCHUCHERT'S CLASSIFICATION OF TECTONIC
ELEMENTS

MONOGEOSYNCLINES
   Linear, deeply subsiding, shallow water
   Located along borderlands at continent margins
   Example: Appalachian Geosyncline

POLYGEOSYNCLINES
   Broad, linear, shallow water
   Give rise to geanticlines and parallel monogeosynclines
   Example: Cordilleran Primary Geosyncline

MESOGEOSYNCLINES
   Elongage oceans between continents
   Deep water, excessive mobility, complex history
   Example: Mediterranean

PARAGEOSYNCLINES
   Lie adjacent to continents
   Deeply subsiding, short-lived
   Example: Japan Sea

EMBAYMENTS
   Extend transversely across continental interior
   Non-deeply subsiding, short-lived
   Example: Sonoran Embayment

BORDERLANDS
   Very mobile geanticlines along continent edges
   Example: Appalachia

GEANTICLINES
   Positive areas related to geosynclines, or rising from them
   Example: Cordilleran intermontane geanticline

NUCLEAR AREA
   Central neutral portion of continent

---

relatively minor features, extending as arms or branches from the main
geosynclines.

The concept of contemporaneous subsidence during geosynclinal sedimentation is an explicit part of Schuchert's classification. Complementary
positive elements are the geanticlines, of which three classes were recognized. The most active positive elements are borderlands, which supply
debris to the subsiding geosynclinal belt. Less active are the intrageosyn-
clinal geanticlines that rise from the geosynclinal area, such as the "Ancestral
Rocky Mountains," considered to have risen out of a geosyncline with seas
remaining on either side. The least active geanticlines are low, localized
features on the nuclear area, such as the Cincinnati Arch.

Schuchert's Paleozoic Framework of North America

Figure 11-1 shows the principal tectonic elements of North America during the Paleozoic Era, according to Schuchert. Three principal geosynclines are shown. The **Cordilleran Geosyncline** is located along the western margin of the continent, the **Franklinian Geosyncline** lies along the northern margin, and the **Appalachian Geosyncline** parallels the eastern margin.

Fig. 11-1. Paleozoic tectonic framework of North America. [After Schuchert (1923).]

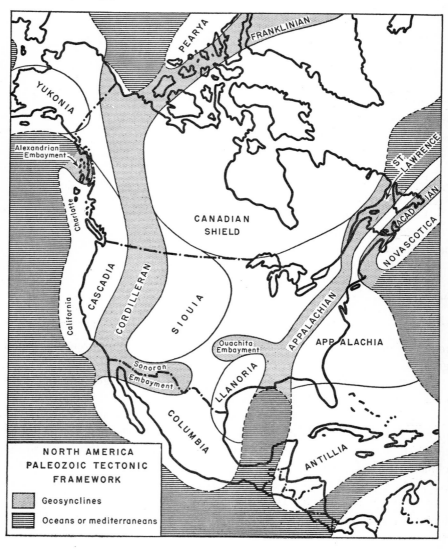

NORTH AMERICA
PALEOZOIC TECTONIC
FRAMEWORK

Geosynclines

Oceans or mediterraneans

The borderlands associated with these geosynclines are **Cascadia** on the west, **Pearya** on the north, and **Appalachia** on the east. The borderlands were considered to be the source areas of sediments deposited in the corresponding geosynclines.

The **Sonoran Embayment** extended eastward from the southern part of the Cordilleran Geosyncline, and the **Ouachita Embayment** extended westward from the southern part of the Appalachian Geosyncline. These embayments were mildly subsiding transverse extensions of the main geosynclinal trends.

The broad central nuclear portion of the continent is divided into **Siouxia**, lying immediately east of the Cordilleran Geosyncline, and the **Canadian Shield**, which occupied much of the northern half of North America. In the north central part of the United States, were several minor geanticlines, such as the **Ozark Dome**, the **Cincinnati Arch**, and others not indicated on the map.

According to Schuchert, the nuclear part of North America has, on the whole, remained only slightly above sea level since the Proterozoic Era, periodically rising or sinking a few hundred feet. Shallow seas have repeatedly covered parts of it, yet as far as outcrop data show, nowhere have Paleozoic sediments accumulated to a depth of one mile on it, in sharp contrast with the five or six miles of Paleozoic sediments in the geosynclines.

Further Development of Geosynclinal Theory

Three Frameworks of Analysis. Progress in understanding the tectonic framework depends, in large measure, on an understanding of geosynclines and their relations to other parts of continents and ocean basins. The study of such relationships may be approached from different points of view, depending on which features are to be emphasized. Glaessner and Teichert (1947) presented a comprehensive review of the development of geosynclinal theory, pointing out that three broad lines of study have been followed.

The **lithogenetic** approach involves a study of the sedimentary filling of the geosyncline, with relatively little emphasis given to its later structural history. The **orogenetic** approach mainly concerns the orogenic history of the geosyncline, without primary regard to its sedimentary filling. The **geotectonic** approach considers the tectonic behavior of geosynclines in relation to other crustal units.

As a result of these several approaches, the definition of the term geosyncline has undergone corresponding changes through the years. This state of flux extends to the present day, with the development of new techniques for studying earth features, and as a better understanding of the three-dimensional relationships among rocks is advanced through subsurface exploration. One of the most important new lines of evidence arises from the application of geophysical methods to the study of ocean basins and archipelagos.

Contributions of Geophysics. Geophysical data collected over the ocean basins has shown that negative gravity anomalies occur in the vicinity of island arcs. The magnitude of these anomalies is so great, and their patterns are so strikingly linear, that they may definitely be interpreted as representing an abnormal mass distribution in the earth's crust.

Theories that account for these linear gravity anomalies are discussed by Hess (1938) and Umbgrove (1947). The anomaly is explained by inferring a downbuckle of the earth's crust as an isoclinal fold into the substratum. Such an isoclinal fold represents the subsidence of a linear tract on the earth's surface, which places island arcs and their associated deep oceanic troughs within the framework of geosynclinal analysis.

A downbuckle of the earth's crust is called a **tectogene** (illustrated in Figure 11-2). During its development, the sial is downfolded into the denser sima, giving rise to the negative gravity anomaly, and producing a buckling of the sediments into the downfold. In present-day island arcs, the tectogene represents the deep sea trench in part.

In early stages of deformation, the unconsolidated sediments on the floor of the ocean are supported by the competent crust, but when a downbuckle occurs, these weak sediments are squeezed out of the tectogene core, forming alpine-type structures. Shear zones may be associated with the tectonic phenomena, resulting in the development of volcanoes near the margin of the tectogene. Other compensatory positive movements produce a slight upbulge on the concave side of the tectogene, usually the side nearest the larger continental mass. This upbulge is referred to as a **geanticline.** An island arc borders the geanticline, the active tectonism of the linear belt being shown not only by volcanic phenomena but also by the occurrence of numerous earthquakes along the general trend of the tectonic zone.

Fig. 11-2

Sketch of tectogene showing deformation of squeezed sediments. [Adapted from Hess (1938).]

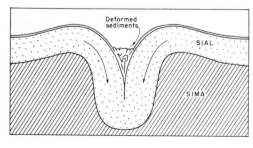

Figure 11-3 shows a portion of the western Pacific island arcs, adapted from Hess (1948). The left hand map shows the depth relations, with the deep oceanic troughs extending in broad arcs east of the Marianas and Caroline Islands. The islands are

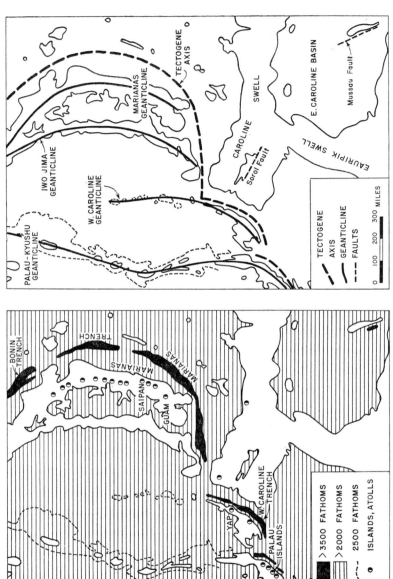

Fig. 11-3. Bathymetric and tectonic maps of portion of the west Pacific island arcs. (*Left*) Bathymetry, showing relation of deep trenches to Marianas and other islands. (*Right*) Tectonic interpretation, showing tectogene axis and associated subparallel geanticlines. The southeastern area apparently represents the craton with its less active tectonic features. [After Hess (1948).]

shown in exaggerated size, to indicate their positions along the inner arc of the deepest areas. Most of these islands, especially those in the Marianas trend, are volcanic in nature.

The second map in Figure 11-3 shows Hess's interpretation of the structural features of the area. The tectogene axis lies along the oceanic trenches, and is paralleled, on the west, by geanticlines. The islands shown are located along the geanticlines, and troughs of intermediate depth lie between the several geanticlines indicated on the map.

On both sides of the more mobile tectogene and anticlinal belt, with their associated deep water troughs, are broad and relatively stable areas shown as **swells** and **basins.** The tectogene, with its associated islands, is believed to represent the active geosynclinal belt. The more stable areas adjacent to the linear zone, with minor swells and downwarps, is more nearly equivalent to the main mass of the continental interior away from the geosyncline.

The western Pacific island arcs seem to differ from some ancient geosynclines in their greater degree of relative submergence. In the more general case, if a veneer of sediments is present where the tectogene develops, it is squeezed upward as the downfold grows, producing highly complex, folded structures. Depending upon a number of factors, such as the rate of subsidence in the trough, the rate of uplift in the compensating positive elements, the degree of volcanism present, and the eustatic level of the sea, the water in the trough may attain abyssal depths or the trough may be filled with sediment almost as rapidly as it subsides.

Deformation along parts of the main geosynclinal element produces folded and faulted uplifts, which, in turn, are eroded and supply sediment to adjacent subsiding parts. During its active life, the geosyncline appears to provide its own source materials. Krynine (1948) has called this a "cannibalistic" process, since the geosyncline tends to "feed" upon itself.

In the broad picture that emerges from the geophysical data, especially when supplemented by stratigraphic and structural studies on continents, it appears that the tectonic framework of island arcs more nearly satisfies the requirements of geosynclinal theory than does the classic concept of a subsiding linear belt with a broad borderland as its source of sediments.

Although the concept of island arcs as major sources for geosynclinal fills has received wide acceptance, there still remain some aspects of the more classical borderland hypothesis that seem to agree with broad paleogeographic considerations of continents as a whole. For example, Pettijohn (1960) points out that the long-continued persistence of paleoslopes, as shown by vector properties of sediments, plus the large volume of debris that came consistently from the southeast during the Paleozoic to accumulate in the Appalachian area, argues against an island arc source. Conceivably, such major extracratonic sources represent the development of large areas above sea level by continental uplift and consolidation of island arc trends.

The Influence of Subsurface Data and Re-examination of Outcrops. Exploration in the subsurface, mainly for oil and gas, has shed much new light on the areal extent, thickness, structural attitude, and lithologic composition of previously inaccessible buried masses of sedimentary rock, the eroded edges of which constitute the outcrop belts. The resulting three-dimensional picture of the rocks that constitute the interior continental platforms demonstrates that this portion of the continent is not as stable or rigid as had been inferred. Instead, sedimentary accumulations in some interior basins are seen to vary greatly in thickness, often attaining thicknesses of the order of magnitude exhibited by geosynclinal rocks.

Kay (1951) discusses the sedimentary fill in some North American interior basins in support of the inference that continued and relatively deep subsidence occurred there, in broadly ovate areas, during the same time-spans in which the thick wedges of classical geosynclinal deposits were being formed nearer to the continental margins.

The three-dimensional view of interior continental sediments furnished by subsurface data has been supplemented by re-examination of metamorphic rocks in exposed geosynclinal areas, with the result that rocks formerly considered to be Precambrian and by implication therefore part of the ancient borderlands of Appalachia, are now recognized as Paleozoic in age and of sedimentary origin. King (1950) reviewed the tectonics of the southeastern United States and expressed doubt that Appalachia ever existed, at least in the manner "envisaged by its proponents." He concluded that the clastic sediments were derived from fold ridges that arose in the interior zones of the geosyncline. These ridges were apparently composed, not of basement rocks, but of material from the inner geosynclinal zones, deformed during the Paleozoic.

STILLE'S FRAMEWORK FOR CLASSIFICATION OF GEOSYNCLINES

Many new principles and concepts have arisen from data obtained in geophysical studies of ocean basins, from the abundant subsurface data obtained in oil exploration, from the re-examination of outcrop belts in classical geosynclinal areas, and from the accumulation of knowledge in less explored areas of rock exposure. Through the years since the early 1920's this expanding knowledge has stimulated reconsideration of many geosynclinal concepts and has resulted in the development of geosynclinal classifications that are markedly different in some respects from classical views.

Stille (1936) was a leader in broadening the definition of the term geosyncline to include any area which subsided through long intervals of time. He placed no restrictions on geosynclines, as to whether they contain marine or nonmarine sediments, and it was incidental to his classification whether or not the deposits were subsequently folded. Stille made a distinction between **pliomagmatic** and **miomagmatic** geosynclines. The former are characterized by contemporaneous volcanism during sedimentation and by synorogenic plutonism during subsequent deformation, in which respects they differ from the miomagmatic geosynclines.

Stille changed these terms to **eugeosyncline** and **miogeosyncline** respectively. The former represents the more mobile tectonic belts, with volcanic rocks associated with their sedimentary fill. Miogeosynclines are relatively less active, without contemporaneous volcanism. Both of these geosynclines were classified by Stille as **orthogeosynclines,** linear belts of tectonic instability lying between more stable oceanic or continental blocks designated as **cratons.**

Stille thus enlarged the concept introduced earlier by Haug, who had stated that geosynclines are mobile belts between continents. Stille also recognized the occurrence of subsiding areas within the craton. These areas, which receive relatively thick sediments, in contrast to other parts of the craton, he called **parageosynclines,** to distinguish them from the more mobile orthogeosynclines between cratons. Schuchert had used the term parageosyncline earlier, but in a different sense, as noted previously in this chapter.

This historical development is examined in detail by Knopf (1960). Kay (1942) had first introduced Stille's terms into the North American literature, and in 1945 he adopted and expanded Stille's classification, especially the class of parageosynclines. Kay's classification has had an important influence on subsequent developments, and is discussed more fully in the next section.

KAY'S CLASSIFICATION OF TECTONIC ELEMENTS

As stated, Kay (1944, 1947) followed Stille in choosing his principal classes of geosynclines, but expanded the class of parageosynclines to include various types of subsiding areas within the craton. In 1951, Kay published a memoir on North American geosynclines in which he reviews the basis of his classification and illustrates his concepts through a detailed discussion of stratigraphic relations on the continental borders, and concludes with a section on continental growth. This memoir ranks, along with

Schuchert's classical analysis of 1923, as one of the definitive integrative studies of geosynclines.

Kay's classification of geosynclines is shown in Table 11-2. It includes Stille's two main classes, which are developed in detail, as well as subordinate features that are more stable or positive in tectonic behavior. The first of the three classes of parageosynclines is the **exogeosyncline**, transitional between the orthogeosynclinal belt and the craton. It extends into the craton, but receives the bulk of its sediments from the orthogeosynclinal source. The best-known example is the Catskill-Chemung (Upper Devonian) "delta" of the Appalachian region.

The **autogeosyncline** is an isolated depositional area within the craton, which accumulates thicker sediments than surrounding areas, receiving its

TABLE 11-2. KAY'S CLASSIFICATION OF TECTONIC ELEMENTS

ORTHOGEOSYNCLINES
  Linear, deeply subsiding, shallow to deep water.
  Located between cratons.
    a. Eugeosynclines
      Actively subsiding, with associated volcanics.
    b. Miogeosynclines
      Less active; no volcanics.

PARAGEOSYNCLINES
  Commonly ovate, less actively subsiding, shorter-lived than orthogeosynclines.
  Located within craton or adjacent to craton.
    a. Exogeosynclines
      Tonguelike extensions from orthogeosyncline.
      Detritus gained mainly from orthogeosyncline.
      Example: Catskill-Chemung (Devonian) "delta."
    b. Autogeosynclines
      Isolated depositional areas within craton.
      Detritus gained from distant cratonic sources.
      Example: Michigan Basin.
    c. Zeugogeosynclines
      Subsiding areas adjacent to complementary uplifts in craton.
      Detritus mainly from uplifts.
      Example: Denver Basin Area in Pennsylvanian Period.

GEOSYNCLINES OF LATER CYCLES
  Subsiding areas that developed later in the sites of older geosynclines.

CRATON
  The consolidated, relatively neutral area which comprises the main part of the continent or of oceanic basins.

Positives:
  Complementary rising areas adjacent to intracratonic geosynclines.

detritus from distant cratonic sources. The Michigan Basin is the type example. The **zeugogeosyncline** also lies within the craton, but receives its sediment from complementary cratonic uplifts. The Denver Basin Area, in Colorado, is an example of a basin "yoked" to its complementary uplift, the Ancestral Rocky Mountains.

Kay's group of geosynclines of later cycles includes fault-bounded basins and other features that may develop after folding in orogenic belts. Details of these special classes may be found in Kay's publications.

KAY'S PALEOZOIC FRAMEWORK OF NORTH AMERICA

Figure 11-4 shows Kay's concept of the tectonic framework for Paleozoic sedimentation in North America. The principal geosynclines (Appalachian and Cordilleran) are divided into outer eugeosynclinal zones, in which volcanism was associated with sedimentary deposition, and inner miogeosynclinal zones were free from volcanic contributions.

The **Llanorian Geosyncline,** in the southern United States, is only partly defined, owing to the present cover of Cretaceous sediments, and the absence of complete subsurface data. It appears, however, that a miogeosynclinal belt extended, as shown, across southern Arkansas and central and western Texas. Presumably, the corresponding eugeosynclinal zone lay in a gulfward direction from the miogeosyncline.

Within the continental craton itself (called the **hedreocraton** by Kay), are intracratonic geosynclines and complementary positive areas, which were active during parts of the Paleozoic. These are not shown in the map. However, a number of intracratonic geosynclines, including the Michigan, Illinois, and Forest City basins, were active during the Paleozoic. Positive areas include the Cincinnati Arch, the Ozark Uplift, the Nemaha Ridge, and others. The Michigan Basin behaved as an autogeosyncline during much of its activity, whereas the Illinois and Forest City basins were zeugogeosynclines at some times.

Comparison of Kay's tectonic framework with that of Schuchert indicates a general similarity in the placement of the main tectonic elements, comprising the Appalachian and Cordilleran geosynclines, and the central more neutral part of the continent. The Llanorian Geosyncline is more accurately located, although its exact relation to the Appalachian Geosyncline is obscure.

The most striking difference between the two frameworks is the absence of borderlands in Kay's map. The presence of these hypothetical land masses was originally inferred from the increasing coarseness of geosynclinal deposits toward their oceanward edges, which implied the existence of

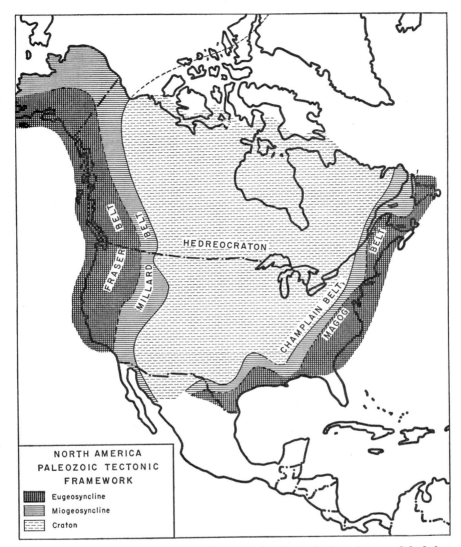

Fig. 11-4. Early Paleozoic tectonic framework of North America, modified from Kay (1947), with adaptations for Barton (1945) and King (1950).

large land masses. Evidence of the former presence of Appalachia was thought to occur in the ancient metamorphosed rocks of the Piedmont. Many of these rocks have since been shown to be Paleozoic in age, which required moving Appalachia still farther east. The present-day absence of such bordering land masses was accounted for in part by foundering of the continental edges.

The frontispiece of Kay's memoir (1951) is reproduced here as Figure

11-5. This shows, more eloquently than words can describe, the conceptual change from broad borderlands, from which sediments are poured into geosynclines, to eugeosynclinal belts (with their volcanic islands and high tectonic mobility) occupying linear zones between the relatively stable oceanic and continental cratons. Kay (1951, p. 31) discusses the theory of borderlands and marginal volcanic geosynclines and gives references to the pertinent literature.

A second point of difference between Kay's and Schuchert's concepts lies in their interpretations of the tectonic behavior of the central part of the continent. Instead of being a relatively stable and rigid mass, as Schuchert suggests, the craton displays its own local subsidence and uplift, generally less intense than in orthogeosynclinal belts. These relative movements give rise to the deposition of markedly greater thickness of sediment in the intracratonic geosynclines than on less rapidly subsiding parts of the craton.

Fig. 11-5. Paleogeography of Early Medial Ordovician of North America. [After Kay (1951).]

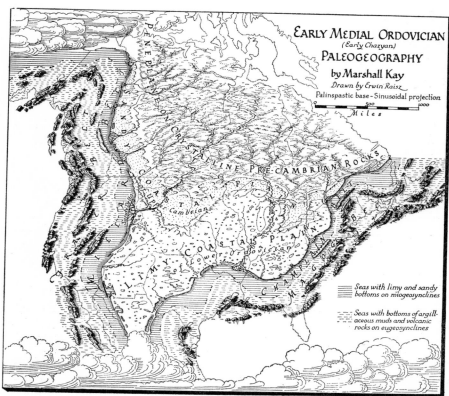

OTHER CLASSIFICATIONS OF TECTONIC ELEMENTS

Although preceding sections have emphasized a particular aspect of the development of geosynclinal classification, many other writers have proposed classifications that take into account the accumulating body of geophysical, oceanographic, and sedimentary data on island arcs. Kuenen (1935) described the features of the East Indian Archipelago, and grouped them into **marginal deeps,** narrow linear zones of deep water; and **intermontane troughs,** subsiding areas that lie among the positive elements in the area. The shallower negative areas are divided into **nuclear basins,** generally conformable to structural trends of the associated positive elements; and **discordant basins,** which cut across the other structural elements.

Umbgrove (1947) developed a classification of tectonic elements represented by ancient sedimentary basins, closely paralleling Kuenen's grouping. In a broad sense, the marginal deeps and intermontane troughs represent the active eugeosynclinal belt. The basins may occur in association with this belt as areas of less active tectonism, or they may represent the intracratonic features of Kay.

Other writers, notably Bubnoff (1931), developed classifications of tectonic elements extending from the continental nucleus to the ocean basins. Bubnoff recognizes **shield areas,** which correspond to the nucleus or craton; **shelves,** essentially neutral areas adjacent to the shield; **geosynclines,** deeply subsiding linear areas; and **oceanic troughs,** which are the deeps of the ocean basin. The shelf areas may be stable or mobile, depending upon whether or not they are subject to oscillations or minor tectonic movements.

Weeks (1952) proposed a classification of geosynclines—sedimentary basins of various sorts—in terms of their occurrence in regions of tectonic mobility or tectonic stability. Geosynclines of the mobile belt include Kay's orthogeosynclines, as well as second-order basins that are developed within the mountains of a mobile belt. Basins in stable regions include the intracratonic geosynclines of Kay (grouped in part according to their position within the craton) and graben-type basins. Week's classification combines aspects of several, and is particularly well adapted to the study of the conditions of oil occurrence within areas of thick sedimentary accumulations. This aspect of the subject is emphasized in his paper.

An important recent integration of earlier tectonic classifications was made by Cady (1950). This is treated in the following section, inasmuch as Cady emphasizes the time sequence of events in geotectonic elements and discusses the association of magmatic and sedimentary fills in geosynclines. In 1951 Krynine presented a thought-provoking critique of geotectonic elements (see below).

TECTONIC CYCLES AND ASSOCIATED IGNEOUS ACTIVITY

A time sequence of events is inherent in geosynclinal theory. In the classical sense, the geosyncline is initially the site of thick sedimentary accumulation and is eventually deformed into a mountain range. With the broadening of the geosynclinal concept, and as the more specific problem of geosynclinal classification was looked into by geologists, the question of the historical geology of geosynclines has been re-examined.

Two aspects of this time framework are treated here. The first comprises the apparently cyclical events that follow one another during geosynclinal development, and the second is the relationship between the developing geosyncline and the sequence of volcanic or plutonic events in the area of tectonic mobility.

Tectonic Cycles

The concept of a tectonic cycle was developed by Krynine (1941). Figure 11-6 shows Krynine's three main geosynclinal stages, in each of

Fig. 11-6. Krynine's tectonic cycle. [From Distinguished Lecture Series, Am. Assoc. Petrol. Geologists (1943).]

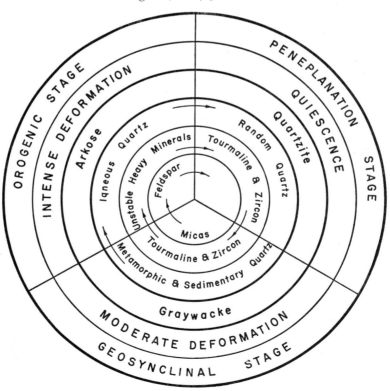

which are implicit certain sets of conditions that control the nature of the sediments formed. The parallelism with the classical stream erosion cycle is evident, as Krynine intended. Certain diagnostic minerals, most readily recognized in sandstone, afford clues to the degree of tectonism that prevailed during each stage of the cycle. These minerals include igneous quartz, metamorphic quartz, feldspar, chert, and mica. Combinations of these minerals with varying amounts of matrix form the typical sandstone in each of Krynine's tectonic stages.

Krynine defined his **peneplanation stage** as a time of widespread cyclic deposition on a relatively stable peneplaned surface. The characteristic sandstone of this stage is quartzite (quartzose sandstone), which contains a highly stable assemblage of minerals. The **geosynclinal stage** is characterized by deposition during subsidence, and its typical sandstone is graywacke. The **orogenic stage** is marked by uplift commonly accompanied by faulting, after folding and magmatic intrusion in the geosyncline. The characteristic sandstone of this stage is arkose.

Whether or not the complex history of geosynclines can be condensed into a single generalized cycle, Pettijohn points out (1957, p. 637) that certain associations of sedimentary rocks are recurrent, and may succeed each other in a systematic manner. He illustrates this in a general cycle that alternates **geosynclinal** and **cratonic** events in terms of a recurrent succession of **oxidizing** and **reducing** conditions, the latter having a **restricted-circulation phase,** during which evaporites and euxinic black shales are typically formed.

Magmatic Relations

The four stages in the development of tectonic elements described by Stille (1940), were applied by Cady (1950) in his classification of geotectonic elements. The four stages are a **primary geosynclinal stage, a primary mountain-building stage,** a **secondary mountain-building stage,** and a **stage of final uplift and local subsidence.**

The primary geosynclines of the first stage are characterized by submarine volcanic rocks, notably spilites. Typical synorogenic plutons, mainly extensive granodioritic batholiths, occur in the stage of primary mountain-building. During or at about the time of secondary mountain-building, a series of hypabyssal intrusives, ranging from andesite to rhyolite, are intruded into secondary geosynclines that develop in the vicinity of geanticlines.

After secondary mountain-building and the consolidation of the geosynclinal belt, alkalic intrusives, typically granitic and syenitic stocks, may be emplaced, as in New Hampshire and the eastern Rocky Mountains. Finally, plateau basalts such as the Columbia River basalts may be extruded during the fourth stage.

Figure 11-7, adapted from Cady, shows the several stages of tectonic history schematically. This diagram is an excellent presentation of the inter-relations among geotectonic elements as they have been defined by various writers. It serves as a readily visualized integration of Kay's classification with those of other writers in terms of positive and negative elements that are associated with each stage of geosynclinal and orogenic events.

Sequence of Events in Major Depositional Cycles

It is instructive to consider a well-documented example of the sequence of events during parts of a tectonic cycle. Kay (1942) describes the development of the northern Allegheny synclinorium in a particularly lucid way. According to Kay, the sequence in the Allegheny belt included the initial deposition of sediments in the main orthogeosynclinal zone. Volcanics, siliceous shale, chert, and some graywacke sandstone formed in the eugeosyncline, whereas shale and limestone dominated in the miogeosyncline. Deposition was succeeded by uplift of Vermontia as an intra-eugeosynclinal geanticline. Folding and thrust of the eugeosynclinal deposits on the miogeosynclinal Champlain deposits occurred during the Taconian disturbance, and intrusion in the eugeosynclinal belt occurred during the Acadian disturbance. Finally, folding and thrust of the miogeosynclinal Champlain on the craton took place during the Appalachian revolution.

In part, the old eugeosynclinal facies is preserved in remnants of the old thrust sheets. This superposition of eugeosynclinal deposits on miogeosynclinal sediments establishes the sequence of events and places the two parts of the orthogeosynclinal zone in their relative geographic positions.

Kay implied a similar history of events for the Cordilleran Geosyncline during Mesozoic and Early Tertiary. In the Ouachitas, the relations are not as clear, but it appears that earlier Paleozoic eugeosynclinal deposits lacking typical volcanics were thrust over the miogeosynclinal Arbuckle facies during some part of the Appalachian orogenic cycle.

During the progress of these events in the main geosynclinal belts, the craton itself was affected by tectonism of various sorts. Pronglike extensions of the miogeosyncline developed in transverse directions marginally into the craton, producing exogeosynclines with source areas in the orthogeosyncline. Farther within the craton, some areas subsided more rapidly than others during parts of the Paleozoic and received correspondingly thicker deposits. The Michigan, Illinois, Forest City, Williston, and other intracratonic geosynclines are examples.

Compensating positive elements on the craton, such as the Cincinnati

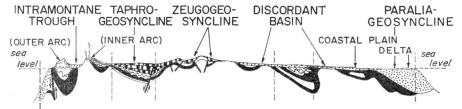

STAGE 4: FINAL DIFFERENTIAL UPLIFT AND LOCAL SUBSIDENCE

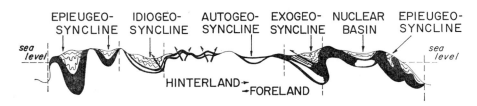

STAGE 3: SECONDARY MOUNTAIN BUILDING

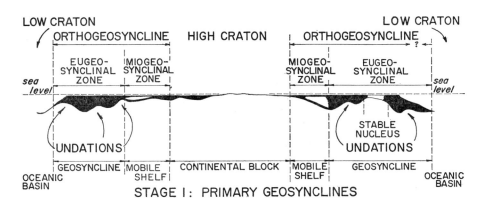

STAGE 2: PRIMARY MOUNTAIN BUILDING

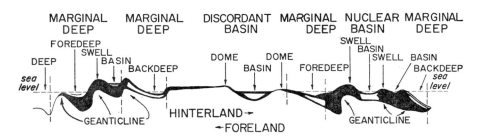

STAGE I: PRIMARY GEOSYNCLINES

Fig. 11-7. Nomenclature of tectonic elements. [From Cady (1950).]

413

Arch, the Nemaha Ridge, and others, showed movements during part of the era. Parts of the Canadian Shield were emergent at times and served as source areas for cratonic deposits. More neutral areas, widespread at times and slowly subsiding, received thin accumulations of limestone and other deposits during times of marine inundation.

The shallow epicontinental seas drained from parts of the craton during times of disturbance in the main orthogeosynclinal belts. Intracratonic positives, the first exposed above water, suffered erosion and developed disconformities in the sections. The seas apparently remained over other parts of the craton during disturbances elsewhere, as shown by continuous limestone deposition from Cambrian through early Ordovician in the midcontinent and other areas.

At other times, such as the close of Lower Devonian, the craton, as a whole, appears to have become a vast neutral area, with general emergence over its whole extent. Subaerial erosion after emergence developed a broad peneplain over which the encroaching Middle Devonian sea spread. In the submergent intervals following such "freezing" of the craton, positive and negative movements were locally resumed. Subsidence in intracratonic geosynclines occurred about the same centers, or showed slight shifts in position.

During major revolutions which fold and thrust the orthogeosynclinal deposits, the craton may respond by a cessation of tectonism in features which were active during much of the life of the main geosynclines. New tectonic elements of the craton, initiated during the ensuing era, may cut across earlier tectonic trends. This is true of some Tertiary basins in the western states, which show little or no parallelism with pre-Laramide or pre-Appalachian structural features.

Added complexity arises as additional stratigraphic studies afford data that imply continuous tectonic activity throughout geological time. The classical concept, which states that each geologic period represents a long interval of quiescence closed by diastrophic disturbances, is not fully supported by these newer data. Instead, it now appears that disturbances in the orthogeosynclinal belts take place continuously, as local basins subside, local positive areas emerge, and as folds and thrusts develop in one part or another of the linear zone. This is in contrast to earlier concepts of discontinuous orogenic episodes.

PRESENT STATUS OF GEOSYNCLINAL THEORY

It is apparent that geosynclinal theory, as well as the classification of geosynclines, is and has been in a state of flux. Knopf (1960), in his analysis of recent geosynclinal theory, points out that the term geosyncline has not yet been adequately defined. Moreover, with respect to the sedimentary filling of geosynclines, he quotes, with considerable justification, Goguel's (1952) remarks that the characteristics of sedimentary accumulations, used by various writers to infer geosynclinal conditions, depend upon the geosynclinal concept held by the geologist who makes the inference. Though it is true that geosynclinal classifications include an element of subjectivity and are influenced by the originator's geological experience, it is equally true that these informal or formal classifications of geosynclines represent progressive stages in the understanding of basically important tectonic features. It may be confidently expected that future changes in classification and terminology of geosynclines will occur; the rate at which geologic knowledge is expanding gives assurance that such modifications will in most instances represent successively closer approximations to an integrated and increasingly objective classification.

One example of geosynclinal classification that is undergoing change has to do with the relationship of the miogeosyncline to the eugeosyncline on the one hand, and the relationship of the miogeosyncline to the continental craton on the other. It appears evident, from recently accumulated subsurface data and from the more detailed outcrop studies in miogeosynclinal areas made during the past decade, that current classifications of orthogeosynclines may need some revision.

The original concept of a miogeosyncline, as a continuous, linear element, exhibiting less intense tectonism than the eugeosyncline, but paralleling it geographically, is not fully supported by this accumulating evidence. The analysis of stratigraphic relations on maps that show the thickness and composition of sedimentary rock bodies lying between the craton and the typical eugeosynclinal deposits with their volcanic associations, demonstrates increasingly that the miogeosyncline is not typically a continuous linear belt, but consists of tectonic elements of limited extent that lie between the craton and the eugeosyncline. It is almost as though the craton deteriorated irregularly along its edges, in a transitional miogeosynclinal zone that may be narrow or broad; that may contain both positive and negative tectonic features; and that may at times receive sedimentary fillings characteristic either of the craton or of the eugeosyncline, depending on the degree of tectonic activity in the eugeosynclinal belt.

Sloss (1956) pointed out the need for reconsidering the original concept of the miogeosyncline in terms of growing evidence that a series of marginal basins, rather than a continuous linear belt of subsidence, characterizes the transitional area between craton and eugeosyncline. It would thus seem to be more appropriate to refer to "*a* miogeosynclinal zone" that embraces a wide range of sedimentary and tectonic features than to speak of *"the* miogeosyncline."

Marginal basins, according to Sloss, are subsiding areas that may occupy marginal parts of the craton proper, or may occur in a transitional band between the major cratonic and orthogeosynclinal elements. Marginal basins sometimes receive their sediment from the adjacent eugeosynclinal element, and at other times from the craton. When the mobile eugeosynclinal belt is active, large volumes of raw, unsorted debris are poured into the basins. During these periods, active structural trends, parallel to the orogenic trends in the eugeosyncline, develop in the basins, which in turn, strongly influence the distribution of the inflowing sediments. During these recurrent bursts of activity, the clastic material from the eugeosynclinal area may overwhelm the marginal basin and spill over onto the craton. At other times, when the tectonism of the mobile belt is less violent, and when orogenic trends are relatively quiescent, the marginal basin receives its sediment from cratonic sources. Kay's definition of exogeosyncline, involving a tongue-like mass of geosynclinal detritus extending onto the border of the craton, recognizes that extracratonic sources are responsible for some of the deposition in miogeosynclinal and bordering cratonic areas.

The complexities encountered at cratonic margins are well illustrated in western North America. Here, numerous mountain uplifts expose the strata of Kay's Millard miogeosynclinal belt and many borings have penetrated these rocks in the search for oil and gas. Regional stratigraphic studies (Dott, 1955; Martin, 1959; and Steele, 1960 are examples) demonstrate the presence of many distinct subsiding basins and emergent uplifts that exhibit patterns of behavior much like those of similar elements in the cratonic interior.

Sloss (1956) uses the Williston Basin as an example of changes in the tectonic setting of what has been considered to be a typical cratonic feature. During its history from mid-Ordovician through Triassic, the Williston Basin behaved as an autogeosyncline, in Kay's terminology, with its source areas on the craton. From at least the middle of the Jurassic through the Paleocene, the Williston Basin area behaved as a complex of subsiding and neutral elements at the margin of the craton, and hence was strongly influenced by events and conditions in the adjoining western orogenic belt.

In this later part of its history, tectonic activity of the Williston Basin changed in various ways. During times of relative inactivity in the adjoining eugeosynclinal trend, the marginal area of the craton contained subsiding areas that were similar to Kay's autogeosynclines and zeugogeosynclines, except that the centers of subsidence tended to shift in position with time somewhat more markedly than did the subsiding areas located well within the craton. As a result, the sedimentary fill in parts of the Williston Basin area shows strong variations, both laterally and vertically. In the final analysis, it is these relations among fill characteristics that offer the best evidence of the changing patterns of tectonic activity through time, and which strongly imply the existence of discontinuous centers of activity rather than a single dominantly linear feature in the transition area of a "miogeosyncline."

As may be seen from this discussion, and from preceding sections, the ramifications of geosynclinal theory have expanded until they now embrace new developments in regional geology, subsurface structure, geophysical study of ocean basins and continents, sedimentation, stratigraphy, and in relations between igneous activity and geosynclinal development, each of which has some bearing on the problem. Until the relative importance of each of these several factors is evaluated, and until a clearer picture emerges of the interactions among them, the subject of geosynclines will necessarily remain in its present healthy state of flux.

TECTONIC CLASSIFICATION USED HERE

Even though no present-day classification of tectonic elements, nor any selected portion of several can fully satisfy the requirements for complete classification, it is evident from the point of view of practical stratigraphy that some sort of framework for the organization of observational data is needed.

The stratigraphic viewpoint in this textbook includes the principle that three-dimensional geological relationships can only be seen if full cognizance is given to subsurface data as well as to outcrop relationships. The authors therefore feel free to select, and if necessary, to modify portions of earlier classifications in order to provide this framework for day-to-day stratigraphic interpretation in a full three-dimensional sense.

Although any such selection is influenced by personal experience, the grouping of tectonic elements used here is based largely on Kay's classification, with some modification of terms, and with major change in the concept of the miogeosyncline as a separate, identifiable, and continuous linear zone of extracratonic geosynclinal behavior.

Orthogeosynclines

This term is restricted to the eugeosyncline of Stille and Kay. It is considered to be an orogenically and volcanically active linear element of long-continued subsidence lying between adjacent cratons. The inference that eugeosynclines receive the bulk of their sedimentary fill from narrow intervening lands or from island arcs within the active tectonic belt is an essential part of this eugeosynclinal concept.

The Miogeosynclinal Transitional Zone

The concept of marginal basins and marginal positive elements arranged discontinuously, or in an interlocked manner along the edges of the craton, suggests that this transitional zone between the eugeosyncline and the main mass of the craton is not a true orthogeosyncline in the sense that it is wholly extracratonic. In many ways this transitional zone is closely related to the craton, and it may ultimately be desirable to classify it as a specific part of the craton, even though the sedimentary fill in marginal basins may have strong affinities with both major tectonic elements. For convenience of discussion, the miogeosynclinal aspect of the transitional zone (in the sense that it lies geographically between the eugeosyncline and the craton) is retained. The transition zone, as the term is used here, consists of marginal basins and marginal uplifts that develop along cratonic edges.

The term **marginal basin** is used for areally limited centers of subsidence that lie between the craton and the eugeosyncline; that is, in the transitional zone commonly referred to as the miogeosyncline. As pointed out earlier, marginal basins may sometimes be dependent upon the eugeosyncline as a source of sediments, as in the exogeosyncline of Kay's classification; but at other times these marginal basins may receive their sediments from cratonic sources.

A **marginal uplift** is a positive area of limited extent associated with marginal basins during periods of high tectonic activity in the adjacent eugeosyncline. Marginal uplifts have structural trends parallel to the orogenic trends in the eugeosynclinal zone.

The Craton

The term **craton,** used here in the same sense as by Kay, designates the broad central part of the continent between the mobile eugeosynclinal belts. Technically it also applies to more stable parts of oceanic basins.

Intracratonic Basins. These are the intracratonic geosynclines of Kay. It seems more appropriate to use the term basin for ovate negative areas within the craton proper. Kay recognizes three main types, the exogeosyncline, autogeosyncline, and zeugogeosyncline. The exogeosyncline, a transverse basin extending into the cratonic margin as an embayment from the mobile tectonic belt, is here considered as a marginal basin.

The term **interior basin** is applied to the autogeosyncline of Kay. These basins are sufficiently remote from the active eugeosynclinal trend such that whatever clastic debris they contain must have been derived from the continental interior. These interior sources may consist of the ancient crystalline rocks of the shield areas or of the rocks in epeirogenic uplifts of one sort or another on the craton.

The term **yoked basin** is used here in place of Kay's zeugogeosyncline. These basins immediately adjoin active orogenic elements of the cratonic platform. With uplift, the relatively thin skin of sediments may be rapidly stripped, exposing basement crystalline rocks that may supply large volumes of arkosic debris as basin fill. The Fountain Arkose, derived from the Ancestral Rocky Mountains in Pennsylvanian time, is an example.

Intracratonic Positive Areas. Positive areas within the craton are grouped into two major classes, depending upon the degree of tectonism which they display. At one extreme are the orogenic elements, such as the "Ancestral Rocky Mountains," and at the other are epeirogenic "uplifts" that appear to be positive because they lag behind the surrounding subsiding areas. During part of its history the Ozark Dome is considered to have behaved as an example of the latter.

Cratonic Shelf Areas. Shelf areas are defined as the neutral parts of the craton, lying between and among more positive or negative areas. The term applies to a degree of tectonism rather than to a specific geographic area. The present continental margins are shelves, but in a stratigraphic sense, the term refers to any portion of the craton which has displayed no marked tectonism during some given cycle of deposition. For identification purposes, the shelves often bear geographic names such as "the Silurian Shelf area of Illinois."

Shelf areas are divided into two categories, between which all gradations may occur. The **stable shelf** is the most neutral part of the craton. The **unstable shelf** is characterized by oscillatory movements that may give rise to cyclical sedimentation. The coal cyclothems of the Pennsylvanian Period as exposed in western Illinois are interpreted as characteristic deposits on an unstable shelf.

Gradations occur between shelves and **intracratonic platforms.** In part, these distinctions depend upon the presence of abrupt marginal slopes at the edges of platforms, in contrast to less abrupt gradations at shelf margins.

A convenient way of visualizing shelves in the sense used here consists in studying the tectonic elements shown on paleotectonic maps. Such maps indicate where uplifts and basins occur, but they may not emphasize those neutral areas of the craton that lie among the positive or negative portions. This situation may be illustrated by the two maps of the central United States, shown in Figure 11-8. The upper one shows two subsiding areas, the Michigan Basin and the Iowa–Kansas Basin, both of which were centers of

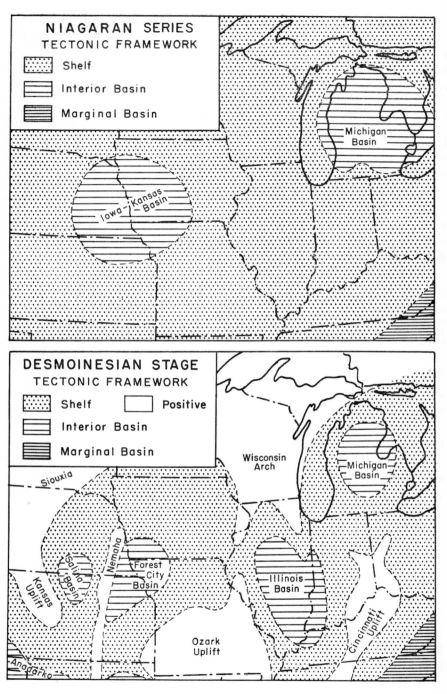

Fig. 11-8. Cratonic elements of the midcontinent during two parts of the Paleozoic era.

420

subsidence during the Niagaran Epoch of the Silurian Period. Since no marked positive elements were present, the dotted area between the subsiding basins falls within the category of essentially neutral terrain, to which the term shelf may be appropriately applied.

The lower map of Figure 11-8 shows the same area as it appeared during the Desmoinesian Stage of the Pennsylvanian Period. During this time interval, several areas of subsidence were counterbalanced by areas of uplift, yielding a much more complex picture than in the upper map. The shelf areas of the Desmoinesian were, in general, narrower than those of the Silurian, and because of their relationship to nearby positive or negative elements, portions of the shelf tended to be unstable. Thus, the narrow shelf that extends essentially from the Wisconsin Arch to the Ozark Uplift between the Illinois Basin and the Rock Island Arch is classified as an unstable shelf, in part because of the well-developed coal cyclothems in western Illinois.

In the southeastern portion of both map areas is the transition zone to the eugeosyncline farther east. This is part of the miogeosynclinal belt of Kay, considered here as the zone of marginal basins. The Forest City Basin is a yoked basin; all other intracratonic basins shown are interior basins. The Nemaha Ridge is a mildly orogenic uplift; all other uplifts on the maps are epeirogenic.

IMPORTANCE OF SEDIMENTARY TECTONICS IN STRATIGRAPHY

From continuing studies of geosynclines come broadened views regarding tectonic behavior of the craton, together with recognition that all degrees of tectonism may proceed simultaneously in geosyncline and craton during major depositional cycles. The degree of tectonism in part controls the distribution of sedimentary environments through its control of the strand line, and hence in part controls the length of time that an environment operates on material before burial. Thus, tectonism and environment are interlocked in that some combination of the two determines to a large extent the final properties of the accumulating deposits.

These developments bear very strongly upon stratigraphic analysis. Principles of correlation must be broad enough to correlate stratigraphic intervals across tectonic boundaries into sediments formed simultaneously under different environmental and tectonic conditions. The problem of correlating time lines through this complex is by no means simple.

Numerous rock units, which persist in their lithology but transgress time lines (such as the Devonian-Mississippian shale of the central states), represent the progressive invasion of a region by certain tectonic or environmental conditions. An intracratonic basin may develop locally and expand with time, carrying its tectonism into a larger area. A stable shelf may expand during the closing stages of a major tectonic cycle, extending across former intracratonic basins and even into orthogeosynclinal belts.

In its wider aspects, therefore, the science of stratigraphy is advanced by developments in the field of sedimentary tectonics. Problems of regional correlation and general stratigraphic analysis, which could not be solved because of conflicting or obscure evidence, can be resolved, in large part, in terms of the new framework of analysis introduced by sedimentary tectonics.

TECTONICS AND SEDIMENTARY ENVIRONMENTS

Questions regarding the relative importance of tectonism and environments in controlling sedimentary properties cannot be answered in simple terms. The characteristics of a sedimentary rock depend on several factors, which include the following:

(a) Nature of the source rock.
(b) Topographic expression and relief of source area.
(c) Distribution of tectonic elements over source and depositional area.
(d) Intensity of tectonism in each tectonic element.
(e) Geologic agents which transport detritus to sites of deposition.
(f) Pattern of environments in the depositional area.

Factors of climate, superimposed on this complex, may affect the degree of weathering of source rocks. In conjunction with restrictions of circulation in depositional areas, climate may determine whether evaporites are formed. Added complexity arises from the interplay of detrital and nonclastic sedimentation in any part of the sedimentary environment.

One or more of the preceding factors may become dominant under the proper conditions. Large-scale, normal faulting of a granitic terrain yields wedge arkose deposits. Here, the petrology and tectonic activity of the source area are controlling factors. On a stable shelf, where environmental agents continually rework the detritus, the sedimentary environment is of first importance. In the more general case, some combination of factors (a) to (f) operates, with sedimentary properties reflecting each combination.

The increasing importance of sedimentary tectonics in sedimentary analysis may be seen by considering the preceding factors in more detail. Factors (c) and (d) are aspects of the general tectonic framework of sedimentation. Krynine showed that factors (a) and (b) are directly related to tectonics, the former in the degree of metamorphism which may be impressed on the source area, and the latter in terms of tectonic intensity. By its control of the strand line, tectonism also affects factor (f).

The sedimentary environment is most important in controlling the detailed patterns of sediment distribution. In part, these patterns are characteristic of particular environments and, in part, they depend upon the relative amounts of detrital and nonclastic sediments being formed. The influence of tectonism on the environmental processes is mainly one of determining the rate at which sedimentary particles pass through the depositional interface. With rapid passage, the particles are buried and protected from the environmental agents. With slow passage, the particles lie at the depositional interface long enough to be thoroughly sorted and otherwise modified in accordance with the physical and chemical processes of the environment.

Study of sediments now forming shows beyond question that the environment of deposition exerts a strong effect on sediment properties, as was developed in Chapter 7. When observations are transferred from a thin veneer of recent sediment to a thick body of ancient sediments, the problem of relating the deposits to specific environments becomes much more difficult.

The reconstruction of the environment is more difficult than the reconstruction of the contemporaneous tectonism, since a degree of tectonism ordinarily prevails for a long enough time in any area to impress its characteristics on the accumulating sediments. During this time, however, the sedimentary environment may pass through many phases.

These relations may be illustrated by conditions on an unstable shelf. As the strand line shifts to and fro in response to mild tectonic oscillations, the pattern of sedimentary environments shifts with it. A stratigraphic section at any point may, accordingly, include deposits ranging from continental clastics to marine clastics and nonclastics, reflecting the change in water depth and distance from shore with time. The lithologic association formed during this time is an unstable shelf association, but the sedimentary environments are expressed by continuous changes in the detailed texture and composition of the sediments.

Inferred Tectono-environmental Conditions in Tectonic Elements

As a basis for the later discussion of classifications that combine tectonic elements and sedimentary environments, it is appropriate here to parallel the thumbnail sketches of sedimentary environments presented in Chapter 7 with a similar treatment of tectonic elements in terms of the conditions of sediment transport and deposition that exist in each. It is to be emphasized that these conditions are mainly inferred rather than known, the basis for inference being the observed associations of sedimentary deposits that suggest occurrence of these conditions.

The term **lithologic association** is applied to groups of sedimentary rocks formed under given tectonic conditions. Normally these associations are described along with their inferred conditions of deposition. The detailed treatment of these associations is deferred to Chapter 13, however, inasmuch as their full interpretation depends upon an understanding of stratigraphic maps, the subject of Chapter 12.

Conditions on Stable Shelves. Shelf areas are among the largest tectonic elements. They suggest conditions like those which exist along the Atlantic Coastal Plain, where the general profile of the land surface extends seaward beneath the ocean. The essential condition for a stable shelf is that a very mild rate of subsidence prevails over the depositional area.

Deposition on shelf areas represents transgressive and regressive phases. Unconformities are typical at the base of sandstone units, and definite transgression of time lines is to be expected. Movement of the strand line shifts the littoral zone over the shelf area and endows much of the section with typical shore-line characteristics. Dune areas developed along the shores may be preserved, intermingling eolian deposits with marine sediments. Dapples (1955), in his study of the St. Peter Sandstone (Ordovician), shows this intermingling relationship in his reconstruction of the conditions under which the sand was deposited.

The supply of detrital material is usually small in comparison with the area of the stable shelf, thus the debris may be repeatedly reworked by environmental agents before it is finally buried. Coarser sediments occur in stream courses and along beaches or in coastal dunes. Finer detrital sediments are formed in quieter parts of the prevailing environments.

Source areas may supply a variety of minerals to the shelf, but the more unstable species are largely eliminated during continued movement in the subaerial, littoral, and shallow-water marine zones. Where the detrital supply is low, the shelf sublittoral environment may become an area of dominant limestone deposition. The limestone commonly contains an insoluble residue of highly spherical quartz grains. Direct gradation from quartz sand to carbonate deposition appears to be commonplace in shelf deposits.

As far as present knowledge extends, no restrictions can be placed on carbonate deposition on shelves with respect to distance from shore. As long as the detrital load is too small to mask the accumulating carbonate, limestone may form close to shore, as it does in the Great Barrier Reef of Australia and along the southeast coast of Florida. Organisms have an important influence on carbonate accumulation in stable shelves. Many benthonic forms contribute directly to sedimentation by the precipitation of carbonate, or by adding their shells to the deposits. Tests of planktonic forms also add to the accumulating sediments.

Conditions on Unstable Shelves. On unstable shelves, the rate of subsidence is greater than that for stable shelves, and may be interrupted by oscillatory movements. On a stable shelf, small eustatic changes of sea level may shift the strand line a considerable distance. Warping may greatly complicate movement of the strand as the shelf itself becomes unstable.

As instability increases, the conditions described under stable shelves are modified. The most important change is introduced by the greater net rate of subsidence, which reduces the length of time during which environmental agents operate on sedimentary material before burial. The lack of continuous reworking is reflected by an increase of finer material in the sandstone, a poorer degree of sorting, and less complete rounding of the grains. Shale responds by becoming more silty, and limestone may become argillaceous or nodular.

Cyclical sedimentation is characteristic of some parts of unstable shelves. If the oscillatory movements shift the strand line over a wide area in rhythmic fashion, typical coal cyclothems may be formed, as in the Pennsylvanian of western Illinois. These and other cyclical deposits are more fully described in chapter 13.

Conditions on unstable shelves grade imperceptibly into those of the stable shelf on the one hand, and toward interior basin conditions on the other. Sharp boundaries between deposits of these tectonic elements seldom occur, but where the depositional area is widespread enough to develop typical unstable shelves, the accumulating deposits tend to reflect the characteristic mild degree of tectonism.

Conditions in Cratonic Basins. Basins within the craton proper are of two main kinds, as mentioned earlier. An **interior basin** develops where a portion of the craton undergoes concentric subsidence, resulting in the formation of a circular or elliptical area in which the rate of subsidence varies from slight at the basin margin to moderate at the center.

Interior basins may show transitional phases to shelf conditions along their edges. Rates of sediment burial may vary accordingly from relatively slow near the margin to rapid in the central portion, producing a range of sediments corresponding to the different rates of burial.

Deposits in interior basins may be marine or nonmarine, depending upon the position of the strand line as a given cycle of deposition progresses. If the open sea covers an interior basin, normal open circulation conditions may prevail. As a result, the sediments may be similar in many respects to shelf sediments, except that the more rapid rate of burial and the increased thickness of the deposits reflect a rate of subsidence greater than normally occurs on shelves.

Circulation in interior basins may become restricted if access to the open sea is limited. Under these conditions, the deposition of evaporites or of euxinic deposits becomes a function of the relationships among the inflow of normal marine waters, the inflow of fresh water from adjacent land areas, and the rate of evaporation in the restricted zone.

The relation between rate of subsidence and rate of sedimentation in interior basins is partly dependent upon relations between the basin and associated source areas. If detritus does not reach the basin, subsidence will exceed deposition. One consequence of this may be the development of a **starved basin,** in which a combination of restricted circulation and lack of inflowing detrital materials may result in the formation of thin deposits in a tectonic setting that is otherwise adapted to the development of thicker accumulations.

When open circulation conditions prevail and detrital inflow is negligible, the basin may be filled with nonclastic sediments, typically carbonates, although interbedded evaporites may form if intermittent restriction occurs.

In contrast to the interior basin, the **yoked basin** is by definition a subsiding area adjacent to a complementary uplift that supplies detritus to the area of subsidence. Yoked basins may have the same range of tectonic intensity as interior basins, though at times the rate of subsidence may be greater than in interior basins, especially if faulting occurs in the boundary zone between rising and subsiding elements. Such faulting tends to develop an asymmetrical cross section in the yoked basin, with thickest deposits normally accumulating adjacent to the fault that bounds the rising source area.

In some respects yoked basins and interior basins may be much the same in that both may contain fills made up of marine or nonmarine deposits, and both may display open circulation or restricted circulation conditions. Generally, however, clastic materials dominate in yoked basins, and the presence of thick carbonate or evaporite deposits is less common than in interior basins.

Disconformities and diastems are less common in yoked basins and interior basins than in shelf deposits. This implies more continuous deposition, or at least less uplift above sea level. The tectonism of a basin may be oscillatory, but if the oscillations do not lift the deposited sediments above sea level or base level, disconformities are not produced, though diastems may be.

The generally more rapid rate at which deposits in intracratonic basins are buried than those on shelves implies that environmental factors have less time to impress themselves on deposits in basins. Thus, one may expect to find the more thoroughly sorted sediments on shelves, though this relation can be complicated should well-sorted material from shelves be washed into and trapped within the basin. Moreover, under some circumstances, such as restriction under arid conditions, thick evaporite deposits may form in basins. Here the deposits clearly reflect environmental control, and the relative tectonism (that is, moderate subsidence) is inferred from the thickness of the deposit.

Conditions in Marginal Basins. Marginal basins, because of their geographic setting at the cratonic edge, may at times display a much higher degree of tectonism than is commonly shown in intracratonic basins located away from the cratonic edges. As pointed out earlier in this chapter, marginal basins may behave very much like interior basins or yoked basins during times of relative inactivity in the eugeosyncline. More typically, during times of greater activity in the eugeosyncline, the marginal basins exhibit the tectonic characteristics of Kay's miogeosynclinal zone. Under these circumstances, rapidly rising positive elements related to the eugeosynclinal belt may be closely associated with the marginal basins, giving rise to a complex interrelationship between marine and nonmarine deposits as the inpouring detrital material from the positive elements at times forces the strand line back. Contemporaneous folding and thrusting in the eugeosyncline may be reflected in corresponding disturbances in the marginal basin, giving rise to folded beds that may be truncated by erosion to produce vacuities in the sedimentary record, as discussed in Chapter 6.

Conditions in Eugeosynclines. The rapid subsidence of the negative elements in the eugeosyncline characteristically traps and buries accumulating sediments before environmental agents can thoroughly sort and winnow them. Rapid deposition in such subsiding areas commonly keeps the troughs filled, or nearly filled, with sediments.

There may be many exceptions to this balanced state. For instance, slackening of subsidence may bring about an excess of accumulation, requiring shifting and reworking of the deposits. This situation establishes, at least temporarily, the dynamic conditions on the shelf. When source areas are low, on the other hand, heavy detrital deposition may be replaced by siliceous limestone or chert accumulations, presumably under bathyal conditions.

The extreme variations in tectonic conditions and the complex association of positive and negative elements that exist in eugeosynclines produce perhaps the greatest variability in the time and space distribution of sedimentary environments. Presumably, environments in the eugeosyncline are dominantly marine, but when deposition exceeds subsidence, alluvial fills terminating in large deltas may form. In addition, it is under these conditions that turbidity currents appear to be most prevalent. Masses of sediment carried down the sides of subsiding troughs by such currents may spread out laterally along the trough axis, giving rise to very complex relationships among the sediments being deposited.

Tectonic "Blurring" of Sedimentary Environments

From the foregoing discussion, it may be inferred that as the degree of tectonism increases, the influence of the sedimentary environment diminishes, in part because the time interval is shortened within which the environment can operate on the inflowing detritus before burial. Thus, tectonism can be considered to exert a "blurring" effect on environmental interpretation. However, certain environments, for instance those within which deposits such as evaporites and euxinic shales are formed, leave their impress on the sediments in spite of the existence of high tectonic activity.

Figure 11-9 shows several environmental groups arranged in rows from

Fig. 11-9. Diagram showing the inferred clouding effect of contemporaneous tectonism on environmental reconstruction of a stratigraphic unit. [From Krumbein, Sloss, and Dapples (1949).]

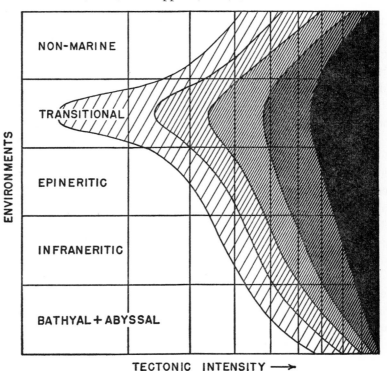

nonmarine at the top to deep-sea at the base. The horizontal axis is a logarithmic scale of tectonic intensity increasing to the right. The diagram may be thought of as a series of environments seen through an overlay of varying transparency. As tectonism increases, the transparency diminishes. This is, the sedimentary environment is obscured as tectonism increases, ultimately to a degree such that it may be impossible to discriminate completely between marine and nonmarine environments. The scale of tectonic intensity is made logarithmic to emphasize the wide range that exists between the stable shelf and eugeosynclinal environments.

The shaded areas in Figure 11-9 attempt to indicate the manner in which the sedimentary environment is obscured by increasing tectonism. It is often difficult to identify an exact shore line, even in some relatively stable shelf areas, because of its sensitive response to sea level changes. This transitional environment is commonly represented by a band of interfingering, intertonguing, and intergradational deposits that are difficult to sort out into individual environments. The blurring effect of tectonism associated with transitional environments in relatively stable situations widens out rather rapidly to include additional environmental groups as the degree of tectonism increases. The blurring effect associated with the high degrees of tectonism prevalent in very mobile eugeosynclinal belts and in marginal basins during their times of greatest tectonic activity may extend over the whole range of environmental conditions. As the diagram suggests, sedimentary environments are more readily distinguished in rocks deposited in areas of low tectonic intensity, mainly on stable and unstable shelves and within intracratonic basins.

Use of a continuous logarithmic scale in Figure 11-9 implies that no sharp "breaks" exist between degrees of tectonism displayed by cratonic and extracratonic elements. Marginal basins, with their great range of tectonism, support the inference that tectonism behaves as a continuous variable and extends over a wide range. In any event, there is no doubt that interpretation of the depositional environment of ancient sedimentary rocks is strongly affected by the degree of tectonism contemporaneous with deposition.

Tectono-environmental Classifications

A tectono-environmental classification is an integrated grouping of tectonic elements, lithologic associations, and sedimentary environments. The framework for such classifications can be developed by pairing each of the thumbnail sketches of sedimentary environments as given in Chapter 7 with each of the sketches of tectonic conditions given in the present chapter. Thus, the shallow marine environment may occur in any tectonic setting, but the kinds of sediments formed in the environment will depend in part on the tectonic conditions present.

Tercier (1940) was among the first to set up a classification of tectonic elements and sedimentary environments. Later, Pettijohn (1949) proposed a comprehensive grouping, and, in the same year, Krumbein, Sloss, and Dapples (1949) explored the subject. In 1952, Weeks presented a classification of sedimentary basins in terms of their relation to mobile belts or stable regions, as described earlier in this chapter. Later, Pettijohn (1957, p. 635) slightly modified his own earlier classification.

Tercier recognized five main classes of environment, as follows:

1. Areas of continental sedimentation on the continental platform. These include alluvial, lacustrine, glacial, and other environments.
2. Areas of **paralic sedimentation** (interfingered marine and continental) on the continental platform. These include alluvial, lagoonal, littoral, and shallow neritic environments.
3. Areas of shallow-marine sedimentation on the continental platform. These include mainly neritic environments, with a predominance of limestone deposition.
4. Areas of geosynclinal sedimentation, with typically thick and heterogeneous accumulation.
5. Areas of deep-sea sedimentation. These include abyssal environments remote from land.

Pettijohn's classification differs from Tercier's in its emphasis on the types of basins in which sediments accumulate. Three main classes are included: **basins of tectonic origin** (nonlinear, mildly negative; and linear, strongly negative); **basins of nontectonic origin** (gradational and volcanic); and "permanent" or deep-sea basins.

Both Tercier's and Pettijohn's classifications place the environments within their tectonic framework and thus include the effects of both tectonism and sedimentary environment on the resulting deposits. It is evident that Tercier's first three classes represent cratonic aspects of sedimentation, and that his fourth class is the typical geosynclinal phase. Pettijohn classifies intracratonic basins and geosynclines as tectonic basins. The abyssal depths of the ocean basins apparently represent suboceanic cratonic elements as well as the deeper troughs that are associated with tectogenes.

In the past decade numerous stratigraphic maps were made available through the literature. These maps add a new dimension to tectono-environmental classification by demonstrating that the problem of sorting out tectonism and environment in a three-dimensional volume of rock must include the consideration of areal variations in the geometry and composition of the rock body.

Thus, a much broader approach to tectono-environmental analysis and interpretation is made possible by examining stratigraphic units in terms of the types of sediments that are distributed vertically and laterally within them over their whole geographic extent. Improved mapping techniques, as illustrated by the wide variety of stratigraphic maps now in the literature, provide the basis for new concepts of stratigraphic models. Treatment of these models and of tectono-environmental classification beyond the historical introduction given here is deferred to Chapter 13.

SUPPLEMENTARY READINGS

1. Cady, W. M., 1950, Classification of geotectonic elements: Am. Geophys. Union, Trans., v. 31, p. 780–785. A very readable integration of several tectonic classifications treated in terms of four tectonic stages.
2. Dunbar, C. O. and Rodgers, J., 1957, Principles of stratigraphy: New York, John Wiley & Sons, Inc. Chapter 18 presents a well expressed integration of the classification of tectonic elements in relation to sedimentation, with some emphasis on classical geosynclinal theory.
3. Glaessner, M. F. and Teichert, C., 1947, Geosynclines: a fundamental concept in geology: Am. Jour. Sci., v. 245, p. 464–482; 571–591. This paper marks an important stage in the analysis of geosynclinal theory at the time when present concepts were developing.
4. Kay, M., 1951, North American geosynclines: Geol. Soc. Am., Memoir 48. This is the definitive publication on modern concepts regarding geosynclines, excellently illustrated with numerous examples.
5. Knopf, A., 1960, Analysis of some recent geosynclinal theory: Am. Jour. Sci., Bradley Volume, v. 258-A, p. 126–136. Concise but penetrating analysis of present geosynclinal theory.
6. Pettijohn, F. J., 1957, Sedimentary rocks: (2nd edition) New York, Harper & Brothers. Chapter 13 discusses relations between sedimentary environments and tectonics.
7. Schuchert, C., 1923, Sites and nature of the North American geosynclines: Geol. Soc. America Bull., v. 34, p. 151–230. This is the definitive paper on the classical approach to geosynclines.
8. Weller, J. M., 1960, Stratigraphic principles and practice: New York, Harper & Brothers. Chapter 9 contains a well organized and detailed discussion of tectonic elements and geosynclinal theory.

CHAPTER 12

Stratigraphic Maps

INTRODUCTION

PERHAPS the single most important device for communicating geologic information is a map. The essential feature for constructing a map is a series of observations made at specific geographic locations. For a topographic map, the observations are elevations of the land surface above or below sea level. In areal geology maps, the observations include the kind of rock exposed at the given locality, the elevation of the outcrop, the thickness, dip, and strike of the beds, and the stratigraphic position of the rock. For a structure contour map, the observation at each geographic point is the elevation of the top of some specific correlated stratigraphic horizon.

In almost all geologic maps, observations are available only in outcrops, boreholes, quarries, roadcuts, and the like. Hence, interpolation is used for filling in the "blank spots." In some instances, the feature being mapped is observable at all points on the surface. Theoretically this is true for a topographic map, though even here certain key positions (bench marks) are used for elevation control, and contours along valleys may in part be sketched in, although aerial photographs permit essentially continuous contouring.

Subsurface data are expressed in terms of (1) known geographic locations (the well sites); (2) known stratigraphic markers; (3) known depths below the surface (which may be converted to elevations with respect to sea level); and (4) known rock composition at the depth of interest. Data for subsurface structure maps, which require only the first three items, became available fairly early in the history of oil and gas exploration. As a result, subsurface structure maps came into early use, and are perhaps the most commonly used of subsurface maps. Maps showing the composition of rocks in stratigraphic units appeared as a later development.

This chapter is concerned with the construction and interpretation of maps that are useful in stratigraphic analysis. A **stratigraphic map** may be defined as one that shows the areal distribution, configuration, or aspect of a stratigraphic unit or surface. Kay (1945) distinguishes between stratigraphic and paleogeographic maps. The former are maps involving a span of geologic time, and the latter represent a moment in the past.

The preparation of stratigraphic maps requires the collection and organization of large amounts of data. Rocks penetrated by the drill must be correlated with outcrop sections so that the maps will be based on the same stratigraphic surface or unit throughout. Stratigraphic correlation is therefore of basic importance in preparing data for map compilation.

The finished map may represent only a single stage in complete stratigraphic analysis. Individual maps may show the areal distribution of structural, lithologic, or stratigraphic characteristics, which provide a basis for reconstruction of the paleogeology, paleogeography, structural history, and historical geology of the unit under study.

ORGANIZATION OF MAP DATA

The fundamental element of stratigraphic mapping is a stratigraphic horizon, commonly called a "key bed," or "marker bed." The horizon is used in preparing subsurface structure maps, paleogeology maps, and others that emphasize the nature or attitude of a **plane** or **surface.** Other stratigraphic maps show attributes of a **three-dimensional body of rock,** and hence require the selection of two horizons, which serve as top and bottom of the stratigraphic unit being mapped.

Table 12-1 lists the kinds of horizons or key beds which may be used in stratigraphic mapping. They are arranged in three classes, and include the lithologic characteristics of the section, biologic attributes, and discontinuities (unconformities) that may be present. Lithologic key beds are most commonly used because of their relative ease of identification in outcrop section, cutting logs, or electric logs.

It is of fundamental importance that the selected horizons or key beds be correctly correlated over the area to be mapped. The purpose of most stratigraphic maps is to show conditions within specified intervals of geologic time, or during some geologic "instant." It is evident that miscorrelation of

TABLE 12-1. STRATIGRAPHIC MARKERS

LITHOLOGIC KEY BEDS	BIOLOGIC MARKERS
Thin limestone bed	Local-range zone
Thin sandstone or conglomerate	Assemblage zone
Coal or lignite bed	STRUCTURAL DISCONTINUITIES
Bentonite (volcanic ash) bed	Angular unconformity
Heavy mineral zone	Disconformity
Insoluble residue zone	Diastem
Phosphate pebble zone	
Characteristic electric log "kick"	
Seismic reflection surface	

the key beds may result in preparation of a map which cuts across the interval to be studied. In general, correlation of the key bed is accomplished by such criteria as its lithologic identity, position in sequence, identity of the interval, and other methods described in Chapter 10.

In compiling data for the map, all available outcrop and subsurface information in the area of interest is assembled. A base map appropriate to the scope of the study is selected or drawn, and the control points are plotted on the base map. The information from each well or measured section is summarized at the control points, and contour lines or other suitable symbols are drawn on the map to bring out the attributes being studied.

Figure 12-1 shows, in summarized form, the data needed for preparing stratigraphic maps. On the right is the base map, with each control point—borehole, outcrop, quarry, or other exposure—numbered, and with its geographic coordinates specified in some manner. The use of U and V coordinates, as shown on the map, will be discussed later. The essential point is that the geographic location of each observation point must be known. On the left in Figure 12-1 is a measured section with its top and bottom elevation indicated, and with conventional symbols for the rocks in the section. This basic diagram will be referred to often as the specific kinds of stratigraphic maps are discussed in turn.

Fig. 12-1. Hypothetical measured section and base map. The coordinates (U_1, V_1) locate the control point illustrated by the measured section. [From Krumbein (1960).]

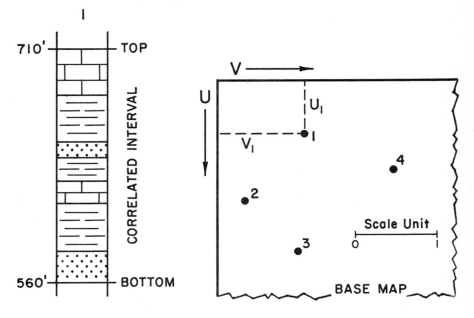

In areas of marked crustal shortening, the present positions of tectonic and other features differ from their original positions. For such areas a **palinspastic base map** is prepared, which restores present-day features to the positions they occupied at some designated time in the geologic past. Detailed discussion of such maps is given by Kay (1945), and Figure 11-5 illustrates such a map for presenting the paleogeography of part of Ordovician time.

CLASSIFICATION OF STRATIGRAPHIC MAPS

Stratigraphic units have many properties that relate to the geometry, lithologic composition, faunal content, and fluid content of the rock body concerned. In this chapter, interest is focused on certain mappable attributes of the stratigraphic unit, especially the geometric and compositional features that can be shown on contour-type maps. Emphasis here is accordingly limited to the areal distribution, structure, thickness, and lithologic composition of the three-dimensional rock body. This permits the development of mapping principles that are related to geometry and lithology, and which are closely paralleled by mapping techniques for other stratigraphic attributes—such as faunal relationships—as will be pointed out as the chapter develops.

Table 12-2 is a condensed classification of stratigraphic maps, which indicates the large variety of specific map types that have been developed. The first class of maps concerns the **external geometry** of the three-dimensional rock body as a whole. Here are included the widely used structure–contour and isopach maps discussed in the following sections of this chapter. In contrast to geometry, the delineation of lithologic composition is more complex in that it involves analysis of the kinds of rocks present, their several thicknesses, and their vertical arrangement within the rock body. Hence, though geometry can be displayed with a few maps, it requires a wide variety of maps to display all the details of lithologic composition.

Table 12-2 subdivides compositional maps into three classes. The first subclass includes maps that display the gross areal variations of lithology—commonly referred to as **conventional facies maps.** These include percentage maps, ratio maps, and other types described later. The second subclass includes maps that show the positions, thicknesses, and vertical sequence of beds. These are **vertical variability maps,** and though shown under composition, they also depict the internal geometry of the stratigraphic unit. The third subclass includes "**internal maps**," which display selected features of particular beds or lithologic types within the stratigraphic unit. Heavy mineral composition of a basal sandstone, for example, can be shown on

TABLE 12-2. CLASSIFICATION OF STRATIGRAPHIC MAPS

A EXTERNAL GEOMETRY OF ROCK BODY
    Thickness and areal extent: *isopach map*
    Attitude of upper surface: *structure contour map*

B COMPOSITION OF ROCK BODY
    I Gross areal variation (Conventional facies) maps
        Thickness of a single rock type: *isolith map**
        Relative amount of a single rock type: *percentage map*
        Ratio of thickness between rock types: *ratio map*
        Relations among three components: *triangle ratio map, entropy map, entropy-ratio map, facies-departure map*
    II Vertical-variability maps
        Position, thickness, and number of occurrences of specific rock types: *limestone center-of-gravity map, limestone mean thickness map, number of limestones map*
        Degree of vertical alternations among beds: *interval-entropy map*
    III Internal geometry and composition
        Internal textures, structures, and composition of selected beds in the stratigraphic unit: *sandstone sorting map, cross-bedding map, heavy mineral map, trace element map*

C DERIVED, INTEGRATIVE, AND INTERPRETATIVE MAPS
    Paleotectonic maps
    Rock volume maps
    Rate-of-change maps
    Trend-surface maps

---

* See qualifications on use of this term in the discussion of isolith maps.

such a map. These maps may also depict internal geometry and composition, though the selection of the beds to be mapped in both the second and third subclasses is commonly made on a lithologic basis, hence they are listed as subclasses under composition.

The fourth category in Table 12-2 represents maps that may be prepared from any of those listed in the preceding classes. The paleotectonic map is an **integrative map,** prepared by combining features of the isopach map and one or more facies maps. The rock-volume map is an example of a derived map, obtained by mathematical treatment of the isopach map or of selected conventional facies maps. The terms integrative and derived are used in a descriptive sense, rather than with respect to the mathematical or statistical procedures used in their preparation.

The several types of map in Table 12-2 are not defined in detail at this stage, inasmuch as the table is primarily an outline of the remainder of this chapter. Structure–contour maps are the first to be considered, because they are perhaps the most familiar to readers of this text.

STRUCTURE CONTOUR MAPS

A **structure contour map** shows the geometric configuration of a rock surface by contour lines passed through points of equal elevation above or below a selected datum. The datum commonly used is sea level, and the elevation of the key bed above or below this datum is indicated at each control point on the map.

Structure contour maps may include both surface and subsurface data. The upper part of Figure 12-2 shows a cross section of several key beds, extending from the outcrop to the subsurface. As indicated, some observation points are located in the outcrop area, and others are seen in wells. The position of the key bed with respect to the datum is computed from the known elevation of the well mouth and the depth to the key bed. In outcrop, the elevation of the key bed is taken from a topographic map or by planetable.

The lower part of Figure 12-2 is the contour map from which the upper cross section was taken. The map scale and contour interval selected for a structure contour map depend on the purposes of the study, the accuracy of the data, and on the spacing of available control points. Maps for broad regional studies may be made on a scale of 1:1,000,000 or less, with contour intervals of 100 feet or more. Detailed maps, such as are used in oil exploration, may be on scales as large as 1:10,000, with contour intervals of 10 feet or less.

In terms of Figure 12-1, the structure contour map is prepared by plotting the elevation of the top of the stratigraphic unit at each control point on the map. The structure contours are drawn through the resulting field of numbers in one of three ways (Bishop, 1960, p. 45). In **mechanical contouring,** interpolation is performed by distributing the differences in elevation arithmetically between any two points. **Equal-space contouring** maintains uniform slope on the map (within the limits of available data), and may thus show highs or lows in places where no actual data are available. **Interpretative contouring** consists in giving a "grain" to the map in accordance with known or inferred structural or other trends in the mapped area.

Bishop gives an example of each method of contouring, and points out that if sufficient control is present, mechanical contouring is perhaps the most accurate. When data are limited, interpretative contouring is probably most satisfactory. Though contouring methods are mentioned here under structure maps, the same principles apply to any kind of contour map in the classification of Table 12-2.

The interpretation of structure contour maps is relatively straightforward.

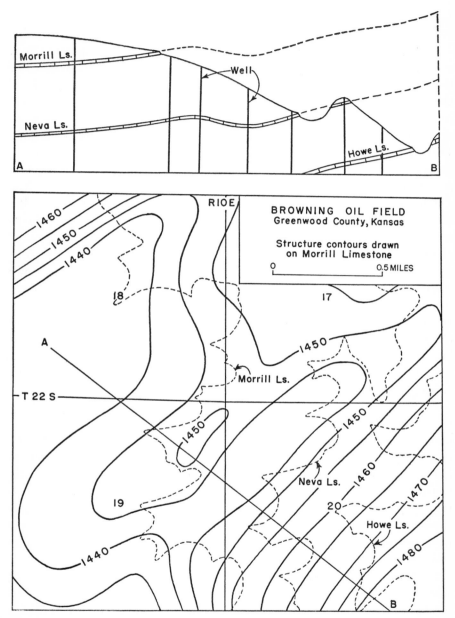

Fig. 12-2. Structure contour map, showing relation of structure contours to outcrop patterns. The upper cross section shows the projection of the contours on the Morrill Limestone beyond its outcrop edge through the use of lower key beds and known intervals. [After Bass (1936).]

Domes and other anticlinal features are shown as "highs," which are closed contours of higher elevation than surrounding points. Synclines and basins are the opposite.

Monoclinal structures or flexures are indicated by more or less parallel structure contour lines increasing or decreasing in elevation in a given direction. Faults are shown by the superposition of contour lines along a linear trend, commonly with some offset of the contours on both sides of the fault zone.

The magnitude of a structure is expressed in terms of its closure and areal extent. The closure is read from the map by noting the elevation difference within the largest closed contour which surrounds the structure.

The spacing of the structure contour lines gives an indication of the steepness of the fold or flexure. As with topographic contour maps, the spacing of the lines is inversely proportional to the steepness of the slope.

Structure contour maps are numerous in the geologic literature. The *Bulletin of the American Association of Petroleum Geologists* includes many examples which accompany descriptions of oil fields. The *Geologic Folios* of the U.S. Geological Survey commonly include structure contours on the economic geology maps. The *Tectonic Map of the United States* (1961) is a regional map of dominant structural elements, expressed by widespread key beds in each structural province.

ISOPACH MAPS

An **isopach map** shows the varying thicknesses of a stratigraphic unit by contour lines (isopachs) drawn through points of equal thickness. Isopach maps require two horizons or key beds, one at the top, and the other at the bottom of the stratigraphic unit.

The upper and lower horizons for an isopach map may be selected on several bases. The interval between two prominent unconformities is commonly used. Such an isopach map furnishes information on structural changes in the area during the time interval between the two unconformities. In other instances, the limits may be selected within conformable groups of rocks, to emphasize contemporaneous tectonism in the depositional site.

Isopach maps may be prepared directly from two structure contour maps by subtracting the elevations of the lower surface from those of the upper surface at each control point, and drawing contours of equal interval between the two surfaces. Isopach maps prepared in this manner are also called **convergence maps.** Preparation and use of these maps are discussed by Levorsen (1927).

Once the stratigraphic unit for an isopach map is selected, the mapping procedure involves essentially the same steps as the structure contour map. The observed thickness is plotted at each control point, and lines of equal thickness are drawn through the points. The vertical interval between isopachs may vary from several hundred feet on a regional map, to intervals as small as 10 feet for detailed studies of thin stratigraphic units.

Inasmuch as the isopach map can be considered as a type of paleostructure map, the contouring method used (mechanical, equal-spacing, or interpretive) is commonly the same as that used in the corresponding structure map of the same unit. However, when the isopach map is used as a record of tectonism contemporaneous with accumulation of the stratigraphic unit, the "grain" of the isopach map may not be related to present structural trends. An isopach map of a Paleozoic unit, for example, may not agree with present-day structure, which may have been superimposed on the rocks during the Laramide orogeny.

With reference to Figure 12-1 again, note that the data for isopach maps are obtained by subtracting the elevation or depth of one boundary from that of the other.

Figure 12-3 is an isopach map of Mississippian rocks in the Williston Basin. This map shows the typical circular or ovate pattern of isopach lines as they reflect subsidence contemporary with deposition in a major cratonic basin. The map also brings out the distinction between a subsiding basin and its adjacent shelf area. The break between the basin and the shelf is commonly selected in terms of the rate of change in the spacing of the isopach lines. The change from slow to rapid subsidence during deposition is at a maximum where the isopach lines are most closely spaced. This zone of closely spaced lines is commonly designated as the **tectonic hinge**, operative during deposition of the stratigraphic unit.

An isopach map differs from other types of contour maps in having its datum at the top of the stratigraphic unit. A topographic contour map, made into a relief model, has a flat base representing sea level, with elevations rising above it. A model of an isopach map has a flat top, with varying thicknesses extending downward from it.

This reversed convention arises from the fact that the top of the interval is the first penetrated by the drill. The upper horizon or key bed is used as the datum in laying out the well logs, and the changing thicknesses project downward from that datum to the lower key bed. By this convention, the isopach map directly shows the structural attitude of the lower marker with respect to the upper horizon taken as a level datum plane.

Figure 12-4, adapted from Levorsen (1927) shows a cross section in eastern Oklahoma arranged on a sea-level datum. The section shows the

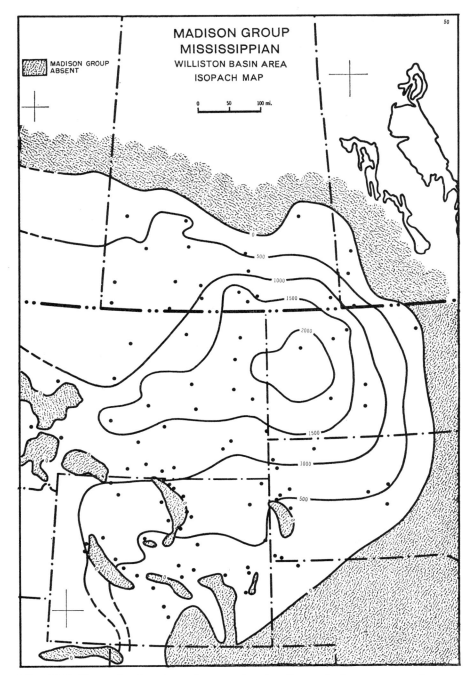

Fig. 12-3. Example of an isopach map, showing the ovate form common to many interior basins. [Adapted from Sloss et al. (1960).]

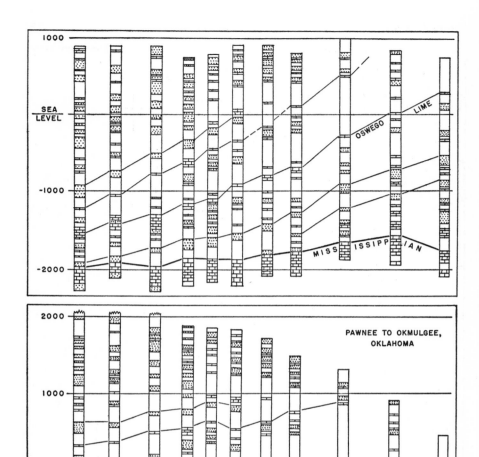

Fig. 12-4. Cross section of Pennsylvanian rocks in eastern Oklahoma. (*Top*) A
structural cross section on a sea-level datum. (*Bottom*) A stratigraphic
cross section, in which the Oswego Limestone is used as a datum, showing the structure of Mississippian rocks at the time the Oswego Limestone was deposited. [Adapted from Levorsen (1927).]

442

present structural attitude of the rocks. The lower cross section uses the Oswego lime as a datum and accordingly shows the structure of the underlying Mississippian rocks at the time the Oswego lime was deposited.

It is apparent that isopach maps have an advantage over cross sections, in that they show the same effects areally. Moreover, by selecting a series of datum planes and preparing a succession of isopach maps, the structural growth of an area can be developed in detail.

It is common practice to restrict subsurface isopach mapping to the area within the limits of cover on the upper marker bed. If the Missourian rocks of the Midcontinent are mapped this way, the map ends where the top of the Missourian appears along the outcrop. By using this convention, the stripping effects of post-Pennsylvanian erosion do not enter the map.

An alternative method is to map the present observed thickness of the unit, regardless of its position under or beyond cover. Such maps have the advantage of showing the complete factual picture of present-day distribution of the stratigraphic unit. On these maps, the zero isopach is the outcrop edge of the bottom of the unit. A line marking the limit of cover may be drawn on the map to indicate the inner edge of the outcrop belt.

In the subsurface, the zero isopach is traced through well data to outline the complete area of occurrence of the unit. In the outcrop area, the zero isopach may be drawn to include outliers, but buried outliers are difficult to locate except in areas of intensive drilling.

The occurrence of zero areas within the main map area presents special problems. In some instances, these "holes" are known to be due to postdepositional uplift and erosion. The absence of some Paleozoic rocks in the Big Horn Mountains, the Black Hills, and other places is explained on this basis, the "holes" being a result of post-Laramide erosion. Where the evidence for erosion is clear, the isopach lines may be carried through the zero areas.

In other instances, the zero area occurs entirely in the subsurface, and the problem becomes one of deciding whether it represents a site of nondeposition, or of postdepositional erosion. Relative spacing of the isopachs and changes in lithology toward the zero edge provide some criteria for solving the problem. Table 12-7, discussed later, lists these criteria.

Interpretation of Isopach Maps

For structural interpretation of isopach maps, it is convenient to select horizons or key beds of sufficiently widespread extent so that the assumption of horizontal datum planes may be made. For isopach maps based on the interval between two widespread angular unconformities, it may be assumed that each unconformity was essentially a plane surface at the time it was developed. In similar manner, an isopach interval with an unconformity at the base and a conformable thin limestone with shallow-water fauna at the top permits the assumption that the surface of the limestone was essentially a horizontal plane at the time of deposition.

An important part of isopach map interpretation includes restoration of the original depositional edge of the stratigraphic unit. In some instances, the present-day zero isopach may represent the shore of the ancient sea which deposited the formations. More commonly, perhaps, the outcrop limit and much of the subsurface limit represent eroded edges.

The problem of extrapolating the isopach map to its original depositional edge is difficult. To a large extent, it depends upon understanding of the sedimentary facies now present near the zero line, and their probable placement with respect to the ancient strand line. As with other aspects of isopach interpretation, combined maps of thickness and facies provide integrated data which permit more critical evaluation of the evidence.

An isopach map that is based directly on two unconformities shows the structure of the lower unconformity at the time the upper unconformity was developed, as has been mentioned. In similar manner, an isopach map based on an interval with a conformable top indicates the structure of the lower surface at the time of deposition.

A series of isopach maps based on successive stratigraphic units provides fundamental data on the sequence of structural changes that occurred in the area. It becomes possible, with such a set of maps, to narrow the times of deformation to specific stratigraphic intervals. The detailed structural history is of basic importance in oil exploration, inasmuch as it sheds light on possible movements and trapping of oil in response to structural controls.

A second important basis for interpreting isopach maps is the evaluation of areas of maximum subsidence during any interval of sedimentation. An isopach map prepared on a conformable interval with no unconformities in the section expresses the relative subsidence of the depositional site during the stratigraphic interval. Demonstration of the relation requires selection of upper and lower key beds or horizons which can be assumed to have been horizontal depositional surfaces at the time of their formation.

Criteria for Contemporaneous Subsidence

Isopach maps are widely used for the study of subsidence contemporaneous with deposition, as well as of local structural growth during deposition. Recognition of the importance of isopach maps in these respects is relatively recent, however. The commonly noted accumulation of sand on structure, grading laterally to shale, was formerly thought to result from the accumulation of sand in shallow water, with mud deposited in adjacent deeper areas. During subsequent burial, the greater compaction of the mud would then steepen dips away from the sand, developing a structural high. Many of the local structures in eastern Kansas and Oklahoma were explained on this basis.

Recognition that local structural growth also occurred during deposition, and added its effects to those of differential compaction, represented a major advance in the understanding of the relations between tectonism and sedimentation. Demonstration of such growth was made by McCoy (1934), who assembled a large amount of data on the subject and presented arguments for and against differential compaction as the main explanation for midcontinent structures. McCoy showed that contemporaneous structural growth could effectively account for many of the observed thickenings and thinnings associated with sand and shale bodies in the stratigraphic section.

Figure 12-5 is an example from McCoy, to show the reasoning involved. The cross section shows the intervals in the El Dorado anticline. Prominent structural movement occurred throughout pre-Pennsylvanian time, as indicated by the section below the Cherokee. Adjustment above the unconformity occurred during the deposition of the Cherokee, and structural growth ceased during the Marmaton. Between the top of the Lansing and the end of Oread deposition, growth of the structure lessened the interval by some 50 feet, according to McCoy. Practically no structural movement occurred from the top of the Oread to the top of the Topeka, but thickness on structure decreases about 40 feet from the top of the Topeka to the top of the Burlingame. The interval from Burlingame to Cottonwood is practically uniform, indicating a time of quiescence.

McCoy concluded that the El Dorado anticline had numerous periods of development and quiescence. Moreover, the zones of thinning are not located in the principal shale deposits, where they should be if compaction accounted for the structure.

McCoy also concluded that compaction is less important in initiating structures than in accentuating those developed by other means. In general, structural growth occurs when a local area subsides less rapidly than its surroundings, maintaining shallower water on the crest, and commonly accumulating thinner sediments as a result. Since the advent of electric logs, evidence for local differential subsidence has greatly expanded. Isopach maps of thin intervals, based on electric logs from closely spaced wells, are used extensively in the oil industry as guides to local structural growth associated with buried salt domes, normal faults, and other diastrophic events. Such studies shed light on the relation between periods of growth and the movement or trapping of oil and gas.

The demonstration, in local areas, of subsidence contemporaneous with deposition requires detailed study of closely spaced data, as stated. The case

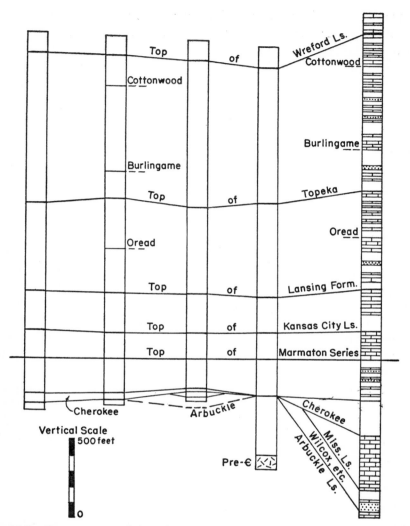

Fig. 12-5. Cross section of the El Dorado anticline and associated structures in Butler County, Kansas. [Adapted from McCoy (1934).]

for regional contemporaneous subsidence is more readily demonstrable than for the local structures. Kay (1945) showed that there are three broad criteria for the evaluation of contemporaneous subsidence in intracratonic basins and other regional elements.

The first criterion involves study of the present structural configuration of the base of the selected stratigraphic unit. The base of any stratigraphic unit in the Pennsylvanian, for example, shows some areas of synclinal downwarp, others of anticlinal uplift, and still others of essentially horizontal attitude.

The question arises whether the present structures are entirely the result of postdepositional warping. If not, how much of the present attitude of the beds may be attributed to subsidence or uplift during sedimentation? A related question is whether the observed variations in thickness of the unit are due to greater accumulation in areas of subsidence, to deposition on buried hills, to compaction after burial, or to stripping of upwarped portions.

Answers to these questions are obtained by consideration of the factors discussed above. For stratigraphic units with conformable upper surface, the regional effects of buried topography and compaction may be relatively minor, and the question resolves itself into evaluation of hiatuses in the section.

Kay's second criterion concerns the form of the lower datum surface during the progress of sedimentation. If the foregoing tests show that contemporary subsidence was present, it permits the statement that, during part of the time, at least, the bottom surface of the stratigraphic unit was warped down during sedimentation.

The third criterion developed by Kay relates to the attitude of the upper surface of the stratigraphic unit during sedimentation. The upper surface of a conformable interval is the depositional surface. The question is raised whether the water was uniformly shallow during sedimentation or increased in depth toward the basin center. Several lines of evidence are available. Bathymetric indicators among fossils and evidences of shallow-water deposition (mud cracks and others) permit some specific answers.

Paleogeomorphologic Maps

An additional important use of isopach maps is for the reconstruction of the geomorphology of some selected stratigraphic horizon. For this purpose, an isopach map is made of a thin stratigraphic interval that rests on a major unconformity, or on an eroded surface of appreciable relief, and which is topped by a conformable key bed within a vertical distance of one or two hundred feet above the unconformity. When such a thin stratigraphic interval can be mapped over a fairly extensive area, the major physiographic features of the unconformable surface are commonly revealed. Cuestas marking the edges of dipping strata are sometimes disclosed by this method, as may be the major drainage pattern of the original eroded landscape. An excellent discussion of paleodrainage patterns, including a summary of mapping methods, is given by Andresen (1962).

Other Uses of Isopach Maps

Isopach maps are commonly used as base maps for lithofacies studies. The isopachs are drawn as relatively heavy lines over which the facies patterns are superimposed with lines of lighter weight. When used in this manner, the relationship between the underlying three dimensional geometry of the stratigraphic unit and the pattern of areal variation in lithologic composition are readily visualized.

The fact that isopach maps may be used to express paleostructure, to indicate the degree of subsidence that occurred during accumulation of a sedimentary deposit, and even utilized as paleogeomorphological maps, indicates the wide range of usefulness of this kind of map. The isopach concept has also been applied to compositional maps to show the thickness of individual rock components in stratigraphic units, as treated in a later section of this chapter.

PALEOGEOLOGIC MAPS

An important advance in stratigraphic mapping was made when geologists realized that it was possible to map the distribution of rock formations on a buried unconformable surface. For example, in many large areas, rocks of Pennsylvanian age are separated by a major unconformity from earlier rocks. It is possible, figuratively speaking, to strip off all rocks of Pennsylvanian age or later, in some area of interest, and to map the areal geology that must have been exposed when the Pennsylvanian seas transgressed the pre-Pennsylvanian erosion surface.

Such maps, called **paleogeologic maps,** were introduced into the literature of geology by Levorsen (1933). Paleogeologic maps are important in the search for oil and gas, inasmuch as they indicate the ages and kinds of rocks that lie beneath major unconformities. As subsurface mapping techniques developed further, it became conventional to examine not only the areal distribution of stratigraphic units beneath an unconformity, but to examine the kinds of rocks and the ages of rock bodies both beneath and above any given stratigraphic unit, whether an unconformity is involved or not. Maps that display the areal geology beneath a stratigraphic unit of interest are commonly called **subcrop maps.** The term subcrop map may be considered a generalization of the term paleogeologic map. In similar fashion, the stratigraphic units that lie above a given rock body may also be mapped. In a sense, such maps are looked at as though from below, and the term **"worm's eye map"** was early applied to these maps. More formally, the term **supercrop map** has come into relatively common use.

Inasmuch as both subcrop and supercrop maps communicate information regarding the geometric relations of a stratigraphic unit to other rock bodies below and above it, full analysis of the three dimensional implications of any stratigraphic unit requires that maps of these external geometrical relations be made in addition to structure contour and isopach maps. Comparison of the areal geology of the subcrop map with the thickness trends in isopach maps of subsequent units provides important information on times and places of regional deformation. In a series of maps that represent several successive stratigraphic units, knowledge of the subcrop and supercrop relations of each succeeding unit is of great practical significance in evaluating the economic potential of each unit.

Data for the construction of paleogeologic maps include identification of the stratigraphic units at the datum surface. In a pre-Pennsylvanian paleogeologic map, the required data are the units immediately below the base of the Pennsylvanian rocks. These data are plotted at the control points, and a geologic map is drawn by indicating the lines of contact among the formations or other stratigraphic units present. When properly drawn, a paleogeologic map shows the distribution and structural attitude of the rocks in the same manner as an areal geology map of the present-day surface.

Figure 12-6 is a pre-Pennsylvanian paleogeologic map that shows large areas occupied by Mississippian rocks in Kansas as well as a broad belt of pre-Cambrian rocks along the Sioux Uplift. In addition, small areas of pre-Cambrian rocks occur along the Nemaha Ridge and in central Kansas, the latter too small to be shown.

Paleogeologic maps may be terminated at the limit of cover, to avoid complications of subsequent erosion. In Figure 12-6, the limits of Pennsylvanian rocks control the areas shown in pattern.

The paleogeologic map indicates that Mississippian rocks had been stripped from large areas before Pennsylvanian rocks were laid down. It appears likely that Mississippian rocks occurred over much or all of the area now occupied by Pennsylvanian rocks, inasmuch as the Mississippian is composed dominantly of limestone to its edges. This suggests that the Mississippian shore line lay beyond the present edge of the system.

The areal geology of the pre-Pennsylvanian surface indicates that structural movements occurred between the close of Mississippian and the beginning of Pennsylvanian. Uplift along the Nemaha Ridge developed local, sharp, angular unconformities between the top of the Mississippian and the base of the Pennsylvanian. These buried structures, not reflected directly by the present attitude of Pennsylvanian rocks, are important oil reservoirs.

In his paleogeologic studies of broad regional unconformities, Levorsen showed that successive pairs of unconformities include "layers of geology"

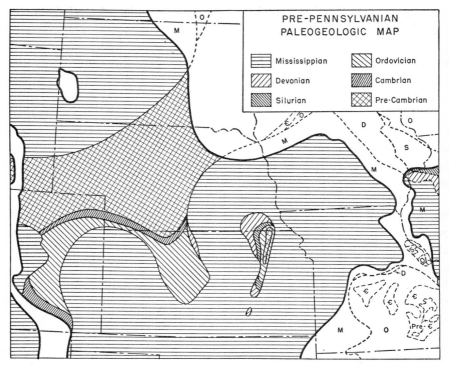

Fig. 12-6. Sub-Pennsylvanian paleogeologic map. The pre-Pennsylvanian rocks are shown in pattern under Pennsylvanian cover, and are sketched beyond the eroded edge. The strong influence of the Sioux Uplift (Transcontinental Arch) in Nebraska during pre-Pennsylvanian time is well shown.

between them which differ from each other in structure and lithologic content. He showed that important structural differences occur beneath the Mississippian overlap of the Midcontinent and under the great Cretaceous overlap in numerous areas. In 1943, Levorsen emphasized the importance of such layers in the search for petroleum because of the widespread occurrence of oil beneath major unconformities in many regions.

Levorsen (1960) has greatly expanded the topic of paleogeologic maps in his book on the subject, and further development of topics touched upon here can be found in his more complete presentation.

FACIES MAPS

A **facies map** shows the areal variation in aspect of a stratigraphic unit. The **aspect** of a stratigraphic unit at any point of observation, as in a borehole or outcrop section, is some observable lithologic or biologic attribute of the section at that control point. Facies maps based on lithologic attributes are **lithofacies maps,** and these will be emphasized here. This emphasis reflects the fact that the amount of lithologic data greatly exceeds the faunal data available on stratigraphic units. Virtually every type of lithofacies map can be paralleled by a corresponding **biofacies map** based on faunal observations.

No single number or symbol that can be shown on a map completely expresses all the compositional aspects of a stratigraphic section. The variety of rock types present, their repeated positions in the stratigraphic interval, and the varying thicknesses of the beds from top to bottom of the section present complex interrelationships that require maps especially designed to bring out features of importance in a given study.

Common practice consists in using an isopach map as a base for showing the distribution of facies. As pointed out, the stratigraphic units used are normally defined by the kinds of marker beds shown on Table 12-1. Some facies maps, however, are made on arbitrary segments of a stratigraphic unit, such as a series of 500-foot intervals above or below a definable datum surface. Such maps are called **slice maps** (Forgotson, 1954, p. 2479), and because they have equal thickness throughout, there is no isopach base. An illustration of such a slice map is given in the next chapter (Figure 13-26).

In most facies studies a series of maps is prepared, each of which communicates information on selected aspects of the mapped unit. A facies map that shows the areal variation in the percentage of sand in a stratigraphic unit communicates no information whatever regarding whether the sand occurs as a single body or many, or whether it is near the top or bottom of the unit. If the positional implications of aspect are important to a given study, maps that communicate this information must be prepared.

Several kinds of lithofacies maps may be distinguished, as brought out in Table 12-2. The distinction between the first two classes under (B) in the table can be illustrated by showing the manner in which lithologic data are compiled from well logs or outcrop sections in these two instances.

Figure 12-7 shows a stratigraphic section with sand, shale, and other rock types distributed through it. Assume that the sand is of immediate interest. In preparing a conventional facies map, the total amount of sand in the section is obtained by adding the thicknesses of each sand occurrence and expressing the result as a total footage. This is equivalent to combining all the sand into a single aggregate as indicated by the arrow pointing to the left in Figure 12-7, thus the position and identity of the individual sand bodies are lost. This value represents one aspect of the measured section, and it may be used to prepare conventional maps of sand thickness, percentage of sandstone in the section, or various sand content ratios.

For vertical variability maps, the original positions and thicknesses of

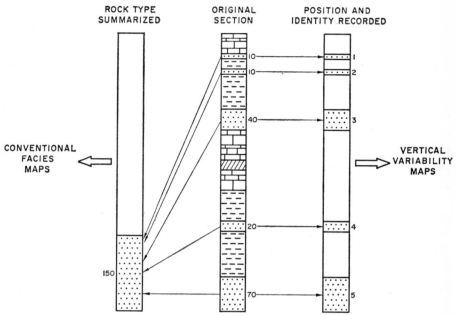

Fig. 12-7. Example of a stratigraphic section, showing methods of compiling sandstone data for stratigraphic maps. [From Krumbein and Libby (1957).]

individual sandstones in the section are maintained, as shown by the arrow leading to the right in Figure 12-7. Preservation of the sandstone identities permits preparation of maps showing the number of sandstones in the section, the average thickness of the sandstone, and their average position in the section. The last two items are summary numbers, but the position and thickness of the individual beds must be recorded to obtain these summarized values.

The distinction between conventional facies maps and vertical variability maps is not always clear-cut. For practical purposes, vertical variability maps may be thought of as facies maps that depend primarily for their preparation on knowledge of the individual positions and thicknesses of selected rock types or other features of interest, such as sandstone beds or porous zones in carbonate sections. Conventional facies maps, on the other hand, may be prepared from data that express the total thicknesses of the several rock types in the section, regardless of the position or thickness of individual beds. The principal distinction between the two map types is that vertical variability maps communicate information about the internal geometry of the stratigraphic unit in terms of some component or property of interest.

Conventional Lithofacies Maps

Lithofacies maps became relatively common in the geologic literature during the 1950's. In addition, the United States Geological Survey has published facies maps for the Jurassic and Triassic Systems in the United States (McKee, 1956, 1959); and Sloss, Dapples, and Krumbein (1960) prepared an atlas of lithofacies maps that includes more than 100 examples. The earliest forms of lithofacies maps may be traced back to the beginning of the present century (Grabau, 1913). In earlier maps, generalized patterns of shading were used to show the areal characteristics of the stratigraphic unit, such as its marine or continental nature.

The importance of contrasting clastic and nonclastic components contained in a section was recognized and emphasized by Ver Wiebe in 1930. In 1942, King published a series of lithofacies maps on the Permian of west Texas, which contrasted areas of typical sedimentary associations. One of these is described later in this chapter. Read and Wood (1947) published a contour-type map based on the ratio of clastic to nonclastic components in the Pennsylvanian of New Mexico. Krumbein (1948) defined the clastic ratio and sand–shale ratio for mapping purposes, and applied the conventional 100-percent triangle to facies studies.

During the 1950's the literature on facies mapping expanded rapidly, owing to the introduction of numerous new mapping techniques and principles of map interpretation; and as a result of the application of statistical and mathematical analysis to map data. Specific references are cited as this chapter develops.

Most stratigraphic maps prepared today are probably based on numerical data for preparation of contour-type maps. Structure maps and isopach maps are contour-type maps, but the use of contours to display lithologic composition is a later development. This does not imply that qualitative pattern maps are of no value. Sometimes the more subtle gradations in stratigraphic aspect can be more effectively shown by patterns than by contour lines. However, when used for studies of rates of change in lithologic composition or for predictive purposes, the contour-type map is superior. Some of these uses are discussed in this chapter under (C) in Table 12-2.

In preparing conventional facies maps, the measurements made at each well or outcrop section are assembled in tabular form, as shown in Table 12-3. The compilation sheet has columns for recording the total thickness of the stratigraphic unit, as well as the thickness of each rock type, individually or assembled as end members. If percentages or ratios are to be computed by desk calculator, additional columns may be added for recording the

TABLE 12-3. DATA SHEET FOR LITHOLOGIC ANALYSIS

Stratigraphic Unit _____

State _____ County _____

WELL LOG OR OUTCROP SECTION	LOCATION			THICKNESS IN FEET				
	SECTION	T	R	TOTAL SECTION	SANDSTONE	SHALE	LIMESTONE + DOLOMITE	EVAPORITE

computed values. In many practical studies, and to some extent in academic research, the computations are performed by automatic data processing equipment. For such processing, the compilation sheets are designed to facilitate punching the data on cards or tape, as described in a later part of this chapter.

Single-component, Conventional Facies Maps. Two main kinds of facies maps fall into this category. They are based either on the absolute thickness of a selected rock type in a stratigraphic unit, or on its relative thickness with respect to the total thickness of the stratigraphic unit itself.

Net Thickness Maps (Isolith Maps). When the total thickness of sandstone in a stratigraphic unit is recorded at each map control point, and lines of equal sandstone thickness are drawn through the field of numbers, the map is a **sandstone thickness map.** This is a form of isopach map, but inasmuch as it is used to present the areal variation in a specific rock type, it is also a form of facies map. Such maps, showing the thickness of a selected rock component, have come to be known as **isolith maps.**

The term "isolith map" was introduced by Grossman (1944) to be applied to maps that depict "lines of equal lithic character." Kay (1954) pointed out that some then current usage violated this definition, but it is likely that the same term was developed in two meanings, one associated with typical subsurface mapping practices. It is probable that many more isolith maps have been prepared as thickness maps than in the sense defined by Grossman. However, to avoid confusion in use of the term it is probably preferable to qualify the kind of map described here as a "thickness isolith map" or, for example, simply as a "sandstone thickness map."

Figure 12-8, top, is an example of a sandstone isolith map. Corresponding maps of the thickness of limestone, evaporite, or other components in a stratigraphic section are prepared in a similar manner—that is, by plotting the values at each control point and contouring the field of numbers.

Percentage Maps. Instead of contouring net sand thickness directly, the percentage of sandstone in the unit may be computed by dividing sand thickness by total thickness at each control point. The resulting map is a **sandstone percentage map** that shows the relative amount of sand in the stratigraphic unit. An example is given in Figure 12-8, center. Percentage maps of other components are made in a similar manner. Percentage data are commonly contoured on an arithmetic interval of 5 or 10 percent.

Comparison of the two maps in Figure 12-8 brings out some of the distinctions between isolith and percentage maps. The sandstone thickness contours show a pattern of areal variation that expresses the absolute amount of sandstone present, whereas the percentage map shows the areal variation in sandstone thickness *relative to* the total thickness of the unit. The map

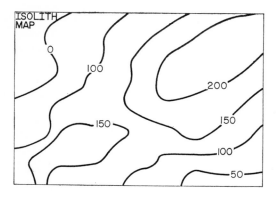

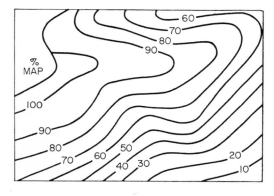

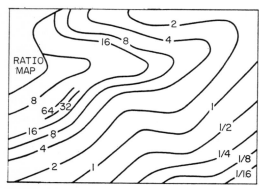

Fig. 12-8

Isolith, percentage, and ratio maps of a hypothetical stratigraphic unit. Contours on the isolith map are in feet. Note the similarity in the form of percentage and ratio maps, with crowding of the ratio contours as they approach infinite values. The percentage contours tend to "bunch up" in the vicinity of 50%.

patterns for the same set of basic data may thus differ markedly in some cases, and in others the patterns may be similar.

Multicomponent Conventional Facies Maps. Several choices of procedure are available when more than one lithologic component is to be included in a conventional facies map. Several sets of percentage lines or isolith lines may be superimposed on the same map, using shading or color to segregate particular combinations of interest. Such superimposition may yield a map that is difficult to interpret, thus methods are usually resorted to that combine more than one component into a single contour system. This can be done effectively for two lithologic components by the use of simple ratios.

Ratio Maps. The thickness ratio of one rock type to another (such as the sand–shale ratio, or the dolomite–limestone ratio) provides an effective means for displaying the interrelations between two lithologic components with a single set of contours. The numerical value of the ratio A/B may vary from zero to infinity. If A and B represent the thicknesses of the lithologic components being compared, the ratio A/B is zero if A is zero; if B is zero, the ratio is infinite. A ratio of 1.0 means that the thickness of A is equal to that of B along a particular contour line.

When the range of computed ratio values lies between the approximate limits of 1/3 and 3, the field of numbers at the control points may be contoured directly with an arithmetic contour interval. That is, the ratio lines may be contoured as 0.5, 1.0, 1.5, and so on up to 3.0. If the range of ratio values is larger, a geometric contour interval is more effective. Usually such maps are contoured values of about 1/32 to 32 by doubling the contour interval at each step, even if extreme values range up to infinity. Values smaller than 1/32 or larger than 32 indicate that one of the components is present to the extent of about 3 percent, and this may approach the limit of accuracy of the data.

Ratios are conventionally named in terms of the component or components in the numerator of the ratio. Thus, if A is sandstone and B is shale, the ratio A/B is called the **sand–shale ratio.** Similarly, for ratios that include more than two components, as described in the next section, the ratio name is determined by the components in the numerator.

Ratios are easily visualized inasmuch as the ratio B/A indicates directly the number of feet of component B per foot of component A. For example, a sand–shale ratio of 3.2 means that the section contains 3.2 feet of sandstone per foot of shale; similarly a sand–shale ratio of 0.32 means that there is about one third of a foot of sandstone per foot of shale in the measured section.

The sand–shale ratio thus contrasts one rock type with another, whereas a percentage expresses the proportion of a given rock type in the section as a whole. The decision to use ratios or percentages depends upon the kind of information to be communicated by the map. If the intention is to emphasize one type of rock in terms of the total thickness of the unit, percentages are appropriate. On the other hand, the interplay between sand and shale, expressed as a ratio, may shed light on interrelations among reservoir and source rocks, especially if porous sandstones are contrasted with typical marine shales.

A mathematical relation exists between percentage and ratio maps in two-component systems, in that the percentage lines 20, 50, and 80 correspond to ratio lines 1/4, 1, and 4 respectively. This need not be so for three or four components. For some purposes of analysis a transformation of the **map data** may be made (Krumbein, 1957) which, among other things, eliminates infinity values from the ratio data.

Figure 12-8, bottom, shows a ratio map of the same stratigraphic interval, as is shown in the upper two maps of the figure. Although the three percentage and ratio lines mentioned in the preceding paragraph are identical in the ratio and percentage maps, it may be noted that the procedures of contouring (equal arithmetic percentage intervals as opposed to geometric ratio intervals) give a somewhat different relative spacing of the contour lines, although the over-all appearance of the maps is similar. The percentage map contours are more closely spaced in the middle range, whereas those in the ratio map are more closely spaced at the extremes.

The Facies Triangle. When three lithologic components are involved in a facies study, it is convenient to express the relations among them by use of the 100-percent triangle, which finds wide use in geology, and which is applied to classification of rocks by composition or texture, as described in Chapter 5; to phase relations among end members in a geochemical study; and to a large variety of facies studies.

The facies triangle is used when the stratigraphic unit has only three components (such as sandstone, shale, and limestone) or when any three components in a stratigraphic unit of N components are selected for study. In the latter case, the selected components are recomputed to 100 percent. Consider a measured 200 foot section of rock, comprising 20 feet of sandstone, 80 feet of shale, 60 feet of limestone, and 40 feet of evaporite. If, in a given study, the evaporite is to be omitted, the other three components add up to 160 feet. In terms of this thickness, sandstone represents 12.5 percent (as against 10 percent in the original four components), shale represents 50 percent and limestone 37.5 percent.

In some four-end-member systems it is advantageous to combine related end members to reduce the system to three. The limestone and evaporite of the preceding example could be combined into a "nonclastic" group to be contrasted with sandstone and shale; or the sandstone and shale could be combined into a "clastic" group for comparison with limestone and evaporite. Selection of end members is a part of **facies map design,** in which components are selected to bring out certain features of interest in a given study.

Figure 12-9, upper left, shows the manner of plotting points on 100-percent triangles. The three vertices are labelled to identify the end members, and the percentage of each end member is measured along the line from a given vertex to the opposite side of the triangle. The scale of percentages then rises from zero at the side to 100 at the vertex. In Figure 12-9, the percentage of limestone (37.5 in the above example) is measured upward from the base of the figure, and the percentage of sandstone (12.5) is measured along the line extending to the sandstone vertex. The intersection of the limestone and sandstone lines defines the point, which is checked by noting that the intersection occurs at 50 percent shale. It is common practice in facies studies to plot all available control points on a triangle in this manner, in order to observe the distribution of points in terms of the changing

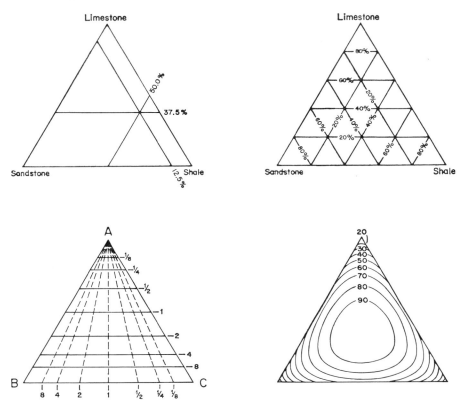

Fig. 12-9. 100-percent triangles, showing (*upper left*) the method of plotting points, and (*upper right*) the arrangement of percentage lines. The lower left triangle shows distribution of ratio lines; the lower right is an entropy overlay. See the text for details.

composition of the stratigraphic unit, independently of the geographic location of the control points. The grid of percentage lines on a triangle is shown in Figure 12-9, upper right.

The percentage triangle is not only a graphic device for showing the composition of a stratigraphic section, but it is a basic tool in the preliminary analysis of the data used in the design of facies maps. Because a large number of facies maps can be used to show the areal variations in composition of a stratigraphic unit, some preliminary analysis of the data is necessary before selecting the particular maps to be prepared. By examining the percentage distribution of the plotted points in their true trilinear relation, plus use of ratio overlays and other graphic devices, it is commonly possible to select two or three facies maps that communicate maximum information in a given study for the time and cost involved.

In this sense, the use of percentages, absolute thicknesses, ratios, or more complicated mathematical functions in facies mapping is not so much one of personal preference as of selecting the kinds of maps that best serve the scientific or economic purposes of the facies study.

Although the 100-percent triangle shows percentage lines directly, it is possible to overlay transparencies that show the ratio relations among the points. Thus, if the end members are A, B, and C, as shown in Figure 12-9, lower left, it is possible to generate two kinds of ratios from the percentage values. The ratio $(B + C)/A$ contrasts one end member with the sum of the other two. The two end members in this *composite ratio* may themselves be expressed as the ratio B/C. The composite ratio may be selected in any of six different ways. For example, the ratio $A/(B + C)$ is the reciprocal of the first ratio mentioned. A second combination is the composite ratio $B/(A + C)$, or its reciprocal. In similar fashion, the ratio B/C may be expressed in reciprocal form; four other ratios involving A, B, and C in pairs are possible, depending upon the choice of the composite ratio. Regardless of the selection that is made, the composite ratio is always a series of straight lines parallel to the edge of the triangle that contains the two end members in the numerator or denominator of the composite ratio. Similarly, the corresponding ratio B/C, or C/B, will always be a series of straight lines diverging from the corner occupied by end member A.

By superimposing a transparent ratio overlay on the percentage triangle, it is possible to read the ratio values directly that correspond to the percentage combinations used in plotting the original points. Moreover, whereas it would require three sets of contour lines to express the percentages of the three end members individually, the use of ratios reduces the number of maps required to two. The use of other mathematical functions permits the development of overlays that, in turn, allow the relations among three end members to be plotted on a single contour map. These special functions are introduced in a later section.

Although transparent overlays permit graphic determination of ratio values from the percentage triangle, it is common practice to compute the ratios directly, either from the original thickness data, as recorded directly on a data sheet like that shown in Table 12-3, or from the percentage values. The overlay method is mentioned here to indicate that the use of ratios instead of percentages does not in any way change the position of the plotted points; ratios are simply transformations of the percentage values.

Construction of Triangle Facies Maps. Numerous facies maps can be designed for three-component systems by using the method of multiple contouring of percentage lines or ratio lines. A common type is the **triangle ratio map,** in which two sets of ratio contours are used to delineate areas having certain compositional features in common. The limiting ratio values can be selected to block out clusters of points on the 100-percent triangle, or for preparation of "rock-inventory maps," a generalized set of limits may be chosen. By using the same limiting values in a set of maps, ready visual comparison of patterns or colors that represent certain conventional facies groups can be made.

Preparation of multiple-ratio facies maps is more complicated than is the preparation of individual isopach, isolith, or percentage maps. The following remarks on map construction facilitate interpretation of the examples to follow. The use of two ratios to prepare a facies map is illustrated in Figure 12-10. Component A includes carbonates (limestone and dolomite) and evaporites (anhydrite, gypsum, and salt). Component B represents sandstone and conglomerate, and C represents siltstone and shale. The ratio $(B + C)/A$ thus expresses the relationship between detrital (clastic) sediments and the nondetrital (nonclastic) sediments. This is the **clastic ratio.** The ratio B/C contrasts coarse and fine clastics and is the **sand–shale ratio.**

Fig. 12-10. Illustration of the procedure used in compiling the triangle ratio map shown in lower right. The isopach base is in the upper left, and the sand-shale ratio and clastic ratio maps are in the upper right and lower left. The facies map with triangular legend (components A, B, and C arranged as in Fig. 12-9) shows the selected ratio contours that divide map into nine facies areas. [From Sloss et al. (1960).]

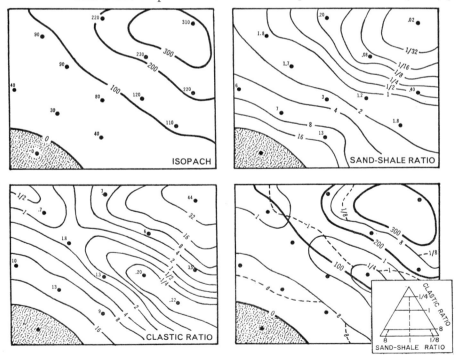

The maps in Figure 12-10 show the several stages in constructing a triangle facies map. The isopach base commonly used in such maps is shown in the upper left. The clastic ratio and sand–shale ratio values are entered at each control point on separate base maps. Contour lines of equal ratio values are then drawn through the fields of numbers, commonly on a geometric contour interval, as shown.

Ratio maps, like ispoach maps, are contoured as continuous functions. Thus, the three upper control points on the clastic ratio map of Figure 12-10 have the values 0.7, 7.0, and 44. The clastic ratio lines 1, 2, and 4 must be drawn between the first and second points, and lines 8, 16, and 32 must pass between the second and third points.

The clastic ratio and sand–shale ratio maps are directly useful for interpretation of some features of the stratigraphic unit. However, for preparing a "rock inventory map" that shows interrelations among all three components, it is conventional to superimpose one map on the other, as shown in Figure 12-10. In this map, the triangle is divided into segments at sand–shale ratio lines 8, 1, and 1/8 and at clastic ratio lines 8, 1, and 1/4. This selection serves two purposes. First, the lines divide the map into selected "pattern areas" that show where the stratigraphic unit is mainly sandstone, shale, or nonclastics or where a given lithologic component constitutes more than 50 percent of the unit. Further simplification is achieved by eliminating the sand–shale ratio line of 1 where the clastic ratio falls below 1/4 (that is, where the strata are more than 80 percent carbonate or evaporite), and by using the sand–shale ratio lines 8 and 1/8 only in those map areas where the clastic ratio exceeds 8 (that is, where approximately 90 percent or more of the section is sandstone or shale). For many conventional facies maps, the limits used in Figure 12-10 have been adopted, and the legend triangle has become known as the "standard" triangle. Table 12-4 summarizes the composition of each of the nine lithologic groups associated with the standard triangle. Use of the standard triangle facilitates comparison of rock inventory maps of different stratigraphic units.

The frontispiece is an example of a conventional facies map illustrating the effective use of color on maps of this type. The limiting ratio values are those indicated in Table 12-4, except for the sand and shale end members, which are here defined by the clastic-ratio line 16 and the sand–shale ratio lines 16 and 1/16. It has become standard practice to use colors that approximate those of the frontispiece; if the shale and shale–sand groups were to appear within the map area, these would be colored bright green and yellowish-green, respectively.

In many facies maps prepared as described, the clastic ratio and sand–shale ratio lines may cross and recross one another, as they do in the area

TABLE 12-4. LIMITS AND CHARACTERISTICS OF LITHOLOGIC
GROUPS

GROUP NAME	CLASTIC RATIO LIMIT	SAND–SHALE LIMIT	GENERAL FEATURES
Sandstone	>8	>8	More than 79% sandstone
Sand-shale	>8	8–1	More sand than shale; less than 11% limestone
Shale-sand	>8	1–1/8	More shale than sand; less than 11% limestone
Shale	>8	<1/8	More than 79% shale
Sand-lime	1–8	>1	More sand than shale; 11 to 50% limestone
Shale-lime	1–8	<1	More shale than sand; 11 to 50% limestone
Lime-sand	1/4–1	>1	50 to 80% limestone; more sand than shale
Lime-shale	1/4–1	<1	50 to 80% limestone; more shale than sand
Limestone	<1/4	any value	More than 80% limestone

immediately above the legend block in the triangle map of Figure 12-10.
When colors or patterns are used on the maps, these crossing ratio lines
outline tongue-like or lens-shaped patches, which may cause some confusion unless the principles of map construction are kept in mind.

In some instances, a stratigraphic unit is dominated by carbonates and
evaporites and lacks significant amounts of sandstone or shale. If this is the
case, the sand–shale ratio may be insignificant, and a different combination
of end members may be selected. Instead of contrasting sand and shale, the
carbonates (B) and evaporites (C) may be contrasted, with sand and shale
combined into a single end member (A). In terms of the general triangle of
Figure 12-11, left, A/(B + C) is the clastic ratio, but B/C now contrasts
evaporites and carbonates, and is called the **evaporite ratio.**

Figure 12-11 is a conventional triangle facies map adapted from Forgotson
(1960) in which the standard triangle is used, and which shows a progressive
change in facies from dominantly clastic materials in the northwest, where
the Trinity sands are exposed in outcrop, to a section composed dominantly
of limestone, which occurs in the subsurface along the general southern part
of the map.

Forgotson's map is based on ratio limits controlled in part by the clustering

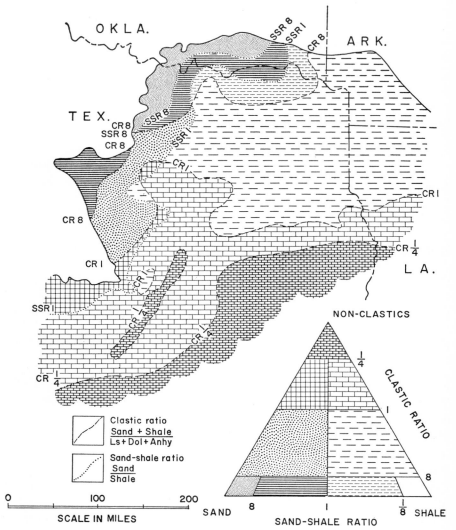

Fig. 12-11. Triangle facies map of Cretaceous Trinity Group. Compare with Figure 12-10 for relations between the sand-shale ratio lines and clastic ratio lines, which may cross, giving rise to small irregular patches. [Adapted from Forgotson (1960).]

of control points on the 100-percent triangle. The limits used by Forgotson have been changed in Figure 12-11 to conform to those of the standard triangle, but Forgotson's original map is a good example of variations that may be followed in defining facies blocks on the 100-percent triangle.

Multicomponent Single-contour-system Maps. The use of selected segments of ratio lines in effect produces a pattern map from the individually contoured ratio maps. Thus, the resulting rock-inventory maps show, through the use of color or shading, the main lithologic groups in a stratigraphic unit. It is to be emphasized that in detailed studies of the interrelations among lithologic components, the various ratio maps are commonly prepared as separate sheets and serve as "working maps" in preparation of the pattern maps.

If the full details from three percentage maps or from two ratio maps for three-component systems are all superimposed on a single base, the network of lines may lead to considerable confusion. In order to simplify the communication of information on several components in one map, various single-contour-system maps have been developed.

Entropy Maps. Pelto (1954) opened this field in facies mapping by applying an entropy-like function to the 100-percent triangle to develop a single set of contour lines that would display the interrelations among three end members. The entropy function expresses the degree of "mixing" of the rock components in a stratigraphic unit. The function is set up so that a section with equal parts of sandstone, shale, and limestone has an entropy value of 100, and as the proportion of one end member or another increases, the entropy value becomes smaller, approaching zero as the composition approaches that of a single end member.

Entropy maps are most conveniently prepared by using an overlay of the entropy function on the 100-percent triangle, which permits direct transformation from percentage points to entropy values. An overlay of this type, adapted from Pelto (1954), is shown in Figure 12-9, lower right. The lines show relative entropy values, with the highest point on the triangle representing 33.3 percent of each component.

Though the entropy overlay is commonly used, Table 12-5 shows how the entropy value may be computed for a control point having the percentages of rock types indicated in the first column. The entropy value of a given component is the product of its proportion in the section, p_i, times the natural logarithm of its proportion, $\log_e p_i$. In the table, the percentage of

TABLE 12-5. COMPUTATION OF ENTROPY VALUE FOR THREE-COMPONENT SYSTEMS

COMPONENT	PERCENT	PROPORTION, p_i	$\log_e p_i$	$p_i \log_e p_i$
Sandstone	13.0	0.13	−2.0402	−0.2652
Shale	7.0	0.07	−2.6593	−0.1861
Limestone	80.0	0.80	−0.2231	−0.1785
Totals	100.0	1.00		−0.6298

sandstone is shown to be 13.0, hence its proportion in the section is 0.13. The natural log of 0.13 (which can be found in standard tables) is -2.0402. The product of these is -0.2652. The sum of the three products is -0.6298, representing $\Sigma\ p_i \log_e p_i$.

The maximum entropy, H_m, that a three-component system can have is 1.0986 (see Pelto, 1954, p. 507). To obtain the entropy value used for mapping, H_r, the ratio of the sum of the products in Table 12-5, $\Sigma\ p_i \log p_i$, to the maximum entropy value, H_m, is multiplied by a negative constant (here, -100); this yields a positive value that lies between 0 and 100. Using the values given in the example above, dividing -0.6298 by 1.0986 and multiplying by -100 gives 57.32, the value plotted. Thus, if the value 100 represents complete "mixing," the section in the table has a relative "mixing value" of about 57 percent.

Figure 12-12, also adapted from Forgotson (1960), is an entropy facies map of the same unit and area shown in Figure 12-11. Forgotson points out that the entropy map, by virtue of the large central area in the triangle selected for the more "mixed" sections, shows less spottiness than the ratio map, in part because it eliminates the criss-crossing of ratio lines.

In preparing entropy maps, the control points must be identified as to the end members that tend to dominate, inasmuch as the value 40, for example, does not of itself discriminate among the three end members. Note also that the entropy map does not indicate whether a dominant end member, such as shale, is sandy or calcareous, whereas this information is commonly given by the contour lines of value 1 on ratio maps. It was partly this feature that led Forgotson to develop a variant of the entropy map that involves combination of the entropy function with selected ratio values.

Entropy-ratio Maps. Figure 12-13 shows this variant of the entropy map, which again depicts the same area and stratigraphic unit. Note that three line segments of ratio value 1.0 have been inserted in the triangle legend between entropy values 60 and 70. These are the **sand-shale ratio** B/C, the **nonclastics–sand ratio,** A/B, and the **nonclastics–shale ratio** A/C of the general ratio triangle in Figure 12-9, lower left. Thus, Forgotson's entropy-ratio map is not strictly a single contour system map.

The ratio lines on the entropy map indicate by map pattern the nature of the lithologic "mixture" through which a given end member is approached. Thus, the nonclastic end member in the map is gradational through shale all along its extent, with no areas in which a transition from sandstone to nonclastics occurs. A map of the Upper Cambrian in the upper Mississippi Valley would show essentially the opposite situation.

As Forgotson points out, single-contour-system maps tend to give an integrative picture of a stratigraphic unit. This feature can be used to advantage

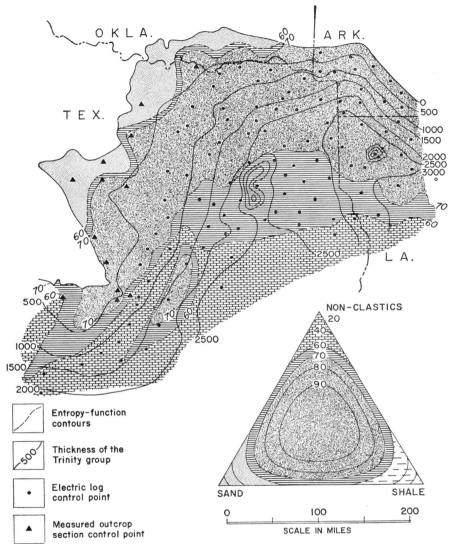

Fig. 12-12. Entropy lithofacies map of Cretaceous Trinity Group. The single-contour system eliminates crossing of facies lines shown in Figure 12-11. [Adapted from Forgotson (1960).]

in designing other kinds of maps that have application in the evaluation of certain over-all features of a stratigraphic unit. Thus, on the basis of a defined average composition that is associated with observed occurrences of oil and gas or with the location of tectonic hinge lines, the development of other kinds of single-contour-system maps has been made possible. The average point selected for reference on the triangle is called the "optimum point."

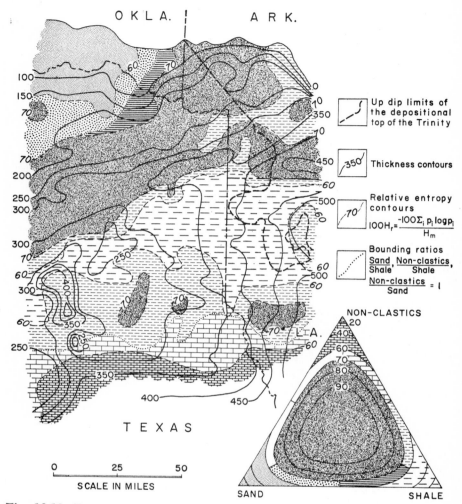

Fig. 12-13. Entropy-ratio lithofacies map of Cretaceous Trinity Group. Identification of end members and inclusion of ratio lines of 1 make the map more meaningful geologically than Figure 12-12. [Adapted from Forgotson (1960).]

Facies-departure Maps. This single-contour map was originally called a "distance-function map" (Krumbein, 1955), because it involves transforming the three trilinear coordinates of the optimum point on the triangle to two Cartesian coordinates and measuring the straight-line distance from the optimum point to all other points plotted on the triangle. Forgotson (1960) suggested the change of name, inasmuch as the "distance" referred to is measured on the triangle and may bear no relation to the geographic distance between the control points.

Figure 12-14 (Forgotson, 1960) shows a **facies-departure map** for the Trinity Group, based on an average rock composition that appears to be associated with the tectonic hinge line for the Trinity, as interpreted from a combination of isopach and facies data. This average composition, shown as a point on the upper right edge of the facies triangle in Figure 12-14, is used as the center for a series of concentric circles that indicate the degree

Fig. 12-14. Facies-departure map of Cretaceous Trinity Group. [Adapted from Forgotson (1960).]

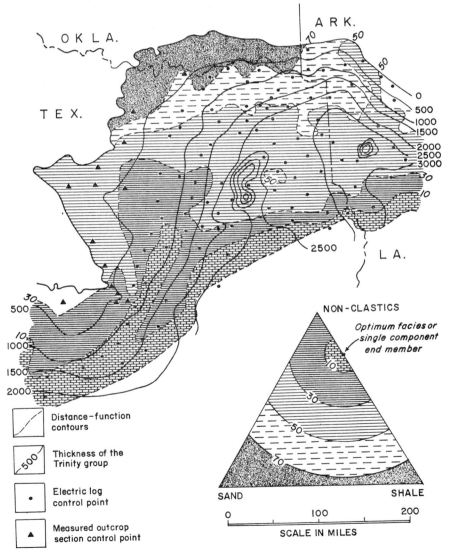

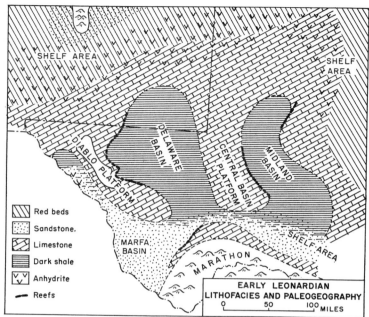

Fig. 12-15. Leonardian (Middle Permian) lithofacies and paleogeography in West Texas and southeastern New Mexico. [After King (1942).]

to which all control points on the map approach (or depart from) this selected value. As the map shows, the **departure contour** of value 10, which presumably contains the tectonic hinge line, lies along the southern part of the map area and defines a general area on the map where the lithologic composition conforms to that of the optimum point.

In some respects, single-contour-system maps, as represented by the entropy map and the facies-departure map, belong in the category of integrative or derived maps, which constitute the last class in Table 12-2. However, these maps are included here because they are a natural outgrowth of the 100-percent triangle.

Facies-pattern Maps. It was mentioned that combinations of ratios in triangle facies maps produce **facies patterns** that are bounded by selected values of the ratios used. More generally, pattern maps can be developed less formally by mapping the occurrence of certain lithologic groups that, owing to their composition, provide data for environmental analysis and other purposes. These need not be based on formal contour systems.

Figure 12-15 presents an excellent map of this type, used by King (1942) in his study of the Permian rocks in west Texas. In preparing his map, King selected certain diagnostic combinations of the sediments that show very clearly the interrelations among environments in terms of associated tectonic states of sediment accumulation. The map area covers parts of Texas and New Mexico, and shows two tongues of dark shale extending northward into an area of dominant limestone, with some reef areas in the narrow transition zone. Red beds with associated sandstone occur to the east and northwest, with a transitional zone of evaporites between the limestone and red beds in the northern and western parts of the map area.

The Facies Tetrahedron. When it is necessary to include more than three end members in a map, for example, if a stratigraphic unit contains significant amounts of sandstone, shale, carbonates, and evaporites, the facies triangle can be extended to its three-dimensional counterpart—the tetrahedron. This extension complicates the preparation of conventional facies maps because it introduces an additional end member and another set of contour lines in most maps.

Figure 12-16, upper left, shows a tetrahedron with several points indicated on and within it, which illustrates the relations that exist among the various combinations of end members. The sand isolith map of Figure 12-8 is an example of a single-end-member map, and the sand–shale ratio map in the same figure is a two-end-member system, represented on the tetrahedron as

Fig. 12-16. The facies tetrahedron. The upper left diagram shows systems comprising from one to four end members. Other diagrams show developed tetrahedrons subdivided in various ways. [After Krumbein (1954).]

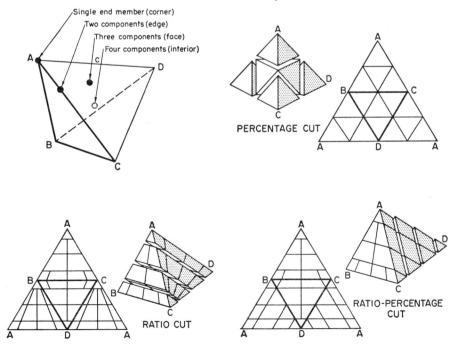

an edge. The triangle facies maps of the preceding section all have three end members, which can be represented on a single face of the tetrahedron.

The same principle of subdividing a triangle into segments or areas to represent facies can be applied to the tetrahedron, except that in the latter the facies segments are three-dimensional blocks cut from the tetrahedron. The tetrahedral diagrams of Figure 12-16 show developed and perspective views of three ways in which the tetrahedron can be cut or sliced. In the upper right is a **percentage cut,** in which the blocks are defined by various percentage planes. The lower left diagram illustrates a **ratio cut,** and the lower right diagram shows a combination **ratio-percentage cut.**

Figure 12-17 is a synthetic facies map based on percentage slices through the tetrahedron. As the diagrammatic legend shows, the slices cut the tetrahedron at 50 percent and 80 percent for all four end members, giving rise in this instance to a fairly simple map. In practice, such maps may become considerably more complex, as is discussed in the following paragraphs.

The facies tetrahedron was used by McKee, in the U.S.G.S. Jurassic and Triassic Paleotectonic Map folios (1956, 1959), to display relations among four end members. Figures 12-18 and 12-19 show the combination of percentage and ratio cuts adopted for the folios and the corresponding form of the map legend. The latter is laid out as a Cartesian diagram with the vertical axes showing the percentages of detrital and chemical components. The

Fig. 12-17. Example of a fictitious stratigraphic map based on a tetrahedron cut along 50 and 80 percent planes. [After Krumbein (1954).]

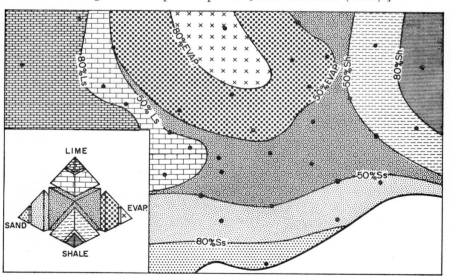

horizontal axis is a ratio axis, with the evaporite ratio along the top and the sand–shale ratio along the bottom. In order to include the interplay between the sand–shale ratio and the evaporite ratio in the four-end-member system, it is also necessary to subdivide the two central rows horizontally to show the sand–shale ratio of 1.0 in the upper block, and the evaporite ratio of 1.0 in the lower block. These relations can readily be seen in the tetrahedron of Figure 12-19.

McKee's legend clearly identifies the color blocks on the maps, the patterns of which are mainly bounded by fixed percentage or ratio values. However, the internal relations among certain ratio lines in McKee's legend, such as the sand–shale ratio 1.0, is not immediately apparent between the upper and lower portions of the legend because of the shift of this ratio line to a horizontal position in the upper half of the legend. The sliced tetrahedron shows how each legend block is bounded, and indicates that the sand–shale ratio cut of value 1.0 extends above the plane of 50 percent chemical components to the 80 percent plane, and thus explains the need for the double blocks in the lower row of the top half of the legend. This arrangement makes it difficult to distinguish relationships where geographically adjacent map patterns are not contiguous on the legend.

These remarks are included mainly to emphasize the practical difficulties in working with four end members, and to suggest that the use of Cartesian coordinates in displaying relations among trilinear or quadrilinear systems may introduce complexities in clear visualization of interrelations among the facies classes. Weller (1960, p. 612) argues for the use of Cartesian coordinates for trilinear legends. The 100-percent triangle and the tetrahedron are particularly adaptable as devices for plotting relations among observations in **closed number systems** in which all components add up to 100 percent. Graphic transformation to a Cartesian system may distort these relations. Chayes (1960) discusses the algebraic and statistical properties of closed number tables.

Vertical-variability Maps

Facies maps may be designed to present simultaneously information on the composition and internal geometry of stratigraphic units. Inasmuch as such maps commonly involve the vertical placement of one or more lithologic components within the stratigraphic unit, they are called **vertical-variability maps.** As with conventional facies maps, vertical variability maps may be based on a single component or on several. If a single component, such as sandstone, is of major interest in a facies study, the basic data obtained from each outcrop section or subsurface control point comprises a tabulation

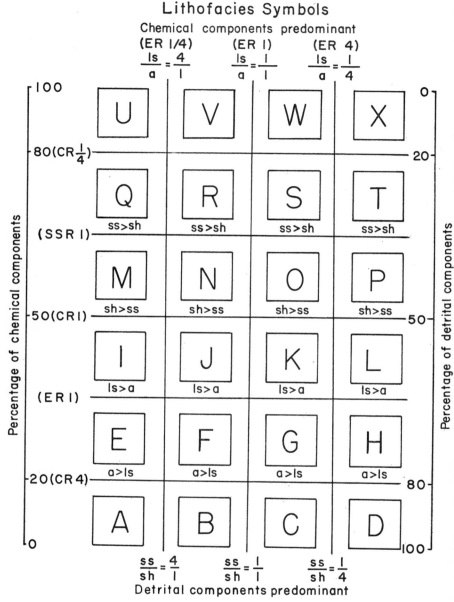

Fig. 12-18. Lithofacies legend used in U.S. Geological Survey paleotectonic maps of the Jurassic System (McKee et al., 1956). Compare Figure 12-19 for corresponding tetrahedron slices.

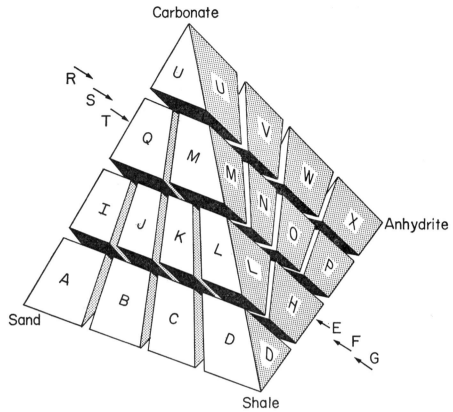

Fig. 12-19. Paleotectonic map legend of Figure 12-18 shown as a sliced tetrahedron to indicate three-dimensional relationships among facies subdivisions.

of the number of sandstones, their individual thicknesses, and the distance to their centers from the top or bottom of the stratigraphic unit, as shown in Figure 12-7.

Single-component Vertical-variability Maps. Several kinds of single component vertical variability maps may be developed from data that preserve the identity and position of rock layers in a stratigraphic section. If the average thickness of the sandstone units in the rock body is of interest, the total thickness of sandstone in the unit is divided by the number of individual sandstones, and the average thickness is entered at each control point on the base map. The resulting contour map then displays the manner in which the average thickness of the rock type varies over the map area. In terms of Figure 12-1, the aspect being mapped at each control point concerns a single lithologic component, mapped in terms of its average bed thickness instead of its absolute amount.

For some facies studies, information about the number of discrete sand-stone units in the stratigraphic body may be of importance. For this purpose, the number of discrete sandstones on each well log is counted and entered at its control point, whereupon the resulting contour pattern communicates information on the increase or decrease in the number of sandstones in any given geographic direction. Similarly, by computing a weighted mean, based on the thickness of each sandstone unit in terms of its distance from the top or bottom of the rock body, the resulting vertical variability contour map will show the change in average vertical position of the sandstone beds within the unit throughout the area of interest. One particular extension of this type of map involves computing the relative vertical dispersion of sand-stone units throughout the rock body, which indicates whether the sand-stones occur relatively close together in some particular portion of the strati-graphic unit, or whether they are scattered throughout the unit from top to bottom.

Figure 12-20 is an example of a number-of-sandstones map, from Forgot-son (1954). The map shows an increase in sandstones southward to a maxi-mum, with a subsequent decrease farther south. For the Upper Jurassic rocks studied, this map shows maximum interfingering of sands and other rock types along the maximum zone; where the sands on one side of such a maxi-mum are dominantly non-marine, and on the other, dominantly marine, the zone of maximum number of sands indicates the "average shoreline" (Krum-bein and Nagel, 1953).

In preparation of number-of-beds maps, it is important that an opera-tional definition be set up in making bed counts, in order that the subjective element in deciding on the number of discrete beds be reduced to a mini-

Fig. 12-20. Sandstone isolith and number-of-sandstones map of the Shuler Forma-tion, Cotton Valley Group (Jurassic), in parts of Arkansas and Loui-siana. [After Forgotson (1954).]

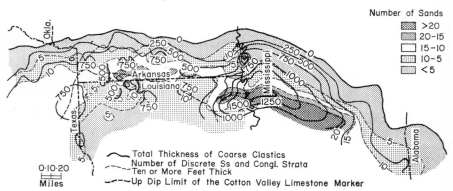

mum. For the map shown in Figure 12-20, Forgotson (1954, p. 2485) gives the explicit definition he used, which included a minimum thickness of 10 feet per sand unit, and a spacing of at least 20 feet of non-sand between his units.

The number-of-sandstones map does not indicate the position of the sand in the stratigraphic unit, but this can be shown on other kinds of maps. Figure 12-21 shows the relative center of gravity and the relative spread, throughout the section, of sandstone beds in the Upper Cretaceous of Wyoming. The **sandstone center-of-gravity map** shows the relative, weighted mean position of the sandstones in terms of their distance from the top of the unit, expressed as a percentage of total thickness of the unit. Thus, in the southwest the mean sand position is near the top of the section, whereas in the northeast, the mean position approaches to within 20 percent of the bottom (that is, the center of gravity has dropped to 80 percent of the distance from the top of the unit). The **standard deviation map** in Figure 12-21 is also expressed in relative terms, such that the 10 percent contour means that the sands are confined, on the average, to a vertical spread of only 10 percent of the thickness of the stratigraphic unit.

Computation of the center of gravity and the standard deviation of beds in a stratigraphic unit is time consuming. The basic data used are illustrated in Figure 12-22, taken from Krumbein and Libby (1957). The center of gravity (in feet) from the top of the unit is obtained by multiplying each sand thickness by its distance from the top of the unit and dividing by the total thickness of sand in the section. In the example this is 128 feet. The relative center of gravity is then obtained by dividing this number by the thickness of the unit at the control point (540 feet). The relative center of gravity is accordingly located at a point 24 percent below the top of the stratigraphic unit. The corresponding standard deviation of the sand beds is obtained by multiplying the individual bed thickness by the square of its distance from the top, and summing these products as indicated in Figure 12-22. As shown in the figure, the approximate standard deviation is 100 feet, which, when divided by the total thickness of the unit, indicates that the sandstones have an average spread of about 19 percent on either side of the center of gravity. Details of the theory of center-of-gravity and standard-deviation maps, generally called **moment maps,** are given in Krumbein and Libby (1957).

Multicomponent Vertical-variability Maps. Although single-component, vertical-variability maps are fairly extensively used in some aspects of oil and gas exploration, multicomponent vertical-variability maps are also needed. These maps are more difficult to design and prepare, inasmuch as they may involve different numbers or thicknesses of several kinds of rock

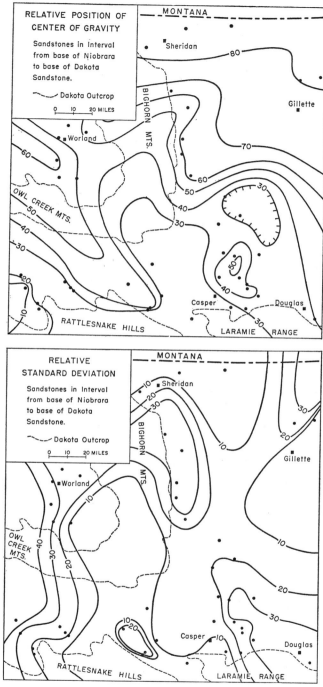

Fig. 12-21. (*Top*) Center-of-gravity map. (*Bottom*) Standard deviation map of sandstones in a Cretaceous operational unit, Wyoming. See the text for details. [After Krumbein and Libby (1957).]

478

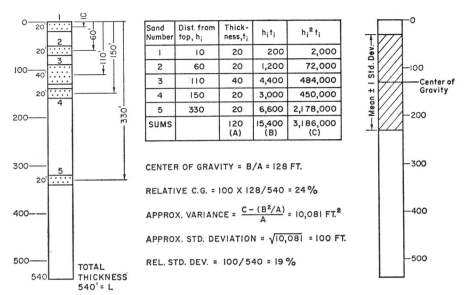

Sand Number	Dist. from top, h_i	Thickness, t_i	$h_i t_i$	$h_i^2 t_i$
1	10	20	200	2,000
2	60	20	1,200	72,000
3	110	40	4,400	484,000
4	150	20	3,000	450,000
5	330	20	6,600	2,178,000
SUMS		120 (A)	15,400 (B)	3,186,000 (C)

CENTER OF GRAVITY = B/A = 128 FT.

RELATIVE C.G. = 100 X 128/540 = 24%

APPROX. VARIANCE = $\dfrac{C - (B^2/A)}{A}$ = 10,081 FT.^{2}

APPROX. STD. DEVIATION = $\sqrt{10,081}$ = 100 FT.

REL. STD. DEV. = 100/540 = 19%

TOTAL THICKNESS 540' = L

Fig. 12-22. Manner of computing the center of gravity and the approximate standard deviation of the sandstone beds shown in Figure 12-21. [From Krumbein and Libby (1957).]

distributed throughout the stratigraphic unit. If porous parts of the section are of interest, these may occur either in sandstones or in carbonate rocks. The simultaneous display of these two kinds of porous rocks requires the development of relatively complex methods of map construction.

Another type of map that may be considered as multicomponent (in the sense that it depicts several parts of a larger stratigraphic interval) is the **multipartite map,** introduced by Forgotson (1954). In this method, the stratigraphic unit is first divided into three equal parts, and the amount of sand, for instance, is measured in each. A facies triangle is then set up with ratios established to contrast the amount of sand in the lower third with the amount in the upper two thirds, as well as to contrast the amount of sand in the middle and upper third. These ratios can then be used to display the geographic variation of the interplay of sandstone in the three parts of the stratigraphic unit. Thus, for a given stratigraphic body, the sandstone may rise from the lower, through the middle, and into the upper third in a given direction. This would imply a time transgression of the sandstone if the limiting boundaries of the stratigraphic unit are selected as being time parallel.

Figure 12-23 shows a tripartite map of the Schuler (Upper Jurassic) formation in parts of Louisiana and Arkansas (Forgotson, 1954). In the south-

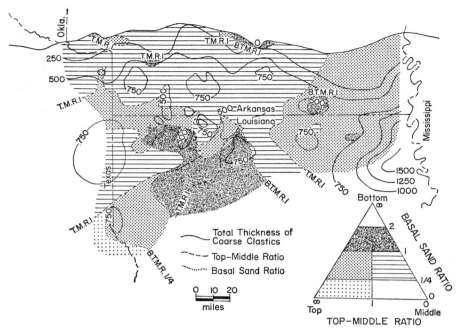

Fig. 12-23. Tripartite map of Shuler Formation, Cotton Valley Group (Jurassic). After Forgotson (1954).]

central area, the sand is in the basal portion of the stratigraphic unit, and tends to extend to the top toward the west and southwest, as well as in the northeast, with an intermediate area of sand mainly in the middle part of the section.

The tripartite map is related to the sandstone center-of-gravity map mentioned earlier, in that it presents data in terms of discrete parts of the stratigraphic section, as compared to a position computed over the whole range of thickness. A succession of slice maps, mentioned earlier, may also be used in vertical variability studies.

A more recent and more general type of multicomponent vertical-variability map was introduced by Forgotson in 1960, in which the technique of Pelto (1954) is applied to the problem of homogeneity or heterogeneity of the rocks in vertical succession. Such maps are called **interval-entropy maps.** Figure 12-24, taken from Forgotson, shows the two extremes, in which the total entropy is either 0 or 100. Interval entropy maps may be prepared for more than three components, but high speed computers are essential for routine preparation of such maps, because of the large amount of computation that is necessary.

Maps of Internal Geometry and Composition of Stratigraphic Units

In addition to the stratigraphic maps discussed in previous sections, there is a large class of maps that communicate information on textures and other features of rock bodies. These constitute the third class under (B) in Table 12-2. Such maps are related to vertical variability maps, in that they may involve the study of particular kinds of rocks within stratigraphic units, although some of the maps in this class are based on single beds in the stratigraphic unit.

A particular bed of sandstone may be chosen to study its average grain size, its degree of sorting, or its average particle shape. Similarly, the porosity or permeability of a sand bed may be mapped for exploration or reserve-estimation purposes in petroleum geology.

Figure 12-25 is a textural map adapted from Pye (1944), which shows the median grain diameter of the Bethel Sandstone in the Chester Series (Upper Mississippian) of the Illinois Basin. The average particle size decreases fairly regularly across the eastern half of the area, with some irregularities in the western part.

The heavy mineral composition of sandstones may also be shown on maps. Such maps may be used to infer the nature of the source rocks involved and the paths of movement of the transported sand; or they may show the changing relations between stable and unstable minerals as the sand moves toward its ultimate site of deposition. A comprehensive study of Recent sediments in the northern Gulf of Mexico by Van Andel and Poole (1960) shows the nature of the heavy minerals supplied to the Gulf by various streams (their Figure 3), as well as heavy mineral provinces within the Gulf (their Figure 5).

Fig. 12-24

Two stratigraphic sections showing the concept of vertical entropy for sections as a whole and for three subdivisions. In both columns the total entropy is 100 (that is, the three end members are equally represented), but in column A each vertically successive interval consists of a single end member; accordingly, the interval entropy is zero. In the corresponding intervals of column B, the end members are equally represented, and the interval entropy is 100. [From Forgotson (1960).]

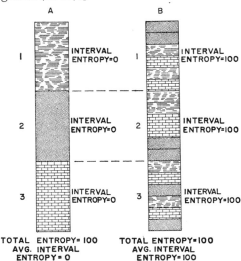

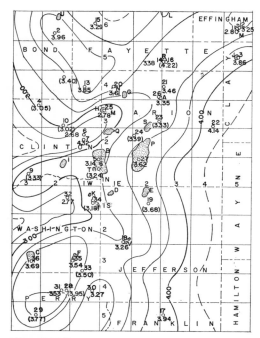

Fig. 12-25

Subsurface map of median grain diameter, in phi units, of the Bethel Sandstone (Upper Mississippian) in southern Illinois. Areas of Bethel Sandstone oil production are shown by the stippled pattern. Inclusion of the many more datum points now available would probably develop a more complex pattern associated with lenticular sands, such as those in the related Palestine sands (Figure 12-26). [After Pye (1944).]

Maps of vectorial properties of sedimentary rocks, such as the direction of cross-bedding or of grain-orientation in sandstone, have applications in a variety of academic and applied studies. Figure 12-26, from Potter and co-workers (1958), shows the cross-bedding directions observed along the outcrop of the Palestine formation (Upper Mississippian Chester Series) in southeastern Illinois. As the map demonstrates, there is good agreement between the mean direction of cross-bedding and the subsurface alignment of the main Palestine sand bodies. Results of this kind suggest that some subsurface features of buried rocks may be highly predictable from surface studies. Note that, in the illustration, the closest point from which abundant subsurface data were obtained lies about 6 miles or more away from the outcrop band.

The general term **sedimentary-stratigraphic map** seems appropriate for the large class of maps that depict the internal geometry and composition of individual lithologic components in stratigraphic units. These are not commonly included in facies map classification, though they may be important for stratigraphic interpretation, for determination of provenance, or for environmental reconstruction.

Integrative and Derived Stratigraphic Maps

Stratigraphic studies commonly include preparation of several kinds of maps for the unit of interest. These maps may be considered as finished products in themselves, or they may be used as a basis for preparation of additional maps, some of which represent combinations of the maps already

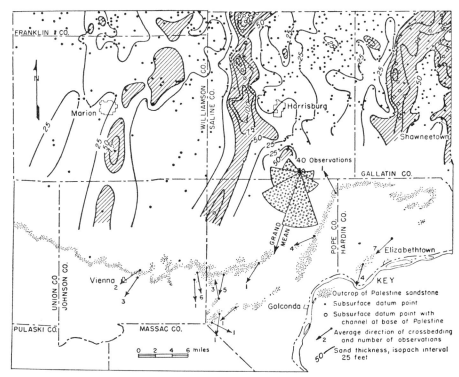

Fig. 12-26. Direction of cross bedding and thickness of sandstone in the Palestine Formation (Upper Mississippian) in southern Illinois. Note the prominent south-southwest lenticular sand bodies generally parallel with the mean direction of cross bedding. [Adapted from Potter et al. (1958).]

prepared. Alternatively, a single map may be further analyzed by subjecting the data used in its preparation to formal mathematical or statistical analysis. In either case, the new maps prepared in these ways are called **integrative** or **derived maps;** several are listed as a class in Table 12-2.

Integrative maps are commonly constructed by combining the data from two or more stratigraphic maps. In one sense, the triangle facies maps that are prepared by superimposition of two sets of ratio lines belong in this category, since they are used to assemble an integrative pattern map. More commonly, the term integrative map is applied to combinations of stratigraphic maps that are normally regarded as end products in individual stratigraphic studies. For example, in a study of the sandstone content of a stratigraphic unit, it may be possible to combine features of the isolith (thickness) map, the vertical-variability map, and perhaps of textural and vectorial maps. Patterns or symbols may be used to depict not only the changing thickness of the sandstone, but may also reveal the directions of sand transport. Maps that show the inferred source area and the direction and distance of transportation of clastic materials are **dispersal maps.** These are treated in detail by Pettijohn (1957, Chapter 12). An example of a **sand dispersal map** is given in the present book in Figure 13-9. Potter and Pryor (1961) examine the problem of dispersal centers of Paleozoic clastics in the Upper Mississippi Valley, and include an effective diagrammatic summary in their Figure 14.

Another kind of integrative map is based on a combination of isopach and facies maps. These **paleotectonic maps** show what the distribution of positive and negative tectonic elements was during the accumulation of a particular stratigraphic unit. Such maps were called **tectofacies maps** in the first edition of this book, but it seems preferable to classify them as integrative maps. Still another example of integrative maps are **evaluation maps,** which summarize the results of stratigraphic analyses made for economic purposes.

In contrast to integrative maps, which combine the information from several stratigraphic maps, derived maps are prepared by further analysis of a map already constructed. An example of this type of map is the **rate-of-change map,** which is based on analysis of the contour lines on the initial map. The rate of change of structure, thickness, or composition of a stratigraphic unit is inversely proportional to the distance between contours, just as the slope on a topographic map is greatest where the contours are most closely spaced. Areas on a stratigraphic map where rates of change are greatest commonly imply conditions under which the aspect of the stratigraphic unit changed more rapidly during deposition than elsewhere. Thus a map that shows the rate of change of thickness of a stratigraphic unit may aid in distinguishing basins from shelves. For instance, a line drawn through the area of maximum change in thickness might show the position of the **tectonic hinge line** as it was during deposition of the stratigraphic rock body. Figure 12-14, it will be recalled, showed an alternative way of identifying the tectonic hinge.

By contrasting rates of change in thickness with rates of change in facies, it is possible in some instances to note whether the principal facies changes generally occur along the tectonic hinge line, or whether they are displaced shelfward or basinward from the position of maximum rate of change in subsidence. Such studies aid in interpreting the conditions under which shelf-formed sediments may spill over into a basin, in contrast to conditions under which sediments may accumulate in a basin more rapidly than can be accommodated by subsidence, resulting in an extension of typical basin sediments shelfward of the tectonic hinge. Facies "spill-over" is referred to again in the section in which facies map interpretation is discussed.

Trend Maps. Within the past decade, geologists have experimented with methods of map analysis that separate local fluctuations in stratigraphic data from the broader patterns of areal variation. A stratigraphic map may be regarded as a means of depicting the combination of tectonic, depositional, and erosional processes that developed the geometry and composition of a rock body. The geologic processes may be divided into two groups; those that operated on a relatively large scale, and others whose effects were relatively local. The first category includes the widespread regional controls that govern shelf, basin, and geosynclinal deposition, that is, the entire tectono-environmental complex, plus those that produce broad postdepositional structural and erosional changes. These large-scale controls give rise to systematic changes that influence the attributes of the rock body as a whole. Less widespread controls develop small-scale features, such as local variations in the sedimentary environment, growth of structures within the broad depositional area, and may be responsible for localized postdepositional disturbances and erosion.

An "observed" contour map based directly on the original stratigraphic data thus reflects the simultaneous effect of the large-scale and small-scale factors operative during accumulation of the deposit. For example, a shoreline zone may show a systematic increase in sand from the offshore area toward the old landmass. However, the shoreline zone often contains bars, barrier beaches, tidal inlets, and other features that locally modify this gradual increase in sand content. The amount of sand observed in a given well would thus depend on its location. The large-scale controls may account for an average of 30 feet of sand in the well area, whereas the occurrence of a local bar might increase this to 50 feet in a particular well. Similarly, if a well penetrates an area of scour, the sand thickness encountered might be abnormally low, say only 10 feet.

The sand thickness encountered in an individual well can be regarded as the sum of two components, one contributed by the large-scale controls and the other by a local control. The well that penetrated the sand bar in the above example can be regarded as comprising a 30-foot contribution from the large-scale controls and a 20 foot contribution of sand from the small-scale control. Similarly, the abnormally thin sand in the subsequent example includes a contribution of 30 feet from the large-scale controls, from which 20 feet of sand were removed by scour. Thus, the local component may be either positive or negative, depending in this case on whether localized deposition or scour occurred in the well area.

The large-scale component may be defined as that part of an observed value which is relatively stable and which varies systematically, if at all, from point to point on the map. The large-scale component gives rise to a relatively smooth surface that may have gradients in various directions and thus controls the main form of the map. In contrast, the small-scale component contributes a relatively unstable part to the observed value and varies in a somewhat irregular manner. It produces no significant gradients, but is represented by a series of nonsystematic (positive or negative) departures from the smooth regional form. Thus, the small-scale component would display a spotty pattern of hills and hollows if it were mapped separately from the large-scale component.

Separation of the observed map data into two main parts representing large-scale and small-scale effects is called **trend surface analysis.** The large-scale component is called the **trend,** and its map is the **trend surface.** The small-scale effects produce **residuals** on the trend. With trend surface analysis, a single stratigraphic map can be divided into two maps, one of which displays the relatively systematic, large-scale features of the stratigraphic unit, and another which displays the small-scaled variations that are superimposed on the underlying pattern. The trend surface aids in the reconstruction of the broad aspects of the sedimentary basin, whereas the residuals may reflect local deltas or other features along the basin margin. In exploration for economic resources, the trend surface may, in some cases, be used as a "predicting surface" for estimation of features to be encountered in new test borings (such as sand thickness, depth to a marker bed, and so forth), with the residuals playing the part of the "uncertainty" in the prediction. In the more general case, the residual maps may shed light on local areas in which special conditions may have prevailed that were favorable for the accumulation of oil, gas, or ore. In some instances, particular local effects, such as the interplay of bars and channels along a shoreline trend, may be shown more effectively on residual maps than on trend maps or even on the original "observed maps."

The theory of trend surfaces and methods of computation are not developed here, but a fairly comprehensive literature is available on the subject. Grant (1957) defines the trend as the polynomial surface of best fit to the observed map data. Miller (1956) applied the method to beach deposits, and Krumbein (1956) showed its application to facies maps. Both of these papers describe computational methods by desk calculator, though most trend analysis is performed with high-speed computers (Krumbein, 1959). Graphic methods have been used (Pelletier, 1958; Bishop, 1960, Chapter 10).

The basic data for trend analysis are the geographic coordinates of each map control point and the magnitude of the mapped variable at each point. In Figure 12-1 the origin is located at the upper left, an arbitrary choice, to give the map a sense of direction similar to that obtained when gridded data are analyzed. First, a linear surface, $X' = A + BU + CV$, is fitted, in which X' is the computed value of the surface at the given point (U,V) and B and C are coefficients that define the slope of the surface. Then the next higher surface, which combines linear and quadratic terms, is fitted, and the analysis proceeds at least to the cubic degree (see Allen and Krumbein, 1962, for details). The residuals (or deviations) on the surfaces are obtained by subtracting the computed value at each point from the observed value.

Figures 12-27 and 12-28 illustrate the use of a quadratic trend surface in the analysis of subsurface data. The stratigraphic unit is the Upper Permian in southeastern Colorado and western Kansas, extending from the top of the Stone Corral Dolomite to the top of the Permian. The left-hand map in Figure 12-27 is the total isopach of the unit; the right-hand map shows the thickness of sandstone in the unit. The total thickness increases toward a center in western Kansas, but the sandstone thickness is greatest along an intermediate area in eastern Colorado.

The 31 control points used in this example (shown on the isopach map) were used to fit the quadratic surface to the sand isolith map. The saddle-shaped trend surface map is shown in Figure 12-28, *left*, which represents the mathematical surface that corresponds to the observed map of Figure 12-27, *right*. The deviation map shown in Figure 12-28, *right*, was obtained by subtracting each computed value from its corresponding observed value.

Fig. 12-27. (*Left*) Isopach map of the Upper Permian in southeastern Colorado and western Kansas, showing the thickened central portion of the unit. (*Right*) Sandstone isolith map with its thickest portion in an intermediate area. See Figure 12-28 for trend analysis of the sandstone data.

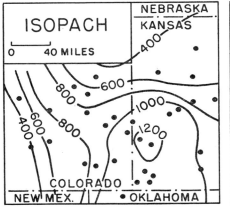
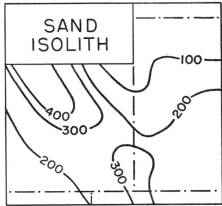

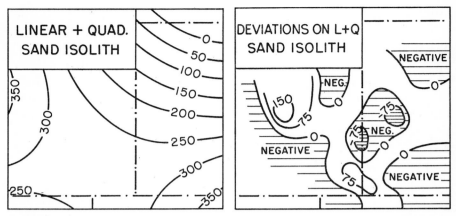

Fig. 12-28. (*Left*) Quadratic trend surface fitted to the sandstone isolith map of Figure 12-27, showing the saddle-shaped regional distribution pattern. (*Right*) Deviations from the regional map, showing residual areas of high sand content along the inferred hinge line. Map scale and control points are the same as on Figure 12-27.

Positive deviations (representing more sand than would be expected on the mathematical surface) occur in a band across eastern Colorado, and negative deviations (shown shaded on the maps) occur on both sides. The geological implication of this deviation map is that the sand accumulated along a hinge line lying between the thin western and thick central areas, as shown on the isopach map.

This example, though based on relatively few control points, illustrates how an original "observed" map can be separated into two portions which may give more information about the stratigraphic unit than is readily visible in the original map. The potential value of deviation maps in the search for local facies "anomalies" that may be associated with economic deposits is apparent from the right-hand map of Figure 12-28.

In addition to the methods of mathematical and statistical analysis used in the preparation of derived maps from observed maps, other systems of statistical analysis have been applied to stratigraphic information. The problem of expressing **stratigraphic variability** numerically and that of measuring its magnitude was investigated by Potter and Siever (1955). They compared the variations in stratigraphic attributes over a sampling range on the county, township, and section levels. In a comparison of Pennsylvanian sands and Upper Chester sands and limestones in Illinois, they observed similar variabilities between observations relatively widely spaced, with relatively greater variability between more closely spaced observations. The variability of the limestones was smaller than for the sandstones, as may be expected.

Interpretation of Lithofacies Maps

Facies studies have expanded so rapidly during the past decade that a voluminous literature has sprung up, in which many new mapping techniques are discussed, and in which numerous isopach and lithofacies maps, based mainly on subsurface data, are depicted.

Stratigraphic maps are of value to the degree that they supply information pertinent to the stratigraphic unit being studied. The interpretation of stratigraphic maps may be facilitated or hindered by the kinds of data that are selected for mapping as well as by the particular map form that is selected for presentation. Thus, stratigraphic mapping includes a large element of design, and the objectives of the study must be considered in terms of the kinds of data available and of the mapping techniques to be used. It is sometimes necessary to prepare a series of working maps for preliminary analysis, in order to select those maps that most effectively communicate information pertinent to the objectives of the study.

A good rule of thumb to apply in becoming acquainted with problems of facies map interpretation is to study published maps and note how the geologist who prepared them tackled his own problem of interpretation. Many such maps appear in the *Bulletin of the American Association of Petroleum Geologists,* as well as in other journals. Examples are Andrichuk (1951), Brill (1952), Amsden (1955), Baillie (1955), and Dickey and Roth (1955).

Relatively few broad principles of facies map interpretation have been stated (Krumbein, 1952). Stratigraphic units differ widely in their patterns of variation, and sometimes the influence of large local fluctuations in the data may obscure the broad trends in the maps. In addition, the number of facies maps that have been published is small in comparison with the number of topographic maps available. Thus, it is not surprising that the principles of stratigraphic map interpretation lag behind those of land form analysis since the latter developed from topographic maps.

A conspicuous feature of many facies maps is the relation between isopachs and facies contours. In some maps, both sets of contours are approximately parallel, but in others they may be discordant in complex ways. The "isopach strike" and "facies strike" concepts are useful in evaluating these relations, and rank in importance with the concept of structural strike in facies map interpretation.

An isopach map is the projection of a three-dimensional solid that is assumed to have a horizontal, planar upper surface. **Isopach strike** may accordingly be defined as the compass direction of an isopach line at a given point on the map. Facies contours represent traces of vertical surfaces that cut the three-dimensional rock body into facies segments. Hence, **facies strike** may also be defined as the compass direction of a facies contour at a given point. **Structural strike,** as is well known, is similarly measured as a compass direction.

One of the first stages in facies map interpretation accordingly includes the study of the relations between composition and geometry of the three-dimensional rock body. Three classes of relationship are involved, as shown in Table 12-6. Thus, the strikes of the three types of contours may all be parallel. When this is the case, the implication is that the thickness and composition of the accumulating sediments express a simultaneous and similar response to contemporaneous subsidence and that no major post-depositional structural disturbances have occurred across the "grain" of the area. This condition is suggested by maps of some stratigraphic intervals in the Michigan Basin, which appear to have undergone no major postdepositional warping of the kind that would develop discordance between structure, composition, and thickness.

The second class of conditions shown in Table 12-6 is by far the most interesting. Where facies and isopach strike are parallel and structure is discordant, the relations imply that structural disturbance followed an initial concurrent response of thickness and facies to subsidence. This relation is characteristic of some Paleozoic deposits in the Rocky Mountains, in which later structures cut across earlier sedimentary and tectonic trends.

Parallelism between isopach and structural strike, with the facies strike discordant, implies, as in the previous case, that no major postdepositional structural disturbances cut across the original "grain" of the deposits. On the other hand, it appears that the composition and thickness of the accumu-

TABLE 12-6. RELATIONS AMONG STRUCTURE, ISOPACH, AND FACIES ''STRIKES''

---

(1) All three are parallel.

(2) Two are parallel; one is discordant.
　　(a) Facies and isopach strike parallel; structure discordant.
　　(b) Isopach and structure strike parallel; facies discordant.
　　(c) Facies and structure strike parallel; isopach discordant.

(3) All three are discordant.

---

lating sediment differed in their response to contemporaneous subsidence. This may reflect special source conditions, or even facies "spill-over" from basin to shelf, or the reverse.

The special case of parallelism of facies and structural strike, with isopachs discordant, seems less common than the others. Where carbonate reefs abut against thick shale accumulations, there may be initial differences between thickness and compositional response of the sediments to contemporaneous tectonism. Subsequent deformation may result in the rigid reefs influencing the structural strike, developing a postdepositional parallelism between composition and structure, with isopach lines discordant.

In the preceding discussion, it is assumed that the stratigraphic unit of interest has not been subjected to postdepositional erosion. Where erosion has occurred, the relations among the three kinds of strike may be very complex. This is especially true if the pattern of erosion was controlled in part by local disturbances along an otherwise systematic trend. In addition, the generalizations given above may not hold if erosional gaps exist in the stratigraphic unit being mapped. It is commonly difficult to interpret the significance of the edge of a given stratigraphic unit as delineated by the zero isopach line inasmuch as this position may represent the margin of the depositional environment or may reflect postdepositional erosion. Table 12-7 lists some of the criteria which are useful in distinguishing depositional strand lines from erosional zero lines.

Although the relationships among structural, isopach, and facies strike are important in setting up a framework for facies map interpretation, other

TABLE 12-7. EROSIONAL VERSUS DEPOSITIONAL SIGNIFICANCE OF ZERO ISOPACH LINES

EROSIONAL	DEPOSITIONAL
Zero line at edge of lower beds of unit mapped.	Zero line at pinchout of upper beds of unit mapped.
Lower beds offlapped by conformable upper beds (where regressive stage preceding exposure and erosion is preserved).	Lower beds onlapped by conformable higher beds.
Top beds of interval thin toward zero line; others constant.	All beds of interval thin progressively toward zero line.
Lithofacies and isopach trends discordant.	Lithofacies and isopach trends concordant.
Rise in clastic ratio and sand-shale ratio through stripping of upper beds and increased influence of basal coarse clastics (revealed by vertical variability maps).	Rise in both ratios without systematic upward shift of component lithosomes.
Isopach rate of change shows abrupt increase.	Isopach rate of change constant to zero line.
Biofacies discordant.	Biofacies show systematic shift from sublittoral to littoral.

features of the maps also need to be examined critically. The detailed patterns of the facies lines, the trends that they show, and the possible geologic significance of residual maps all bear on facies interpretation. Moreover, the relationships among the maps, such as the similarities or differences between maps showing different aspects of the stratigraphic unit, need to be taken into account. Thus, if two maps look much alike, the question arises as to whether there is some geologic relation between the features mapped. If so, one or the other may be selected as being more closely related to the objectives of the study. That is, one may prepare too many facies maps, just as he may err in constructing too few.

The interpretation of broad-scale rock inventory maps is commonly fairly straightforward, inasmuch as such maps supply information on the source areas of detrital materials, on the occurrence of special environments, and on the tectonic elements present in the mapped area at the time of sediment accumulation. For example, presence of evaporites implies a restricted arid environment; the nature of a basin, as brought out by isopachs and facies patterns, sheds light on degrees of contemporaneous subsidence over the area of interest.

Interpretation of maps is facilitated when the maps are designed for specific purposes. For instance, end members may be selected to emphasize environmental conditions. In carbonate sections, the limestones can be grouped into "rough-water" types (those formed in agitated shallow water areas) and "quiet-water" types (those formed in deeper, quieter waters). By thus designing a map that includes or contrasts selected stratigraphic attributes, it becomes possible to set up more definitive principles of map interpretation in terms of the specific attributes under study.

BIOFACIES MAPS

As stated earlier, the techniques of lithofacies mapping can be applied directly to biofacies data. If numerical biofacies data are available, a set of contour-type biofacies maps can be made to parallel any given set of lithofacies maps. The basic data for such maps includes knowledge of the kinds of fossil species present, as well as of the number of individuals in each category. From such data, it is possible to set up end members that distinguish ecological groups, clear-water versus muddy-water inhabitants, and the like. With data arranged as end members, all the maps based on the facies triangle, including even the facies departure maps, can be applied to biofacies studies. The "bio-departure" map, for example, may be used to show the extent to which the faunal assemblage "departs" from some selected central type.

Though one may visualize a wide variety of biofacies maps, the compilation of biofacies data is beset by much more difficulty than lithofacies data. As pointed out in the first edition of this text, sedimentary rocks, as a class, are much less affected by diagenesis than are the fossils they contain, which may be wholly destroyed during dolomitization, for example. Moreover, data on megafossils are seldom obtained in subsurface cores, and are usually difficult to identify even if they are included among rock cuttings. In addition to these limitations, buried fossil faunas may not be wholly representative of the forms that lived on the bottom and in superjacent waters. Nevertheless, considerable work is being done in the analysis of biofacies data. Two papers by Imbrie (1955) illustrate this approach.

Despite these difficulties, however, much can be accomplished with biofacies data if allowances are made for their limitations. Outcrop studies, which do not suffer the limitations of subsurface data, as far as megafossils are concerned, lend themselves well to biofacies studies. Figure 12-29, reproduced from the first edition of this book, provides an illustration of this kind of approach.

The Upper Cretaceous Mancos shale of New Mexico has been extensively studied, and Figure 12-29 shows three columnar sections of the Mancos in which the chief components of successive faunas are indicated. It is appar-

Fig. 12-29. Cross section of Mancos Shale from south to north in northwestern New Mexico. See Figure 12-30 for line of section. [Data from Pike (1947).]

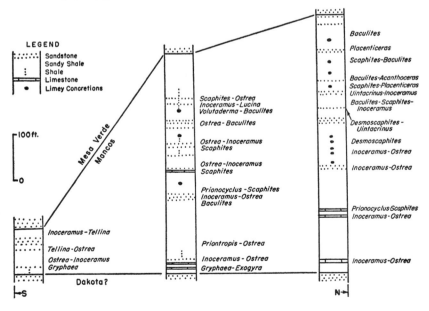

ent that the thin southern section is characterized by an abundance and diversity of pelecypods. Thus, the percentage of cephalopods in molluscan faunules in the Mancos would appear to be related to changes in thickness.

In testing this hypothesis, biosomes are established by determining those portions of each section bearing cephalopods alone, to the exclusion of other mollusks. Other biosomes are based on thicknesses bearing pelecypods and gastropods alone to the exclusion of cephalopods. Intermediate biosomes are designated according to the species of cephalopods, gastropods, and pelecypods recorded. A 100-foot interval, for instance, which bears three species of cephalopods and one of pelecypods, has 75 feet assigned to a cephalopod biosome and 25 feet assigned to a gastropod-pelecypod biosome.

Following the determination of the biosomes, the biologic aspects are calculated by deriving ratios between cephalopods and gastropods-plus-pelecypods for each section. That is, the number of feet assigned to cephalopod biosomes is divided by the number of feet assigned to gastropod-pelecypod biosomes. The resulting ratios for each of the eighteen sections studied constitute the nonspecific biologic aspects in this case. These values are plotted on a map (Figure 12-30, right), and lines of equal ratio value are drawn, dividing the map area into subdivisions of varying biologic aspect.

Comparison of the biofacies map with a sand-shale lithofacies map (Figure 12-30, left) of the same stratigraphic unit aids interpretation of the biofacies. The trends of the two maps are parallel, and it is evident that cephalopod values decrease with increasing sand-shale ratio values. Since

Fig. 12-30. Lithofacies and biofacies maps of the Mancos Shale and equivalents in the Four Corners area. Reciprocal relations between the sand-shale ratio and the biofacies ratios are shown by the two maps. [Data mainly from Pike (1947).]

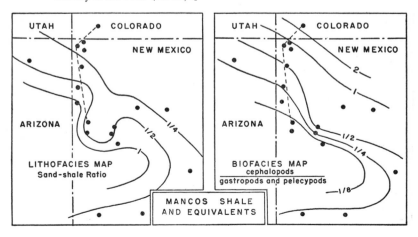

the sand tongues in the Mancos are northeastward extensions of lithosomes that dominate the largely nonmarine Mesaverde Formation, it is clear that increase in gastropod-plus-pelecypod values indicates approach toward shore.

Conversely, an increase in cephalopod percentages indicates seaward departure from the littoral zone. The example suggests that variation in the biologic aspect of the Mancos may be significant beyond the line where a significant lithologic rate of change is apparent.

AUTOMATIC DATA PROCESSING IN STRATIGRAPHIC ANALYSIS

There has been an almost explosive expansion in the amount of data that has become available to the stratigrapher in the past decade or two, owing largely to the development of various kinds of mechanical well-logging devices. Electric logs, for example, in conjunction with sample logs, permit the extraction of large amounts of numerical data on elevations of marker beds, on thicknesses of rock layers, on number of sand occurrences, and so on, which constitute the basic data for preparation of the kinds of maps treated in this chapter.

The storage problem alone for data from some 30,000 exploratory wells each year in North America is a formidable task, to say nothing of the compilation and use of the data contained in the records. In part, the magnitude of the problem is such that, in many instances, the essential day-to-day information is read directly from the well logs, which are then filed for later reference. Thus, many geological data are relatively inert; when special stratigraphic studies are undertaken, it is sometimes necessary to comb through the files to obtain the data needed for the particular study.

Automatic data processing provides the essential means for coping with such large masses of data, inasmuch as it affords a mechanism by which data-searching, arranging, and analysis can be performed with a minimum of hand labor.

Geologists as a professional group have been hesitant in their use of data-processing equipment, though within the past several years considerable strides have been made. There seems little doubt that geologists will take increasing advantage of the benefits that accrue from automatic data handling as they become more familiar with the techniques; in this section, five main topics associated with the subject will be briefly treated. These are: acquisition, storage, retrieval, processing, and presentation of data.

Data acquisition includes all techniques for obtaining information bearing on a given subject. To a very large degree, data acquisition in stratigraphy is performed by the geologist, who correlates the sections on the well logs by himself and measures or supervises measurement of lithological, faunal, physical, and chemical information about the rocks penetrated by the well or observed in outcrop.

Some aspects of data acquisition can be handled by automatic or semi-automatic devices. Electric logs, for example, may be **digitized** by converting the continuous curves into numerical readings at fixed intervals of depth, or in terms of the magnitude of the "kicks." These numerical data, automatically punched on cards, are then used for further analysis.

Data storage refers to the preservation of information or data, usually in such form that it may later be retrieved. The basic requirements for the storage of electric logs, for example, are a filing cabinet and a system of coding that permit the log of any well to be found conveniently. In the sense of automatic data processing, the term refers to the storage of data on punched cards or magnetic tape. In this phase of data processing the design of punched cards becomes basically important, since all pertinent items must be recorded, and each item of information must be keyed as to source, stratigraphic unit, geographic location of well or outcrop, and so on.

For example, in compiling information on wells drilled for oil or gas in the Rocky Mountain region, Petroleum Information, Inc. (Denver), estimated that on the basis of six data cards for each well, the total file includes approximately 300,000 punched cards to cover the 50,000 wells drilled in that region.

Data acquisition and storage are interrelated in that decisions must be made regarding the information that is to be recorded; and the punched card must have its columns of data arranged such that specific items always occupy the same positions on the card. Data sheets and card design are mentioned at the end of this section.

For the relatively small amounts of stratigraphic data used by geologists in most academic projects, punched cards are most suitable for storage, inasmuch as they can be handled and sorted in various ways as the study progresses. A project that includes 200 control points within a single stratigraphic unit seldom requires more than a few cards per control point, which would form a deck of IBM cards less than 5 inches thick. For many studies, the pertinent data for each point of observation can be stored on a single card.

For projects with economic implications, where hundreds of control points may be involved in a stratigraphic study, and where the rocks in the stratigraphic unit are classified into a dozen or more categories, it may be necessary to devote the major portion of a filing cabinet to the storage of punched cards on one project alone. For such projects the use of magnetic tape is almost mandatory.

Data retrieval includes all procedures by which the information stored on cards or tape is made quickly available as printed lists or for use in any kind of analysis or processing that may be required. In large installations data may be transmitted from cards or tape through teletype devices and made directly available in some other city or in a centralized computing center.

Data processing includes a wide range of accounting, statistical, and mathematical procedures through which information stored on cards or tapes can be passed. In stratigraphic analysis, for example, processing includes sorting procedures for arranging the data geographically or by magnitude; the computation of percentages and ratios; and the much more complicated computations that are involved in trend surface analysis. The high speed computer is only one element in an array of machines for data processing, and it is used either for very large amounts of data handled in some routine manner or for complex computations when only relatively small sets of data are involved. A review of some aspects of data analysis in geology, including some discussion of models, is given in Krumbein (1962).

Data presentation refers to the automatic construction of graphs, maps, and other visual devices utilized in the study and analysis of data. Plotting machines can be used in conjunction with computers to display or print charts (scatter diagrams) in which one variable is plotted against another. On this chart may be superimposed the smooth curve that best "fits" the observations. Map-plotting devices are available that print thicknesses, percentages, or ratios at the proper control-point position on maps; some such machines print whole fields of numbers that show directly the pattern of the contoured surface being studied.

The rapid development and increasing versatility of automatic data-processing equipment suggests that the stratigrapher become acquainted with these ways of eliminating the "busywork" associated with stratigraphic analysis in order that he may spend more of his time studying the geologic aspects of his problem. In addition to computations involving the numerical data of stratigraphy, computers can be used with qualitative data of various sorts to aid in setting up classifications of rocks, distinguishing among paleoecologic faunal assemblages, and the like.

As mentioned earlier, an important preliminary consideration in using automatic data processing equipment is the design of the data sheets and of the punched-card formats used for storing the data in convenient form. Figure 12-31 shows a data sheet that may be used for the kind of strati-

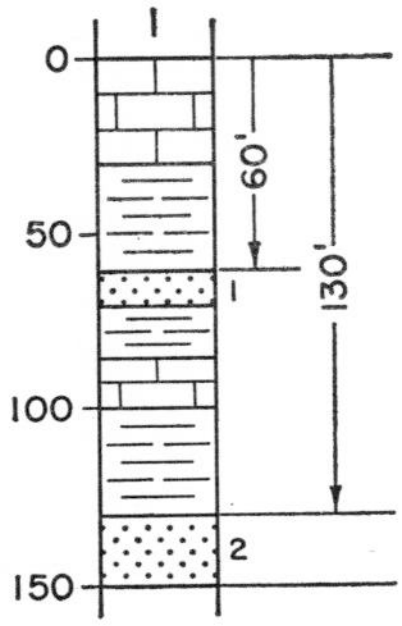

SUMMARY   DATA   SHEET

CONTROL PT.	U MILES	V MILES	TOP ELEV.	TOTAL TH.	SS. TH.	SHALE TH.	LS. TH.	
1	0.7	1.1	710	150	30	75	45	

VERTICAL RELATIONS DATA SHEET (SANDSTONE EXAMPLE)

CONTROL PT.	U MILES	V MILES	TOP ELEV.	NO. OF SANDS	TOTAL SS. TH.	SAND 1		SAND 2	
						TH.	DIST.*	TH.	DIST.*
1	0.7	1.1	710	2	30	10	60	20	130

* See Remarks in Caption

Fig. 12-31. Data sheets for conventional stratigraphic maps and for sandstone vertical variability maps at control point 1 of the section shown on the base map of Figure 12-1. In measuring the position of a sandstone bed, the distance to the center of the bed, instead of its top, is used for center-of-gravity maps such as Figure 12-21. [After Krumbein (1960).]

graphic section illustrated in Figure 12-1. The upper part of the sheet includes the gross data for conventional stratigraphic maps; the lower part is used for vertical variability data. In sections containing numerous sandstones the vertical variability data for a single well may require several cards, which can be keyed by identification codes to the same well.

A somewhat generalized card used for student projects in conventional stratigraphic studies is shown in Figure 12-32. The first part of the card is used for coding the outcrop or well number and the geographic U and V coordinates shown in Figure 12-1. Specific "fields" of digits are used for total thickness of the rock unit and the thicknesses of sandstone, shale, and nonclastics in the section. In addition, six fields labeled with Roman numerals may be used for recording data on more specific rock types that may be needed in a detailed analysis.

The card form shown in Figure 12-32 is a combination **data transcript card** and **computer-input card**; that is, the card serves the dual purpose of storing the basic data and of having the data in proper form for direct input to a high-speed computer. The use of such combined transcript and computer-input cards for ratios and percentages is described by Krumbein and Sloss (1958) in connection with an IBM 650 computer program that yields 150 percentages and 100 ratios per minute.

CONCLUDING REMARKS

The wide range of mapping techniques described in foregoing sections indicates the many ways in which stratigraphic data may be combined to bring out their varying aspects. It is apparent that a series of maps of any stratigraphic interval involving structure, thickness, facies, and paleogeology gives an insight into three-dimensional implications of the stratigraphic unit that earlier methods could not supply.

To a large extent, the expansion of stratigraphic methods and the sharpening of stratigraphic concepts owe their development to the influx of subsurface data from oil exploration. Many of the mapping techniques described in this chapter arose from the need for improved methods of analyzing and integrating large masses of data for more effective subsurface exploration.

Stratigraphic analysis, especially with regard to facies mapping, has undergone a phenomenal growth during the past decade. This has arisen in part from the many new and improved techniques of map design that have become available; and in part the growth has come from increased realization that areal geologic data are presented more effectively in maps than in cross sections. This in no way implies that cross sections are not useful; indeed, they are indispensable both for setting up the initial correlation network and for showing in two dimensions some of the complex interrelations among the rocks that make up a three-dimensional stratigraphic unit.

It is increasingly apparent that full three-dimensional treatment of stratigraphic units is essential for their understanding and analysis. This will become especially true as stratigraphers move ahead in their search for underlying generalizations of wide applicability. The concept of a stratigraphic model, developed in the next chapter, builds on the three-dimensional aspects of stratigraphic analysis as brought out by the mapping techniques presented here.

Fig. 12-32. Example of a punch card, with fields designed for stratigraphic data. Many other formats are in current use. [From Krumbein and Sloss (1958).]

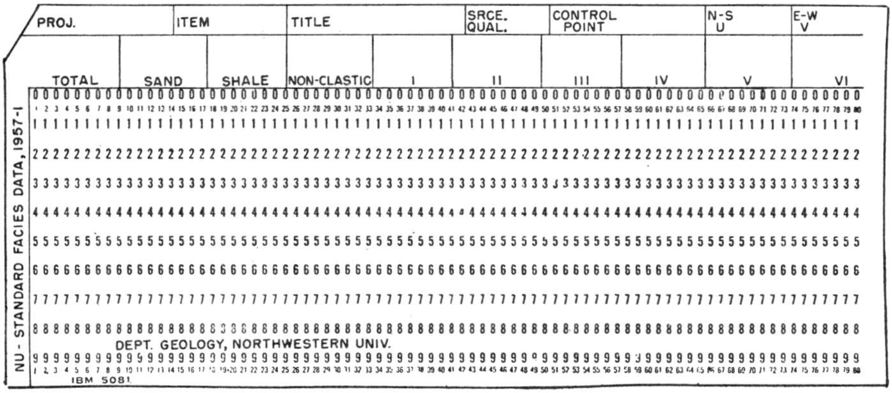

SUPPLEMENTARY READINGS

The amount of literature on stratigraphic mapping has increased tremendously during the past decade. The following selected references include several papers that introduce specific concepts, as well as papers and books that present a general treatment of the subject.

1. Andrichuk, J. M., 1960, Facies analysis of Upper Devonian Wabamun Group in west-central Alberta, Canada: Am. Assoc. Petrol. Geologists Bull., v. 44, p. 1651–1681. An excellent example of a facies study of a complex carbonate–evaporate unit, in which the end members and the ratios among them are clearly defined.
2. Bishop, M. S., 1960, Subsurface mapping: New York, John Wiley & Sons, Inc. This is an excellent presentation of the principles used in the construction of a wide variety of stratigraphic maps, and includes discussion of methods of contouring and other related topics.
3. Forgotson, J. M., Jr., 1960, Review and classification of quantitative mapping techniques: Am. Assoc. Petrol. Geologists Bull., v. 44, p. 83–100. This is the definitive article on modern facies maps, with discussion of the usefulness of each of the map types discussed.
4. Goodlet. G. A., 1957, Lithological variation in the Lower Limestone Group in the Midland Valley of Scotland: Geol. Surv. Great Britain, Bull., No. 12, p. 52–65. An especially well-designed facies study presented in a lucid manner.
5. Krumbein, W. C., 1954, The tetrahedron as a facies mapping device: Jour. Sed. Petrology, v. 24, p. 3–19. Discussion of the ways in which four end members may be mapped and the relation between points within a tetrahedron and their projections onto various triangular faces.
6. McKee, E. D. et al., 1956, Paleotectonic maps, Jurassic System: U.S.G.S. Misc. Geol. Investigation, Map I-175. This is the first facies map folio published. See also the folio on the Triassic System, issued in 1960.
7. Pelto, C. R., 1954, Mapping of multicomponent systems: Jour. Geology, v. 62, p. 501–511. The original reference on entropy maps, recommended as an illustration of the application of mathematical principles to map design.
8. Sloss, L. L. et al., 1960, Lithofacies maps: an atlas of the United States and southern Canada: New York and London, John Wiley & Sons, Inc. This is a presentation of more than 100 two-color facies maps, prepared mainly by students at Northwestern University.
9. Weller, J. M., 1960, Stratigraphic principles and practice: New York, Harper & Brothers.

    Chapter 14. Lateral variation and facies.
    Chapter 17. Graphic presentation.

CHAPTER 13

Stratigraphic Analysis

INTRODUCTION

Stratigraphic practice calls for a degree of familiarity with almost all other fields of geology and their fundamental principles. In addition, the literature of stratigraphy is burdened with a seemingly endless array of formation and fossil names, each with a particular connotation in the coordinates of space and time. No completely satisfactory objective method for classifying sedimentary rocks has emerged, hence students must cope with yet another awkward terminology that is in a state of restless evolution. At the same time stratigraphers, as confirmed Uniformitarians, attempt to relate the conditions of deposition of ancient sediments to present-day conditions, which are only now being intensively investigated.

In short, as was true of other sciences at the times of their most rapid evolution, stratigraphy lacks those generalizing laws and guiding principles which provide in more mature disciplines a basis for precise explanation and accurate prediction. Nevertheless, the authors believe that the apparent complexity of stratigraphic phenomena is but another manifestation of an ordered universe, and this last chapter is devoted to a search for a rationale or system among stratigraphic observations. All the materials of preceding chapters are employed, and there is heavy emphasis on the integrative techniques of stratigraphic mapping. No claim is made for complete coverage, nor should the reader assume that the syntheses and interpretations presented are more than tentative. New data, new investigative techniques, and more mature consideration will inevitably contribute to a continuing evolution of concept.

THE CONCEPT OF A STRATIGRAPHIC MODEL

In the search for generalizing principles it is a useful philosophical device to recognize *models*—actual or conceptual frameworks to which observations are referred as an aid in identification and as a basis for prediction. The model concept is an old one in many engineering applications and has a

501

long history in the study of processes active on beaches and in stream drainage basins. More recently there has been an increased interest in the development of models (such as the environmental models touched upon in Chapter 7) to represent more complex geologic situations. Some of the inherent possibilities of using models to solve stratigraphic problems were outlined in a conference on "facies models" in 1958 (Potter, 1959), and much of the present chapter represents an effort to expand this subject.

Generally speaking, models are of several kinds. For example, a flume, in which the movement of sedimentary particles by running water may be studied in the laboratory, is a **physical model.** Such models are used in deriving mathematical relationships that explain the processes of particle transportation. Another kind is the **mathematical model,** in which some physical phenomenon is described in mathematical symbols. The validity of such models may be tested by means of laboratory experiments, or even under field conditions. Closely related to the mathematical model is the **statistical model,** in which relationships among simultaneously varying quantities are analyzed to evaluate the contribution of each variable in the process under study. The statistical model may include a **probability model,** which specifies the way samples are to be drawn.

The common factor in all these models is that they provide a framework for organizing observational data. Models, not necessarily explicitly identified as such, have been used in geology for many years. In his classic paper on multiple working hypotheses, Chamberlin (1897) came very close to the application of modern concepts of models when he set up a series of alternative hypotheses to account for geological observations. Each of these was an implied model, and a geological generalization was accepted when it could be shown to fit all or most of the elements in a given hypothesis.

With respect to modern environments, where the results of energy applied to sediments may be directly observed, it is possible to set up a process model on the one hand, and a response model on the other. The **process model** specifies the kinds of activities that occur in the environment, and it predicts what the responses should be. The **response model** is thus a structuring of the resultant deposits within the framework of the causative factors that are included in the process model. Process models and response models are analytical models in which a distinction can be made between dependent and independent variables. For examples of stratigraphic process and response models, see Sloss (1962).

Thus, one may establish a beach environment as a physical concept, in which wave energy is released along a relatively narrow band on the shoreline. The energy supplied by breaking waves may be used in three ways. Part may be used to stir up the bottom particles; part may be used to develop a shore current; and part is used in the uprush of the wave across the foreshore. Thus, waves, their angle of approach, and the shore currents are the process elements of the model. In the presence of movable materials (sand and pebbles) the energy relationships necessarily produce a linear beach deposit as a response, in which the observable changes in beach properties change more rapidly across the beach than along it.

It may be noted that stratigraphic observations are referable to response models in the sense used above and that the process models have vanished long since. Although no longer observable, the responsible process model is nevertheless commonly identifiable. For example, the deposition of evaporites requires certain restrictions of circulation, plus an excess of evaporation over inflow. Thus, important elements of the process model and its environment may be strongly inferred. Similarly, as discussed in Chapter 11, tectonic behavior at a depositional site sets up a complex of responses that are impressed upon many attributes of the accumulating sediment. Each tectonic state tends to be represented in the stratigraphic record by a particular suite of rock types. These individual suites—the *lithologic associations*—may be thought of as *tectonic response models*.

LITHOLOGIC ASSOCIATIONS

The relationships between sedimentary tectonics and their sedimentary responses, long recognized in general terms by stratigraphers, were more explicitly stated in a paper by Dapples, Krumbein, and Sloss (1948) and constitute one of the topics emphasized in the first edition of this book. The response patterns are now so widely accepted as to require no elaborate treatment in this revision. Nevertheless, as an early phase in the consideration of stratigraphic analysis it is useful to review lithologic associations as relatively simple **tectonic response models.** Lithologic associations may be grouped according to the dominant tectonic state that they represent and, within each tectonic heading, may be categorized according to lithology.

Stable Shelf Associations

Table 13-1 lists the lithologic associations of the stable shelf. The sediments are commonly limited to thin sequences of continental or marine deposits, marked by numerous disconformities and diastems.

Stable shelf sandstones characteristically contain abundant, well rounded quartz grains. They belong to the class of quartzose sandstone (quartz arenite, pure quartz sandstone) described in Chapter 5. Four varieties are found, as shown in Table 13-1. Pure quartz sandstones are the most widespread

TABLE 13-1. STABLE SHELF ASSOCIATIONS

SANDSTONES
    Quartzose
    Quartz-gluconite
    Quartz-iron oxide
    Quartz-muscovite

SHALES
    Chiefly clay shales
    Gray, green, red, brown, black
    Calcareous, glauconitic, carbonaceous
    Quartz common in silt

CARBONATES
    Fossiliferous micrite and sparite
    Biohermal
    Dolomitization common; secondary chert common

EVAPORITE
    Anhydrite and gypsum

---

and representative stable shelf type. Quartz-glauconite sandstones are also relatively common and are intergradational with the pure quartz variety.

Quartz-iron oxide sandstones are found in typical red bed associations, and may occur with red shale and with shelf evaporites. Quartz-muscovite sandstones are not as common as the other varieties, but may occur as channel fillings or as thin sheets of limited extent. Stable shelf shales commonly consist of claystone or soft clay shale containing abundant silt-size quartz particles.

Fossiliferous biomicrites and sparites are the most common of the stable shelf carbonates, but their original textures and structures are characteristically masked by dolomitization. The resulting dolomites display a texture of intergrown rhombic crystals in which voids mark the former position of fossils and fossil fragments. Biolithites occur as sheet-like masses or biostromes, as in the Nisku (Devonian) of Alberta, or as randomly distributed reefs, as in the Silurian of Illinois and Indiana.

Evaporites appear on the stable shelf as sheets of anhydrite or gypsum (rarely as halite) in close association with quartz-iron oxide sandstone, red shale, and thin nodular limestone, as in parts of the Permian of the Great Plains states.

Certain groups of the sedimentary rocks listed in Table 13-1 are found more commonly than others in stable shelf associations. Quartzose sandstone, greenish-gray clay shale, and fossiliferous micrite form a typical group, as illustrated by the Middle and Upper Ordovician of the upper Mississippi

Valley. Dolomitized fossiliferous micrite and biolithite form another common association, as in the Silurian of the Great Lakes region.

Unstable Shelf Associations

Table 13-2 shows the lithologic associations of the unstable shelf. These sediments occur in relatively thin sequences, being slightly thicker locally than they are on stable shelves. The cyclical repetition of beds is commonplace.

Sandstone of the unstable shelf type is less well sorted than the stable shelf type, though all gradations occur between the two. Quartz wacke is widespread and occurs as sheets or lenticular masses. In local, apparently more turbulent areas, such as stream channels or shorelines, the sands may "clean up" to form quartzose varieties, as in the shoestring and channel sandstones associated with Pennsylvanian coal cyclothems.

Thin deposits of "blanket" arkose may occur on unstable shelves, representing periods during which their adjacent granitic source area was not strongly positive. This type of sandstone is typical of the basal portion of transgressive beds on a granite terrain. Feldspathic sandstone is a closely related type that occurs locally on unstable shelves.

Shales formed on the unstable shelf tend to be more silty than their stable shelf counterparts. They belong to the class of micaceous shale described in Chapter 5. Gray and drab colors predominate, although red and black shales also occur. Unstable shelf limestones are dominated by very fine grained varieties containing a considerable clay mixture. Such limestones appear mainly as interbeds in dominantly clastic sections.

Characteristic groups of sedimentary rocks occur among the broader, un-

TABLE 13-2. UNSTABLE SHELF ASSOCIATIONS

SANDSTONES
Feldspathic arenite and wacke
"Blanket" arkose
Muscovite quartz wacke

SHALES
Chiefly silty shales
Gray, green, red, brown, black
Micaceous, carbonaceous, calcareous
Feldspar may be common in silt

CARBONATES
Argillaceous, nodular micrite
Thickened stable shelf types
Dolomitization less common

---

stable shelf associations. The Pennsylvanian coal cyclothems, mentioned earlier, consist, in their lower half, of quartz wacke, thin, fresh-water clay shale with nodular limestone, and coal. Typical marine beds (including silty shale, nodular or thin fossiliferous micrite and sparite) and thin-bedded black shale comprise the upper portion. Cyclothem associations are treated at greater length later in this chapter.

Certain red bed associations, those consisting of quartz wacke and quartz-iron oxide sandstone, red silty shale, evaporites, and thin, nodular limestone, are interpreted as unstable shelf deposits. Parts of the Chugwater Formation of Wyoming apparently belong in this category.

Interior Basin Associations

Table 13-3 lists the lithologic associations found in interior basins. Several groupings are shown in order to distinguish between restricted and open basins. The deposits typically occur in thick sequences, which may be about four or more times that of shelf deposits.

Disconformities are less common in interior basin deposits than in those of the shelf. This suggests more continuous sedimentation, or at least less frequent uplift above depositional base level. Basin tectonism may be oscillatory, but if the oscillations do not lift the sediments above sea level, typical disconformities are not produced.

Interior basin sandstones resemble those of the unstable shelf. Quartz wacke is the dominant type, with somewhat more matrix and finer average grain size than shelf equivalents. Shales in interior basin associations are commonly micaceous, although other types also occur. The nature of the shales is dependent upon the physicochemical environment revealed by associated rocks. Interbedded shales in limestone sequences are commonly calcareous. Black shale is typical of sediments formed in some restricted basins. In general, this shale is more silty than its shelf equivalents.

Carbonate deposition in interior basins may follow any of several paths. Fossiliferous micrite and sparite, dependent upon shallow water and slow burial rate, become subordinate away from the basin margins. Thick accumulations of micrite devoid of benthonic elements may form in the central portions of the basin. Dark bituminous limestone occurs in deeper portions under conditions of impeded circulation.

The margins of interior basins meet ecologic requirements for persistent reef growth more frequently than they do for any other forms of epicontinental sedimentation. Fairly continuous zones of biolithite limestone mark the peripheries of active basins during times of dominant nonclastic sedimentation. The details of reef development and morphology are treated in a later section.

TABLE 13-3. INTERIOR BASIN ASSOCIATIONS

1. Normal "open basin" association

SANDSTONES	Quartz arenite
SHALES	Chiefly siltstones Gray, brown, red, black; chiefly dark Calcareous, carbonaceous, siliceous, micaceous Variety of minerals in silt
LIMESTONES	Thickened shelf types Micrite; often argillaceous

2. Arid "restricted basin" association

SANDSTONES	Quartz arenite
SHALES	Chiefly siltstones Gray, brown, red, black; chiefly dark Calcareous, carbonaceous, siliceous, micaceous Variety of minerals in silt
LIMESTONES	Fine textured, calcitic types Fine grained "primary" dolomites Marginal belts of reefs, fossiliferous sparite, Oolite, and pellet limestones
EVAPORITES	Gypsum and anhydrite Halite and potash salts

3. Black Shale "restricted basin" association

SANDSTONES	Quartz arenite Thin quartzose types
SHALES	Chiefly black, with aberrant faunas; pyritic, carbonaceous
LIMESTONES	Dark, fine grained micrite with much organic matter

Yoked Basin Associations

Although Table 13-4 lists a number of rock types found in yoked basin associations, thick wedges of arkose completely dominate the lithologic assemblage.

Marginal Basin Associations

As noted in Chapter 11, marginal basins occupy a transitional realm between eugeosynclines and cratons. During times of relative eugeosynclinal inactivity, or where eugeosynclinal trends are distant from the stable cratonic margins, accumulation in marginal basins results in lithologic associations identical with those of interior basins. Subsidence tends to be somewhat more continuous, and thicknesses are commonly greater than those that

TABLE 13-4. YOKED BASIN ASSOCIATIONS

SANDSTONES
　　Arkose

SHALES
　　Silty, micaceous, kaolinitic
　　Red and brown
　　Abundant feldspar in silt

NONCLASTICS
　　Nodular limestone
　　Special evaporite sequences

---

accumulate in interior basins and are interrupted by fewer disconformities. Otherwise, the associations are those listed in Table 13-3 and discussed under Interior Basin Associations.

At times of marked orogenic activity in adjacent eugeosynclinal trends, marginal basins fall under the influences of extracratonic conditions and are filled with sedimentary suites representing the lithologic associations common to the eugeosyncline, as discussed below. Typically, the sediments of a marginal basin exhibit intertonguing and intergradation of eugeosynclinal and cratonic associations both vertically and laterally.

Eugeosynclinal Associations

One of the outstanding characteristics of eugeosynclinal sediments (Table 13-5) is the great thickness to which they accumulate. It is not unusual to encounter tens of thousands of feet of sediment without discernible interruptions, although complex structures that make accurate measurement difficult are common. The typical sandstone is graywacke, greenish gray in color, and rich in fragments of pre-existent eugeosynclinal sediments, metamorphic rocks, and volcanics. Graded bedding, load casts and other bedding-plane structures, and evidences of slump are typical features of the graywackes and associated shales.

Tectono-environmental models

The groupings of lithologic associations reviewed in the preceding section are referred to specific tectonic models without significant consideration of environmental vectors. The closing portion of Chapter 11 points out the importance of environment in modifying sedimentary responses to tectonism, and it is obvious that pure tectonic models are an oversimplification. The role of the tectono-environmental couple was discussed in a paper by Krumbein, Sloss, and Dapples (1949), and, as was the case for the simple tectonic response patterns, requires no more than passing notice here.

Table 13-6 is a condensed and idealized grouping of lithologic associations as responses to given combinations of environment and tectonism. A columnar arrangement of environments, ranging from nonmarine to deeper sublittoral is shown in the table, with restricted environments on the right. The rows of the table summarize the environments and their sediments in general terms and according to tectonic conditions ranging from stable shelf to eugeosynclinal. Thus, each block in the table represents the lithologic response to a particular combination of tectonism and environment—a tectono-environmental model.

Despite limitations on interpretations of highly variable and complex lithologic associations, Table 13-6 permits several generalizations regarding the interrelationships of tectonism and environments of deposition. It is seen that, throughout all sedimentary environments, quartzose sandstone is common under stable shelf conditions; quartz wacke, under unstable shelf and interior basin conditions; and graywacke, under orthogeosynclinal conditions. Arkose is characteristic of special source areas adjacent to active yoked basins and may accumulate in marine or continental environments.

The presence of a certain sandstone type in a particular tectonic setting, regardless of sedimentary environment, means that such an occurrence must be discounted as having any bearing on direct environmental interpretation. That is, the occurrence of a quartz wacke is, by itself, no certain criterion of any particular sedimentary environment. However, the detailed characteristics of the quartz wacke, and the nature of the fossils enclosed in it, may furnish significant data about the environment.

In contrast to sandstone, some sedimentary types afford excellent criteria of the sedimentary environment. Thick evaporite deposits interbedded with

TABLE 13-5. EUGEOSYNCLINAL ASSOCIATIONS

SANDSTONES
    Graywacke and graywacke conglomerate
    Tuffs and pyroclastics

SHALES
    Black siliceous shale and siltstone
    Gray, green, common in marine associations
    Red silty shale in nonmarine associations

CARBONATES
    Fine grained, dark, siliceous micrite
    Dolomitization very uncommon

OTHER ROCKS
    Bedded chert; commonly black, yellow, green
    Subaerial and submarine volcanics

TABLE 13-6. TECTONO-ENVIRONMENTAL CLASSIFICATION

	FLUVIAL-LACUSTRINE-EOLIAN ENVIRONMENT	TRANSITIONAL ENVIRONMENT (FLUVIAL-LAGOONAL-LITTORAL)	INFRALITTORAL ENVIRONMENT	CIRCALITTORAL ENVIRONMENT
General conditions; types of specific environments	Alluvial plains, stream channels, lakes, swamps, local or extensive wind action.	Alluvial plains, lagoons, marshes or swamps, barrier beaches, deltaic conditions.	Shallow wave and current-agitated marine waters, open circulation.	Water depths exceed 120 feet; relatively quiet off-shore zones.
General colors and properties of sediments; main faunal elements	White, gray, yellow, red, brown, maroon, mottled. Lenticular or sheet sandstones. Blocky to poorly bedded shales. Limestones very subordinate; coal and lignite beds. Plant impressions and remains; land vertebrates; fresh-water gastropods and pelecypods.	Gray, brown, red, green, blue, dark gray, and black. Lenticular sandstones; some sheet sands. Shales blocky to well bedded; coal and lignite beds. Limestones subordinate; here and there a tongue of marine limestone. Plants; land vertebrates, gastropods, pelecypods, phosphatic brachiopods, and ostracodes common.	Gray, light brown, greenish gray, bluish gray, dark gray to black. Sheet sandstones; local linear bodies. Shales commonly bedded; limestones range from argillaceous to biosparite types. Great variety of stout-shelled benthonic invertebrates (mollusks, brachiopods, echinoderms, corals, etc.)	Sediment colors gray, greenish gray, bluish gray, brownish gray, dark gray, black. Reds and browns subordinate. Sheet sands mainly fine-grained; shales well bedded. Limestones show wide variety, with normal marine types dominant. Great variety of benthonic and nektobenthonic types, including more delicate forms. Significant percentages of planktonic types.
Stable Shelf Occurrence	Quartzose sandstones, cross-bedded. Massive clay shales, commonly mottled. Carbonaceous; seldom calcareous. Fresh-water limestones, nodular, micritic, local.	Quartzose sandstones, cross-bedded, commonly lenticular. Clay shales dominant, brackish varieties bedded; carbonaceous, locally calcareous, marly. Fresh-water limestone subordinate.	Quartzose sandstone cross-bedded. Siltstones ripple-marked. Shales commonly fine clayey, and greenish. Limestones with clastic textures, evenly bedded or locally cross-bedded. Sandstone may grade directly to limestone.	Fine-grained quartzose sandstones. Clay shales common, well bedded; calcareous, carbonaceous. Biomicrite, chalk; numerous planktonic components.
Unstable Shelf Occurrence	Quartz wacke sandstones, some linear quartzose channel sands. Shales mainly siltstones, massive to banded, micaceous, carbonaceous, seldom calcareous. Fresh-water limestones subordinate, nodular micrite to uneven sugary texture.	Lenticular quartzose sandstones; sheet sands are quartz wacke. Shales mainly siltstone; claystones commonly bedded; micaceous, carbonaceous, calcareous. Fresh-water to marly limestones.	Quartzose to quartz wacke sandstones, cross-bedded, ripplemarked. Shales commonly siltstones, carbonaceous, calcareous, light colors. Limestones thicker stable neritic types, argillaceous, locally micritic.	Fine-grained to quartz wacke sandstones, evenly bedded. Silty claystones, carbonaceous, calcareous. Limestones as above, locally denser, less widespread.
Interior Basin Occurrence	Quartz wacke sandstones, local arkose associations. Shales mainly uneven-textured siltstones; micaceous, carbonaceous, semi-waxy, seldom calcareous. Limestones nodular to uneven thin-bedded.	Quartzose, quartz wacke, arkosic sandstones; thick shales commonly change characteristics from top to bottom. Micaceous, carbonaceous, calcareous. Fresh-water limestones may locally be thick.	Quartz wacke sandstones, arkosic sheets or wedges. Shales silty, carbonaceous, micaceous, calcareous. Limestones nodular, uneven, may be argillaceous or micritic.	Quartz wacke sandstones, thin-bedded. Shales fine siltstones to clay shales; dark colors common. Limestones thin, commonly dark; may be nodular.
Geosynclina Occurrence	Graywacke sandstones with subordinate quartz wacke channels. Shales massive to banded, chloritic or feldspathic. Fresh-water limestone may form thick lenticular bodies.	Graywacke sandstones with subordinate quartz wackes. Massive to banded shales, mainly silty to sandy. Local fresh-water limestones.	Graywacke sandstones with thinner quartz wackes. Shales commonly uneven-bedded; may show dark colors. Limestones subordinate, nodular.	Graywacke sandstones subordinate. Shales mainly siltstones with uneven texture. Limestones rare; siliceous, dark.

TABLE 13-6. (Continued)

	INFRALITTORAL, BIOSTROMAL ENVIRONMENT	BATHYAL-ABYSSAL ENVIRONMENT	RESTRICTED LAGOONAL HUMID	RESTRICTED LAGOONAL ARID
General conditions; types of specific environments	Shallow clear waters, open circulation, little or no land-derived sediment. Temperature, salinity, oxygen content, and depth are controlling factors.	Water depths exceed 600 feet; these conditions may locally be fulfilled in rapidly subsiding geosynclines. Rare or absent on craton.	Mainly sublittoral neritic depths; volume may be constant, but circulation restricted by barriers, sills, or biohermal control.	Mainly infralittoral depths; evaporation exceeds inflow. Circulation restricted by barriers, sills, or biohermal control.
General colors and properties of sediments; main faunal elements	Light colors, with tan, bluish, cream dominant. Sandstones and shales subordinate; main bulk of sediments are carbonates, with abundant evidence of life forms and associated debris. Corals, algae, oysters, specialized brachiopods and larger foraminifera, crinoids, etc.	Sediment colors commonly dark; blue, green, red, dark gray to black. Land-derived sediments relatively rare; shales siliceous, diatomaceous. Limestones dark siliceous. Chiefly planktonic types, smaller foraminifera, diatoms, pteropods, etc.	Sediment colors commonly dark gray to black. Sandstones rare; shales dominate; bituminous, pyritic; calcareous, mainly claystones. Limestones dark, bituminous, thinbedded. Phosphatic brachiopods, conodonts, certain mollusks, spores, algae.	Sediment colors commonly light; white, cream, brownish, greenish, bluish, pink, red. Sandstones rare. Clay shales dominate, gypsiferous, calcareous. Limestones micritic, primary dolomites, nodular to thinbedded. Evaporites may range from subordinate to dominant. Fauna aberrant, depauperate or lacking.
Stable Shelf Occurrence	This is a typical environment of stable to mildly unstable shelves, in widespread shallow seas. The biostromal areas may occur locally or over large areas. Sporadic bioherms common. Limestones include biosparite, oösparite, biomicrite, biolithite. Subordinate clay shales, marls, and thin quartzose sands in the association.	These environmental conditions doubtfully present on shelf areas; may occur locally in intracratonic basins. Typical but rare occurrence in eugeosynclinal association at times of rapid subsidence and slow deposition. No sandstones known; shales very siliceous, splintery; primary chert beds or nodules; limestone dark, micritic, very siliceous. Turbidity current deposits may occur.	In shelf occurrences, this environment may form widespread black shales behind barrier beaches or fringing reefs. The sequence may grade into continental sands and shales on one or more sides. Within the environment sandstones and limestones are rare.	In shelf occurrences this environment may form widespread evaporite sequences dominated by gypsiferous shales and thin evaporite beds, grading landward to typical redbed continental and transitional sequences. Limestones thin and subordinate within sequence.
Unstable Shelf Occurrence				
Interior Basin Occurrence	Under basin or geosynclinal conditions, biostromes may rarely occur in local optimum areas. Significant is the growth of biohermal zones along tectonic hinge lines at edges of intracratonic basins. Here biolithite, biosparite, oösparite limestones are the rule, with other types subordinate.		Thick sequences of dark shales, bituminous, waxy, mainly clay types. Sandstones rare, fine grained. Limestones subordinate, dark, bituminous varieties.	Thick sequences of typical evaporite associations; gypsum, anhydrite, salt, thin limestones, and dolomites; bright-colored shales, commonly clayey and gypsiferous. Cyclical evaporites common.
Geosynclinal Occurrence			Dark gray, brown, greenish silty shales, uneven textures. Some fine graywackes or lithic wackes. Limestones rare or absent.	It is doubtful whether true evaporite basins occur in geosynclinal conditions, although local sheets of evaporitic beds and gypsiferous shales may be associated with deltaic parts of geosynclinal sedimentation.

marine limestone and dolomite definitely point to the existence of a restricted environment in which there was an excess of evaporation over inflow. Similarly, biosparite limestone is almost always a good index to the marine sublittoral environment, more probably shallow than deep. Weaver (1958) has shown how clay mineralogy may be applied to the interpretation of depositional environments.

Limitations of tectono-environmental models

The recognition that lithologic associations are responses to specific combinations of tectonism and environment was a major step toward achieving a rational system of stratigraphic analysis. However useful, tectono-environmental models have a number of severe limitations that circumscribe their application to stratigraphic problems.

Pure Versus Mixed Models. The stratigraphic models discussed thus far are represented by lithologic associations assumed to be essentially *pure.* That is, all of the rock types found in association are referable to the same combination of tectonism and environment. In the real world of stratigraphy it is common to find many rock types, presumably related to entirely different models, in intimate association. So frequently are such mixtures observed that they cannot be considered "unnatural" or anomalous; rather, they must represent *mixed models* not taken into account by the classification presented earlier. For example, the occurrence of pure quartz sandstone in an otherwise typical eugeosynclinal association of graywackes and siliceous shales ought not to be considered a complete invalidation of the tectono-environmental concept. As the concept is broadened to admit mixed models it is seen that virtually any kind of rock may be associated with any other kind. Nevertheless there is an identifiable thread of natural association that may be followed to a natural interpretation. Thus, the deposition of quartzose sand in a eugeosyncline may have required nothing more than an interval of relative quiescence during which mature sediment from an adjoining shelf, possibly from the craton, could be washed into the trough.

Discrete Versus Integrated Data. The development of more refined procedures (such as the mapping techniques of the previous chapter) for integration among many fields of data and among separate and discrete points of observation render the relatively simple lithologic association inadequate as a basis for satisfactory and practical stratigraphic models. Some of the most significant attributes of sedimentary rocks are revealed only through stratigraphic mapping to determine internal and external geometric properties and rates and directions of change in various parameters.

Conceptual Models Versus Observable Associations. The sedimentary tectonic and tectono-environmental associations of Tables 13-1 to 13-6 are *conceptual models* in that both the tectonic state and the environment are inferred. Contrasted with these are the actual *observable associations* of sedimentary rocks, as they are seen in nature. One of the cardinal principles of any analytical procedure is the progression from observation to inference. Experience gained in recent years suggests that the stratigraphic record contains numerous natural associations of lithology, form, internal geometry, and other attributes of sedimentary rock masses that are directly observable. Moreover, these observable associations lead to the establishment of models to which observations may be referred for interpretation and analysis.

The characterization and categorization of observable stratigraphic models is clarified by consideration of an example of current stratigraphic analysis. The following example outlines the steps of observation, decision, and integration that permit the recognition of natural associations and a master model of greater flexibility, scope, and applicability than those treated previously.

EXAMPLE: THE FRONTIER FORMATION OF WYOMING*

Let us assume that a stratigrapher is asked for an interpretation of a unit of strata such as the Frontier Formation of Wyoming. This is a prominent succession of sandstones and shales well exposed on the flanks of numerous uplifts in the western and central areas of the state and penetrated by many wells represented by samples, cores, and mechanical logs.

Primary observations and decisions

Among the most essential of primary observations is the determination of the position of the unit to be studied in the stratigraphic column of the area. The Frontier is recognized by its position; it overlies a prominent siliceous shale (the Mowry Shale), and underlies a thick gray shale unit variously termed Hilliard, Baxter, Cody, or Carlile. Recorded observations indicate that the Frontier ranges in thickness from 500 to 900 feet and that it consists of as many as eight individual sandstone members separated by shales. Primary observations of this type may be anticipated in areas of mature stratigraphic study, but in "new" areas they may consume man-years of effort before the analytical phases of investigation may be undertaken.

Stratigraphic analysis, unless related to the time framework of earth history, is relatively meaningless. One of the most important primary deci-

* The authors are indebted to H. G. Goodell, whose doctoral dissertation is the source for many of the data and materials included in this section.

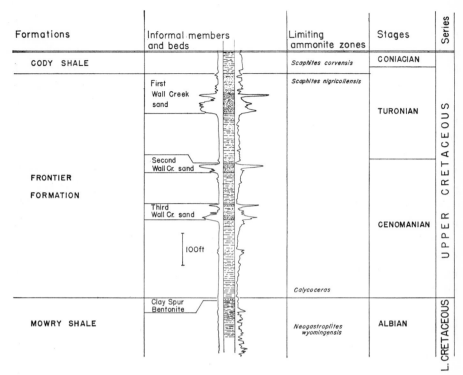

Formations	Informal members and beds		Limiting ammonite zones	Stages	Series
CODY SHALE			*Scaphites corvensis*	CONIACIAN	
	First Wall Creek sand		*Scaphites nigricollensis*	TURONIAN	UPPER CRETACEOUS
FRONTIER FORMATION	Second Wall Cr. sand				
	Third Wall Cr. sand			CENOMANIAN	
	100ft		*Calycoceras*		
MOWRY SHALE	Clay Spur Bentonite		*Neogastroplites wyomingensis*	ALBIAN	L. CRETACEOUS

Fig. 13-1. The Frontier Formation of Wyoming. Primary observations on the stratal and biostratigraphic successions lead to placement of the units to be studied in a time-stratigraphic and lithostratigraphic framework. [Modified after Goodell (1957).]

sions is the time placement of the units investigated and the recognition of significant lacunas representing episodes of nondeposition or erosion. For example, it would be relatively unprofitable to attempt analysis of a succession of strata ranging in age from Pennsylvanian to Jurassic and embracing a lacuna representing Late Pennsylvanian, Permian, Triassic, and Early Jurassic. Fortunately the paleontology of the Frontier Formation has been studied for decades, and clearly indicates an Upper Cretaceous age ranging from Cenomanian to Coniacian. Here again a primary and fundamental decision has been arrived at through the efforts of previous investigators. The primary observational data and the first-order decisions that they in turn permit are summarized in Figure 13-1.

Integration of Observations

The primary observational phase of investigation consists in recording data from discrete geographic points. The observations can be made by studying individual outcrops or by examining individual wells; the first-order decisions can be made without recourse either to geographic integration or to detailed petrologic and mineralogic investigation.

External Geometry. The integration of observational data normally begins with the assembly of information on the spatial relationships of the body of rock under investigation. These include the vertical and lateral relationships with other groups of strata, the thickness and shape of the subject rock body, and its structure.

Vertical relationships. The relationships between a given group of strata and units above and below are best displayed by preparing subcrop and supercrop maps at each boundary. The Frontier Formation rests everywhere with conformity on Mowry Shale, the contact being marked by a distinctive bentonite that is traceable in the subsurface into the Clay Spur Bentonite of the Black Hills. This horizon can be followed over much of the state of Wyoming and provides an easily recognizable operational base for the interval to be studied. In the few localities where the bentonite zone is locally thin or absent, the top of the siliceous Mowry Shale, recognized in the subsurface by its distinctive resistivity pattern on electric logs, is used as the base of the unit without introducing significant error. Although similar sandstones occur in younger strata of the western part of Wyoming, for this investigative example, the top of the Frontier is taken to be the top of the First Wall Creek sand zone and its lithologic correlatives. Thus, for the

Fig. 13-2. Generalized stratigraphic cross section of the Frontier Formation. [After Goodell (1957).]

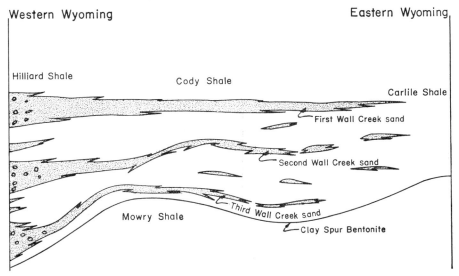

purposes of the study, the Frontier Formation is defined as those strata between the regional marker provided by the Clay Spur Bentonite and the top of the First Wall Creek sandstone and its correlatives. Since both contacts are conformable, no mapping techniques are required to demonstrate the vertical relationships of the unit.

Lateral Relationships. As noted in Figure 13-2 the eastern limit of the Frontier Formation is defined by the pinchout of the First Wall Creek sandstone. It would require a very large number of cross sections to illustrate the geographic distribution of this stratigraphic cutoff, but the relationship is easily portrayed by constructing a map showing the known distribution of the First Wall Creek sandstone (Figure 13-3). Beyond the eastern and southern limits of the area thus defined, the Frontier Formation passes into an unbroken succession of shales. To the west and northwest the Frontier Formation has been eroded from uplifts related to the thrust-fault belt of western Wyoming and adjacent parts of Idaho. Hence the observational data do not of themselves directly indicate the original nature of the western and northwestern lateral relationships of the Frontier.

Thickness. Figure 13-2 illustrates the irregular wedge-shaped character of the Frontier Formation. However, a more complete three-dimensional integration of separate observations on thickness of the unit may be obtained by preparing an isopach map (Figure 13-4). The isopach map shows that the Frontier Formation is over 1500 feet thick at its southwestern extremity, thinning rapidly to an average of about 700 feet in a few tens of miles. A number of areas of local thickening and thinning (sometimes termed "thicks" and "thins") are seen to complicate the pattern in central Wyoming.

Fig. 13-3

Distribution map of the First Wall Creek sand. The eastern and southern pinchout of the sandstone tongue, shown diagrammatically in the preceding figure, provides the cutoff for the Frontier Formation. [After Goodell (1957).]

Limit of 1st Wall Creek SS. Arbitrary cutoff for operational unit.

Structure. In areas of complex structure and steep dips stratigraphic analysis is made more difficult because the thicknesses of units penetrated by wells are exaggerated. In such areas it is useful to prepare a structure-contour map and to use the map in correcting drilled intervals to true stratigraphic thickness before preparing isopach and other integrative maps. Although the area of the Frontier Formation includes many steeply inclined strata most of

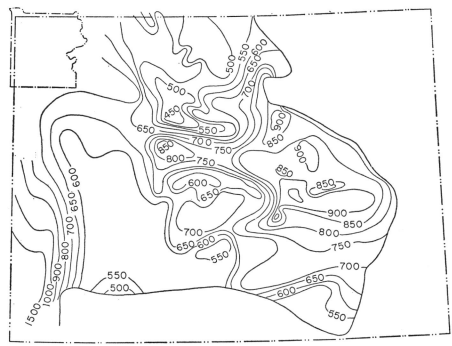

Fig. 13-4. Isopach map of the Frontier Formation in Wyoming. [After Goodell (1957).]

these are observable in outcrop, where true stratigraphic thicknesses are directly measurable; therefore, preparation of a structure-contour map would not add significantly to the present study.

Internal Geometry and Composition. Once the framework of the external geometry and shape of the body of strata under investigation have been established, the investigator is ready to assemble those observational data which pertain to the geometry and interrelationships of rock masses within the major unit and to their sedimentary structures, textures, and composition.

Lithosomes. As indicated by the cross section (Figure 13-2) the Frontier Formation comprises two major intertongued lithosomes: a mass of sandstone on the west and northwest that intertongues easterly and southeasterly with a shale mass. These relationships are most easily studied by reference to map representations. Figure 13-5 is a sand-shale ratio map of the Frontier superimposed on the isopach map of the interval. The map clearly demonstrates the predominance of sandstone at the western border of the area and the gradation to shale at the eastern and southeastern margins. Figure 13-6, which is a sandstone isolith map combined with a map of the number of individual sandstones, is a measure of the vertical variability within the

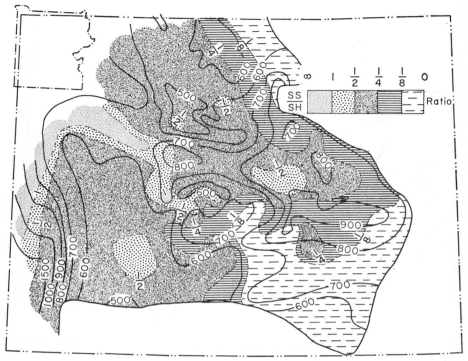

Fig. 13-5. Sand-shale ratio and isopach map of the Frontier Formation. [After Goodell (1962).]

section. Note that sand thickness has a strong correlation with the number of sandstone tongues present. In a more complete study the distribution of sandstone tongues through the vertical dimensions of the Frontier would be developed by the presentation of tripartite or "center of gravity" maps that would determine whether the sand bodies are evenly distributed in a vertical sense or concentrated at some particular level within the unit.

In exposures of the western part of Wyoming the sandstones are characterized by a lack of marine fossils and by numerous intercalations of coal and lignitic shale. In the central part of the state the sandstones are markedly gradational with sandy shales below, except where the contact is abrupt and marked by minor channelling. The basal parts of the sand tongues vary from thinly bedded to massive with common cut-and-fill structures and some local cross bedding. In many instances the basal sandstone is overlain by a shaly interval bearing wood fragments and thin lignites. Above the shaly interval the succession reverts to sandstone, commonly cross-bedded, light in color, and lacking the chert and rock fragments that give a "salt and pepper" appearance to the lower sandstones. The upper sands, in turn, pass by gradation into shales containing marine fossils. These relationships are diagramed in Figure 13-7.

Still farther to the east, in east-central Wyoming, no shaly interruption within individual sandstone tongues is found, and the sandstone members are marked by thickened elongate lenses near their eastern and south-eastern termini.

In a more complete study the orientation of cross-bedding, channels, and grain fabric would be integrated in map form, as would all available observational data on the shale bodies. There are so many aspects of the field and microscopic petrography to be observed and integrated that no more than a few can be treated here. Figure 13-8 shows the manner in which certain parameters of mineral composition may be integrated on a map. The example is taken from the lower part of the First Wall Creek sand, and shows that a central trend of the sandstone tongue from northwest to southeast is characterized by a high content of chert, rock fragments, and feldspar. Goodell (1962) has demonstrated a strong, positive correlation between chert content and grain size. Therefore, the quartz-chert-ratio map (Figure 13-8) serves to illustrate the distribution of grain sizes. Obviously

Fig. 13-6. Sandstone isolith and number-of-sands map of the Frontier Formation. [After Goodell (1962).]

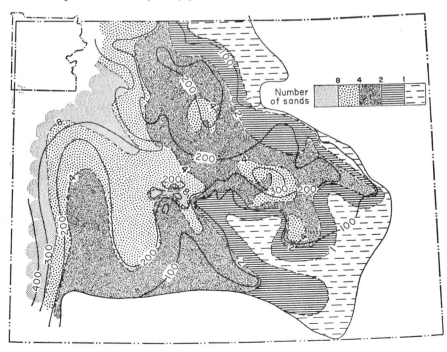

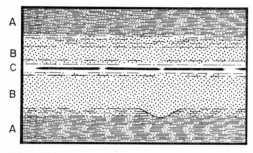

Fig. 13-7

Cyclical units in the Frontier Formation of central Wyoming. (*A*) Marine shale; (*B*) sandstone; (*C*) dark shale with nonmarine fossils and lignite.

there are many other mineralogic and petrographic parameters that can be treated.

In each parameter studied the data produced are of greatest value in interpretation when they are integrated with the three-dimensional geometry of the unit concerned. The stratigraphic mapping techniques discussed in Chapter 12 are particularly appropriate for use in preparing observational data for analysis and interpretation. It is becoming more and more apparent that the techniques of automatic acquisition, storage, retrieval, processing, and presentation of stratigraphic data will make it possible for a stratigrapher to assemble and treat masses of a great variety of data within practical limits of cost and time. Regardless of the method, however, whether by hand and pencil or by high-speed computer, it remains essential to maintain a clear separation between observation and interpretational analysis.

Observable Associations within the Frontier Formation

The Frontier Formation and its correlatives to the west and northwest in Idaho and southwestern Montana can be seen to comprise four intergradational response patterns to a range of tectonic, environmental, source, and transport conditions. At the northwestern and western extreme, separated from the main body of the Frontier by thrust faults, are graywackes of nonmarine origin intercalated with andesitic flows and tuffs and aggregating thicknesses in excess of 5000 feet. According to the classification of Table 13-6 this would be termed a *nonmarine eugeosynclinal association* in purely tectono-environmental terms. The environmental setting is obvious, but the tectonic assignment is a debatable inference in view of the internal and external geometry of the associated strata. The discussion will return to consideration of the interpretation of this association, but, for the moment at least, it seems preferable to assign it to an observational model and call it simply a *graywacke association*.

In western and northwestern Wyoming the Frontier Formation, averaging over 1000 feet in total thickness, remains predominantly nonmarine and is characterized by lithic wackes bearing numerous thick coal beds. This association is difficult to place with reference to pure tectono-environmental models, falling somewhere between *eugeosyncline* and *marginal basin* on a tectonic basis. Without attempting inference and interpretation this can be called a *lithic wacke association* on straight observational grounds.

Another pattern of sedimentation is found in central Wyoming. Here the Frontier Formation is but half as thick as in the western part of the state and is made up of about two-thirds marine shale, interrupted by cyclical units of sandstone enclosing thin coals and nonmarine silts. The sandstones are chiefly quartz wackes with minor quartz arenites, the latter appearing in close vertical succession with marine shales. In the older classification this association would be referred to an *unstable shelf* or to an *interior basin* or both. In observational terms it can be assigned without prejudice to a *quartz wacke association.*

At the eastern and southeastern margins of the sand bodies, quartz arenite sandstone accounts for a small fraction of the total thickness, which is almost entirely clay shale, bearing a few thin calcareous shales and biomicrite and biosparite limestones. Tectono-environmental

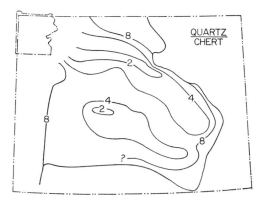

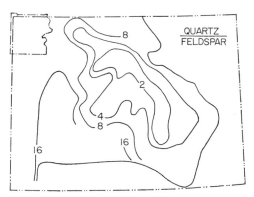

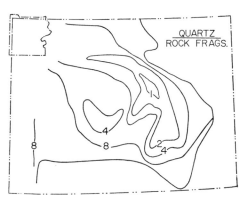

Fig. 13-8

Mineral composition maps of the First Wall Creek sand. [Modified after Goodell (1962).]

assignment would be to *littoral and shallow sublittoral stable shelf* and/or *interior basin.* Since the sands, although volumetrically small, remain the most prominent and easily observed rock type, it is appropriate to apply the term *quartz arenite association* to the observed shale-sandstone complex.

Two major questions are raised by this suite of observable lithologic associations in the Frontier. First, is it possible to recognize other observable associations of this type and categorize them without resorting unnecessarily to inferential reasoning? This question is discussed in the next section. Second, does the ordered transition from graywacke association to quartz arenite represent a systematic and recurrent larger-scaled relationship among lithologic associations, and, if so, are there other such master plans or models which may be discerned?

OBSERVATIONAL LITHOLOGIC ASSOCIATIONS

Most stratigraphers would agree that there are natural associations of sedimentary rocks in which each association is characterized by a combination of compositional, structural, and geometric attributes. Much of the disagreement as to the classification of these natural associations arises from attempts to proceed directly to an interpretation and to categorize associations on the basis of tectonic and environmental assumptions. Here an attempt is made to recognize the principal natural associations of rock types and to describe these in strictly observational terms before proceeding to analysis and interpretation. Thus, each lithologic association is a kind of natural empirical model defined without recourse to abstract interpretation. For purposes of reference the model associations are identified with a lithologic term, modified by a geometric prefix in certain cases. It should be noted, however, that lithology is only one of the fields of observation that are integrated in the description and definition. In fact, placement within the framework of classification presented here is possible only after consideration of a number of contributing fields of observational data ranging from detailed petrography of individual specimens to stratigraphic maps and cross-sectional diagrams.

Essential Observations

Table 13-7 lists a number of the empirical associations that may be recognized and indicates the nature of the essential observations upon which the identities of the associations are based. A few paragraphs of explanation will aid the reader in understanding the table.

Lithology. Rock types, identified by the standard classification used in this text, are listed in order of their relative prominence in each association. "Relative prominence" is not strictly a measure of volumetric relationships but refers, rather, to the most characteristic lithology. In the graywacke association, for example, shale is commonly the most important rock type volumetrically; but, since shales are difficult to observe and classify, they are of lesser significance than the sandstones in characterizing the association. Within a single major association certain lithologies occupy particular positions. Therefore it is difficult to describe the lithologies involved without reference to the geometry of the rock bodies in which they occur. The geometric terms applied are defined below.

Geometry. Thickness is one of the most important parameters of a lithologic association. Expressing thickness merely in terms of feet is misleading, however, inasmuch as a given association may represent deposition during either a short or a long interval of time. In an attempt to arrive at a more meaningful measure of thickness this parameter is expressed in terms of feet per million years. It is obvious that a degree of interpretation is involved when the time value of a succession of strata is estimated. Fortunately, the errors in time estimates, even if these be in the 50–100 percent range, are insignificant when compared to the variations in thickness encountered. The thicknesses used are those taken from the stratigraphic record after compaction of the sediments, and bear no simple relationship to rates of sedimentation.

Adequate terms have not been developed for a purely descriptive definition of positions within lithologic associations. For present purposes terms that require inference and interpretation are used in the interests of clarity. The terms proximal and distal refer to positions close to and away from assumed source areas or close to and away from the margins of depositional basins. In undisturbed successions the terms updip and downdip would serve equally well, but this usage would be confusing where younger structure has affected the succession.

Postdepositional Effects. At first glance it seems illogical to apply characteristics resulting from postdepositional episodes to the classification of lithologic associations. Yet there is a clear relationship between certain of the associations and structural and metamorphic history. The frequency with which the graywacke association, for example, is found involved in regional metamorphism is such that metamorphic effects of this type are recognized as one of the hallmarks of the association. This is not to suggest that metamorphism is requisite to recognition of the graywacke association, but it does indicate that this and other postdepositional effects are among the observations that, through integration, contribute to the identity of the association models.

Other Observations. Under the heading "sedimentary structures" no attempt is made to list all of the internal structures that may occur. Instead, those structural features which aid in typifying each association are noted.

TABLE 13-7. OBSERVATIONAL BASIS FOR THE LITHOLOGIC ASSOCIATIONS.

OBSERVATIONS					
			ROCK TYPES	GEOMETRY	SEDIMENTARY STRUCTURES
CLASTIC ASSOCIATIONS	**WACKE-ARENITE ASSOCIATIONS**	**GRAYWACKE ASSOCIATIONS**			
		DEEP BURIAL GRAYWACKE ASSOCIATION	Graywacke, slate and phyllite, bedded chert, greenstone (including pillow lavas) and metatuff.		Graded bedding; bedding-plane features rarely observable.
		INTERMEDIATE GRAYWACKE ASSOCIATION	Graywacke, lithic and feldspathic wacke; dark siliceous shale; volcanics (including pillow lavas and tuffs); minor quartz arenite, micrite, and biolithite.	Linear-arcuate trends 10's to, more commonly, 100's of miles in length; Thicknesses in 1000's of feet per million years.	Graded bedding, oriented sole markings, slump and flow structures, large exotic blocks.
		SHALLOW BURIAL GRAYWACKE ASSOCIATION	Lithic, feldspathic, and arkosic wacke in graded units that may include quartz wacke and arenite; siliceous shale and subordinate volumes of other rocks as above.		
		NONMARINE GRAYWACKE ASSOCIATION	Poorly sorted boulder conglomerate with clasts of older sediments and volcanics; interbedded lithic wacke, tuff, and volcanics.		Conglomerate poorly stratified in thick units; sandstone with torrential cross bedding.
		CLASTIC WEDGE ASSOCIATION	Proximal coarse wacke, frequently red, grading distally to finer, more mature sandstone with interbeds of marine shale and coal; proximal tuffs, distal bentonite.	Proximal thicknesses in 1000's of feet per million years, thinning distally; typically fan-shaped or series of coalescent fans in plan view; regional orientation marked.	Distally thinning sandstone tongues exhibit channels, cross bedding, medial coal cycles.
		COAL CYCLE ASSOCIATION	Quartz, lithic, feldspathic wacke and arenite in cyclical succession.with variety of shale and carbonate; coal common but not everywhere present.	Low rate of change of thickness, 10's to 100's of feet per million years, marked vertical cyclicity with disconformity, channeling between units common.	Regionally oriented channels, cross bedding; systematic cyclical succession.
		DELTAIC ASSOCIATION	Quarts wacke and arenite; lesser. feldspathic, lithic, wacke and arenite; siltstone and shale of various colors including red and black.	Proximal thicknesses in 10's distal thicknesses approaching 1000's of feet per million years; fan-or coalescent fan-shaped in plan view.	Radiating elongate and sheet sand bodies; radial orientation of cross bedding, other vector properties.
	QUARTZ ARENITE ASSOCIATIONS	BLANKET SAND ASSOCIATION		Thicknesses in 10's of feet per million years with low rate of change and very broad areal extent.	Commonly strongly cross bedded; bedding surfaces ripple marked and dessication cracked.
		UNCONFORMITY SAND ASSOCIATION	Pure quartz arenite; quartz-glauconite arenite; quartz-hematite arenite.	Lenticular bodies elongate parallel to strike of overstepped strata and/or faults.	As above; thin basal conglomerate with clasts of underlying units.
		STILLSTAND ASSOCIATION		Elongate lenses parallel to buried topography or to trends of increased rate of thickening of synchronous units.	Primary dip and cross bedding concordant with buried topography or direction of thickening.
	ARKOSE ASSOCIATIONS	WEDGE ARKOSE ASSOCIATION	Arkose, arkosic and feldspathic arenite and wacke; lithic arenite and wacke; commonly conglomeratic and interbedded with red quartz wacke; volcanics commonly present.	Linear trends 10's, rarely 100's of miles in length; proximal thicknesses in 1000's of feet per million years, rapid distal thining.	Distally radiating cross-bedding directions in coalescent fan patterns.
		BASAL ARKOSE ASSOCIATION	Arkose, arkosic wacke, lithic wacke, conglomerate with clasts of underlying units.	Highly irregular thin sheets at base of overstepping succession.	Lenses of varying texture and composition related to lithology and topography of overstepped surface.
NONCLASTIC ASSOCIATIONS	**BLANKET CARBONATE ASSOCIATIONS**	BLANKET BIOSPARITE ASSOCIATION	Crinoid, fusulinid biosparite, etc.; well sorted, not commonly sandy; light colored shale, quartz arenite.	Thicknesses in tens of feet per million years and lower with low rate of change and very broad areal extent.	Cross bedding, cut-and-fill, other arenite structures.
		BLANKET BIOMICRITE ASSOCIATION	Crinoid biomicrite; many other types with small or fragmented tests.		Well-defined bedding; lenses of biosparite, biolithite.
		BLANKET MICRITE ASSOCIATION	Micrite, light to dark, with variable clay admixture and interbedded with shale.		Dessication cracks, algal (?) nodules.
		BLANKET BIOSTROME ASSOCIATION	Biolithite, subordinate biosparite, biomicrite, oomicrite, pelmicrite.		Tests and fragments with sediment binding, commonly algal, framework.
	LENTIFORM CARBONATE ASSOCIATIONS	LENTIFORM BIOMICRITE ASSOCIATION	Like blanket biomicrite but commonly with more matrix, darker color.	Subcircular or ovate in plan view, diameters from 10's to a few 100's of miles; lenticular in cross section, 10's of feet per million years at margins to 100's of feet near centers.	Like blanket biomicrite.
		LENTIFORM MICRITE ASSOCIATION	Dark micrite, commonly clay-rich and interbedded with shale shale.		Fine lamination common, bedding obscure in absence of shale partings.
	CARBONATE BANK ASSOCIATIONS		Bio-, oo-, and pelsparite; subordinate micrite and evaporite.	Elongate trends miles to 10's of miles in length; upward convex lenticular cross section; thicknesses from 10's to 100's of feet per million years.	Well sorted, cross bedded; sparite types arranged in systematic lateral order parallel to long axis of deposit.
	CARBONATE REEF ASSOCIATIONS	RANDOM REEF ASSOCIATION	Reef core:— biolithite; subordinate micrite and biomicrite. Reef flank:— intrasparite and -micrite with clasts of core rock; biosparite and -micrite. Interreef:— biomicrite and micrite commonly clay rich, cherty.	Irregular mound shapes, 10's to 100's of feet thick, 10's of feet to mile or more in diameter. Reef core:— massive, vugular, with framework or algal and other organic binding laminae; commonly upward expanding. Reef flank:— quaquaversally"dipping beds with clasts of core rock; intertongued with, and commonly transgressed by, reef core; intertongued distally with interreef. Interreef:— finer grained, well bedded, lacking appreciable initial dip.	
		BARRIER REEF ASSOCIATION	Reef core:— like random reef association. Forereef:— like reef flank. Backreef:— micrite and oomicrite; evaporite (typically anhydrite).	Elongate shapes miles to 10's of miles and more in length, 1000's of feet to mile or greater in width; 100's to 1000 feet or more in thickness; typically assymetrical, steep forereef, gentle backreef slopes. Reef core:— like reef flank but confined to front (basinal) flank. Backreef:— like interreef but confined to back (basin-margin) flank.	
	EVAPORITE ASSOCIATIONS	BASIN-CENTER EVAPORITE ASSOCIATION	Anhydrite (commonly gypsum in outcrop), halite, polyhalite, sylvite, micritic dolomite, dolomitized biomicrite; other carbonates and black shale not uncommon.	Strongly lentiform, thicknesses to 100's of feet per million years; K and Na chlorides most prominent in areas of thickest accumulation.	Markedly cyclical vertical succession from marine carbonates, through laminated micritic dolomite, sulfates, to chlorides (if present); complete cycle with upper part in reverse order seldom preserved.
		BASIN-MARGIN EVAPORITE ASSOCIATION	Anhydrite and gypsum most common, halite much less common, potash salts very rare; carbonates as in basin-center association plus oo- and pelsparite and -micrite.	Gently lentiform, thicknesses in 10's of feet per million years; irregular elongate trends parallel to basin circumference.	
		SHELF EVAPORITE ASSOCIATION	As in basin-margin association but with higher proportions micrite, less oolite, pelletoid carbonate; interbedded red shale, silt, arenite common.	Thicknesses in 10's of feet per million years with low rate of change and very broad areal extent.	

TABLE 13-7 (Continued)

		O B S E R V A T I O N S			
		FOSSILS	POSTDEPOSITIONAL EFFECTS	LATERAL RELATIONSHIPS	EXAMPLES
C L A S T I C A S S O C I A T I O N S — GRAYWACKE ASSOCIATIONS	DEEP BURIAL GRAYWACKE ASSOCIATION	Megafossils rarely preserved; planktonic and bathyal-abyssal benthonic microfossils.	Diagenetic effects minor or obscured by low-to high-rank regional metamorphism and migmatization.	Lateral relationships typically obscured by thrust contacts with igneous-metamorphic blocks and by intrusion or migmatization.	"Francisan" (Jurassic-Cretaceous, California); Knife Lake (Precambrian, Ontario).
	INTERMEDIATE GRAYWACKE ASSOCIATION	Dominantly planktonic and nektonic, bathyal-abyssal benthonic; displaced sublittoral assemblages; reworked older faunas.	Regional metamorphism of chlorite grade and lower.	Proximal limits commonly thrusts; distal portions may intertongue with many other associations.	Vinini (Ordovician, Nevada); "graptolite facies" (Early and Mid Paleozoic, Great Britain and Western Europe).
	SHALLOW BURIAL GRAYWACKE ASSOCIATION		Unmetamorphosed; diagenetic effects minor.		Tertiary of California basins; Alpine flysch (Tertiary, France and Switzerland).
	NONMARINE GRAYWACKE ASSOCIATION	Scarce plant fossils.	Commonly poor cemented, except limestone conglomerates that are typically carbonate cemented and stained red.	Proximal limits defined by thrusts; distal portions intertongue with clastic wedge.	Hoback Conglomerate (Paleocene, Wyoming); Beaverhead Conglomerate (Paleocene, Montana).
WACKE-ARENITE ASSOCIATIONS	CLASTIC WEDGE ASSOCIATION	Dominantly plant and tetrapod forms proximally; variety of planktonic, nektonic, and benthonic fossils in distal portions.	Moderate to extreme diagenesis; quartz enlargement, silicification, calcification, authigenesis of feldspar, glauconite, clays.	Proximal limits typically in thrust relationship to graywacke association or defined by igneous contact; distal intertonguing with deltaic or other associations.	Catskill-Chemung (Devonian, New York); Mesaverde (Cretaceous, Utah).
	COAL CYCLE ASSOCIATION	Rare in sandstones; highly diversified fauna and flora in shales, limestones, coals.	Diagenetic effects low to moderate.	Lateral transition to distal margin clastic wedge, wedge arkose; to proximal margin deltaic association; or to many other associations (except graywacke).	McLeansboro (Pennsylvanian, Illinois); Dakota Group (Cretaceous, South Dakota).
	DELTAIC ASSOCIATION	Plants; abundant nonmarine, littoral and sublittoral invertebrates.		Transitional with all other associations, most commonly with arenites and, distally, with opposed distal margins of clastic wedges.	Cotton Valley (Jurassic, Mississippi); Claiborne (Eocene, Texas - Louisiana).
QUARTZ ARENITE ASSOCIATIONS	BLANKET SAND ASSOCIATION	Very scarce fossils of littoral forms; more abundant in associated shale and carbonate.	Quartz enlargement weakly to completely developed; silica-to-carbonate replacement not uncommon.	Transitional and intertongued with blanket carbonates and shales.	St. Peter (Ordovician, Illinois); Tensleep (Pennsylvanian, Wyoming).
	UNCONFORMITY SAND ASSOCIATION			Pinchout against irregularities of overstepped surface.	Numerous Pennsylvania oil sands of Midcontinent.
	STILLSTAND ASSOCIATION			Intertongue down dip with marine shales, updip with lagoonal shales or pass into blanket arenites.	Simpson sands (Ordovician, Oklahoma); Frio sands (Oligocene, Texas).
ARKOSE ASSOCIATIONS	WEDGE ARKOSE ASSOCIATION	Very scarce; typically nonmarine.	Minor, except for feldspar alteration and debatable secondary acquisition of red color.	Limited proximally by high-angle faults; distally transitional and intertongued with quartz arenite, coal cycle, evaporite, other associations.	Fountain (Pennsylvanian, Colorado); Newark (Triassic, New Jersey).
	BASAL ARKOSE ASSOCIATION	Reworked fossils from underlying units.		Pinchout on higher areas of overstepped surface; transitional with unconformity arenite, others.	Basal Lamotte (Cambrian, Missouri); "granite wash" and "detrital" oil sands of Midcontinent.
N O N C L A S T I C A S S O C I A T I O N S — BLANKET CARBONATE ASSOCIATIONS	BLANKET BIOSPARITE ASSOCIATION	Crinoid columnals, benthonic foraminifera, abraded and fragmented tests of robust forms.	Dolomitization moderately common, chert replacement less frequently observed.	Transitional and intertongued with blanket sand and shale, oosparite, pelsparite, biomicrite, biolithite.	Ste. Genevieve (Mississippian, Illinois).
	BLANKET BIOMICRITE ASSOCIATION	Small tests or fragments of dominantly benthonic, some planktonic, forms.	Dolomitization and chertification common.	Intertongued and transitional with all other carbonate associations, evaporite, reef, blanket shale, etc.	Viola (Ordovician, Oklahoma); Madison (Mississippian, Wyoming).
	BLANKET MICRITE ASSOCIATION	Scarce, well preserved delicate fresh, brackish, marine forms.	Dolomitization uncommon except in association with evaporites.	Transitional with shale, biomicrite, shelf evaporite.	#3 limestone (Pennsylvanian cyclothems, Illinois); Alcova (Triassic, Wyoming).
	BLANKET BIOSTROME ASSOCIATION	Great variety of benthonic types, dominantly sessile.	Dolomitization common.	Transitional with reef, bank, sparite associations.	Huntington (Silurian, Indiana); Nisku (Devonian, Alberta).
LENTIFORM CARBONATE ASSOCIATIONS	LENTIFORM BIOMICRITE ASSOCIATION	Greater proportion of planktonic forms than in blanket biomicrite.	Dolomitization uncommon except in association with evaporites.	Micrite commonly in area of greatest thickness, gradational to biomicrite which passes into blanket associations in direction of thinning.	Arbuckle (Cambro-Ordovician, Southern Oklahoma); Lower Mission Canyon (Mississippian, Montana).
	LENTIFORM MICRITE ASSOCIATION	Scarce planktonic and nektonic forms; few phosphatic brachiopods.	Dolomitization very uncommon.		Ratcliffe (Mississippian, North Dakota); Bone Spring (Permian, West Texas).
CARBONATE BANK ASSOCIATIONS	CARBONATE BANK ASSOCIATION	Littoral and sublittoral small tests and fragments, commonly in distinct zones parallel to long axis of deposit.	Dolomitization not uncommon and accompanied by destruction of primary textures; anhydrite cement common where associated with evaporites.	Intertongued with lentiform biomicrite in direction of thickened contemporaneous deposits, with evaporite or black shale in direction of thinning.	Mississippian of southern Saskatchewan; "Horseshoe atoll" Pennsylvanian-Permian, Texas).
CARBONATE REEF ASSOCIATIONS	RANDOM REEF ASSOCIATION	Calcareous algae and other sediment binding organisms, robust sessile benthonic forms in variety and commonly in distinct zonation.	Dolomitization common, decreasing in direction of thickening of contemporaneous strata; chert development marked near circumference of reef complex.	Intertongued or transitional with blanket carbonate associations; less commonly with shelf evaporite, shale.	Silurian of Illinois; Upper Devonian of Alberta.
	BARRIER REEF ASSOCIATION	Like random reef association.	Dolomitization less common than in random reef association; vug-and pore-filling by anhydrite and salt not uncommon.	Forereef intertongued with lentiform biomicrite, micrite, black shale, basin-center evaporite. Backreef intertongued with blanket carbonates, basin-margin evaporite.	Permian of West Texas - New Mexico; Triassic of Italian Tyrol.
EVAPORITE ASSOCIATIONS	BASIN-CENTER EVAPORITE ASSOCIATION	Very rare to unknown (except for scattered spores) in dolomitic micrite, sulfates, and chlorides.	Marked dolomitization of associated limestones; variable degree of replacement of carbonate by sulfate, sulfate by chloride, Na by K.	Commonly surrounded by intertongued carbonate bank and/or reef; less commonly transitional with blanket association.	Solina (Silurian, Michigan); Castile (Permian, West Texas).
	BASIN-MARGIN EVAPORITE ASSOCIATION			Intertongued basinward with backreef or bank deposits; intertongued or transitional peripherally with blanket associations, commonly including red beds.	Wabamun (Devonian, Alberta); Mission Canyon (Mississippian, Saskatchewan).
	SHELF EVAPORITE ASSOCIATION			Intertongued and transitional with all blanket arenite and carbonate associations, especially with red arenite and siltstone; transitional with basin-margin association.	Blaine (Permian, Kansas); Gypsum Spring (Jurassic, South Dakota).

Similarly, the paleontologic heading does not involve recounting all of the fossil types to be observed; entries are confined to broad environmental groupings having some qualitative measure of abundance. The examples of rock units chosen as representative of the several associations are not intended as holotypes to which other groupings are referred for comparison and identification. Rather, they are no more than appropriate examples that the writers have selected as typical. Individual readers in other regions will find numerous equally good examples within their own areas. "Related associations" are those commonly occurring in close geographic or temporal juxtaposition.

Interpretations of Lithologic Associations

Table 13-8 presents in capsule form the interpretations that may be drawn from an integration and synthesis of the observations listed in Table 13-7. Source materials of clastic associations, source areas, and transport media are interpreted from consideration of the compositions, textures, and structures of the accumulated sediments. The inferred tectonic habit of each association is stated in terms of the ratio between the rate of sediment supply and the rate of subsidence. This figure is estimated in general terms and applied, along with data on the geometric form of the lithosomes represented, to the consideration of an appropriate tectonic classification stated in terms of the tectonic elements involved. In like manner, all contributing lines of evidence are integrated to arrive at an environmental state typical of each major association.

The brief entries in Tables 13-7 and 13-8 can scarcely do justice to the wealth of descriptive and interpretational detail that is available on lithologic associations; nor is it possible within the limitations of this text to present anything approaching a complete coverage. However, some expansion of treatment is required to permit the introduction of illustrative examples and a modest amount of discussion.

CLASTIC ASSOCIATIONS

The Graywacke Association

This is one of the most easily recognized associations and yet one of the more difficult to define. No single sedimentary rock type, structural habit, metamorphic grade, geometric form, or relationship to igneous activity is confined to the association or is uniquely characteristic of it. Even the sandstone that lends its name to the association is differently defined by various workers, tending to cause the inclusion or exclusion of particular occurrences on what are almost semantic grounds. Nevertheless the common association of immature detrital sediments of apparent turbidite type, great thickness in elongate belts, and volcanic admixture, combine to present an identifiable pattern. Where the depositional pattern has been affected by compressional forces leading to major oriented overthrusts and regional metamorphism, and where metasomatic granites and ultrabasic intrusions are evident, the relationship to eugeosynclinal conditions is clear and incontrovertible. Given these observations and their interpretations, the assignment to a conceptual *eugeosynclinal model* is almost less involved than recognition of the observational graywacke association.

Deeply Buried Graywacke Associations. The structural, metamorphic, and igneous hallmarks of the eugeosynclinal graywacke association are prominent in the older Precambrian and in the Paleozoic and Mesozoic of certain areas. In these older occurrences subsequent uplift and erosion have exposed the once deeply buried axial portions of depositional troughs while enormous volumes of more shallowly seated sediment have been removed, along with much of the evidence of transitional conditions between eugeosynclinal and cratonic sedimentation. As a result, the rocks of the graywacke association bear the characteristic impress of metamorphism and intrusive activity and are sharply delimited by unconformities and faults from obviously different associations. Pettijohn (1943) presents an excellent description of older Precambrian sedimentation in the Lake Superior area. Paleozoic successions of the Magog belt (Kay, 1951) in the Appalachian Piedmont trend and the "Franciscan" rocks of the California Coast Ranges are younger examples.

Intermediate Graywacke Associations. There are many sedimentary successions that are readily recognizable as graywacke associations but which do not exhibit the degree of metamorphism, metasomatism, and intrusive igneous involvement of the deeply buried associations. The early Paleozoic rocks of the classic North Wales areas, where they constitute the so-called graptolite facies (Jones, 1938; Wood and Smith, 1959; Bassett and Walton, 1960) are well-documented examples. Other representatives are found in the Ordovician of north-central Nevada (Roberts, Hotz, Gilluly, and Ferguson, 1958) and in the Stanley-Jackfork strata of the Ouachita area (Cline, 1960).

Rocks of the intermediate graywacke association, although they may have suffered some grain reorientation, typically exhibit the internal primary structures of turbidites and the prominent bedding-plane sole markings that permit the direction of transport to be determined. Fossils of planktonic and nektonic organisms, such as graptolites and ammonoids, are relatively common in the dark shales; in certain areas, the association includes huge "root-

TABLE 13-8. INTERPRETATION OF LITHOLOGIC ASSOCIATIONS BASED ON INTEGRATION AND SYNTHESIS OF OBSERVATIONS.

		INTERPRETATIONS		
		SOURCE AREA	SOURCE MATERIAL	TRANSPORT MEDIUM
CLASTIC ASSOCIATIONS	**GRAYWACKE ASSOCIATIONS** — DEEP BURIAL GRAYWACKE ASSOCIATION / INTERMEDIATE GRAYWACKE ASSOCIATION / SHALLOW BURIAL GRAYWACKE ASSOCIATION	Linear-arcuate, volcanic and non-volcanic welts, associated with extra-cratonic, eugeosynclinal, orogenesis. Topographic relief above sea level low to moderate with widely spaced episodes of development of higher relief.	"Cannabalized" sediments and volcanics of graywacke associations, their regionally metamorphosed equivalents, migmatic granitoid rocks; some source rocks almost contemporaneous or but slightly older than accumulating strata; detritus markedly immature at point of yield to transport agency.	Submarine transverse (with respect to long axis of depositional trough) and longitudinal turbidity currents; lesser contribution by transverse gravity slide of major blocks.
	NONMARINE GRAYWACKE ASSOCIATION	Strongly emergent, linear-arcuate mountain trends, typically representing impress of extracratonic orogenesis on miogeosynclinal zone.	Carbonates, wackes, arenite, and volcanics, commonly unmetamorphosed, of marginal basin associations; more rarely graywacke associations noted above.	Subaerial mass down-slope movement, steep-gradient streams.
	WACKE-ARENITE ASSOCIATIONS — CLASTIC WEDGE ASSOCIATION	Linear-arcuate, volcanic and (more commonly) non volcanic trends associated with extracratonic orogenesis of eugeosynclinal border of miogeosynclinal zone; relief fluctuating from low to high. Specific source area commonly identifiable.	Same as for graywacke associations with some greater prominence of sedimentary source, including partial age-equivalence of source rocks and deposits.	Proximal steep-gradient streams leading to low-gradient streams and flood plains, to distributary channels, and, distally, to strandline agencies (waves and littoral currents).
	COAL CYCLE ASSOCIATION	Positive elements of cratonic interior typically within shield areas of shallowly buried basement crystallines; some contribution possible from remote extracratonic uplifts and related emergent trends of miogeosynclinal zones. Specific source areas not identifiable; commonly multiple.	Very wide variety reflecting multiple provenance areas yielding maturely to immaturely weathered detritus from basement crystalline and sedimentary rocks of earlier cycles; may also have volumetrically less important admixtures of nearly concurrent graywacke association materials.	Low-gradient streams and their distributaries; waves and littoral currents.
	DELTAIC ASSOCIATION			Same as above; turbidity currents effective (but volumetrically unimportant) in pro-delta deposits.
	QUARTZ ARENITE ASSOCIATIONS — BLANKET SAND ASSOCIATION	Epeirogenic positives and remote orogenic uplifts of craton; specific source rarely identifiable.	Same as above except possible greater maturity of detritus (reflecting greater stability of craton and larger contribution from reworked sedimentary rocks).	Waves and littoral currents; wind action effective as last agent in some regressive deposits.
	UNCONFORMITY SAND ASSOCIATION	Commonly very local; rarely from remote cratonic area.	Dominated by locally derived maturely weathered residual soil.	Transport distance commonly very short; waves and littoral currents.
	STILLSTAND ASSOCIATION	Generally unidentifiable epeirogenic and remote orogenic elements of craton; possible remote extra-cratonic source as in deltaic association; clastic-wedge arenites same source as clastic wedges.	Same as coal cycle and deltaic associations except clastic-wedge arenites formed by maturation of graywacke association materials.	Waves and littoral currents.
	ARKOSE ASSOCIATIONS — WEDGE ARKOSE ASSOCIATION	Readily identified cratonic orogenic elements, typically of limited extent, bounded by high-angle faults, without systematic orientation except in presence of controlling basement trend.	Highly immature detritus of granitoid and other crystalline basement rocks; typically with great age difference between source rocks and deposits, except contributions by nearly concurrent volcanics.	Proximal mass down-slope movement and steep-gradient streams, to low-gradient streams and distributaries (distal terminus of some examples), to marine or lacustrine-border waves and currents.
	BASAL ARKOSE ASSOCIATION	Local; commonly identifiable as topographic irregularity of overstepped surface.	Immature residual soil developed on feldspar-rich rocks.	No effective transport.
NONCLASTIC ASSOCIATIONS	**BLANKET CARBONATE ASSOCIATIONS** — BLANKET BIOSPARITE ASSOCIATION / BLANKET BIOMICRITE ASSOCIATION / BLANKET MICRITE ASSOCIATION / BLANKET BIOSTROME ASSOCIATION			
	LENTIFORM CARBONATE ASSOCIATIONS — LENTIFORM BIOMICRITE ASSOCIATION / LENTIFORM MICRITE ASSOCIATION		*ENDOGENETIC*	
	CARBONATE BANK ASSOCIATIONS			
	CARBONATE REEF ASSOCIATIONS — RANDOM REEF ASSOCIATION / BARRIER REEF ASSOCIATION			
	EVAPORITE ASSOCIATIONS — BASIN-CENTER EVAPORITE ASSOCIATION / BASIN-MARGIN EVAPORITE ASSOCIATION / SHELF EVAPORITE ASSOCIATION			

ABLE 13-8   (Continued)

INTERPRETATIONS

Group	Association	RATE OF SUPPLY / RATE OF SUBSIDENCE	TECTONIC CLASSIFICATION	ENVIRONMENT
GRAYWACKE ASSOCIATIONS	DEEP BURIAL GRAYWACKE ASSOCIATION		Deeply subsiding troughs of eugeosynclinal complex; less commonly extracratonic border of marginal basin in miogeosynclinal trend; strongly affected by continuing subsidence and orogenesis.	All marine bathymetric zones, sublittoral and hadal rare; typically but not exclusively low mechanical energy, low pH, negative Eh.
	INTERMEDIATE GRAYWACKE ASSOCIATION	Predominantly <1, leading to bathyal to hadal depths, interrupted by brief episodes of turbidite current activity when ratios are much >1; net effect over long time period ≈1 with both factors high.	Eugeosynclinal troughs and, more commonly, eugeosynclinal flank of marginal basin; slightly affected by depth of burial and continuing orogenesis.	
	SHALLOW BURIAL GRAYWACKE ASSOCIATION		Eugeosynclinal troughs and adjoining flank of marginal basin; composition, texture, and primary structures unaffected by orogenesis or depth of burial.	
	NONMARINE GRAYWACKE ASSOCIATION	> 1, leading to subaerial deposition.	Eugeosynclinal flank of marginal basin.	Subaerial talus cones and alluvial fans; mechanical energy high, variable pH and Eh.
WACKE-ARENITE ASSOCIATIONS	CLASTIC WEDGE ASSOCIATION	Fluctuating between >1, leading to regression, and <1, leading to transgression; both factors high proximally, decreasing distally.	Marginal basin, extending from border of eugeosyncline (proximal) to border of stable craton (distal).	Proximal piedmont plain with high-energy streams, positive Eh; to low-energy streams, distributaries, floodplains with variable pH and Eh; to deltas and marine strandlines of variable energy, pH, and Eh.
	COAL CYCLE ASSOCIATION	Repeated fluctuation from >1 to <1; rates for both factors low to moderate.	Unstable shelf and mildly negative cratonic interior basin.	Complex of environments varying periodically and systematically with time; marine to nonmarine, moderate to low energy, high to low pH, positive to negative Eh.
	DELTAIC ASSOCIATION	Predominantly in equilibrium; both factors moderate to high.	Cratonic border (proximal) to axial portion (distal) of marginal basin; less commonly from shelf border to axial portion of interior basin.	Complex of environments with more-or-less systematic areal variation; distributary channel and flood plain, swamp and lagoon, littoral and prodelta marine; wide variation in pH and Eh.
QUARTZ ARENITE ASSOCIATIONS	BLANKET SAND ASSOCIATION	Slightly >1 or slightly <1; both factors low.	Stable shelf.	Strand line; high energy, high pH, positive Eh.
	UNCONFORMITY SAND ASSOCIATION	Slightly <1; both factors low.		
	STILLSTAND ASSOCIATION	Predominantly in equilibrium; both factors moderate, rarely high.	Cratonic-border hinge line of marginal basin; hinge line of interior basin.	
ARKOSE ASSOCIATIONS	WEDGE ARKOSE ASSOCIATION	≈1; both factors proximally high.	Yoked basin.	Subaerial alluvial fan (high energy, positive Eh); to stream channel and flood plain; to marine or lacustrine with high pH, dominantly positive Eh.
	BASAL ARKOSE ASSOCIATION	Slightly <1; both factors low to moderate.	Stable shelf, unstable shelf, flank of epeirogenic uplift.	Littoral, moderate to high energy variable pH, commonly positive Eh.
BLANKET CARBONATE ASSOCIATIONS	BLANKET BIOSPARITE ASSOCIATION	Slightly >1 or slightly <1.	Stable shelf, unstable shelf.	Littoral and infralittoral, high energy, high pH, positive Eh.
	BLANKET BIOMICRITE ASSOCIATION	≈1.		Sublittoral; dominantly low energy, occasionally high; high pH; positive Eh.
	BLANKET MICRITE ASSOCIATION			Sublittoral, lagoonal, lacustrine; low energy; dominantly high pH; variable Eh.
	BLANKET BIOSTROME ASSOCIATION	Slightly >1 or slightly <1.		Littoral and infralittoral, high energy, high pH, positive Eh.
LENTIFORM CARBONATE ASSOCIATIONS	LENTIFORM BIOMICRITE ASSOCIATION	≈1; both factors moderate.	Interior basin, marginal basin.	Sublittoral; dominantly low energy, occasionally high; high pH; variable Eh.
	LENTIFORM MICRITE ASSOCIATION	≈1 to slightly <1; both factors moderate.		Sublittoral to bathyal; low energy; dominantly high pH; variable Eh, commonly negative.
CARBONATE BANK ASSOCIATIONS		≈1; both low to moderate.	Hinge line of interior and marginal basins.	Infralittoral, littoral, and lagoonal; high to moderate energy; high pH; dominantly positive Eh (lagoon margin may be negative Eh, euxinic or evaporitic restricted).
CARBONATE REEF ASSOCIATIONS	RANDOM REEF ASSOCIATION	≈1 to slightly >1, less commonly <1; both factors low.	Stable shelf and border of mildly negative interior basin lacking well-defined hinge line.	Infralittoral, littoral, and lagoonal; high energy (littoral) to low (lagoonal); high pH (infralittoral and littoral) to possible low (lagoonal); positive Eh except lagoon which may be negative with evaporitic or euxinic restriction.
	BARRIER REEF ASSOCIATION	≈1, both factors moderate.	Cratonic-border hinge line of marginal basin; hinge line of interior basin.	Littoral and infralittoral, high energy, high pH, positive Eh.
EVAPORITE ASSOCIATIONS	BASIN-CENTER EVAPORITE ASSOCIATION	≈1 to slightly <1; both factors moderate to high.	Axial portion of strongly negative interior basin; less commonly in marginal basin.	Sublittoral or indeterminate marine zone; low energy; dominantly high pH; Eh cyclically positive; evaporitic restriction to saline and, less commonly, supersaline phase.
	BASIN-MARGIN EVAPORITE ASSOCIATION	≈1 to slightly <1; both factors low, less commonly moderate.	Border of interior basin; cratonborder of marginal basin.	Lagoonal; dominantly low energy, high pH, positive Eh; evaporitic restriction to penesaline, rarely to saline, phase.
	SHELF EVAPORITE ASSOCIATION	≈1 to slightly <1; both factors low.	Stable shelf.	

Left margin labels: CLASTIC ASSOCIATIONS · NONCLASTIC ASSOCIATIONS less" exotic blocks of older strata apparently transported by gravity sliding. These are the *olistoliths* defined by Marchetti (1957) in the Tertiary of Sicily and Italy. (See also Goguel, 1952, 1961.)

The unqualified attribution of intermediate graywacke associations to a eugeosynclinal site is not warranted. Rather, the majority of occurrences appear to represent deposition in a transitional zone between the eugeosyncline and the marginal basins of the miogeosynclinal trend. Typically, rocks of the intermediate graywacke association grade into strata of cratonic derivation, and there is commonly a degree of interfingering, such that relatively thin units of quartz arenite or biosparite may interrupt the generally dark succession of graywackes and siliceous shales.

Graywacke Associations of Shallow Burial. Areas of later Mesozoic and Cenozoic orogenic activity of eugeosynclinal type, and the belts adjacent to such areas, are characterized by sedimentary successions less easily identifiable with the graywacke model. The sandstones lack the abundant chloritic matrix and consequent dark color of typical graywackes, and the feldspar content in some cases exceeds the admissible values for graywackes in some systems of sandstone classification. These are the arkosic wackes of Gilbert (Williams, Turner, and Gilbert, 1954). The shales lack the highly developed bedding-plane fissility or slaty cleavage of deeply buried and intermediate associations; intercalations of carbonates and mature clastics, being unaltered, are conspicuous. Exotic blocks (olistoliths) of gravity-slide derivation are relatively common, as in intermediate associations.

These characteristics, except for the presence of the olistoliths, suggest that the sediments have not been buried as deeply and have not been subjected to the consequent elevated pressures and temperatures of the more typical graywacke associations. Therefore they lack metamorphic and metasomatic effects and are not commonly involved with the ultrabasic plutons. It seems probable, however, that both the deeply buried and intermediate associations had the characteristics of these "shallow" graywacke suites before being transformed by burial beneath younger sediments and continuing orogenesis. If it were possible to re-examine the "shallow" associations after the passage of hundreds of millions of years and after repeated diastrophic cycles, they could be expected to have taken on all of the identifying hallmarks of what are here termed deeply buried associations.

Two types of "shallow" graywacke associations can be recognized. One of these can be shown to have accumulated in sharply downwarped troughs within a eugeosynclinal complex. Active uplifting welts on either or both sides of the troughs appear to be the sources of very immature detritus that has been transported by turbidity currents down the flanks of the welts and to the axes of the troughs, in some instances reaching abyssal depths. Further transport along the axes of the troughs toward their points of greatest topographic depression is indicated by near right-angle changes in current direction as shown by measurable vector properties. Reworking and redeposition of older fossil assemblages are common, as are occurrences of sublittoral forms mixed with or intercalated with deep-water forms. Examples are found in the Tertiary of the California Coast Ranges and their intervening basins. An excellent discussion of certain California examples is provided by Natland and Kuenen (1951).

A second "shallow" graywacke type is exemplified by Cretaceous and Early Tertiary sediments of Alpine areas. These sediments, characterized by great thicknesses of shale, marl, and graywacke or arkosic wacke sandstones of turbidite type, have long been termed **flysch**. The term has reached little currency in North America, but has been extended in Europe to include many sedimentary suites thought to represent "preorogenic" or "synorogenic" deposition related to geosynclinal activity. In this expanded application, flysch has become a conceptual model that is closely related to an inferred mode of origin. A recent interpretation is presented by Wassojewitch (1959).

The "type" Alpine flysch appears to represent deposition in marginal basins on either flank of the Alpine orogenic trend and can be considered to be the shallowly buried equivalent of what is termed the intermediate graywacke association. Examples of flysch occurrences, the successions of stratal units involved, and their primary structures are illustrated by Lombard (1956), Bouma (1961), and many other European workers.

Nonmarine Graywacke Associations. Yet another type of observable association, with more tenuous or debatable linkage to graywacke associations in general, is found among nonmarine conglomerates located in or immediately adjacent to actively orogenic eugeosynclinal trends. Here, as exemplified by the Late Cretaceous rocks of westernmost Wyoming and southwestern Montana (discussed in earlier paragraphs of this chapter), there are very thick accumulations of unsorted debris dominated by boulder conglomerates and exhibiting the rude stratification of fanglomerates and talus breccias. Volcanic conglomerates and tuffs are common, and there may be thick successions of flows. The associated sandstones have the mineralogic and textural attributes of lithic graywackes, but are characterized by torrential cross-bedding and plant fossils. The conglomerates are dominated by fragments of older sedimentary rocks; commonly a single formation can be identified as the source of hundreds, or even thousands, of feet of section. Thrust faulting of considerable magnitude is a normal feature of the association, and the relationships indicate movement concurrent with deposition, suggesting that the conglomerates were deposited at the front of an advancing thrust sheet and were overridden by continued movement.

As noted in the discussion of the Frontier Formation, nonmarine graywackes are related to lithic wacke associations rather than to other graywacke suites.

Lithic Wacke-Feldspathic Wacke Associations

The distinction between observable associations characterized by lithic
wackes and feldspathic wackes is difficult to draw. Lithic wackes are distinguished from feldspathic wackes by their higher content of rock fragments compared with feldspar, but, particularly where chert grains and
cherty cement are present, this defining ratio is commonly obscure. Moreover, the two sandstones are often found in close association, which makes it
both practical and convenient to consider them together. Lithic wacke and
feldspathic wacke associations are known in a variety of tectonic and environmental circumstances which lead to recognition of several distinct
types. One of these is illustrated by the Frontier Formation of Wyoming; in
the following paragraphs, consideration of the Frontier example is continued from earlier portions of the chapter.

Clastic Wedge Associations. The Frontier Formation is seen (Figure
13-4) in map view as an assymetric fan-shaped or lobate mass. It is wedge
shaped in cross section and is thickest at its northwestern and western
margins. Many of the geometric, textural, and compositional parameters
(Figures 13-5, 13-6, and 13-8) have geographic distribution patterns roughly
similar to the gross form established by the isopach map. Note the high
values at the western and northwestern margins, the axial "high" trending
to the southeast, and the diminishing values encountered to the northeast,
east, and south of the axial "high." The obvious inference is that the same
factors of source, transport, depositional environment, and tectonics are
reflected in the majority of the attributes observed.

Frontier sandstones are both marine and nonmarine and are intertongued
with marine shales. Although no data are available on the regional distribution of grain sizes in the sandstones, Goodell (1962) has shown a strong
correlation between grain size and chert content, with markedly higher
proportions of chert in the coarser grades. Therefore, the quartz-chert ratio
map (Figure 13-8) of the First Wall Creek sandstone is a measure of grain-
size distribution. The map suggests a concentration of coarser sizes along
the southeast trending axis of the tongue-shaped sand body, with smaller
grain sizes at the northeastern, eastern, and southern borders of sand distribution. Similar patterns are exhibited by the distributions of unstable rock
fragments and feldspar, sand-shale ratios, and the number of individual
sand tongues. These combine to indicate a source area northwest of Wyoming, with distribution in a fan-shaped pattern toward the southeast. The

mineralogy of the sandstones indicates a derivation from a source area dominated by sedimentary rocks, including carbonates, quartzite, chert, and argillite. Additional volumes appear to have been supplied by volcanic rocks dominated by andesitic flows and tuffs, and there are lesser volumes represented by low-rank metamorphics.

The majority of the sandstone bodies in the Frontier Formation exhibit vector properties (orientation of grains, wood fragments, channels, and cross bedding) that indicate the paths of sediment transport shown diagrammatically in Figure 13-9. There is a progressive diminution of grain size following the same paths, which fan out in a radial pattern away from the assumed western and northwestern source areas. These sand bodies are most logically interpreted as representing successive stages in a complex system of stream channels and flood plains as elements of a shifting distributary system. The lack of marked downstream increase in the mineralogic maturity of the sands suggests a lack of significant reworking of the sediments after primary deposition.

The distal margins of the sand bodies are markedly involved with marine beds, and there is evidence that individual sand tongues end in elongate pods or lenses having the internal structures of beach sands. Thus it appears that the major agent of transport consisted of a distributary complex of streams carrying sand grains to the margin of a sea where further, if limited, distribution was accomplished by shoreline agencies.

The pattern of radiating distributary channels and flood plains leading to a marine basin suggests a delta such as that of the present-day Mississippi River. Yet the concentration of conglomerates at the western and northwestern borders of the area and the presence of accumulations of very coarse conglomerate in equivalent strata still farther west indicate high stream gradients scarcely typical of known delta systems. Further, the conspicuous volcanic admixture and the imputation of orogenic character to the source area indicate accumulation on a broad piedmont plain lying between the sea and the elevated mountains.

Fig. 13-9

Interpreted paths of sediment transport (dispersal) in the Frontier Formation of Wyoming. [After Goodell (1957).]

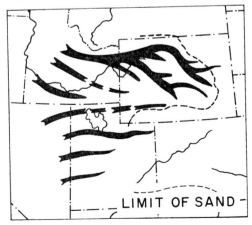

LIMIT OF SAND

Cyclical repetitions strikingly similar to those in the Mesaverde-Mancos of New Mexico (Figure 10-17) are apparent where vertical relationships among Frontier lithosomes are exposed. Regression and offlap are clearly indicated where marine shales are succeeded by sandstones, and these by nonmarine sediments including coals. As in the Cretaceous of New Mexico, the transgressive phases are less well represented, and it is common to find marine shale resting directly upon coal-bearing strata, reflecting rapid transgression and onlap without significant development of strand-line sands. The sandstone tongues of the Frontier of course represent regressive-transgressive episodes, and the pod-like distal sand bodies may be bar accumulations formed during temporary still-stands marking the maxima of regression.

In tectonic terms the source area of Frontier sediments appears to have been a mountainous region related to the eugeosynclinal belt that extended the length of the continent in Late Cretaceous time. The rock fragments in the Frontier conglomerates and lithic wackes were "cannibalized" from older sediments, volcanics, and low-rank metamorphics at nodes or loci of greater vertical displacement along the eugeosynclinal trend, one of which would be the apparent elevated source west of Yellowstone Park.

Consideration of the Frontier's western trend of thickening (Figure 13-4) and its proximity to an active eugeosyncline farther west permits identification of the trend of greater thickness as the flank of a marginal basin, such as may be demonstrated to have occupied this position since Late Precambrian time. Deposition to the east appears to have taken place under the typically cratonic conditions of a broad shelf area interrupted by local interior basins of more rapid subsidence. The presence of the coarsest sediment in the trend of greatest thickness, it should be noted, is the reverse of the normal deltaic pattern and is another reason for avoiding the term "delta" for this and similar accumulations.

The repeated regressive-transgressive cycles represented by the sandstone tongues might suggest eustatic shifts in sea level with concomitant advances and retreats of the strand line. However, there is no evidence of coincident bathymetric changes in marine shales farther to the east such as would indicate widespread eustatic events. In view of the known pulsational character of eugeosynclinal orogenic activity, it seems more logical to attribute the sand tongues to such pulsations. At times of quiescence, continued subsidence of the marginal basin and adjoining shelf would result in broad marine transgression to the west. At times of orogenic activity in the eugeosyncline, great volumes of debris would be carried to the east and southeast, overwhelming the subsiding tendencies of the marginal basin and building the entire western part of the area above sea level as a wide piedmont plain traversed by aggrading distributary streams. With relaxation of the orogenic pulse, renewed marine transgression over the piedmont plain would be initiated.

The Tertiary of the Alpine foreland is characterized by similar thick, alternating marine and nonmarine clastics of orogenic derivation to which European geologists have long applied the term **molasse**. The term would be applicable to the association model under discussion; however, as is true of the term flysch, the name molasse has been used so broadly in connection with similar, but not necessarily related, suites as to have lost its original connotations. From Ordovician through Mississippian the Appalachian marginal basin was the site of accumulations readily referable to the Frontier model, but here they have been termed "deltas" (Queenston and Catskill are examples). As noted, the term is inappropriate, since it creates a false picture and expends a term more useful in another connection, as will be noted later. It seems preferable to apply the term **clastic wedge**—a term introduced by Pettijohn (1957) and enlarged upon by King (1959).

The Appalachian clastic wedges differ from the Frontier and other Cretaceous examples of the Rocky Mountain area in that they were formed largely before the evolution of plants suitable for the development of coal. Further, the nonmarine units are characteristically red, possibly reflecting a different climatic condition. Pelletier (1958) describes and illustrates a Mississippian clastic wedge in Pennsylvania and Maryland and shows the application of paleocurrent measurements to analysis of the paleogeographic setting. The similarity to the Frontier example is striking in all important attributes, although Pettijohn (1960) arrives at a different interpretation of the nature of the source area.

Wackes and Related Arenites of Coal-cycle Type. Among the most common of all clastic associations are those characterized by quartz wackes and lithic wackes (less commonly feldspathic and lithic arenites) essentially indistinguishable in hand specimen or thin section from those of the clastic wedges, but lacking the well defined external and internal geometry of the wedge associations. Included here are the Pennsylvanian strata of the Eastern Interior and Western Interior provinces, and the Cretaceous strata of the Western Interior beyond the toes of the clastic wedges discussed above. Regional isopach-lithofacies maps show relatively low rates of change (except where the effects of erosion are marked) and only moderate response to the gently expressed intracratonic elements that form the tectonic framework of deposition. Maps of regional scale are presented in Sloss, Dapples, and Krumbein (1960, maps 64, 73, 74, and 135–150). Detailed local studies reveal a high degree of both vertical and lateral variability and complexity, which make possible the recognition of a number of subsidiary, but closely related, associations.

Cyclothems. The Pennsylvanian coal measures of the midcontinental and eastern interior states display a remarkable succession of cyclical deposits. The cyclical repetition of beds was recognized by Udden in 1906, but it remained for Weller (1930) to develop the definitive concept. Wanless (1931), Moore (1931), and others extended the study, until, today, an extensive literature covers the subject.

A **cyclothem** is defined as a series of beds deposited during a single sedimentary cycle of the type that prevailed during the Pennsylvanian Period. Weller defined an "ideal cyclothem" of ten members for western Illinois. Figure 13-10 illustrates the ideal cyclothem and summarizes the characteristics of its members.

As the figure indicates, the ideal cyclothem has quartzose, quartz wacke, or lithic wacke sand at the base (member 1), commonly lying unconformably upon the upper member of the previous cyclothem. The basal sandstone grades upward into sandy shale and clay shale (member 2), with fresh-water limestone nodules (member 3) near the top. This is succeeded by gray to drab underclay and coal, constituting members 4 and 5. Problems of origin of Pennsylvanian sands were discussed by Rich (1923) and Bass (1936).

Fig. 13-10

The ideal cyclothem. [Adapted from Willman and Payne (1942) and other sources.]

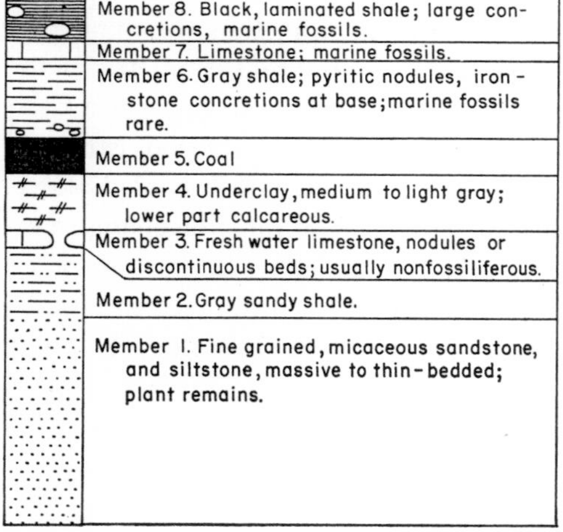

Member 10. Gray shale, sandy at top; marine fossils and ironstone concretions in lower part.

Member 9. Limestone; marine fossils

Member 8. Black, laminated shale; large concretions, marine fossils.

Member 7. Limestone; marine fossils.

Member 6. Gray shale; pyritic nodules, ironstone concretions at base; marine fossils rare.

Member 5. Coal

Member 4. Underclay, medium to light gray; lower part calcareous.

Member 3. Fresh water limestone, nodules or discontinuous beds; usually nonfossiliferous.

Member 2. Gray sandy shale.

Member 1. Fine grained, micaceous sandstone, and siltstone, massive to thin-bedded; plant remains.

Immediately above the coal in the ideal cyclothem is a thin marine shale (member 6) succeeded by micrite or argillaceous limestone with a dominant productid fauna (member 7). Black laminated shale (member 8), with an aberrant fauna composed of much flattened forms, lies above the fine grained limestone, and is succeeded by clean biosparite, commonly foraminiferal, limestone (member 9). The uppermost member of the ideal cyclothem is a bluish-gray marine shale that becomes more silty near the top. Plant fossils may occur in its upper portion.

The concept of the ideal cyclothem was developed to represent the optimum succession of deposits during a complete sedimentary cycle. The ideal cyclothem has not been observed fully developed in any one locality, but numerous partial cycles show that the members would occur in this ideal order. In western Illinois, the cyclothems consist typically of members 1, 4, 5, 7, 9, and 10. This "normal" type for western Illinois depends upon the dominance of certain environmental and tectonic conditions in that area, which produce cyclothems emphasizing certain members.

Cyclothems are typically associated with unstable shelf or interior basin conditions in which alternate marine submergence and emergence occur. During the emergent stages, local disconformities may be developed in the previously deposited sediments before the succeeding basal sandstone is deposited. Sand and silt, derived from rising elements in source areas, are deposited over the low emergent plain, mainly as alluvial detritus. As the source area is lowered by erosion, sand is succeeded by mud, also distributed over the alluvial plain and in shallow lakes and ponds. Marl and fresh-water limestone may occur locally.

With continued lowering of the source area, the inflow of detrital material diminishes, and the broad plain is occupied by swamps or marshes. Where conditions are suitable, peat accumulates and is later transformed to coal. The accumulation of peat requires restricted fresh or brackish water, under the general environmental conditions described in Chapters 6 and 7.

The lower five members of the ideal cyclothem are typically nonmarine deposits. This continental stage draws to a close at the end of peat formation. Slow negative movements or eustatic changes of sea level initiate submergence and start the marine phase of the cyclothem, which develops the upper five members.

Marine mud, transformed to a thin, clay shale, is deposited first, followed by a relative clearing of the sea during which dense or argillaceous limestone is deposited. Restricted shallow marine conditions commonly develop after the initial limestone deposition, to form the black laminated shale. It is believed that these restricted conditions involve stagnation of the sea or of broad lagoonal areas by a prolific growth of algae, which contribute their organic matter to the accumulating sediment.

As the cycle of sedimentation progresses, the environment loses its restrictions, develops open circulation, and eventually forms biosparite limestone in the shallow, current-agitated water. Toward the close of the cycle, initial disturbances in the source area supply mud to the environment and develop the uppermost shale of the cyclothem. As the mud accumulates, the environment grades from marine to brackish, foreshadowing the emergence that introduces the succeeding cycle.

The ideal cyclothem is subject to numerous variations, depending on the distribution of tectonic elements in source and depositional areas and on relative times and intensities of movement. Combinations of these factors determine the kind and succession of deposits, thereby controlling the members present in any cyclothem. Over any large area, such as may extend across several states, the cyclothems show lateral variations as the controlling factors themselves vary.

Two lateral variations of the ideal cyclothem are important in stratigraphy in that they illustrate lateral changes associated with nearness of source on the one hand and with dominance of marine conditions on the other. Wanless and Shepard (1936) described the three types of coal cyclothems shown in Figure 13-11. The Southern Appalachian type (called piedmont type by Wanless and Shepard) is intermediate between the regressive-transgressive cycles typical of the Rocky Mountain-Colorado Plateau Cretaceous and of the cratonic shelf conditions of the ideal cyclothem; as such, it is as closely related to the clastic wedge as to the low rate of change circumstances typical of accumulation in the cratonic interior. The thick cyclothems of the Southern Appalachian type are characterized by dominant continental clastic

Fig. 13-11. Three types of cyclothems. [Modified from Wanless and Shepard (1936).]

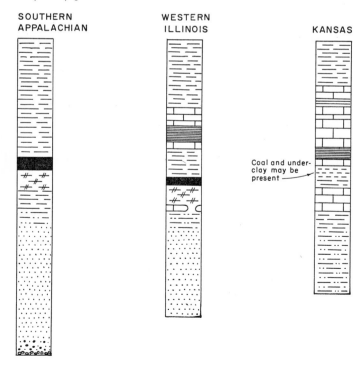

SOUTHERN
APPALACHIAN

WESTERN
ILLINOIS

KANSAS

Coal and under-
clay may be
present

sediments, good development of coal, and very subordinate marine beds. Unconformities and basal conglomerates mark the base of many cycles.

The ideal cyclothem (called deltaic type by Wanless and Shepard, 1936) has about equal representation of continental and marine deposits and is best developed in western Illinois. Environmentally, the western Illinois type represents the maximum alternation of marine and nonmarine conditions. Southeastward the nonmarine content increases, and the cyclothems approach the composition of those of the Southern Appalachian type; westward, where seen again at the margin of the Western Interior Basin, the cyclothems are dominated by marine deposition, and grade into the Kansas type.

Cyclothems of Kansas type (called neritic type by Wanless and Shepard, 1936) show a marked dominance of marine conditions, with alternations of limestone and shale. Basal sandstones are thin and bear marine fossils; underclay and coal are minor and subordinate. Of interest is the common occurrence of marine limestone below the underclay, possibly representing the marine equivalent of the fresh-water limestone (member 3) of the ideal cyclothem. Southwestward from the Kansas outcrop area, Pennsylvanian sedimentation is increasingly dominated by marine deposits, and, although cyclical phenomena are apparent in the Pennsylvanian of many North American areas, coal cyclothems are most typically developed east of a line from central Nebraska to the Llano Uplift of Texas.

Wanless is constructing a series of detailed facies and paleogeographic maps of individual cyclothem members. On completion, this collection of data and interpretations will add significantly to our knowledge and understanding of cyclothems.

A number of hypotheses have been proposed to account for the cyclical nature of Pennsylvanian deposits. Weller (1930) attributed them to mild positive and negative diastrophic movements. Wanless and Shepard (1936) concluded that the cyclothems were related to glacial episodes recognized on other continents in the later stages of the Paleozoic Era. More recently, the glacial control hypothesis has been revived and enlarged by Wheeler and Murray (1957), who interpret the ideal cyclothem as a two-phase cycle involving two upward and two downward shifts in base level and solar radiation.

The question of the source of the incompletely matured sandstones of Pennsylvanian cyclothems has long been a matter for speculation. Levorsen (1931) early recognized the strictly cratonic Transcontinental (Sioux) Arch and Canadian Shield as important contributors to Early and Middle Pennsylvanian sediments. Potter and Siever (1956), after careful statistical analysis of the petrology and of the vector properties of basal Pennsylvanian sandstones in the Eastern Interior Basin, concluded that the sediments of eastern Illinois and adjacent parts of Indiana and Kentucky were transported down a southwesterly directed regional slope, possibly from source areas in the Appalachian geosynclinal trend and parts of the Canadian Shield. Further consideration of Pennsylvanian data, in conjunction with study of the sources and dispersal paths of all sandstones in the Eastern Interior area, reinforce opinion on the importance of the "Appalachian reservoir" as a source (Potter and Pryor, 1961).

Channel Sandstones. Commonly associated with deposits of coal-cycle type is the development of narrow, elongate, downwardly convex sand bodies at the base of cyclothemic units. The importance of such bodies as productive oil sands and the interruptions ("cutouts") that they form in coal beds have led to detailed study of these sand bodies in a number of areas and to their recognition as the filling of stream channels. Although by no means confined to Pennsylvanian cyclothemic associations, some of the most thoroughly documented examples are found in the Eastern Interior Basin. Siever (1951) has mapped channel sands at the base of the Pennsylvanian in southern Illinois, as shown in Figure 13-12A. The dendritic pattern is clear, as is the general southwesterly course of the channels, which is in agreement with the regional slope defined by cross-bedding and other vector properties (Potter and Siever, 1956). In detail the basal Pennsylvanian channels range from broad features two to three miles wide to narrow valleys less than three-quarters of a mile wide and as much as 300 feet deep. The downward convexity of the sand bodies, the apparent terraces occasionally noted, the conformity to paleoslopes, the erosion of underlying strata, and the dendritic patterns of numerous examples strongly indicate that the sands represent the fillings of stream-eroded channels. A distinction must be drawn between channel fills of two types: (1) those that are clearly nonmarine, considered to be deposits of an aggrading stream, and which pass laterally into thinner, more widespread, finer grained sandstones and siltstones, interpreted as floodplain accumulations; (2) Channel fills, commonly arenitic, which lack evidences of stream associations and which may bear marine fossils. These indicate transgressive sedimentation of a depositional cycle subsequent to the channel-cutting phase. Examples of the latter type are well documented in the Bedford Formation (Mississippian) of the northern Ohio area. Figure 13-12B adapted from Pepper, De Witt, and Demarest (1954) illustrates Bedford deposits that fill the meandering and braided channels of an earlier erosional episode.

Deltaic Arenites and Wackes. It will be recalled that under the discussion of clastic wedges a distinction was drawn between these accumulations and those formed under conditions resembling modern delta systems. Clastic

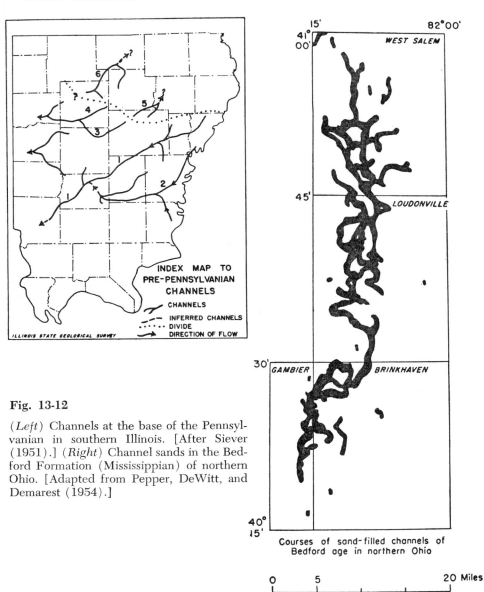

Fig. 13-12

(*Left*) Channels at the base of the Pennsylvanian in southern Illinois. [After Siever (1951).] (*Right*) Channel sands in the Bedford Formation (Mississippian) of northern Ohio. [Adapted from Pepper, DeWitt, and Demarest (1954).]

wedge deposits include a large measure of sediments formed in the deltaic environment, representing the mouths of streams crossing a piedmont plain to drop their load at the margin of the sea. Three factors combine, however, to prevent a significant impress of the deltaic environment on clastic wedge associations: (1) the dominant subsiding tendencies of the marginal basins, in which clastic wedges form, cause burial of the sediments before the immediate depositional environment can strongly influence the composition and geometry of the sediments; (2) the position of the strand line and of deltas along it is governed by the rate of supply of sediment, which in turn reflects the highly variable tectonic activity or the orogenic source area; and, (3) largely as a result of factor (2), the border of the sea is subject to nearly continuous large-scale advance and retreat and consequent short duration of the deltaic environment at any point. As pointed out earlier, clastic wedges are found at the eugeosynclinal borders of marginal basins where the greatest preserved thickness coincides with the position of coarsest grain sizes.

In contrast to clastic wedges (see Figure 13-13), but commonly confused with them, are other wedge-shaped accumulations of sandstone and shale developed at the hinge lines of interior basins or, more typically, at the cratonic border of marginal basins. Here the coarsest grain sizes are concentrated at the thin, proximal wedge edge, and shale is the dominant sediment where the accumulation is thickest. Forgotson's maps (in Sloss, Dapples, and Krumbein, 1960; maps 119–122 and 126–128) illustrate typical ancient deltaic deposits in the state of Mississippi during Late Jurassic and Early Cretaceous time.

A number of ancient deltaic deposits, where studied in detail, reveal a sedimentary framework similar to the Mississippi Delta, as illustrated and analyzed by Fisk and his co-workers (1954, 1955). Figure 13-14, adapted from Fisk (1961), shows the major distribution of sands and clays in parts of the modern, or birdfoot, delta of the Mississippi, as well as the distribution of sediment types along South Pass and Southwest Pass. As the

Fig. 13-13. Diagrammatic cross sections illustrating the difference in geometry between clastic wedge and deltaic associations.

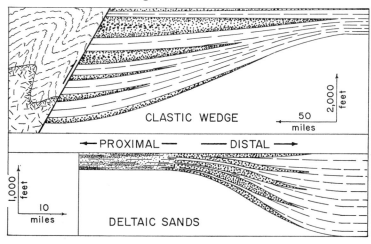

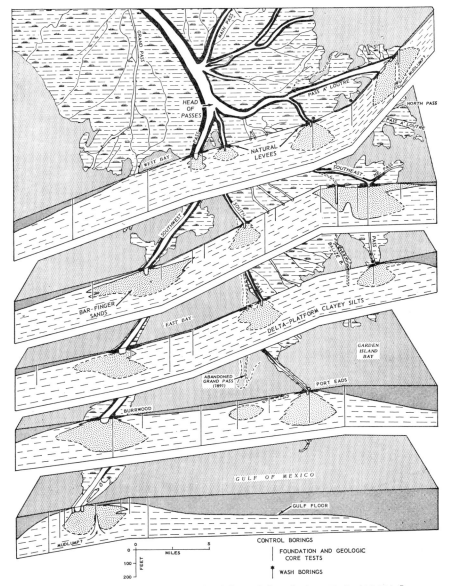

Fig. 13-14. Diagram of Mississippi bird-foot delta. [After Fisk (1961).]

diagram shows, the delta platform is made up of elongate **bar-finger sands** underlying the distributaries and of wedges of silty clay beneath the inter-distributary troughs and the delta front. The natural levees rest directly on the bar-finger sands, and consist of bedded clayey silts and silty clays. In their basal portions they are transitional to the bar-finger sands.

The bar-finger sands diverge from the Head of Passes and extend to the delta front bulges, where they underlie the distributary mouth bars, as shown in Figure 13-15. These sandy deposits are gradational to more silty and clayey deposits, described by Fisk as the **pro-delta facies.** These finer deposits form a belt covering the delta front and the surrounding Gulf floor. They are divided into inner and outer zones on the basis of grain size.

Between the distributaries are spits and subaqueous bars, composed of well sorted clean sands that grade into more silty deposits. The marsh deposits exposed just above sea level are organic-rich clayey silts. Typically, they form a brown to black spongy mass a few feet thick, in places made up mainly of grass roots. Laterally the marsh deposits grade into levee and bay bottom deposits.

Core-drilling in the Mississippi bird-foot delta has shown (Fisk, 1961) that the bar-finger sand bodies originate as distributary-mouth bar deposits that grow to elongate deposits with long-continued seaward lengthening of the distributary "passes" of the river. As such they are regressive deposits that appear to be typical of many advancing major deltas, reaching thicknesses in excess of 250 feet and maximum widths of about five miles. In contrast to channel-fill sands (described in the preceding section), which occupy eroded channels in pre-existing sediments, bar-finger sands sink into the underlying clayey silts through gravity displacement of these waterladen deposits.

Bar-finger sand bodies, identified by their branching distributary pattern and nonerosional relationship to underlying strata, have been recognized as important elements of a number of ancient deltaic deposits. Sandstone isoliths of the Booch sandstone (pronounced "Boke") in the Pennsylvanian of eastern Oklahoma clearly demonstrate the distributary pattern of elongate sand bodies, as shown by Figure 13-16, adapted from Busch (1961). According to some interpretations, the oil-productive Oficina sands (Oligocene) of eastern Venezuela, described by Probst (1953), are representative of similar deltaic environments.

Fisk (1955, 1961) draws a distinction between **deep-water delta sands** characterized by bar-finger sand bodies amid pro-delta clays and **shoal-water delta complexes** formed where wave action and longshore currents effect further transport of sediments carried to the shoreline by distributary streams. With progradation (marine regression) along a delta front the sands reworked by shore agencies may be spread as a regressive **delta-front sheet-sand** body. If delta progradation and marine regression are accompanied by subsidence the shoal-water delta and its redistributed sands are carried over the complex distributary channel pattern cut in an earlier phase, and the channels are filled with delta-front sands. The channel fills form

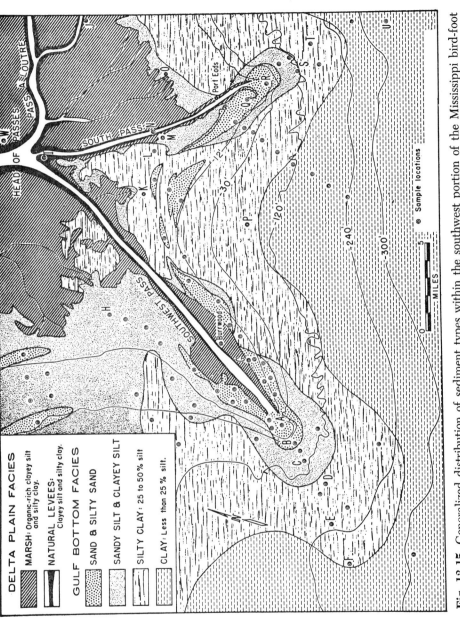

Fig. 13-15. Generalized distribution of sediment types within the southwest portion of the Mississippi bird-foot delta platform. The "facies" are lithotopes in the terminology adopted in this book. [After Fisk et al. (1954).]

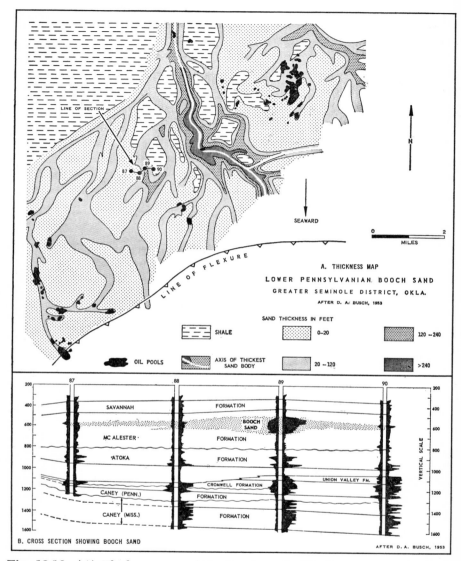

Fig. 13-16. (*A*) Thickness map of the Booch sand. (*B*) Cross section of related Pennsylvanian strata in central Oklahoma. [From Fisk (1961); after Busch (1953).]

elongate, bifurcating, thickened trends in the sheet-sand lithosome. Fisk (1955) has called attention to the Oligocene sand of southwest Texas, described by Nanz (1954) as an example of an ancient shoal-water delta complex. Such channel fills represent a special type associated with deltaic sedimentation; as is true of other channel sands, however, they tend to be oriented parallel to the regional slope and normal to the regional isopach and facies strikes.

Mixed Arenite and Wacke Associations. It should be clear that the stratigraphic record rarely exhibits a neat segregation of associations into clastic wedge, coal cycle, and deltaic types. Where the distal portions of a clastic wedge spread across a marginal basin or reach the margin of a subsiding interior basin, a belt of deltaic deposits is produced whose relationships to the clastic wedge become apparent only after broad regional study. Figure 13-17, adapted from Pepper, De Witt, and Demarest (1954), shows a paleogeographic reconstruction of conditions in the northern part of the Appalachian marginal basin at the time of deposition of the lower part of the Bedford Shale (Early Mississippian). Deposits in northern Ohio, identified as the "Red Bedford Delta," are derived from sources in the cratonic interior, chiefly the Canadian Shield, and are deltaic sediments in the sense applied here. To the east, deposits identified as the "Cussewago Delta," Gay-Fink Delta," "Cabin Creek Delta," and "Virginia-Carolina Delta" represent the distal zone of an eastward-thickening clastic wedge derived from the orogenically active Appalachian eugeosynclinal trend. A mixture of sediments from separate sources and representing distinct transportational histories is found in the basin interior.

Similarly, where a clastic wedge extends onto a stable shelf (where environments are controlled by eustatic sea-level changes), there is gradation into typical cyclothems that are indistinguishable from those unrelated to clastic wedges. In a like manner, cyclothemic and deltaic associations are commonly intimately mixed within the same succession, producing an alternation of channel-fill and bar-finger sand bodies. In general, vertical continuity of the same association suggests long-continued maintenance of a steady state in tectonic behavior; conversely, intercalation of associations suggests lateral shifts of tectonic habit without fixed hinge lines. As discussed in a later paragraph, there are also many degrees of mixing between arenite-wacke associations and the more mature arenite associations considered below.

Arenite Associations

The point has been made that the wackes were transported by agents such as turbidity currents and streams, which are incapable of producing significant textural or mineralogic maturity in a single cycle of transportation and deposition. Further, there is general agreement that these sediments were deposited under tectonic conditions leading to burial before the chemical and mechanical energy of the depositional environment could profoundly alter the texture and mineralogy. There is no unanimity of opinion, however,

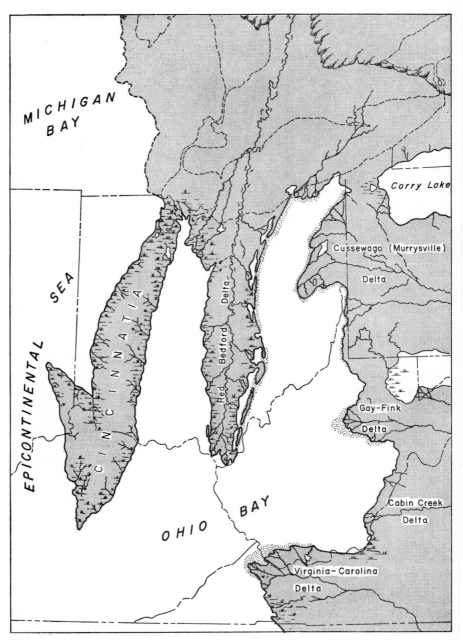

Fig. 13-17. Paleogeographic reconstruction of a part of Early Mississippian time in Ohio and adjoining areas. [After Pepper, DeWitt, and Demarest (1954).]

on the origin of the well sorted quartzose sands and the distinctive associations of which they form the most characteristic parts.

It is possible that the mineralogic purity of sandstones results from post-depositional effects, discussed as **interstratal solution** by Pettijohn (1941)—a theory compellingly refuted by Krynine (1942) and van Andel (1959). The most widely accepted view (reviewed by Potter and Pryor, 1961) considers quartzose sandstones of wide extent to be the product of erosion and *recycling of older mature sandstones,* two or more cycles being required before maximum purity is attained. There is experimental evidence (Kuenen, 1959) of the very long transport indicated by the well rounded quartz grains typical of quartzose accumulations, and these data are used in support of the multicycle hypothesis.

The present authors are inclined to reject the multicycle explanation on the grounds that (a) the almost universal occurrence of quartzose sandstones under conditions of great tectonic stability, (b) their occasional intermixing with sands of lesser maturity, (c) their distribution without relation to potential mature source materials, (d) the apparent lack of any relation to position in geologic time, and (e) the sheer volume of such sandstones in the stratigraphic record, which would have to be both source and product, render this explanation untenable. Rather, it appears probable that many quartzose accumulations represent long-continued chemical and mechanical maturation of grains under stable tectonic states in a *single cycle* of erosion, transportation, and deposition. Under the extreme stability envisaged, each grain would remain in the depositional environment, continuously subject to reworking before ultimate burial, until the sediment attained maturity. Insofar as roundness is concerned, Folk (1960) presents evidence in support of this view.

If mature quartz sandstones can, indeed, be formed in a single cycle, then it follows that the degree of maturity attained is a function of the energy released in the depositional environment and the length of time over which the accumulating sediments are subject to this energy. The first factor—energy—is most abundantly available in the zone of breaking waves along marine strandlines, and the great majority of quartzose sand accumulations can be shown, by their internal structures and textures and by their relationships to marine, transitional, and continental sediments, to represent beaches, offshore bars and cheniers, or associated dune ridges.

The second factor—time in the depositional environment—as emphasized earlier, is controlled by the rate of subsidence at the depositional site. With few exceptions, mature sandstones give every evidence of having accumulated under conditions of tectonic stability, where slow subsidence permits long exposure to mechanical and chemical energy before ultimate burial.

These conditions are met on stable shelves and at the shelf margins of subsiding basins. The exceptions to this rule are represented by sediments that matured under conditions of stability and which were carried into a tectonically negative regime.

Thus, given a supply of quartz-rich detritus and a stable tectonic state, any marine strandline is capable of producing quartzose sands. Nevertheless, the geometry and distribution of the sand body formed reflect subtle equilibria between rates of sediment supply and rates of subsidence. A number of patterns can be observed in the stratigraphic record.

Blanket Sands. The stratigraphy of broad and stable shelf areas is commonly punctuated by pure quartz sandstone sheets or blankets of unusually wide distribution. The St. Peter Sandstone and its correlatives form a typical example on the North American craton (see Kistler; in Sloss, Dapples, and Krumbein, 1960, Map 10). This blanket sand extends in an unbroken sheet 100–200 feet thick from Colorado to Indiana and is matched by equivalents in the areas of the Cordilleran marginal basin, the Williston Basin, Hudson's Bay Basin, and elsewhere. An excellent review of the St. Peter is presented by Dapples (1955).

Accumulations of this type represent an abundance of detritus fed to a stable area undergoing very slow subsidence at a steady rate such that strandline deposits are spread as a nearly continuous succession of parallel beaches, which are buried by the transgressing offshore sediments. At any moment during the transgression it must be assumed that the normal geomorphic features and sedimentary environments of a coastal plain are present, but the record of these is commonly destroyed by continuing transgression and reworking of lagoonal, dune, and deltaic deposits. The result is the production of a sheet of quartzose sand (Figure 13-18A) bearing the primary structures, textures, and bedding-plane markings identified with beach phenomena. A well documented example is presented by the Lyons Sandstone (Permian) of Colorado, as discussed and illustrated by Thompson (1949). The Tensleep Sandstone, a typical blanket sandstone (Pennsylvanian and early Permian) of the Wyoming Shelf area, is illustrated in the frontispiece. Note the characteristic low rate of change in isopach values so commonly associated with sandstones of this type.

The sedimentary record of regression on stable shelves is rarely preserved, because the deposits formed do not normally remain long below base level and are subject to erosion. Therefore, the majority of blanket sandstones represent transgressive phases punctuated by minor and volumetrically insignificant regressive tongues. Under special circumstances—apparently those that occur where regression on a shelf is accompanied by sufficient subsidence to permit the retention of sediments at or slightly below base level—regressive blanket sands are preserved. Examples are certain of the Cambrian-Early Ordovician sandstones (Galesville, Jordan, New Richmond) (Bell, Berg, and Nelson, 1956) of the Mississippi Valley area, discussed in Chapter 2, and parts of the Late Paleozoic to Early Jurassic sandstones of the Colorado Plateau. The latter examples include large volumes of sandstone with dune cross-lamination, suggesting a sheet formed by a succession of innumerable dune ridges along a regressive strand line.

Finally, if it is accepted that blanket quartz arenites indicate extreme tectonic stability, then their wide distribution is a measure of the extent of this tectonic state during parts of the history of a continent, regardless of the previous or subsequent behavior of specific areas. Thus, the St. Peter Sandstone extends across a number of interior basins without changing in character or in thickness, indicating an almost complete lack of tectonic differentiation during the time involved.

During the interminable and restless working and reworking of grains to produce a mature quartz arenite, it is possible that substantial volumes of mature sediment may be carried to the margin of a subsiding basin and "spilled over the edge," as it were, to be deposited and buried in an alien tectonic milieu. Here, because of the greater rate of subsidence, clean arenites can accumulate to surprising thicknesses, although their maturity is inherited from the stable shelf over which they have been transported. The Kinnikinic Quartzite (Ordovician) of central Idaho, for example, consists of nearly 3000 feet of pure quartz arenite, whereas the equivalent Eureka Quartzite of southwestern Nevada exceeds 1000 feet (see Kistler; in Sloss, Dapples, and Krumbein, 1960, map 10). Correlative sands (Winnipeg, Lander, Harding) covering shelf areas, over which the component grains of the thickened units must have passed, average much less than the thickness of those mentioned above. Other correlatives in the Simpson Group of Oklahoma are also markedly thickened in the Anadarko Basin, but the lithosomes include some units with a different geometry; these are discussed under Stillstand Sands.

"Unconformity Sands." Where other conditions appropriate for the formation of a blanket sand are present but an inadequate supply of quartz grains is provided, the scene is set for the development of blanket carbonates, as discussed in a later paragraph. If the organisms requisite to the formation of carbonates are lacking because of one or more environmental factors, clay is deposited at the base of the transgressive sequence, and whatever sand is present is concentrated along irregularities of the transgressed surface. These irregularities (either fault- and fault-line scarps or ridges and cuestas formed by the truncated edges of overstepped strata) trap sand in long, narrow sand bodies (Figure 13-18B) called **"strike-valley sands"** (Busch, 1961). The

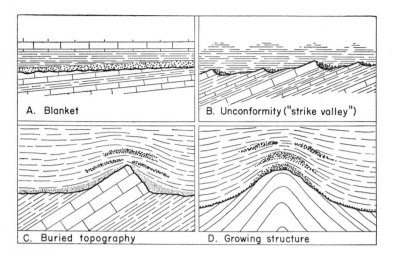

Fig. 13-18. Generalized diagrams of arenite associations.

association of such occurrences, with the onlapping succession above an unconformity, has led to the more common term **"unconformity sand."**

Stillstand Sands. It seems apparent that blanket sand bodies represent a steady state in the progressive transgression (or, more rarely, regression) of stable shelf areas, producing broad lateral shifts in depositional environments at a relatively constant rate. It is also apparent that other sand bodies and their associations represent approximations of a steady state of a different sort. Among these are the isolated lenticular bodies or linear trends of sandstone that are found within dominantly shale and siltstone lithosomes. Such ocurrences suggest the interruption of quiet-water, low-energy depositional environments by the localization of high-energy, strandline conditions. Where sand concentrations of this type reach significant thicknesses, they indicate a **stillstand** of the strandline achieved by the maintenance of an equilibrium between subsidence and deposition such that shoreline agencies remain fixed for appreciable periods along a relatively narrow zone. There are a number of mechanisms or circumstances under which stillstand sand bodies are formed.

Buried Topography. The localizing effect of minor irregularities on an overstepped erosion surface has been discussed under "Unconformity Sands." Where the topographic relief on a buried surface amounts to some tens of feet, the hills and valleys may have a strong effect on the composition, thickness, and attitude of the overstepping succession. Although valleys on the old surface tend to become filled, the differential compaction of thin shale accumulations on hills and ridges and thick accumulations in valleys tends to maintain a subdued reflection of the buried topography at the depositional surface during the development of a significant thickness of strata. Where the influence of buried topography results in local shoals shallower than wave base, beaches or offshore bars may form from sand winnowed or "cleaned up" from predominantly quartz-poor source material. The result (Figure 13-18C) is the development of sands along the crest of buried hills or along their flanks.

Because the sand trends thus formed are less subject to compaction than the surrounding shales, they tend to reinforce the effect of buried topography on subsequent sea floors and permit the possible formation of vertically successive sand bodies.

Growing Structures. Anticlinal folding contemporaneous with deposition provides the same opportunities for the development of localized stillstands and strandlines by buried topography. Typically, anticlinal uplift is irregular and sporadic, and only the active episodes create stillstand conditions. In some situations (Figure 13-18D) wave base is reached along the anticlinal axis, which is the site of sand accumulation. Continued uplift may cause erosion of sand from the higher parts of the anticline, creating a "bald-headed" structure. In other circumstances, strandlines are held at a stillstand, girdling the anticline with sand deposited on the flanks and with lagoonal fine grained sediments at higher structural positions. Such anticlines are also spoken of as "bald."

Numerous examples of quartz-arenite sand bodies developed on the flanks and crests of contemporaneous structures are known in oil fields of Pennsylvanian age in the Midcontinent. Salt domes whose upward growth has resulted in their penetration of Tertiary sediments of the Gulf Coast area constitute other easily recognized examples of sand bodies of this type.

Hinge-line Sands. During the activity of an interior basin or of the cratonic border of a marginal basin, these subsiding elements are separated from adjoining neutral or positive elements by a linear zone along which the amount of subsidence changes at a high rate—the hinge line. Where a hinge line has remained fixed for a significant amount of time, the isopach map of the sediments formed will illustrate this change; structural cross sections will show a point of inflection, and facies patterns will commonly show an abrupt change at the hinge line. Among other lithologic changes to be anticipated at hinge lines is the development of quartzose sand bodies related to strandline associations.

Hinge lines are the natural loci of marine stillstands. Along the hinge line, minor adjustments in the equilibrium between sediment supply and subsidence can be attained with minor lateral shifts, in contrast to the very broad shifts in the strand line that are brought about by such adjustments on stable shelves. As has been discussed, stream-borne detritus reaching a rapidly subsiding basin tends to be deposited in a deltaic complex, the sands being buried and preserved in a relatively immature state. Where lesser rates of subsidence are encountered the detritus remains in the littoral environment and is subject to long exposure to maturing processes and to lateral transport for significant distances along the shoreline. Much information regarding this pattern of sedimentation on the present Gulf Coast and on associated lagoonal and nearshore environments has appeared as a result of studies supported by Project 51 of the American Petroleum Institute (see Shepard, Phleger, and Van Andel, 1960). These conditions appear to have prevailed for tens of millions of years in that area as well as at the cratonic borders of other marginal basins and at the hinge lines of numerous interior basins.

Sand percentage maps of Tertiary units in the Gulf Coast area, presented by Waters, McFarland, and Lea (1955), illustrate the degree of concentration of strandline deposits along Cenozoic hinge lines. Each accumulation is confined by the gulfward and landward extremes of regression and transgression, and these, in turn, are limited by the degree to which relative changes in sea level can outweigh the stabilizing effect of the hinge line. It is noteworthy that, in contrast to shelf conditions, the subsiding tendencies at basinal hinge lines permit the preservation of regressive deposits, and complete cycles of regression and transgression are commonly represented (well illustrated by Lowman, 1949, Figure 23, and Storm, 1945). The net effect of Cenozoic transgressions and regressions has been a gradual gulfward shift of the average positions of strandlines, reflecting the gulfward retreat of successive hinge lines.

A somewhat different, but related, pattern is revealed in the Simpson Group (Ordovician) of the Anadarko Basin in Oklahoma. Here a succession of onlapping sandstones, with numerous regressive phases, oversteps older units on the north flank of the basin to become the blanket Wilcox sand and St. Peter Sandstone of the Kansas Shelf and areas to the north. Within the basin the extreme purity of the sands indicates a maturity inherited from long transport on the adjacent shelf in the manner of the basinal extensions of the blanket arenites previously discussed. Some of the more tabular sand bodies are simple blanket deposits formed at times of little or no relative subsidence of the basin. Other prominent masses, however, are elongate bodies oriented parallel to the isopach trends and normal, presumably, to the paleoslope. These elongate lithosomes pass basinward into fine grained carbonates and shales; and updip, into dark, finely laminated shales of possible lagoonal origin. Stillstands in the general transgression of the basin flank are believed to be responsible for the sand "build ups." Here, then, is yet another example of naturally occurring mixtures in which at least three model associations can be identified.

Other basins of less continuous subsidence have, of course, lesser stability of hinge lines and strandlines and offer opportunities for the isolation of deposits representing relatively temporary stillstands. Figure 13-19 shows part of the Appalachian Basin at a moment in Early Mississippian time. A temporary stillstand in the advance of the "Red Bedford" delta (or regression of the Early Mississippian seaway) permitted the growth of a number of offshore bars subsequently buried under expanding deltaic sedimentation. One of these, the "Second Berea" sand, has been penetrated by a great number of gas wells and is shown (Figure 13-19) by Pepper, De Witt, and Demarest (1954) to be an elongate sandstone-siltstone lithosome lying between finer grained terrestrial and lagoonal sediments on the west and marine shales on the east. Fisk (1955) refers to this type of occurrence as a **delta-margin island sand,** pointing to Grand Isle, Louisiana, as a modern exemplar and to the Olympic sand (Pennsylvanian) of Oklahoma as an example in the stratigraphic record. Fisk (1955) illustrates both occurrences, and Dillard (1941) presents further details on the Olympic sand. Although the relationships of the "Second Berea" sand and of Grand Isle to individual deltas are clear, there seems to be no major distinction between these sand bodies and others formed at basinal hinge lines without the necessary association with a specific deltaic system. Offshore bars and barrier islands characterize the present Texas coast, and, if buried as isolated masses, would have the same hallmarks in the stratigraphic record—lagoonal deposits on one side, marine on the other; the internal structures of beaches; and upward convexity. Very much the same may be said of **chenier sands,** identified by Fisk (1955) as a special type of delta-associated accumulation. Cheniers are oak-covered beach ridges in the coastal marshlands of Louisiana and appear to represent temporary stillstands along a regressive shore. Fisk (1955, Figure 8) illustrates the typical forked shape of present-day cheniers and refers to certain of the Pennsylvanian "shoe-string sands" of Kansas (discussed by Dillard, Oak, and Bass, 1941) as ancient examples.

Clastic-Wedge Arenites. The point was made in the earlier discussion of clastic wedges that the rapid transport by streams and the early burial of sediments in a subsiding marginal basin permit little development of textural and mineralogic maturity by the accumulating deposits. It was also noted, however, that where clastic-wedge sediments encounter the energy states and longshore transportational agencies of the strand line, opportunity is afforded for significant increase in maturity of sandstones. Indeed, lithic, feldspathic, and quartz arenites petrologically indistinguishable from sandstones of quite different derivation may be formed.

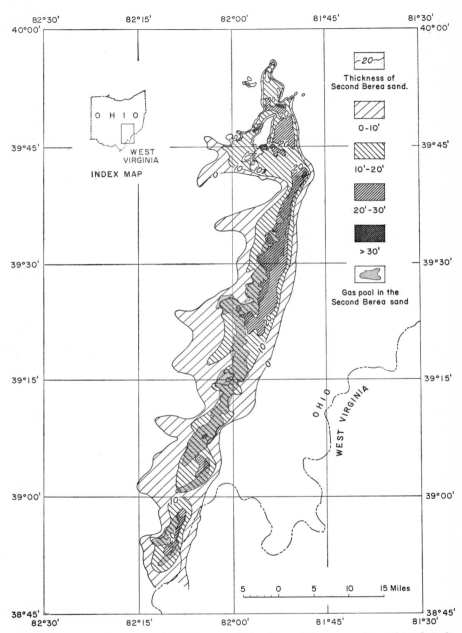

Fig. 13-19. Distribution and thickness and the Second Berea sand in Ohio. [Modified from Pepper, DeWitt, and Demarest (1954).]

Stillstands may occur in the regression or transgression of the strandlines of clastic wedges as a result of temporary equilibria between sediment supply and subsidence. As at hinge lines, such stillstands permit the maturation of accumulating sediment on beaches and barrier islands. Hollenshead and Pritchard (1961) illustrate the occurrence of clean sand trends or "benches" in the Point Lookout and Cliff House Formations, regressive-transgressive units of the Cretaceous Mesaverde Group of New Mexico. Figure 13-20 is adapted from their paper and clearly shows, on an electric-log cross section, the successive step-like arrangement of thickened sand trends. Scruton (1961) has related sand occurrences of this type to modern sand accumulations on regressive beaches on the Pacific Coast of southern Mexico. Here, at the edge of a narrow piedmont plain, aerial photographs reveal closely spaced beach ridges having a pronounced linearity that strikingly resembles patterns developed in Mesaverde gas-producing sand bodies (Scruton, 1961,

Fig. 13-20. Clastic wedge arenites in the Cretaceous of the San Juan Basin. The "benches" noted on this electric log cross section represent stillstands in the regressive (Point Lookout Formation) and transgressive (Cliff House Formation) development of a sandstone tongue of the type shown in Figure 10-17. The marked irregularity, and absence in some areas, or the Cliff House Sandstone is characteristic of clastic wedge transgressive units. [After Hollenshead and Pritchard (1961).]

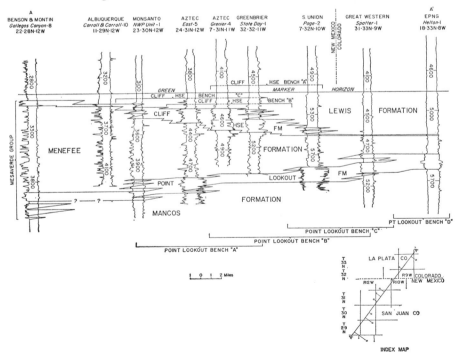

Figures 1 and 3). Similar relationships of strandline sand bodies oriented at right angles to the paleoslopes of clastic wedges (that is, parallel to arcuate shores at the margins of clastic wedges) have been noted in the Silurian, Devonian, and Mississippian of the Appalachian area (Yeakel, 1962; Pelletier, 1958; Dickey et al., 1943). Pryor (1961, Figure 10) presents a conceptual model illustrating relationships among paleoslope, direction of transport, depositional strike, and sand-body trends.

The significant distinction between clastic-wedge arenite lithosomes and those representing stands at hinge lines is, of course, the regional association of the former with a distally thinning, extracratonically derived mass of debris, whereas the latter, of intracratonic derivation, pass distally into thickening basinal accumulations. Inasmuch as the terminus of a clastic wedge is largely controlled by the rate of sediment supply—and this is a function of conditions in an adjoining tectonic belt—there is no predictable superposition of vertically successive sand bodies as may be the case with stillstands on the craton or cratonic margin.

Arkose Associations

An attempt to construct purely observational lithologic associations approaches a breakdown where markedly feldspathic sediments are encountered, since these occur in widely differing sedimentary suites representing a broad spectrum of tectonic and environmental habits. Thus, the recognition as "arkose associations" of all sedimentary successions that include sandstones having a significant feldspar content makes for very strange lithologic bedfellows and for confusion in stratigraphic analysis. For example, turbidite sandstones deposited in deep waters and interbedded with radiolarian chert, siliceous shale, and submarine volcanics of an obvious eugeosynclinal habit may closely resemble, in hand specimen and thin section, the basal few inches of a predominantly carbonate sheet that oversteps a cratonic erosion surface.

Such incongruities are avoided by considering separately those arkoses, arkosic wackes, and arkosic arenites which exhibit clearly defined relationships to graywacke associations and clastic wedges (that is, those derived from extracratonic sources), as distinguished from other associations that include similar high-feldspar sandstones without eugeosynclinal affinities (that is, those derived from sources in the interior of the craton) and which are here treated as *arkose associations*. At first glance it would appear that a strong admixture of inference and subjectivity is required in identifying these associations, but in practice the availability of data on the geometry of the rock masses, the other associations with which they are mixed, and the degree and kind of structural, metamorphic, and igneous involvement make the acceptance or rejection of a given observable association as a member of the arkose group relatively easy.

Wedge Arkoses. By far the most significant of the cratonic arkoses are those wedge-shaped masses in which the thickest part of the wedge contains the coarsest material and is obviously proximal with respect to source. The proximal margin of the wedge is commonly formed by a high-angle fault delineating a typical yoked basin coupled to an adjacent orogenic uplift. Arkose associations of this geometry are relatively narrow linear belts which may be many tens of miles long and from a few hundred to several thousands of feet thick. Where they occur, such masses make imposing interruptions among thinner and more mature cratonic sediments, but they tend to be widely scattered in both space and time in the depositional history of a continent. In middle North America wedge arkoses are virtually limited to the Late Precambrian (Belt of southern Montana and the Keweenaw of the Lake Superior region); Late Paleozoic and Early Mesozoic [Absaroka Sequence of Sloss (1963) in the southern Midcontinent, southern and central Rockies, and discontinuously from the Maritime Provinces to the Appalachian Piedmont and Atlantic Coastal Plain]; and Cenozoic of the Cordilleran area. These are the times and positions of cratonic orogenesis with which wedge arkoses are inevitably linked.

Where the uplifts complementary to yoked basins involve granitoid basement rocks covered by no more than a thin veneer of sediments, the resulting immature, feldspar-rich debris accumulates as a typical wedge arkose in which individual hand specimens may be difficult to distinguish from the parent granite. Characteristically, but not universally, the arkosic sediment is red, in part colored by an abundance of pink potash feldspar, but primarily as a result of ferric oxide coatings on the grains. It had long been common practice to attribute the necessary oxidizing conditions to an arid climate, but according to Clark (1962), who has reviewed the earlier writings of Van Houten (1948), Wahlstrom (1948), Krynine (1949), and Swineford (1955), the red color reflects at least seasonal influences of a warm humid climate in which the lateritization of arkosic sediments took place after deposition or was inherited from lateritic soils.

Among the more completely investigated wedge arkoses are those of Pennsylvanian and Permian age that flank the Front Range, Uncompahgre, and Apishapa positive elements of the central and southern Colorado area. In a single volume, "Symposium on the Pennsylvanian Rocks of Colorado and Adjacent Areas" (Rocky Mountain Association of Geologists, 1958), the reader will find a number of well documented papers on regional relationships of the wedge arkoses and their local details. Figure 13-21, modified from Mallory (1958), illustrates the mountainous uplifted blocks fringed by

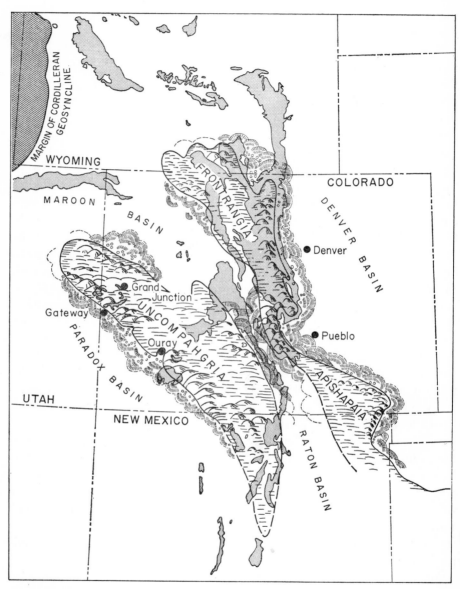

Fig. 13-21. Middle Pennsylvanian paleogeography of the Colorado area. The named elements are orogenic positives yoked to the adjacent basins and are the sources of arkose wedges whose proximal portions are shown as alluvial fans flanking the uplifts. The gray areas mark present outcrops of basement crystalline rocks exposed on Tertiary uplifts. [After Mallory (1958).]

coalescent alluvial fans. The regional panel diagram, Figure 13-22 (from Bissell and Childs, 1958) shows the wedge-arkose masses (Cutler, Minturn; Maroon, Fountain) flanking the uplifts and passing northward into blanket quartz arenites (Weber and Tensleep), southward into blanket carbonates and quartz arenites. Extension of the section to the east across the Denver Basin (as shown by Taylor, 1958, Figure 4) would indicate contemporaneous relationships with the dominantly marine cyclothemic Permo-Pennsylvanian strata of the Midcontinent.

Note (Figure 13-22) the intertonguing of the arkosic red beds on the

Fig. 13-22. Regional relationships of Pennsylvanian and Lower Permian lithosomes in the Colorado area. The uplifted blocks of basement crystallines are flanked by thick wedge arkoses—Cutler, Fountain, and Maroon (includes Minturn Formation of present usage). These intertongue with a variety of other lithosomes in the interiors of the yoked basins and on adjoining shelves. [After Bissell and Childs (1958).]

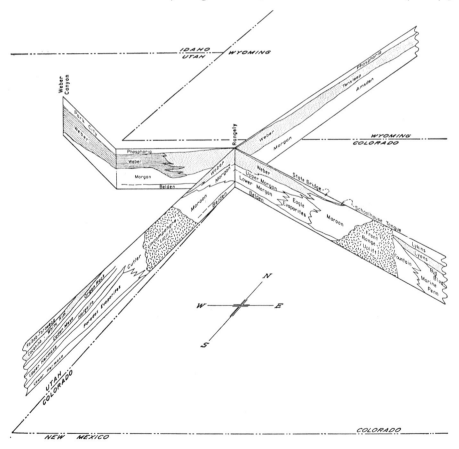

flanks of the yoked basin with the evaporites (Paradox and Eagle) in the interiors of the Paradox and Maroon Basins. Details of the relationships between evaporite and arkose lithosomes and the numerous marine limestone tongues that form synchronous markers are presented in Figure 13-23

Fig. 13-23. Pennsylvanian lithosome relationships in the interior of the yoked Maroon Basin of Colorado. Note that the vertical exaggeration is over 20×. [From Murray (1958).]

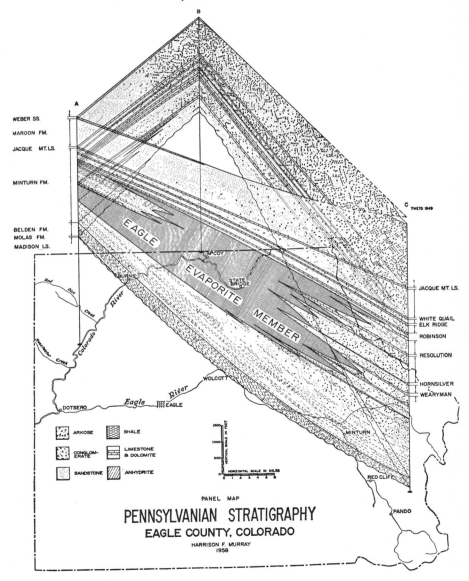

PANEL MAP

PENNSYLVANIAN STRATIGRAPHY

EAGLE COUNTY, COLORADO

HARRISON F. MURRAY
1958

(modified from Murray, 1958). Black shales, complexly intertongued with both arkoses and evaporites, are volumetrically important in the basin interiors, especially so in the Paradox Basin.

Wedge-shaped conglomerate and sandstone masses of similar geometry and similar relationships to contemporaneous structure and intertonguing lithosomes, but characterized by quite different petrology, are known in a number of areas where thick sedimentary successions were present before uplift of orogenic positive elements. In the area of the Ardmore Basin of southern Oklahoma, for example, some 10,000 feet of Paleozoic strata, largely carbonates, cherty carbonates, and chert, had accumulated before latest Mississippian time (see the paleogeographic maps in Tomlinson and McBee, 1959). Early Middle Pennsylvanian vertical movement (Atoka and Des Moines) of such elements as the Criner Hills and the Healdton Uplift, and complementary subsidence of adjacent yoked basins, created conditions for the accumulation of vast alluvial fans of carbonate-chert conglomerate and breccia. These grade basinward into dark shales (Atoka) and cyclothemic deposits (Des Moines). Upward in the section the carbonate-chert clastics give way to arkose, marking the exposure to erosion of rhyolitic and granitic basement rocks and confirming the common genesis of the carbonate-chert and arkosic debris. Farther to the west in the area of the Wichita Mountains, where a thinner sedimentary cover was present above basement rocks, arkoses form the dominant fill on the flanks of the yoked Anadarko Basin (Edwards, 1959).

Other variations among wedge arkose associations are formed by relationships with purely nonmarine basin sediments (as in the Triassic Newark basins of the eastern states and in the Cenozoic of the intermontane west), intercalation with extrusive rocks (Keweenaw, Newark, western Cenozoic), and involvement with sill-like intrusives. None of these variants, however, serves to mask the essential similarity of the associations, their wedge-shaped geometry, immature petrology, and relationships to steeply faulted basins and rigid, mountainous, uplifted blocks.

Basal Arkoses. Of lesser significance, although widespread in the stratigraphic record, are the texturally and mineralogically immature sediments at the base of successions that transgress an unconformity. Here, apparently because of limited mechanical energy release at the strandline, or because of swift transgression, residual materials on the ancient erosion surface are reincorporated as part of the overstepping unit without undergoing much reworking. Such accumulations are particularly characteristic of transgressions across a crystalline basement terrain, and the resulting basal strata are typical arkoses that grade upward in a few inches or a few feet to clean quartz arenites or to carbonates. If there is sufficient relief on the erosion surface, the buried hills tend to be flanked by particularly thick masses of residuum. The more permeable units may be oil-bearing (the "granite wash" of numerous productive oil fields), and it may be difficult in subsurface samples to differentiate the slightly reworked residual material from the weathered parent rock below.

A basal arkose cannot, of course, form as a result of the transgression of an erosion surface cut on nonfeldspathic rocks. However, basal conglomerates containing a high percentage of carbonates and other labile rock fragments derived from immediately underlying units are subject to similar interpretations. Such basal accumulations, the "detrital zones" of drillers, may, in the subsurface, be equally difficult to distinguish from the parent materials.

Red Bed Associations

The obvious nature of red beds leads to the ready assumption that they represent a natural lithologic association. Yet, if humans were color blind, the presence of ferric oxide films on clastic grains probably would not seem a sufficiently significant character to permit the establishment of a unique association. Indeed, red beds are common in all of the major associations discussed thus far, save only the deeply buried and intermediate graywackes; they are especially prominent in clastic-wedge associations (Pocono, for example), deltaic wackes and arenites (Moenkopi, Cotton Valley), and wedge arkoses. Red beds are far from uncommon among quartzose associations (Amsden, Wingate), and occur as basal arkoses, basal carbonate conglomerates, and associated siltstones and shales.

Despite the variety of tectono-environmental settings within which red beds may accumulate, they do represent special occurrences or combinations of source, depositional environment, and diagenesis. Such special occurrences or combinations appear to be overwhelmingly more common in nonmarine than in marine sedimentation. Krynine (1949) has recognized four major categories of red beds: primary, postdepositional, secondary, and chemical.

Primary Red Beds. These are sediments whose red color is derived from lateritic soils and is preserved in oxidizing depositional and diagenetic environments. Primary red beds are thought to form on piedmont surfaces and the upper reaches of alluvial plains. The "red clay conglomerates and associated mudstones" of Clark (1962) fall into this type.

Postdepositional Red Beds. It is Krynine's view that, on the lower reaches of streams and deltas, exposure of non-red sediments to oxidizing conditions results in the acquisition of red color. Clark classifies sediments having postdepositionally acquired red color as "variegated reds."

Secondary Red Beds. Where older red beds are subject to erosion and transportation they form the source of secondary red sediments—the "shale-pebble reds" noted by Clark.

Chemical Red Beds. In these the red ferric oxide pigment is precipitated from solution in either fresh or marine waters. Many of the great sedimentary iron formations of the world represent economically vital, if volumetrically insignificant, exceptions to the rule of dominant terrestrial environments in the formation of red sediments. But since the iron formations are nonclastic, they have only their red color and inferred oxidizing depositional environment to relate them to a "red bed association" that is sufficiently heterogeneous without their inclusion.

Black Shale Associations

As is true of red beds, black shales are such visually prominent elements of many stratigraphic successions as to suggest that they constitute a natural lithologic association. Black shales, even more than red beds, are present in all the major observable associations noted in this chapter; taken as a group the black shales cannot be interpreted as being indicative of more than deposition in a *euxinic environment*—a quiet-water, reducing environment leading to the preservation of the organic matter that forms the black pigment. **Humic black shale** contains visible fragments or tissues of plants, whereas **bituminous black shale** contains finely comminuted, fatty, waxy, or resinous materials, and is commonly characterized by abundant pyrite or marcasite. All gradations are found between the two varieties, and clay-ironstone concretions may be present in both types. Most black shales are thinly laminated and fissile, and contain a fauna dominated by planktonic and nektonic forms.

It is apparent that the reducing conditions requisite to black-shale deposition may be encountered in a variety of tectonic and environmental circumstances. Among these, three major types of occurrence may be discerned.

Black Shales in Graywacke Associations. The greatest volume of rock associated with prominent graywackes, bedded cherts, and submarine volcanics is black shale, commonly metamorphosed to slate by the regional metamorphism typical of eugeosynclinal troughs. Where such eugeosynclinal shales extend beyond the limits of significant metamorphic effects and into the transition between eugeosyncline and marginal basin, they occur as enormous volumes of black shale, commonly in part siliceous and gradational with chert. These are the **grapotolite shales,** so named from the fossils preserved on bedding planes, typical of the Ordovician and Silurian of many eugeosynclinal margins. Older and younger accumulations outside the graptolite range-zone are equally common.

Black shales of this type in eugeosynclinal troughs and along the eugeosynclinal borders of marginal basins give every evidence of deep-water deposition—the **fondo environment** of Rich (1951a). Here, depth below wave base provides the necessary lack of mechanical energy for the accumulation of clays, whereas the lack of overturn and circulation leads to deoxygenation and a negative Eh potential.

Black Shales in Restricted Basin Associations. The problem of basins characterized by restricted circulation and the accompanying geochemical effects is treated in greater detail under carbonate-evaporite relationships. For present purposes it is sufficient to note that restraints imposed upon normal marine circulation, whether by encircling reefs and banks or by tectonic effects on topography, may create deoxygenated, still bottom environments not markedly different from those formed in deep water. Black shales, commonly interbedded and intergradational with dark argillaceous carbonates, are important elements in cratonic interior basins and marginal basins. The presence of a benthonic fauna, meager and impoverished except in calcareous phases and carbonate interbeds, belies the notion of a deep-water origin, although this has been proposed by some workers (Rich, 1951b). Others have proposed that thin basinal black shales represent basin interiors from which normal sediments have been excluded by barriers (the "starved-basin hypothesis" of Adams et al., 1951).

Black shales in marginal basins pass uninterruptedly into the graywacke associations noted above, and there is no easily recognized line of demarcation. In general, intercalated carbonates and a bottom-dwelling fauna denote cratonically related marginal-basin black shales, and these are commonly identical in lithology and stratigraphic position to the black shales found in obvious interior-basin settings. Conversely, the shales of the graywacke association are identified by their siliceous admixture, their purely planktonic or nektonic fauna, and their passage into a eugeosynclinal graywacke suite.

Black Shales in Lagoonal Associations. Restricted circulation, deoxygenation, and resulting euxinic bottoms are also characteristic of lagoons cut off from the main body of the sea by barrier beaches, banks, or reefs. Restricting topographic features of this type may be related to the blanket deposits of sand or carbonate, distal margins of clastic wedges, deltaic accumulations, or complex associations represented by cyclothems. In contrast to typical examples of the other black shale types discussed, lagoonal black shales tend to be relatively thin, although some, such as the Late Devonian—Early Mississippian Chattanooga Shale and its correlatives, may cover extraordinarily large areas. Rich (1951b) has argued for a deep-water origin for such deposits, but the evidence in associated sediments and biotas, and in relationships to transgressed erosion surfaces, seems to weigh heavily in favor of a shallow-water environment.

NONCLASTIC ASSOCIATIONS

The analysis and interpretation of associations among clastic rocks require an awareness of the influences brought to bear by diagenetic and other post-depositional effects on the petrology of the rocks and on their internal structures and textures. Nevertheless, in the normal course of work on the majority of clastic associations, the stratigrapher may make his interpretations with confidence in the preservation of significant mineralogic, textural, and structural detail. As regards nonclastic rocks (those representing precipitation from aqueous solutions with or without the intervention of a biologic agent) equal confidence may be placed in the belief that postdepositional mineralogic and textural alterations are the rule rather than the exception. Therefore the recognition and identification of process models operating today, which may be used to explain the observable response models in ancient nonclastic sediments, is much more obscure and subject to error. The combined obscurity and fallibility involved here is attested by the variety of classifications, analyses, and interpretations proposed for nonclastic associations; and the classification that follows in this chapter is certain to require modification and revision.

Blanket Carbonate Associations

Blanket carbonates have the geometry and distribution of blanket quartz arenites and are commonly associated with them. Carbonate sheets a few tens of feet in thickness may cover tens or hundreds of thousands of square miles on the stable shelf areas of the craton, varying in mineralogy, texture, and structure, in apparent response to environmental and tectonic controls.

Blanket Biosparites. The close association of quartz arenites with certain coarse-textured carbonates composed largely of well sorted fossil fragments (or whole tests, commonly abraded, of the larger foraminifera) and exhibiting cross-bedding and cut-and-fill structures suggests a common origin for both the arenites and carbonates. The limestones and their dolomitized equivalents may be considered to represent carbonate beaches that, through transgression or regression, are spread as blankets in the manner previously described for blanket sandstones. Oolites (oosparites) and pelletoidal limestones (pelsparites) are commonly intercalated with blanket biosparites. Under stillstand conditions, successive beaches and related deposits are superimposed to form carbonate banks, as discussed later in this chapter. Examples of blanket biosparites are found in the Ste. Genevieve Formation and in the Chester of Illinois and among Pennsylvanian limestones in cyclothems of the southern Midcontinent.

Blanket Biomicrites. In terms of volume and widespread distribution the most important blanket limestones and dolomites are well bedded, light-colored sheets in which fossils and fossil fragments are present, richly or sparsely, in a matrix of microcrystalline carbonate. Beds or lenses of well sorted biosparite may form an appreciable percentage at any point of observation, but there is a lack of the lateral persistence characteristic of the sparites noted above. The predominance of fine material is interpreted to indicate deposition below average wave base, whereas the intercalations of sorted coarser particles suggests occasional interventions of higher energy states, perhaps as a result of repeated storm cycles. The pervading light colors of these rocks reflect the thorough oxidation of organic debris; the abundance of fossils, especially crinoids and other benthonic forms dependent on a supply of microorganisms, indicates deposition in the shallow sublittoral realm within the sunlit photic zone. The Mississippian limestones (Madison, Leadville, Redwall, and so on) of the Rocky Mountain area and Colorado Plateau are examples of undolomitized or partially dolomitized blanket biomicrites.

Dolomitization is the rule for carbonates deposited on stable shelves, and blanket biomicrites are no exception. Recrystallization during dolomitization greatly alters the primary textures. Typical examples such as the Galena Dolomite (Ordovician) exhibit a dominant matrix of fine to medium grained dolomite rhombs in which the fossils and larger fossil fragments are represented by voids or casts.

Many dolomitized limestones (the Ordovician Bighorn Dolomite of Wyoming is an example) are marked by mottles or segregations of coarse dolomite rhombs in a matrix of finer, commonly less dolomitized, material. Beales (1953), after studying the mottled Palliser Formation (Devonian) of Alberta, suggests that the coarse rhombs indicate an incomplete second phase of dolomitization controlled by original porosity differences related to the presence of algal fronds, fossils, and worm burrows.

Blanket Micrites. Thin sheet-like microcrystalline limestones, closely associated with shales, and passing laterally into coarser grained carbonates, are found with other sediments of the cratonic shelf. Benthonic fossils are rare but may be perfectly preserved; their presence, and the presence of desiccation cracks, indicates deposition in the shallow waters of protected lagoons. Examples of blanket micrites are found in parts of the Decorah Formation (Ordovician) of Iowa among other types of obvious marine affinity, the "fresh-water" limestones of coal cyclothems, and carbonate tongues such as the Alcova Limestone (Triassic) of Wyoming. Quite similar low-energy carbonates are encountered (but with more limited areal distribution) in lagoonal deposits associated with reefs, as described later.

Blanket Biostromal Carbonates. The term **biostrome** was introduced by Cumings (1932) to include sheet-like structures such as crinoid beds, coral beds, and the like, which are composed of the hard parts of benthonic organisms. These sheet-like structures are contrasted with mound-like structures, the **bioherms**. Recent usage has stressed the distinction between *wave-built* structures, such as the blanket biosparites, and *wave-resistant* structures, such as reefs, in which the mass of organically precipitated carbonate is held together by a framework of encrusting growths, especially calcareous algae. The original definition of biostrome covered what are now recognized as both wave-built and wave-resistant, sheet-like bodies, but it has become common practice to limit the term biostrome to the latter; that is the usage followed here.

The presence of blanket biostromal carbonates implies organic reef development (as discussed further under a separate heading) under conditions of transgression or regression such that a relatively narrow zone of wave action and reef growth is effective with advancing time over a major area. The Nisku Formation (Devonian) of Alberta and the Huntington (Silurian) of Indiana are examples. As the rate of transgression or regression decreases, blanket biostromes pass into less sheet-like and more mound-like masses identified as reefs.

Lentiform Carbonate Associations

There is a group of carbonate associations that are characteristically lens-like in shape as viewed in regional cross sections and regional isopach maps. Such deposits obviously occupy subsiding cratonic basins, and might be termed "basinal carbonates"; but, the descriptive term "lentiform" is more appropriate, since it carries no genetic implication and stands in contradistinction to the low rates of change in the thickness of blanket carbonates.

Lentiform Biomicrites. Some lentiform biomicrites (for example, the Cambro-Ordovician Arbuckle Limestone of the Ardmore Basin and the Mississippian Mission Canyon Limestone of Central Montana) are no more than thicker extensions of blanket types. That is, a progressive increase in thickness is not accompanied by significant differences in grain size, sorting, or color, and it is apparent that the more rapid rate of subsidence and sedimentation was insufficient to affect the environment of deposition and diagenesis. More commonly, and especially where the rate of change of thickness is more marked, the lentiform biomicrites are darker in color, have a higher percentage of micritic matrix (with clay and silt admixtures), and have a smaller percentage of intercalations of well sorted biosparite. Dolomitization is much less common, except in association with evaporites and fracture zones, and decreases progressively toward areas of maximum thickness. A mapped example of dolomitized blanket limestones and un-dolomitized lentiform equivalents is found in the Madison Group (Mississippian) of the Williston Basin area, as presented by Thomas (in Sloss, Dapples, and Krumbein, 1960, Map 49). Other typical lentiform biomicrites are developed in the Silurian of the Illinois Basin, in the Sycamore Limestone (Mississippian) and the Arbuckle Group (Cambro-Ordovician) of the Anadarko Basin, and in many of the Paleozoic limestones of the miogeosynclinal marginal basins. Figure 13-24 is an isopach map (after Fuller, 1961) of the lower operational unit of the Red River Formation (Ordovician) in the Williston Basin, the same unit identified in Figure 10-16. The lentiform shape of the unit is readily discernible, and, as is the case with many similar examples, the thicker portions are dominated by calcitic carbonates, whereas the thinner margins in adjoining South Dakota and Montana are markedly dolomitized.

Lentiform Micrites. Dark gray to black micrites, commonly with a high clay content and gradational with black shales, typically occupy interior

Fig. 13-24. Isopach map of a lentiform biomicrite in the Ordovician of the Williston Basin. This is the operational unit termed "Lower Red River beds" on the cross section of Figure 10-16. [After Fuller (1961).]

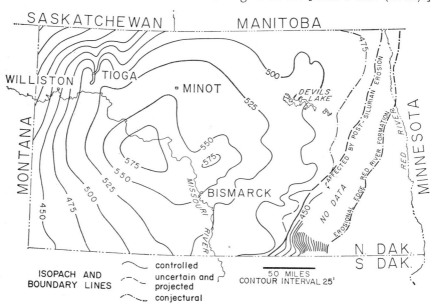

basins and marginal basins. Here they represent a degree of euxinic restriction and quiet bottoms inimical to the growth of shelled benthonic organisms, but within the *p*H stability field of calcium carbonate. Dolomitization is quite rare, and fossils are limited to planktonic and nektonic types plus such hardy mud-dwellers as the phosphatic brachiopods. Examples include the Bone Spring Limestone (Permian of West Texas-New Mexico) and parts of the Lodgepole Limestone (Mississippian) of the interior of the Williston Basin.

Carbonate Bank Associations

The point has been made that blanket biosparites are the nonclastic equivalents of blanket quartz arenites and that both represent transgressive or regressive strand lines. Where stillstands are encountered, as at the hinge lines of basin margins, quartz arenite accumulations of appreciable thickness may develop if the strand line maintains a relatively fixed position. Similarly, stabilization of the strandline under conditions favorable for the organic and inorganic precipitation of calcium carbonate tends to encourage the development of an elongate buildup of well sorted biosparite and related limestones. Such structures that are wave-built and lack a framework of organically derived sediment-binding material are here termed **carbonate banks** to differentiate them from the carbonate reefs discussed under a subsequent heading.

The organisms that contribute importantly to carbonate-bank deposition, and the inorganically precipitated carbonates as well, are sensitive to minor differences in mechanical energy, sunlight, and salinity, and, as a result, carbonate banks display greater textural and compositional variations than stillstand quartz arenites. These variations may be interpreted to indicate the positions of the margin of the open sea occupying the basin, the slightly elevated bank proper, and the lagoon that typically lies between the bank and nonmarine environments beyond. Figure 13-25 (modified after Edie, 1958) shows a reconstruction of a typical bank in the Mississippian of southern Saskatchewan, on the north rim of the Williston Basin. The inferred tectonic and environmental settings are indicated at the top of the diagram; the dominant fossils and lithologic types are shown below the profile of the bank. Note that carbonate-precipitating organisms are concentrated along the bank margin where normal salinity, high oxygenation associated with wave action, and nutrients from the marine basin would be anticipated. An increase in salinity in the shoal waters of the bank and in the lagoon is marked by decreasing organic contribution to the sediment and by a rise in the proportion of chemically precipitated carbonate and sulfate.

In the area in question, minor transgressions and regressions are repre-

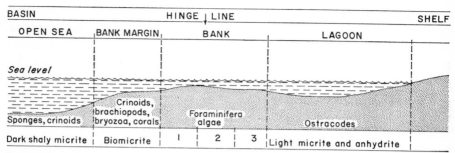

Bank deposits: (1) open marine edge- endothyroid and crinoid biosparite, oösparite, pelsparite;
(2) central shoal- oösparite, pelsparite, intrasparite; (3) lagoon edge- oömicrite, pelmicrite.

Fig. 13-25. Reconstruction of a Mississippian carbonate bank in southern Saskatchewan. [Modified after Edie (1958).]

sented by complex intertonguing of the lithosomes and biosomes. However,
the hinge line provides sufficient stability of environments such that facies
mapping reveals the positions of the carbonate bank and related sediments,
as shown by Figure 13-26 (modified from Edie, 1958). The map shows a 200-
foot slice at the top of the Mission Canyon Formation—an essentially isochronous unit except at the northern margin where pre-Jurassic erosion has
been effective. The southwestern portion of the map area, with "bio" ratios
greater than 4, includes the deposits of the edge of the open sea and of the
bank margin. The progressive northeastward decrease in "bio" ratios marks
the approach toward the shoal waters of the bank, and the abrupt rise in
evaporite ratios is a clear indication of the position of the lagoon during
deposition of the unit mapped. It is obvious that erosion has removed most
of the lagoonal sediments and part of the bank sediments in the central and
northwestern parts of the map area. Other well documented examples of
carbonate bank deposits, also of Mississippian age, have been described by
Stockdale (1931) and Harbaugh (1957).

Figure 13-27 shows the location of the Horseshoe atoll, a carbonate mass
that extends for a hundred miles in the Middle and Late Pennsylvanian and
Early Permian of the Midland Basin of West Texas. The stratigraphic cross
section (modified after Myers, Stafford, and Burnside, 1956), erected on the
base of the carbonate succession, illustrates the profile of the two limbs of
the atoll. Note that a vertical exaggeration of ten is required to bring out
the elevation of the limestone buildup over the central lagoonal area, and
yet the relief is sufficient to localize important oil accumulations, particularly
in the eastern, structurally higher, limb.

The Horseshoe atoll has been termed a somewhat questionable reef
(Myers, Stafford, and Burnside, 1956; Stafford, 1959; Burnside, 1959) by
many of its students, but the structure seems more logically included as a

particularly spectacular and long-lived example of a carbonate bank, since there is a lack of evidence regarding the existence of a sediment-binding framework. Much of the limestone mass is biomicrite and coarse to fine biosparite that contains fusulinids, crinoid columnals, and fragments of brachiopods and bryozoans. Oosparite and intramicrite are also present, the latter containing intraclasts of bank-type limestones apparently eroded by wave action from higher parts of the bank. Such inclusions indicate lithification of the bank rock, perhaps by recrystallization and "setting" of the micritic matrix, suggesting that the wave-resistant character of true organic reefs was approached during part of the life history of the bank.

Carbonate Reef Associations

Recognition of the oil-trapping potentials of mound-like carbonate masses and the relationship of some of these to modern organic reefs has led to the rather indiscriminate application of the term "reef" to almost any permeable carbonate mass that exhibits a degree of upward convexity. The development of a definition that would cover ancient organic reefs, but which would exclude unrelated masses of similar geometry, is hampered by a number of factors. There is a need to identify ancient carbonate masses that

Fig. 13-26. A 200-foot slice map at the top of the Mission Canyon Formation (Mississippian) in southern Saskatchewan. The map shows the distribution of lithologic types in a carbonate bank of the form illustrated by Figure 13-25. Note that the northern limit of the slice is affected by post-Mississippian erosion, which has removed much of the bank and back-bank sediments, except in the southeastern portion of the map area. [Modified after Edie (1958).]

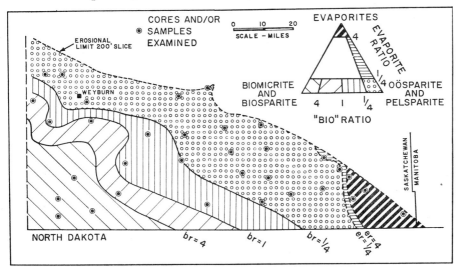

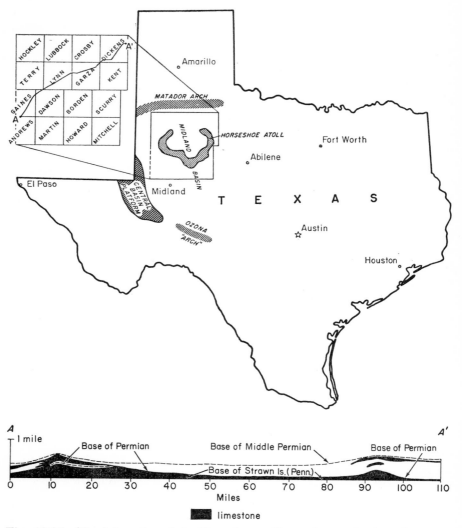

Fig. 13-27. (*Top*) Location of the Horseshoe atoll, a carbonate bank in the Pennsylvanian and Lower Permian of Texas. (*Bottom*) A stratigraphic cross section across the two limbs of the bank, along the line shown on the inset map. Note the vertical exaggeration of 10×. [After Myers, Stafford, and Burnside (1956).]

represent the ecologic conditions of present-day organic reefs. The latter are largely known as topographic or hydrologic features existing at an instant in time, whereas in ancient structures the geologist views the product of a time span that may cover tens of millions of years. Thus, it is probable that at any instant during the formation of a blanket biostrome the topography and ecologic complex of an organic reef would be recognizable, only to be lost in the "smearing" effect of transgressive or regressive environments with the passage of time. Further, much of our knowledge of modern reefs is derived from the study of oceanic realms in which reefs are found on seamounts or islands that rise from abyssal depths. The data have but little applicability to the majority of ancient reef masses available for investigation, since the latter are products of relatively shallow epicontinental seas, commonly associated with restricted euxinic or evaporitic environments that are not duplicated among modern settings. Finally, the dolomitization and recrystallization of carbonate rocks serve to obscure many of the details of structure, texture, and paleontology that would aid in relating ancient reefs to their modern counterparts.

The problem of definition was early recognized by Cumings and Shrock (1928), who proposed that the term **bioherm** be applied to mound-like fossil structures built by sessile benthonic organisms and enclosed in sediments of different type. The definition fails to discriminate clearly between wave-built and wave-resistant structures, and has not been uniformly adopted. Many other definitions have been proposed, stemming both from oceanographic studies of modern reefs and from stratigraphic studies of ancient ones (see, for example, MacNeil, 1954; Ladd, 1950; Lowenstam, 1950).

The Reef Complex. There is agreement that modern organic reefs are characterized by a framework that is the product of organisms that precipitate, bind, and/or retain carbonate and which show a potential of upward growth toward the surface of the sea. Once the surface is approached, the growing reef is capable of exerting a strong influence on its own environment and those adjacent to it. Further, when the reef has penetrated to the zone of breaking waves, it is subject to erosion, and its flanks become mantled with debris torn by wave and current action from its upper levels. Thus, reef growth establishes a complex of environments and a variety of depositional settings appropriately termed the **reef complex.** Ancient reef complexes are recognizable where environmental stability has been maintained for a sufficient length of time to permit the impress of reef growth and related environments on a significant thickness of sediment. Such environmental stability through time is typical of basin hinge lines and other tectonic sites where the upward growth potential of reef organisms may be matched by the downward effect of tectonic subsidence, and it is here that many major ancient reef complexes are found.

Present-day reef complexes exhibit a considerable range of geomorphic types and of relationships to other oceanographic features. (The classification of modern reefs is reviewed by MacNeil, 1954.) An even greater variation in environmental relationships is evident among ancient reefs, and these are further complicated by responses to tectonic influences during the development of individual complexes that may involve time spans of millions to tens of millions of years. A classification of ancient reef complexes based on the ultimate geometric form attained has been proposed by Ingels (1960). For present purposes a simple two-fold distinction is suitable.

Random Reef Complexes. Where reefs are developed without a clearly observable relationship to tectonic hinge lines, as revealed by isopachs of the enclosed strata, they tend to occur in more-or-less random (meaning irregularly-spaced) positions rather than in definite trends. Such **random reef complexes** may occupy broad shelf areas of little tectonic differentiation, or they may form under apparent shoaling conditions that have been localized by growing structures (such as salt domes) or buried topography. Examples of the first type are found among Silurian reef complexes of the Illinois-Indiana area that are scattered broadly over the shelf-like Kankakee Arch and adjoining parts of the temporarily inert Illinois Basin area (the distribution is shown by Lowenstam, 1950, Figure 11). Reefing related to salt domes is well developed in the Cenozoic of the Gulf Coast area, as illustrated by Murray (1961, Figure 6.47). There are numerous examples of reef complexes formed on growing anticlines in the Pennsylvanian of the southern Midcontinent, and apparent random reefs form important oil reservoirs in the upper part of the Paradox Formation (Pennsylvanian) of the Paradox Basin in Utah and Colorado (for a description see Clair, 1958). The reef complexes of the Upper Devonian of Alberta are particularly well documented. Their recognition as important oil reservoirs during the years following World War II has led to their close study (supported by a wealth of subsurface data), and their evolution from a carbonate bank has been traced in a number of detailed investigations (Waring and Layer, 1950; Andrichuk, 1958a, 1958b, 1961). Each random reef complex, as well as the barrier reef complexes to be discussed later, typically exhibits three major petrologic and morphologic subdivisions, representing three major ecologic and depositional settings: reef core, reef flank, and interreef.

Reef Core. The fundamental identifying feature of an ancient reef complex is the presence of reef-core rock characterized by massive, unbedded carbonate, commonly pitted with vugs of varying size and not necessarily fossiliferous in terms of obvious megascopic forms. The hallmark of core rock is the presence of a pervading framework or network of closely spaced laminae, which constitute the sediment-binding and wave-resistant structure of the core. In Late Paleozoic and younger reefs the laminae may be shown to be the products of blue-green algae. These, as seen on modern reefs, grow as mats over older algal structures, and over and around the tests and hard-part fragments of other organisms inhabiting the reef. The mats become covered with finely divided particles of carbonate, either by precipitation or by adherence and retention of suspended material, and this is in turn covered by algal tissue in a succeeding mat and carbonate lamina. In this way, the bulk of the reef core is built, aided by a host of other organisms whose shells and tests are entombed in the core rock and solidly bound with algal laminae. The precise biologic affinities of many of the core-forming organisms in Early and Middle Paleozoic reef complexes have not been fully determined, but stromatoporoids and other coelenterates are important contributors, as are structures that are of presumed algal origin.

Relatively large masses of bedded micrite and biomicrite are common within the cores of some ancient reef complexes. These masses probably represent the fillings of surge channels and other cavities in the reef core, filled with suspended sediment after further reef growth has reduced the wave and current activity.

The relationship of the reef core to other elements of the reef complex is illustrated by Figure 13-28, which is a reconstruction of the Silurian Thornton Reef Complex of northeastern Illinois by Ingels (1963). The reef core represents a highly specialized environment of optimum oxygenation, light penetration, and nutrient supply that is encountered only in the zone of breaking waves at the margin of the complex. The volume of core rock is therefore limited, and amounts to 25 percent or less of the volume of the complex. Expansion of the complex takes place by outward growth of the core over flank beds, continuously seeking the optimum conditions in the zone of breaking waves. Note the greater expansion in the presumed windward direction from which the maximum supply of oxygen and nutrients would be expected.

Reef Flank. The greater part of a reef

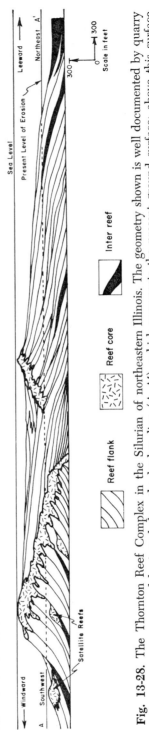

Fig. 13-28. The Thornton Reef Complex in the Silurian of northeastern Illinois. The geometry shown is well documented by quarry exposures and borings below the broken line (A–A'), which represents the present ground surface; above this surface the reef form is reconstructed by projection and extrapolation of observable geometric relationships. Horizontal and vertical scales are equal. [After Ingels (1963).]

complex is composed of bedded strata that dip quaquaversally away from the core. These, the reef-flank beds, are rhythmic alternations of biosparite and intrasparite with biomicrite and intramicrite. The particles are small tests (commonly foraminifera), fossil fragments (crinoid columnals and broken bits of the hard parts of many other organisms), and small-to-large fragments of core rock. It is evident that the flank rock is formed by fragments of the core that have been torn loose by waves and rolled downslope to form talus, plus much additional material derived from organisms inhabiting the reef flank. Algal and other frame-builders contribute to parts of the flank rock, binding and cementing the fossil fragments and other clasts into material much like that of the core. In many circumstances core and flank may be differentiated only by the oriented bedding of the flank rock. Significant masses of wave-resistant core rock are commonly present on the flanks, as at Thornton (Figure 13-28), and these must represent the establishment of satellite cores whose upward growth is ended by burial beneath loose flank debris.

Thus, as shown by Figure 13-28, reef flank is largely derived from reef core, and reef core grows outward over reef flank in an intricately intertongued manner. The resulting form is illustrated by another Silurian reef complex in Illinois that has been completely preserved in the subsurface and is documented by numerous wells. This, the Marine Reef Complex, is shown in Figure 13-29, taken from Lowenstam's (1948) classic study. Note the southwesterly development of the complex, suggesting the influence of prevailing southwest winds, as at Thornton.

Interreef. Fine grained material, representing relatively low states of mechanical energy release, typically occupies the lagoonal areas between and around random reefs. Such interreef rock is a part of the reef complex where it is intertongued with reef-flank deposits, as shown in the cross section of the Thornton Complex (Figure 13-28). In response to the very different environment of the interreef, the fossils there tend to be quite distinct from those of the core and flank, and, where the interrelationships of core rock to flank rock and of flank rock to interreef rock are obscure, interreef beds are commonly placed in a time-stratigraphic position younger than the remainder of the reef complex. In Illinois and Michigan, for example, core and flank rocks of Silurian reef complexes are generally identified as Niagaran (Mid Silurian), whereas interreef strata are placed in the Salinan (Late Silurian). This relationship would suggest that core and flank were built at one stage and that, at a later stage, interreef deposits filled the depressions between reefs. A corollary to this hypothesis would be the existence of reefs standing as isolated masses hundreds of feet above the surrounding sea bottoms. No sound physical or paleoecologic evidence of relief of such mag-

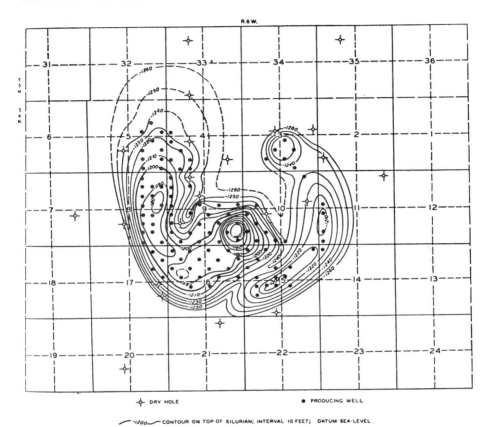

Fig. 13-29. Structure contour map of the Marine Pool, a productive reef complex in the Silurian of Illinois. The structure contours represent the elevations at which reef core or reef flank rocks were penetrated in wells, effectively delineating the form of the complex. [From Lowenstam (1948).]

nitude has been forthcoming, and, at least so far as random reef complexes of cratonic shelf areas are concerned, the synchrony of reef and interreef development is demonstrable.

Shales, argillaceous micrites, dolomitized micrites, and evaporites (typically anhydrite or gypsum) may occur as interreef deposits. With approach toward intertonguing or intergradation with flank beds there is an increase in grain size and in fossils and fragments of reef-related organisms. In a number of cases of interreef carbonates there is a noticeable increase in chert content near the margin of the reef flank, forming a siliceous "halo" around the reef complex.

Barrier Reef Complexes. The biggest and most imposing of ancient reef complexes are those that form linear or curving trends along the hinge lines of interior and marginal basins. Here, under ideal conditions, the persistent downward vector of subsidence is equaled by the upward-growing potential of the reef complex, and reefs may thrive for tens of millions of years while building hundreds, or even thousands, of feet of reef core and reef flank in vertical succession. As with other hinge-line deposits, a degree of regression and transgression is common (see discussion by Link, 1950) but the product of long-continued reef growth at the margin of basins is such that the reef complex becomes an effective barrier between environments in a lagoon behind the complex and quite different environments in the basin located in front of the complex. Thus, barrier reef complexes have a markedly greater asymmetry than is exhibited by typical random complexes. In response to deeper water and greater wave activity at the basinward side of the reef, the reef-flank deposits are largely confined to this **forereef** position. **Backreef** deposits reflect the quiet-water conditions of the lagoon and are commonly evaporitic in response to the restriction on circulation imposed by the growing crest of the barrier reef complex.

Permian barrier reef complexes of the West Texas-New Mexico area are exposed in outcrop and penetrated by thousands of wells, providing a classic example for study. Exhaustive work by King (1942, 1948) and others demonstrated the significance of reef trends on the hinge lines of the Delaware and Midland Basins and of their effects on environmental and depositional patterns. Figure 12-15 (after King, 1942) illustrates the regional tectonic setting and the distribution of forereef dark shales and backreef carbonates and evaporites. A restored cross section of the northwest margin of the Dela-

Fig. 13-30. The Capitan Barrier Reef Complex in the Permian of West Texas and New Mexico. The diagram illustrates inferred relationships at the end of Guadalupean Epoch (vertical exaggeration = 2×). Reef core is shown by the blank areas of Goat Seep and Capitan Limestones; forereef is indicated by the dipping limestones; the bedded limestones of the Carlsbad Group represent part of the backreef succession. The diagram also includes the underlying Leonardian strata, which comprise the Victorio Peak Limestone, a carbonate bank deposit, and its basinal equivalent, the Bone Spring Limestone, a euxinic lentiform micrite. [After King (1948), as modified by Newell et al. (1953).]

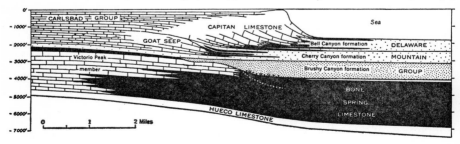

ware Basin at the close of the Guadalupean Epoch (Late Middle Permian) is presented as Figure 13-30, taken from *The Permian Reef Complex*, by Newell et al. (1953), as modified after King (1948). Newell and his co-authors consider the Victorio Peak Limestone to be a carbonate-bank deposit upon which there developed barrier reefs represented by the Goat Seep and Capitan Limestones. The carbonates of the Carlsbad Group are backreef lagoonal sediments, whereas the inclined and bedded portions of the Goat Seep and Capitan are forereef flank beds ("reef talus"). The euxinic Bone Spring Limestone is a basinal response to restriction imposed by the bank and reef; the clastics of the Delaware Mountain Group are fine grained, dark-colored, quartz arenites containing intercalations of dark shale and impure carbonate. The sands were presumably bypassed through the barrier trend to depositional sites in the euxinic-restricted Delaware Basin.

Other examples of barrier reef trends on the hinge lines of euxinic basins are noted by Newell et al. (1953) in the Lower Carboniferous of the Pennine area in the north of England, the Permian of East Greenland, and the Triassic of the Italian Tyrol. Silurian reef complexes at the margin of the Michigan Basin appear to have constituted a barrier that isolated the evaporitic basin interior, a role duplicated by Middle Devonian reef trends of the Williston Basin area of Saskatchewan (Baillie, 1955) and, possibly, by Tertiary complexes of the Iranian Gulf area (Henson, 1950; Dunnington, 1958).

Evaporite Associations

Primary sedimentary accumulations that include sulfates (gypsum and anhydrite), chlorides (halite, polyhalite, and sylvite), and certain inorganically precipitated carbonates constitute the major evaporite successions of the stratigraphic record. Such successions have been identified in Precambrian rocks and in all younger systems (the distribution of deposits in the United States is reviewed by Krumbein, 1951). Although rarely exposed to any significant extent, except under the most arid climatic conditions, evaporites measuring thousands of cubic miles in volume have been disclosed by the drill in many cratonic and cratonic-margin areas.

The Evaporite Cycle. The majority of evaporite deposits exhibit a marked cyclical repetition of members representing stages in the restriction of a seaway and the concentration of soluble salts. A typical evaporite cycle is illustrated by Figure 13-31, which shows the vertical succession of lithologic types commonly present and the corresponding stages of evaporitic restriction defined by Lang (1937). Many cycles lack the halite member, and some contain a record of a supersaline stage marked by potash salt. Higher members of the cycle, representing a gradual return to normal open-

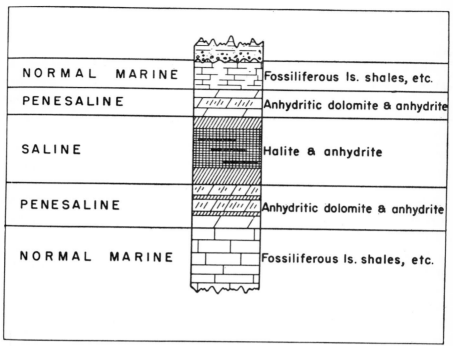

NORMAL MARINE		Fossiliferous ls. shales, etc.
PENESALINE		Anhydritic dolomite & anhydrite
SALINE		Halite & anhydrite
PENESALINE		Anhydritic dolomite & anhydrite
NORMAL MARINE		Fossiliferous ls. shales, etc.

Fig. 13-31. The ideal evaporite cycle. The normal marine stage is characterized by biomicrites and other fossiliferous limestones indicative of open circulation marine waters; the uppermost carbonates of this stage are commonly dolomitized. The penesaline stage includes finely laminated dolomitic micrites interbedded with anhydrite and dolomite, with anhydrite replacements and vug fillings. The saline stage begins with massive anhydrite beds and progresses upward to intercalations of salt and anhydrite and, ultimately, to massive salt. A fourth stage (supersaline), characterized by potash salts, is achieved in some basin-center deposits. This succession of stages has been called the advancing restricted hemicycle; less commonly observed is the relaxing restricted hemicycle in which the stages appear in reverse order, as shown in this diagram. [After Sloss (1953).]

circulation marine conditions, may be lacking as a result of the rapid transgression of normal marine waters after the saline stage or because erosion preceded deposition of the succeeding cycle. Black shales or siltstones, as in the Pennsylvanian of the Paradox Basin (Herman and Barkell, 1957), may intervene between the normal marine and penesaline stages, or fine siltstone and sandstone may interrupt the cycle, as in the Ordovician of the Williston Basin (Porter and Fuller, 1959). Numerous other variations from the "standard cycle" are developed as idiosyncrasies of particular areas or individual parts of the stratigraphic column.

The vertical succession that constitutes the evaporite cycle is duplicated by the lateral relationships of evaporite deposits, commonly in a roughly concentric pattern, with the closest approach to saline or supersaline sediments in the center. As is the case with most stratigraphic relationships, the vertical succession is observable in feet (or tens of feet) of section, whereas the lateral succession cannot be detected unless observations extend for miles or tens of miles. Nevertheless, it has been apparent to all workers investigating the regional distribution of evaporites that two circumstances require explanation: (1) at any point in an area of evaporite deposition, there is a progressive change *with time* in the concentration of soluble salts, establishing a systematic order of precipitation; (2) at any instant of time, there is a systematic *areal* variation in concentration and precipitation.

It has long been recognized that the vertical (temporal) succession would result from maintenance of a restricted marine basin in which the inflow of normal marine water is exceeded by the loss of water through evaporation, with the result that the salts successively reach their limits of concentration in order of their solubilities. The typical process model envisaged is an isolated bay or arm of the sea having restricted access to open marine waters across a shallow sill. Evaporation in the isolated body creates an influx of light, normal sea water; but the sill prevents the dense, concentrated brine from flowing out.

Many explanations have been proposed for the lateral (synchronous) succession, including multiple basins and sills and epigenetic replacement. More recently R. H. King (1947) made use of a "reflux" model to account for areal distribution patterns in the Late Permian of the West Texas–New Mexico area. King's conceptual dynamic model calls for a continuous flow of undersaturated water across the surface of the evaporite basin, matched by a counterflow of dense brines at depth across the sill and out of the basin. By this mechanism he was able to account for the vast volumes of anhydrite deposited in relation to the amount of halite precipitated.

Fig. 13-32. Model evaporite basin. Numbered lines indicate water densities that increase from the inlet and sill at the right to the distal portions of the basin at the left. Arrows show the paths of water movement; note the reverse flow of dense brine at the bottom. The lateral segregation of the precipitated minerals conforms with the concentrations of the overlying brines. [Modified from Weller (1960); after Briggs (1957).]

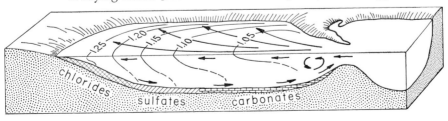

Refinement of the dynamic equilibrium reflux model with the addition of oceanographic and chemical data was achieved by Scruton (1953) as diagramed, with further modifications by Briggs (1957), in Figure 13-32. Lines of equal water density are shown to increase in value from the inlet to the distal margins of the basin, where they assume a nearly vertical attitude, thus accounting for the lateral segregation of salts of differing solubilities. Dynamic equilibrium, subject to shifts produced by changes in temperature, sea level, meteoric water, and wind, is maintained by balance among inflow, evaporation, and the dense bottom current moving across the sill and out of the basin. Continuation of the equilibrium state through a significant span of geologic time would result in the side-by-side accumulation of thicknesses of salt, anhydrite, and carbonate. Briggs (1958) has calculated the mineral composition to be expected by precipitation from various density ranges of brines in a model evaporite basin, as shown by Figure 13-33. The basin is circular, and the major influx of normal sea water enters across a sill at the right. Basinward from the sill there is a systematic increase in water density (concentration) and a corresponding change in the mineralogy of the precipitated minerals until the salinities are reduced by a minor influx of waters from the periphery of the basin. The model is valid for an almost landlocked basin partially supplied by streams crossing a carbonate terrain, or for a restricted marine basin surrounded by the open sea and confined within an almost complete encirclement of banks and reefs. Briggs

Fig. 13-33. Model evaporite basin. The figure on the right is a map view of the distribution of brine densities in a basin model characterized by a major inlet at the right and surrounded by open shelf seas or by numerous streams crossing a carbonate terrain. The patterns indicate the distribution of minerals precipitated at these concentrations, the compositions being those noted on the triangular diagram at the left. [Modified after Briggs (1958).]

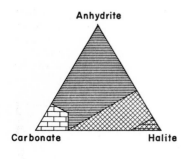

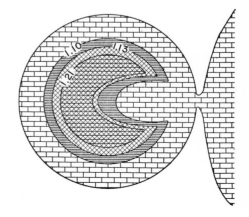

(1958) shows that evaporite distribution patterns in the Silurian of the Michigan Basin are met by the model, as is illustrated in Figure 6-13.

Tectonic-environmental Distribution of Evaporites. Individual evaporite cycles studied by means of discrete observations in bore holes exhibit differences in mineralogy, thickness, and succession, but major relationships are not made clear without consideration of the tectonic position and regional environmental setting of each deposit. Where facies studies of evaporites and isochronous nonevaporitic sediments are available, a reasonably clear grouping of evaporite occurrences emerges.

Basin-center Evaporites. By far the greatest volume of preserved evaporites, especially those representing the saline and supersaline stages, is found at or near the centers or axes of interior cratonic basins and, in great volume but less frequently, in marginal basins. Isopach studies suggest that basin-center evaporites are formed during times of maximum subsidence of such basins when tectonic differentiation from adjoining shelf areas and concurrent development of hinge lines are most marked. When these conditions prevail in the absence of an abundance of clastics, bank and barrier reef development on the hinge lines is expected, and numerous basin-center evaporites can be shown to be the products of restrictions imposed by these structures.

Depositional environments varying from uncomplicated marine carbonates to nonmarine beds may be represented behind the barriers formed by wave-resistant reef complexes or wave-built banks surrounding basin-center evaporites. Some surrounding shelf areas are known to have been the sites of deposition of nonmarine clastics that intertongue with fine grained marine carbonates in transitional lagoons peripheral to bank or reef trends.

The Silurian of the Michigan Basin, intensively studied by Briggs (1958), Melhorn (1958), Alling and Briggs (1961), is an example of a reef-enclosed basin-center evaporite. Figure 13-34 illustrates the relations among limestone, dolomite, evaporite, and the isopach pattern. Basin-center evaporites exhibiting low rates of facies change to surrounding carbonates, and lacking well defined encircling barriers, are more difficult to interpret. Figure 13-35 illustrates facies and isopachs in the upper part of the Charles Formation (Mississippian) of the Williston Basin. Here the classic picture, in which salt is confined to the position of greatest thickness and surrounded by zones of anhydrite and carbonate, is clearly shown, yet no restricting carbonate buildup can be demonstrated. Other basin-center accumulations, such as the Late Permian of West Texas-New Mexico, grade laterally into continental deposits without encountering intervening penesaline or marine phases.

Basin-margin Evaporites. Basin-margin evaporites lie at the peripheries of interior or marginal basins occupied by normal or euxinic marine environ-

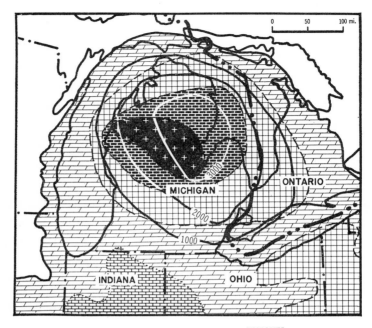

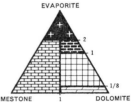

Fig. 13-34. Basin-center evaporites in the Silurian of the Michigan Basin. Note
the westward displacement of the evaporite in accordance with a basin
model influenced by eastern inlets as shown in Figures 6-13, 13-32,
and 13-33. [After Sutterlin, *in* Sloss, Dapples, and Krumbein (1960).]

ments, and are separated from these by barrier trends or sills of some topographic relief. As before, the barrier shoal environment may represent a
barrier reef complex of relatively narrow width, a broad biostrome, or a carbonate bank. Back-reef evaporites are exemplified by the Middle Permian
West Texas-New Mexico lagoons behind the barrier reef trends already discussed. The Late Devonian Nisku Formation of Alberta (Andrichuck and
Wonfor, 1954) is associated with evaporites involved with barrier biostromes. A back-bank evaporite deposit is shown in Figure 13-36, which
illustrates facies and isopach patterns of a Mississippian unit in the Williston
Basin immediately underlying the strata mapped in Figure 13-35. The northern edge of the basin is strongly affected by pre-Jurassic erosion, but the
concentric pattern of basin-margin evaporites is clearly expressed. Here the

confining structure is a complex carbonate bank described earlier in this chapter and illustrated by Figure 13-25.

Basin-margin evaporites tend to be as consistently cyclical as intrabasin types, but the cycles less commonly attain the saline (halite) stage and the supersaline (potash salt) stage is almost unknown. Landward from the basin margin the evaporites intertongue with and pass into nonmarine clastics, typically red beds. In certain situations the evaporites and continental sediments are separated by a zone of carbonates containing marine fossils. Lang (1937) has termed this the "pseudomarine zone" and has interpreted it as resulting from the dilution of lagoonal brines by streams.

Shelf Evaporites. Although basin-center and basin-margin deposits include perhaps 95 percent of the volume of evaporites preserved in the stratigraphic record, extensive accumulations exist that show no relation to persistent basinal subsidence during deposition. Isopach maps of units including these evaporites show no preferential centers, or axes, of greater thickness; facies patterns have no markedly oriented trends that can be shown to have a clear relationship to depositional tectonics. Paleogeographic considerations indicate that these deposits formed at or near the margins of shallow shelf seas covering broad areas of relatively slow and uniform subsidence. Two

Fig. 13-35. Basin-center evaporites in the upper part of the Charles Formation (Mississippian) of the Williston Basin. [After McCabe (1961).]

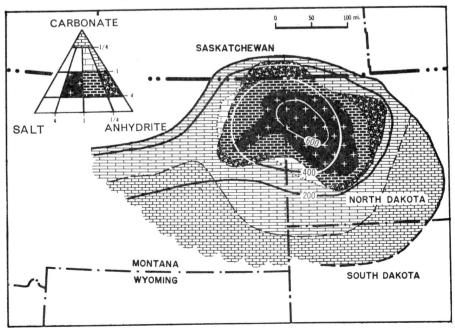

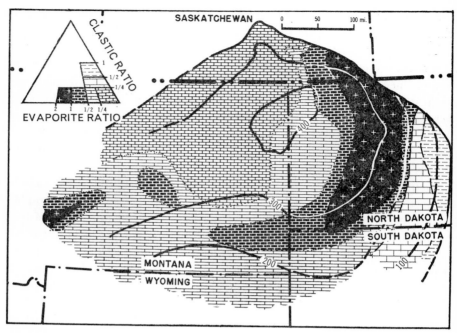

Fig. 13-36. Basin-margin evaporites in the lower part of the Charles Formation (Mississippian) of the Williston Basin. These are back-bank evaporites confined behind carbonate banks such as that illustrated by Figures 13-25 and 13-26. The margin of the basin north of the Canadian border has been severely affected by post-Mississippian erosion; it may be presumed that high evaporite ratios at one time encircled the northern as well as the eastern and southern margins. [After McCabe (1961).]

types of shelf evaporites are recognized; both are known as extensions of basin-margin deposits, but both can occur at great distances from basin influences.

In one type the evaporites are intercalated with red silts and shales, which may carry the remains of land animals and plants. Although there is a tendency to consider these red bed evaporites as representations of completely nonmarine conditions, they can commonly be shown, through regional tracing of individual units, to be connected with strata that are obviously marine. Evaporites of this type, exemplified by the Permo-Triassic of the Rocky Mountains and Great Plains, are considered to be the products of broad saline lagoons formed by the marine transgression of deltaic environments.

Of another type are those shelf evaporites characterized by repeated thin cycles involving blanket marine carbonates and lacking significant thicknesses of land-derived clastics. These associations have many of the characteristics of back-bank lagoonal evaporites, but no relationship to the geometry of a basin can be shown. Rather, the associations appear to represent irregularly distributed shoals (banks and biostromes) and intershoal areas of slightly deeper water in which anhydrite and evaporitic carbonates were formed. Salt is rarely present, and many of the cycles do not advance beyond an early penesaline stage characterized by laminated micrites, oolites, and other apparent precipitates. If these evaporitic carbonates are considered with the anhydrite, distinct facies patterns emerge from mapping—patterns that would be obscure if only carbonate-sulfate ratios were considered. Figure 13-37 presents part of Andrichuk's (1955) findings on the Madison Group (Mississippian of the Wyoming Shelf area). In this broad region, south of the area influenced by the subsiding Williston Basin, the low rate of change in thickness values is obvious. The areas in which the values of evaporite ratios are low consist largely of high-energy carbonates (biosparites and oosparites) thought to have accumulated as shoals within wave base. The areas of high evaporite ratios are dominated by anhydrite and laminated micrite, interpreted as forming in the deeper waters of intershoal lagoons. The dolomitization of the areas of greatest evaporitic tendency is a commonly observed feature in evaporite associations of many types.

Fig. 13-37. Shelf evaporites. Attention is directed to the evaporitic concentration on the Montana-Wyoming border, a shelf area of low rate of thickness change in Madison (Mississippian) strata. These shelf evaporites are isolated from the basin-margin evaporites shown in the northeastern part of the map area and in the preceding figure. Associated areas of dolomitized carbonate are indicated by the light cross-hatched pattern. [After Andrichuk (1955).]

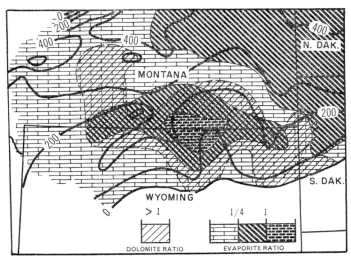

CONCLUDING REMARKS

This completes the discussion of the readily observable associations recognized by the authors at this time. Other workers with different experience will find the list incomplete and will wish to add to it by identification of associations not noted here or by recognition of significantly different patterns within the broad groupings of the present treatment. More important than these inevitable modifications is the awareness among stratigraphers that there is order and system in stratigraphic phenomena. This order and system is manifested by the repeated and recurrent associations of materials and geometric forms that can be discerned among the rocks of the earth's crust. When these patterns are recognized as distinct response elements in integrated models, stratigraphers will then be in a position to synthesize all of the fields of sedimentation into a rational reconstruction of the process elements responsible—invoking the sophisticated methods and procedures that have been so fruitful in other physical sciences.

Each of the preceding chapters has closed with a list of supplementary readings selected to provide the reader with additional background material on the subject matter of the chapter and to draw attention to alternative principles not fully covered in the text. Well over one hundred references are called upon in the present chapter, more than forty of which were published during the five years that this book was under revision. The authors are unable to choose from this list any small group of readings that would be suitable for professional stratigraphers and students. Rather, it is hoped that readers and instructors will make their own selections from the bibliographic listing to expand the treatment of particular topics of interest.

Bibliography

Chapter 2. The Stratigraphic Column

AMERICAN COMMISSION ON STRATIGRAPHIC NOMENCLATURE, 1947, Note 1—Organization and objectives of the stratigraphic commission: Am. Assoc. Petroleum Geologists Bull., v. 31, p. 513–518.

AMERICAN COMMISSION ON STRATIGRAPHIC NOMENCLATURE, 1947, Note 2—Nature and classes of stratigraphic units: Am. Assoc. Petroleum Geologists Bull., v. 31, p. 519–528.

AMERICAN COMMISSION ON STRATIGRAPHIC NOMENCLATURE, 1961, Code of stratigraphic nomenclature: Am. Assoc. Petroleum Geologists Bull., v. 45, p. 645–665.

ANDRICHUK, J. M., 1958, Stratigraphy and facies analysis of Upper Devonian reefs in Leduc, Stettler, and Redwater areas, Alberta: Am. Assoc. Petroleum Geologists Bull., v. 42, p. 1–93.

ARKELL, W. J., 1946, Standard of the European Jurassic: Geol. Soc. America Bull., v. 57, p. 1–34.

———, 1956, Comments on stratigraphic procedure and terminology: Am. Jour. Sci., v. 254, p. 457–467.

ASHLEY, G. H., 1932, Stratigraphic nomenclature: Geol. Soc. America Bull., v. 43, p. 469–476.

———, et al., 1933, Classification and nomenclature of rock units: Geol. Soc. America Bull., v. 44, p. 423–459.

BAIN, H. F., 1906, Zinc and lead deposits of the upper Mississippi Valley: U. S. Geol. Survey Bull. 294.

BERG, R. R., NELSON, C. A., and BELL, W. C., 1956, Upper Cambrian rocks in southeastern Minnesota, p. 1–23, in Lower Paleozoic of the Upper Mississippi Valley: Geol. Soc. America American Guidebook series, Minneapolis meeting, field trip 2.

BERKEY, C. P., 1897, Geology of the St. Croix Dalles: Am. Geol., v. 20, p. 345–383.

CHADWICK, G. H., 1930, Subdivision of geologic time: Geol. Soc. America Bull., v. 41, p. 47–48.

CHAMBERLIN, T. C., 1909, Diastrophism as the ultimate basis of correlation: Jour. Geology, v. 17, p. 685–693.

DANA, J. D., 1880, Manual of geology, treating of the principles of the science: New York, Ivison, Blakemen, Taylor & Co.

DUNBAR, C. O., 1960, Historical geology (2nd ed.): New York, John Wiley & Sons, Inc.

———, and RODGERS, J., 1957, Principles of stratigraphy: New York, John Wiley & Sons, Inc.

FENTON, C. L., and FENTON, M. A., 1945, The story of the great geologists: Garden City, Doubleday, Doran & Co., Inc.

GEIKIE, A., 1897, The founders of geology: New York, The Macmillan Co.

GIGNOUX, M., 1955, Stratigraphic geology: San Francisco, W. H. Freeman and Co.

GILLULY, J., 1949, Distribution of mountain building in geologic time: Geol. Soc. America Bull., v. 60, p. 561–590.

GRABAU, A. W., 1913, Principles of stratigraphy: New York, A. G. Seiler & Co.

HEDBERG, H. D., 1948, Time-stratigraphic classification of sedimentary rocks: Geol. Soc. America Bull., v. 59, p. 447–462.

———, 1954, Procedure and terminology in stratigraphic classification: 19th Internat. Geol. Cong. Rept., sec. 13, fasc. 13, p. 205–233.

HENBEST, L. G. (ed.), 1952, Symposium on distribution of evolutionary explosions in geologic time: Jour. Paleontology, v. 26, p. 297–394.

HILL, M. L., CARLSON, S. A., and DIBBLEE, T. W., JR., 1958, Stratigraphy of Cuyama Valley, Caliente Range area, California: Am. Assoc. Petroleum Geologists Bull., v. 42, p. 2973–3000.

JELETZKY, J. A., 1956, Paleontology, basis of practical geochronology: Am. Assoc. Petroleum Geologists Bull., v. 40, p. 679–706.

LANGENHEIM, R. L., JR., 1952, Pennsylvanian and Permian sratigraphy in Crested Butte quadrangle, Gunnison County, Colorado: Am. Assoc. Petroleum Geologists Bull., v. 36, p. 543–574.

LYELL, C., 1833, Principles of geology: London, John Murray Ltd.

———, 1872, Principles of geology (11th ed.): New York, D. Appleton & Co.

MILLER, S. A., 1889, North American geology and paleontology: Cincinnati, Western Methodist Book Concern.

OWEN, D. D., 1852, Report of a geological survey of Wisconsin, Iowa, and Minnesota: Philadelphia, Lippincott, Grambo & Co.

PHILLIPS, J. A., 1838, A treatise on geology: North Bridge, Scotland, Adam and Chas. Black.

RODGERS, J., 1959, The meaning of correlation: Am. Jour. Sci., v. 257, p. 684–691.

SCHENCK, H. G., and MULLER, S. W., 1941, Stratigraphic terminology: Geol. Soc. America Bull., v. 52, p. 1419–1426.

SCHNEER, C., 1954, The rise of historical geology in the 17th century: Isis, v. 45, p. 256–268.

SCHOLTEN, R., 1960, Sedimentation and tectonism in the thrust belt of southwestern Montana and east-central Idaho: Wyoming Geol. Assoc. Guidebook, 15th Ann. Field Conf., p. 73–83.

SCHUCHERT, C., 1910, Paleogeography of North America: Geol Soc. America Bull., v. 20, p. 127–606.

SLOSS, L. L., 1963, Sequences in the cratonic interior of North America: Geol. Soc. America Bull., v. 74, p. 93–114.

———, KRUMBEIN, W. C., and DAPPLES, E. C., 1949, Integrated facies analysis, p. 91–124 in Geol. Soc. America Memoir 39.

STILLE, H., 1940, Einfuhrung in den bau Amerikas: Berlin, Gebruder Borntraeger.

———, 1944, The geotectonic subdivisions of earth history: Berlin, Akademie der Wissenschaften.

TEICHERT, C., 1958, Some biostratigraphical concepts: Geol. Soc. America Bull., v. 69, p. 99–120.

TWENHOFEL, W. H., et al., 1954, Correlation of the Ordovician formations of North America: Geol. Soc. America Bull., v. 65, p. 247–298.

ULRICH, E. O., 1911, Revision of the Paleozoic systems: Geol. Soc. America Bull., v. 22, p. 281–680.

WESTOLL, T. S., 1954, Mountain revolutions and organic evolution, p. 251–263, in Huxley, J., Hardy, A. C., and Jord, E. B. (eds.), Evolution as a process: London, Allen & Unwin, Ltd.

WHEELER, H. E., 1960, Early Paleozoic tectono-stratigraphic patterns in the United States: 21st Internat. Geol. Cong. Rept., pt. 8, p. 47–56.

WINCHELL, A., 1872, Report of a geological survey of the vicinity of Belleplaine, Scott County, Minnesota: St. Paul.

WINCHELL, N. H., 1874, The geological and natural history survey of Minnesota: Minn. Geol. Survey, 2nd Ann. Rept, for the year 1873, p. 73–219.

ZITTEL, K. A., 1901, History of geology and paleontology to the end of the Nineteenth Century: New York, Charles Scribner's Sons.

Chapter 3. Stratigraphic Procedures

BRAMLETTE, M. N., 1934, Heavy mineral studies on correlation of sands at Kettleman Hills, California: Am. Assoc. Petroleum Geologists Bull., v. 18, p. 1559–1576.

BRIDGE, J., BARNES, V. E. and CLOUD, P. E., JR., 1947, Stratigraphy of the Upper Cambrian, Llano Uplift, Texas: Geol. Soc. America Bull., v. 58, p. 109–123.

BUSCH, D. A., 1950, Subsurface techniques, p. 559–578, in Trask, P. D. (ed.), Applied sedimentation: New York, John Wiley & Sons, Inc.

COGEN, W. M., 1940, Heavy-mineral zones

of Louisiana and Texas Gulf Coast sediments: Am. Assoc. Petroleum Geologists Bull., v. 24, p. 2069–2101.

FEO-CODECIDO, G., 1956, Heavy mineral techniques and their application to Venezuelan stratigraphy: Am. Assoc. Petroleum Geologists Bull., v. 40, p. 984–1000.

HAUN, J. D., and LEROY, L. W., 1958, Subsurface geology in petroleum exploration: Golden, Colo. School of Mines.

HILL, M. L., 1942, Graphic method for some geologic calculations: Am. Assoc. Petroleum Geologists Bull., v. 26, p. 1155–1159.

HILLS, J. M., 1949, Sampling and examination of well cuttings: Am. Assoc. Petroleum Geologists Bull., v. 32, p. 73–91.

IRELAND, H. A. et al., 1947, Terminology for insoluble residues: Am. Assoc. Petroleum Geologists Bull., v. 31, p. 1479–1490.

IRELAND, H. A., 1958, Insoluble residues, p. 75–94, in Haun, J. D. and LeRoy, L. W. (eds.), Subsurface geology in petroleum exploration: Golden, Colo. School of Mines.

KUMMEL, B., JR., 1943, New techniques for measurement of stratigraphic units: Am.

Assoc. Petroleum Geologists Bull., v. 27, p. 220–221.

LAHEE, F. H., 1961, Field geology: New York, McGraw-Hill Book Co., Inc.

LEROY, L. W., and LOW, J. W., 1954, Graphic problems in petroleum geology: New York, Harper & Bros.

MCCRACKEN, E., 1955, Correlation of insoluble residue zones of the upper Arbuckle of Missouri and southern Kansas: Am. Assoc. Petroleum Geologists Bull., v. 39, p. 47–59.

MERTIE, J. B., JR., 1922, Graphic and mechanical computation of thickness of strata and distance to a stratum: U. S. Geol. Survey Prof. Paper 129.

MILNER, H. B., 1962, Sedimentary petrography: New York, The Macmillan Co.

SCHENCK, H. G. and ADAMS, J. E., 1943, Operations of commercial micropaleontologic laboratories: Jour. Paleontology, v. 17, p. 554–583.

SHROCK, R. R., 1948, Sequence in layered rocks: New York, McGraw-Hill Book Co., Inc.

TRASK, P. D., 1950, Applied sedimentation: New York, John Wiley & Sons, Inc.

Chapter 4. Properties of Sedimentary Rocks

AHRENS, L. H., 1954, The log-normal distribution of elements: Geochim. et Cosmochim. Acta, v. 5, p. 49–73.

ALLEN, P., 1949, Wealden petrology—the top Ashdown pebble bed and the top Ashdown sandstone: Quart. Jour. Geol. Soc. London, v. 104, p. 257–321.

ALLING, H. L., 1943, A metric grade scale for sedimentary rocks: Jour. Geology, v. 41, p. 259–269.

———, 1945, Use of microlithologies as illustrated by some New York sedimentary rocks: Geol. Soc. America Bull., v. 56, p. 737–756.

ASCHENBRENNER, B. C., 1955, A photogrammetric method for the tridimensional measurement of sand grains: Photogrammetric Engineering, v. 21, p. 376–382.

———, 1956. A new method of expressing particle sphericity: Jour. Sed. Petrology, v. 26, p. 15–31.

BAGNOLD, R. A., 1941, The physics of blown sand and desert dunes: London, William Morrow & Co.

BAILEY, E. B., 1936, Sedimentation in relation to tectonics: Geol. Soc. America Bull., v. 47, p. 1713–1725.

BATES, J. D., and BATES, B. H., 1960, Evaluation of heavy mineral separations using artificial samples: Jour. Sed. Petrology, v. 30, p. 148–153.

BEAL, M. A., and SHEPARD, F. P., 1956, A use of roundness to determine depositional environments: Jour. Sed. Petrology, v. 26, p. 49–60.

BERMAN, R., 1953, A nomogram for obtaining per cent composition by weight from mineral-grain counts: Jour. Sed. Petrology, v. 23, p. 120–123.

BIRCH, F., SCHAIRER, J. F., and SPICER, H. C., 1942, Handbook of physical constants: Geol Soc. America Special Paper 36.

BISQUE, R. E., and LEMISH, J., 1959, Insoluble residue—magnesium content relationship of carbonate rocks for the Devonian Cedar Valley Formation: Jour. Sed. Petrology, v. 29, p. 73–76.

BOKMAN, J., 1957, Suggested use of bed-thickness measurements in stratigraphic descriptions: Jour. Sed. Petrology, v. 27, p. 333–335.

BUCHER, W. H., 1919, On ripples and related sedimentary surface forms and their paleogeographic interpretations: Am. Jour. Sci., series 4, v. 47, p. 149–210, 241–269.

CADIGAN, R. A., 1954, Testing graphical methods of grain-size analysis of sandstones and siltstones: Jour. Sed. Petrology, v. 24, p. 123–127.

CALDWELL, L. T., 1940, Areal variations of calcium carbonate and heavy minerals in Barataria Bay sediments, Louisiana: Jour. Sed. Petrology, v. 10, p. 55–64.

CARPENTER, G. C., and SCHMIDT, R. G., 1962, Insoluble residues in a portion of the Ordovician Cynthiana Formation, north-central Kentucky: Jour. Sed. Petrology, v. 32, p. 423–434.

CARROLL, D., 1957, A statistical study of heavy minerals in sands of the South River, Augusta County, Virginia: Jour. Sed. Petrology, v. 27, p. 387–404.

COGEN, W. M., 1940, Heavy-mineral zones of Louisiana and Texas Gulf Coast sediments: Am. Assoc. Petroleum Geologists Bull., v. 24, p. 2069–2101.

CROWLEY, A. J., and HENDRICKS, L., 1945, Lower Ordovician and Upper Cambrian subsurface subdivisions in north-central Texas: Am. Assoc. Petroleum Geologists Bull., v. 29, p. 413–425.

CURRAY, J. R., and GRIFFITHS, J. C., 1955, Sphericity and roundness of quartz grains in sediments: Geol. Soc. America Bull., v. 66, p. 1075–1096.

CURRAY, J. R., 1956, The analysis of two-dimensional orientation data: Jour. Geology, v. 64, p. 117–131.

———, 1956, Dimensional grain orientation studies of recent coastal sands: Am. Assoc. Petroleum Geologists Bull., v. 40, p. 2440–2456.

DAPPLES, E. C., and ROMINGER, J. F., 1945, Orientation analysis of fine-grained clastic sediments—a report of progress: Jour. Geology, v. 53, p. 246–261.

DIXON, W. J., and MASSEY, F. J., 1957, Introduction to statistical analysis (2nd ed.): New York, McGraw-Hill Book Co., Inc.

DUNBAR, C. O., and RODGERS, J., 1957, Principles of stratigraphy: New York, John Wiley & Sons, Inc.

EARDLEY, A. J., 1938, Sediments of Great Salt Lake, Utah: Am. Assoc. Petroleum Geologists Bull., v. 22, p. 1359–1387.

FLINN, D., 1958, On tests of significance of preferred orientation in three-dimensional fabric diagrams: Jour. Geology, v. 66, p. 526–539.

FOLK, R. L., 1959, Practical petrographic classification of limestones: Am. Assoc. Petroleum Geologists Bull., v. 43, p. 1–38.

———, 1962, Of skewnesses and sands: Jour. Sed. Petrology, v. 32, p. 145–146.

FREEMAN, T., 1962, Quiet water oolites from Laguna Madre, Texas: Jour. Sed. Petrology, v. 32, p. 475–483.

FRIEDMAN, G. M., 1961, Distinction between dune, beach, and river sands from their textural characteristics: Jour. Sed. Petrology, v. 31, p. 514–529.

———, 1962, Comparison of moment measures for sieving and thin-section data in sedimentary petrological studies: Jour. Sed. Petrology, v. 32, p. 15–25.

GAITHER, A., 1953, A study of porosity and grain relationships in experimental sands: Jour. Sed. Petrology, v. 23, p. 180–195.

GODDARD, E. N., et al., 1951, Rock color chart: distributed by Geol. Soc. America, New York.

GOLDICH, S. S., 1938, A study in rock-weathering: Jour. Geology, v. 46, p. 17–58.

GRATON, L. C., and FRASER, H. J., 1935, Systematic packing of spheres—with particular relation to porosity and permeability: Jour. Geology, v. 43, p. 785–909.

GRENDER, G. C., 1961, Note on measurement of grain size in phi units: Jour. Sed. Petrology, v. 31, p. 608.

GRIFFITHS, J. C., 1953, Estimation of error in grain size analysis: Jour. Sed. Petrology, v. 23, p. 75–84.

———, 1960, Frequency distribution in accessory mineral analysis: Jour. Geology, v. 68, p. 353–365.

———, 1961, Measurement of the properties of sediments: Jour. Geology, v. 69, p. 487–498.

GRIFFITHS, J. C., and ROSENFELD, M. A., 1954, Operator variation in experimental research: Jour. Geology, v. 62, p. 74–91.

————, and MCINTYRE, D. D., 1958, A table for the conversion of millimeters to phi units: University Park, Min. Ind. Expt. Sta., Penn. State Univ.

HARRISON, P. W., 1957a, New technique for three-dimensional fabric analysis of till and englacial debris containing particles from 3 to 40 mm. in size: Jour. Geology, v. 65, p. 98–105.

————, 1957b, A clay-till fabric—its character and origin: Jour. Geology, v. 65, p. 275–308.

HAUN, J. D., and LEROY, L. W. (eds.), 1958, Subsurface geology in petroleum exploration: Golden, Colo. School of Mines.

HERDAN, G., 1953, Small particle statistics: New York, Elsevier Pub. Co.

HIRST, D. M., and NICHOLLS, G. D., 1958, Techniques in sedimentary geochemistry, (1) Separation of the detrital and non-detrital fractions of limestones: Jour. Sed. Petrology, v. 28, p. 468–481.

HOEL, P. G., 1957, Introduction to mathematical statistics: New York, John Wiley & Sons, Inc.

HSU, R. J., 1960, Texture and mineralogy of the recent sands of the Gulf Coast: Jour. Sed. Petrology, v. 30, p. 380–403.

HUBERT, J. F., 1962, A zircon-tourmaline-rutile maturity index and the interdependence of the composition of heavy mineral assemblages with the gross composition and textures of sandstones: Jour. Sed. Petrology, v. 32, p. 440–450.

HUMPHRIES, D. W., 1956, Some problems of size and sorting in sands: Geol. Magazine, v. 153, p. 491–503.

INGRAM, R. L., 1954, Terminology for the thickness of stratification and parting units in sedimentary rocks: Geol. Soc. America Bull., v. 65, p. 937–938.

INMAN, D. L., 1952, Measures for describing the size distribution of sediments: Jour. Sed. Petrology, v. 22, p. 125–145.

IRELAND, H. A., 1958, Insoluble residues, p. 75–94, in Haun, J. D. and LeRoy, L. W. (eds.), Subsurface geology in petroleum exploration: Golden, Colo. School of Mines.

JOHNSON, N. M., 1960, Thermoluminescence in biogenic calcium carbonate: Jour. Sed. Petrology, v. 30, p. 305–313.

KAHN, J. S., 1956, The analysis and distribution of the properties of packing in sand-size sediments: Jour. Geology, v. 64, p. 385–395, 578–606.

KARLSTROM, T. N. V., 1952, Improved equipment and techniques for orientation studies of large particles in sediments: Jour. Geology, v. 60, p. 489–493.

KELLER, W. D., 1945, Size distribution of sand in some dunes, beaches, and sandstones: Am. Assoc. Petroleum Geologists Bull., v. 29, p. 215–221.

————, 1953, Illite and montmorillonite in green sedimentary rocks: Jour. Sed. Petrology, v. 23, p. 3–9.

KELLEY, V. C., 1956, Thickness of strata: Jour. Sed. Petrology, v. 26, p. 289–300.

KRUMBEIN, W. C., 1937, Sediments and exponential curves: Jour. Geology, v. 45, p. 577–601.

————, 1939, Preferred orientation of pebbles in sedimentary deposits: Jour. Geology, v. 47, p. 673–706.

————, 1941, Measurement and geological significance of shape and roundness of sedimentary particles: Jour. Sed. Petrology, v. 11, p. 64–72.

————, 1954, Applications of statistical methods to sedimentary rocks: Am. Stat. Assoc. Jour., v. 49, p. 51–66.

————, 1960, The "geological population" as a framework for analysing numerical data in geology: Liverpool & Manchester Geol. Jour., v. 2, pt. 3, p. 341–368.

————, and MILLER, R. L., 1953, Design of experiments for statistical analysis of geologic data: Jour. Geology, v. 61, p. 510–532.

————, and MONK, G. D., 1942, Permeability as a function of the size parameters of unconsolidated sand: Am. Inst. Mining & Met. Eng., Tech. Publ. 1492.

————, and PETTIJOHN, F. J., 1938, Manual of sedimentary petrography: New York, Appleton Century Co., Inc.

————, and SLACK, H. A., 1956, Statistical analysis of low-level radioactivity of Pennsylvania black fissile shale in Illinois: Geol. Soc. America Bull., v. 67, p. 739–762.

KRYNINE, P. D., 1948, The megascopic study and field classification of sedimentary rocks: Jour. Geology, v. 56, p. 130–165.

————, 1949, The origin of red beds:

N. Y. Acad. Science Trans., series 2, v. 2, p. 60–68.

KUENEN, PH. H., 1953, Significant features of graded bedding: Am. Assoc. Petroleum Geologists Bull., v. 37, p. 1044–1066.

——, and MIGLIORINI, C. I., 1950, Turbidity currents as a cause of graded bedding: Jour. Geology, v. 58, p. 91–126.

LEVORSEN, A. I., 1954, Geology of petroleum: San Francisco, W. H. Freeman and Co.

MANNING, J. C., 1953, Application of statistical estimation and hypothesis testing to geologic data: Jour. Geology, v. 61, p. 544–556.

MARSCHNER, A. W., 1953, A method for the size analysis of sand on a number frequency basis: Jour. Sed. Petrology, v. 23, p. 49–59.

MARTINEZ, J. D., 1958, Photometer method for studying quartz grain orientation: Am. Assoc. Petroleum Geologists Bull., v. 42, p. 588–608.

MASON, C. C., and FOLK, R. L., 1958, Differentiation of beach, dune, and aeolian flat environments by size analysis, Mustang Island, Texas: Jour. Sed. Petrology, v. 28, p. 211–226.

MCKEE, E. D., 1957, Primary structures in some recent sediments: Am. Assoc. Petroleum Geologists Bull., v. 41, p. 1704–1747.

——, and WEIR, G. W., 1953, Terminology for stratification and cross-stratification in sedimentary rocks: Geol. Soc. America Bull., v. 64, p. 381–390.

MIESCH, A. T., et al., 1960, Chemical composition as a guide to the size of sandstone-type uranium deposits in the Morrison Formation on the Colorado Plateau: U. S. Geol. Survey Bull. 1112-B, p. 17–61.

——, and RILEY, L. B., 1961, Basic statistical measures used in geochemical investigations of Colorado Plateau uranium deposits: Am. Inst. Mining & Met. Eng., Transactions (Mining), v. 220, p. 247–251.

MILLER, R. L. (editor), 1953, Statistics issue: Jour. Geology, v. 61, p. 479–568.

——, and GOLDBERG, E. D., 1955, The normal distribution in geochemistry:

Geochim. et Cosmochim. Acta, v. 8, p. 53–62.

MILNER, H. B., 1962, Sedimentary petrography: New York, The Macmillan Co. 2 vols.

MURRAY, R. C., 1960, Origin of porosity in carbonate rocks: Jour. Sed. Petrology, v. 30, p. 59–84.

NAIRN, A. E. M., 1960, Paleomagnetic results from Europe: Jour. Geology, v. 68, p. 285–306.

NANZ, R. H., 1955, Grain orientation in beach sands—a possible means for predicting reservoir trend (abstract): Jour. Sed. Petrology, v. 25, p. 130.

National Research Council, 1948, Rock-color chart: New York, Geol. Soc. America.

O'NEIL, R. L., 1959, Analytical procedures applicable to fine-grained sedimentary rocks: Jour. Sed. Petrology, v. 29, p. 267–280.

ORR, W. L., and EMERY, K. O., 1956, Composition of organic matter in marine sediments, preliminary data on hydrocarbon distribution in basins off Southern California: Geol. Soc. America Bull., v. 67, p. 1247–1258.

OTTO, G. H., 1939, A modified logarithmic probability graph for the interpretation of mechanical analyses of sediments: Jour. Sed. Petrology, v. 9, p. 62–76.

PAGE, H., 1955, Phi-millimeter conversion table: Jour. Sed. Petrology, v. 25, p. 285–292.

PARKS, J. M., JR., 1953, Use of thermoluminescence of limestones in subsurface stratigraphy: Am. Assoc. Petroleum Geologists Bull., v. 27, p. 125–142.

PAYNE, T. G., 1942, Stratigraphical analysis and environmental reconstruction: Am. Assoc. Petroleum Geologists Bull., v. 26, p. 1697–1770.

PECKHAM, A. E., 1961, Heavy minerals of the Miocene Harrison Formation in northwestern Nebraska: Jour. Sed. Petrology, v. 31, p. 52–62.

PETTIJOHN, F. J., 1926, Intraformation phosphate pebbles of the Twin-City Ordovician: Jour. Geology, v. 34, p. 361–373.

——, 1931, Petrography of the beach sands of southern Lake Michigan: Jour. Geology, v. 39, p. 432–455.

———, 1941, Persistence of heavy minerals and geologic age: Jour. Geology, v. 49, p. 610–625.

———, 1949, Sedimentary rocks (1st. ed.): New York, Harper & Bros.

———, 1957, Sedimentary rocks (2nd ed.): New York, Harper & Bros.

PINCUS, H. J., 1953, The analysis of aggregates of orientation data in the earth sciences: Jour. Geology, v. 61, p. 482–509.

———, 1956, Some vector and arithmetic operations on two-dimensional orientation variates, with applications to geological data: Jour. Geology, v. 64, p. 533–557.

PLUMLEY, W. J., and DAVIS, D. H., 1956, Estimation of recent sediment size parameters from a triangle diagram: Jour. Sed. Petrology, v. 26, p. 140–155.

POOLE, D. M., 1958, Heavy mineral variations in San Antonio and Mesquite Bays of the central Texas coast: Jour. Sed. Petrology, v. 28, p. 65–74.

PORTER, J. J., 1962, Electron microscopy of sand surface texture: Jour. Sed. Petrology, v. 32, p. 124–135.

POTTER, P. E., 1955, The petrology and origin of the Lafayette gravel: Jour. Geology, v. 63, p. 115–132.

———, and OLSON, J. S., 1954, Variance components of cross-bedding direction in some basal Pennsylvanian sandstones of the Eastern Interior Basin—geological application: Jour. Geology, v. 62, p. 50–73.

———, and SIEVER, R., 1955, A comparative study of upper Chester and Lower Pennsylvanian stratigraphic variability: Jour. Geology, v. 63, p. 429–451.

———, et al., 1958, Chester cross-bedding and sandstone trends in Illinois Basin: Am. Assoc. Petroleum Geologists Bull., v. 42, p. 1013–1046.

POWERS, M. C., 1953, A new roundness scale for sedimentary particles: Jour. Sed. Petrology, v. 23, p. 117–119.

PROKOPOVICH, N., 1955, The nature of corrosion zones in the Middle Ordovician of Minnesota: Jour. Sed. Petrology, v. 25, p. 207–215.

REICHE, P., 1938, An analysis of cross-lamination—the Coconino Sandstone: Jour. Geology, v. 46, p. 905–932.

RILEY, N. A., 1941, Projection sphericity: Jour. Sed. Petrology, v. 11, p. 94–97.

RITTENHOUSE, G., 1943, The transportation and deposition of heavy minerals: Geol. Soc. America Bull., v. 54, p. 1725–1780.

ROBSON, D. A., 1958, New technique for measuring roundness of sand grains: Jour. Sed. Petrology, v. 28, p. 108–110.

ROGERS, J. J. W., 1959, Detection of lognormal size distributions in clastic sediments: Jour. Sed. Petrology, v. 29, p. 402–407.

———, and POWELL, W. F., 1958, Size distribution of zircon grains in some samples of the lower Beaumont Clay: Jour. Sed. Petrology, v. 28, p. 36–39.

———, and HEAD, W. B., 1961, Relationships between porosity, median size, and sorting coefficients of synthetic sands: Jour. Sed. Petrology, v. 31, p. 467–470.

ROSENFELD, M. A., and GRIFFITHS, J. C., 1951, A new approach to the problem of porosity measurement: Producers Monthly, v. 15, p. 23–28, 31–39.

———, 1953, An experimental test of visual comparison technique in estimating two-dimensional sphericity and roundness of quartz grains: Am. Jour. Sci. v. 251, p. 553–585.

RUSNAK, G. A., 1960, Some observations of recent oolites: Jour. Sed. Petrology, v. 30, p. 471–480.

RUSSELL, R. D., and TAYLOR, R. E., 1937, Roundness and shape of Mississippi River sands: Jour. Geology, v. 45, p. 225–267.

SCHMOLL, H. R., and BENNETT, R. H., Axiometer—a mechanical device for locating and measuring pebble and cobble axes for macrofabric studies: Jour. Sed. Petrology, v. 31, p. 617–622.

SHEPARD, F. P., and MOORE, D. G., 1955, Central Texas Coast sedimentation—characteristics of sedimentary environment, recent history and diagenesis: Am. Assoc. Petroleum Geologists Bull., v. 39, p. 1463–1593.

———, and YOUNG, R., 1961, Distinguishing between beach and dune sands: Jour. Sed. Petrology, v. 31, p. 196–214.

SHEPPS, V. C., 1958, "Size factors," a means of analysis of data from textural studies of till: Jour. Sed. Petrology, v. 28, p. 482–485.

SHOEMAKER, E. M., et al., 1959, Elemental composition of the sandstone-type uranium deposits, p. 25–54, *in* Garrels, R. M. and Larsen, E. S., 3rd., Geochemistry and mineralogy of the Colorado Plateau uranium ore: U. S. Geol. Survey Prof. Paper 320.

SHROCK, R. R., 1948, Sequence in layered rocks: New York, McGraw-Hill Book Co., Inc.

SMITHSON, F., 1941, The alteration of detrital minerals in the Mesozoic rocks of Yorkshire: Geol. Mag., v. 78, p. 97–112.

SNEED, E. D., and FOLK, R. L., 1958, Pebbles in the lower Colorado River, Texas—a study in particle morphogenesis: Jour. Geology, v. 66, p. 114–150.

STEINMETZ, R., 1962, Sampling and size distribution of quartzose pebbles from three New Jersey gravels: Jour. Geology, v. 70, p. 56–73.

SWINEFORD, A., and SWINEFORD, F., 1946, A comparison of three sieve shakers: Jour. Sed. Petrology, v. 16, p. 3–13.

TALLMAN, S. L., 1949, Sandstone types—their abundance and cementing agents: Jour. Geology, v. 57, p. 582–591.

TANNER, W. F., 1958, The zig-zag nature of type I and type IV curves: Jour. Sed. Petrology, v. 28, p. 372–375.

————, 1960, Shallow water ripple mark varieties: Jour. Sed. Petrology, v. 30, p. 481–485.

TEN HAAF, E., 1959, Graded beds of the northern Appenines: Rijksuniversiteit te Groningen.

TICKELL, F. G., and HIATT, W. M., 1938, Effect of angularity of grain on porosity and permeability of unconsolidated sands: Am. Assoc. Petroleum Geologists Bull., v. 22, p. 1272–1279.

TOMLINSON, C. W., 1916, The origin of red beds: Jour. Geology, v. 24, p. 153–179, 238–253.

TRASK, P. D., 1932, Origin and environment of source sediments of petroleum: Houston, Gulf Publ. Co.

TRASK, P. D. (ed.), 1950, Applied sedimentation: New York, John Wiley & Sons, Inc.

TRASK, P. D., and PATNODE, H. W., 1942, Source beds of petroleum: Tulsa, Am. Assoc. Petroleum Geologists.

TREFETHEN, J. M., and DOW, R. L., 1960,

Some features of modern beach sediments: Jour. Sed. Petrology, v. 30, p. 589–602.

TWENHOFEL, W. H., 1950, Principles of sedimentation (2nd ed.): New York, McGraw-Hill Book Co., Inc.

————, and TYLER, S. A., 1941, Methods of study of sediments (1st ed.): New York, McGraw-Hill Book Co., Inc.

VAN ANDEL, TJ. H., 1959, Reflections on the interpretation of heavy mineral analyses: Jour. Sed. Petrology, v. 29, p. 153–163.

————, and POOLE, D. M., 1960, Sources of recent sediments in the northern Gulf of Mexico: Jour. Sed. Petrology, v. 30, p. 91–122.

VAN HOUTEN, F. B., 1948, Origin of redbanded early Cenozoic deposits in Rocky Mountain region: Am. Assoc. Petroleum Geologists Bull., v. 32, p. 2083–2126.

WADELL, H., 1932, Volume, shape and roundness of rock particles: Jour. Geology, v. 40, p. 443–451.

————, 1933, Sphericity and roundness of quartz particles: Jour. Geology, v. 41, p. 310–331.

WASKOM, J. D., 1958, Roundness as an indicator of environment along the coast of panhandle Florida: Jour. Sed. Petrology, v. 28, p. 351–360.

WEEKS, L. G., 1953, Environment and mode of origin and facies relationships of carbonate concretions in shales: Jour. Sed. Petrology, v. 23, p. 162–173.

WEISS, M. P., 1954, Feldspathized shales from Minnesota: Jour. Sed. Petrology, v. 24, p. 270–274.

WELLER, J. M., 1960, Stratigraphic principles and practice: New York, Harper & Bros.

WENTWORTH, C. K., 1922, A scale of grade and class terms for clastic sediments: Jour. Geology, v. 30, p. 377–392.

WEYL, P. K., 1960, Porosity through dolomitization—conservation-of-mass requirements: Jour. Sed. Petrology, v. 30, p. 85–90.

WILLMAN, H. B., and PAYNE, J. N., 1942, Geology and mineral resources of the Marseilles, Ottawa, and Streator quadrangles: Illinois State Geol. Survey Bull. 66.

WOLF, K. H., 1960, Simplified limestone

classification: Am. Assoc. Petroleum Geologists Bull., v. 44, p. 1414–1415.

WOLMAN, M. G., 1954, A method of sampling coarse river-bed material: Am. Geophys. Union Trans. v. 35, p. 951–956.

WRIGHT, A. E., 1957, Three-dimensional shape analysis of fine-grained sediments:

Jour. Sed. Petrology, v. 27, p. 306–312.

YOUDEN, W. J., 1951, Statistical methods for chemists: New York, John Wiley & Sons, Inc.

ZINGG, TH., 1935, Beitrag zur Schotteranalyse: Schweiz. Min. u. Pet. Mitt., Bd. 15, p. 39–140.

Chapter 5. Classification and Description of Sedimentary Rocks

BISSELL, H. J., and CHILINGAR, G. V., 1961, Comments on Teodorovich's "Structural classification of limestones and dolomites," and Shvetsov's "Genetic classification of limestones": Jour. Sed. Petrology, v. 31, p. 611–616.

BOKMAN, J., 1955, Sandstone classification; relation to composition and texture: Jour. Sed. Petrology, v. 25, p. 201–206.

BRAMLETTE, M. N., 1946, The Monterey Formation of California and the origin of its siliceous rocks: U. S. Geol. Survey Prof. Paper 212, p. 15–16.

CADY, G. H., 1942, Modern concepts of the physical constitution of coal: Jour. Geology, v. 50, p. 337–356.

CLOUD, P. E., JR., 1955, Physical limits of glauconite formation: Am. Assoc. Petroleum Geologists Bull., v. 39, p. 484–492.

COX, B. B., 1946, Transformation of organic material into petroleum under geologic conditions ("the geologic fence"): Am. Assoc. Petroleum Geologists Bull., v. 30, p. 645–659.

DAPPLES, E. C., KRUMBEIN, W. C., and SLOSS, L. L., 1953, Petrographic and lithologic attributes of sandstones: Jour. Geology, v. 61, p. 291–317.

DUNBAR, C. O., and RODGERS, J., 1957, Principles of stratigraphy: New York, John Wiley & Sons, Inc.

FISCHER, G., 1933, Die Petrographie der Grauwacken: Jahrb. Preuss. Geol. Landesanstalt, v. 54, p. 320–343.

FOLK, R. L., 1954, The distinction between grain size and mineral composition in sedimentary-rock nomenclature: Jour. Geology, v. 62, p. 344–359.

———, 1956, The role of texture and composition in sandstone classification: Jour. Sed. Petrology, v. 26, p. 166–171.

———, 1959, Practical petrographic classification of limestones: Am. Assoc. Petroleum Geologists Bull., v. 43, p. 1–38.

GALLIHER, E. W., 1935, Geology of glauconite: Am. Assoc. Petroleum Geologists Bull., v. 19, p. 1569–1601.

GOLDMAN, M. I., 1929, Lithologic subsurface correlation in the Bend series of north-central Texas: U. S. Geol. Survey Prof. Paper 129A.

GRABAU, A. W., 1904, On the classification of sedimentary rocks: Am. Geol., v. 33, p. 228–247.

———, 1913, Principles of stratigraphy: New York, A. B. Seiler & Co.

HAM, W. E. (ed.), 1962, Classification of carbonate rocks—a symposium: Am. Assoc. Petroleum Geologists Memoir 1.

HAY, R. L., 1952, The terminology of fine-grained detrital volcanic rocks: Jour. Sed. Petrology, v. 22, p. 119–120.

———, 1956, Pitchfork Formation, detrital facies of early basic breccia, Absaroka Range, Wyoming: Am Assoc. Petroleum Geologists Bull., v. 40, p. 1863–1898.

ILLING, L. V., 1954, Bahaman calcareous sands: Am. Assoc. Petroleum Geologists Bull., v. 38, p. 1–95.

JAMES, H. L., 1954, Sedimentary facies of iron-formation: Econ. Geology, v. 49, p. 235–293.

JEFFREY, E. C., 1915, The mode of origin of coal: Jour. Geology, v. 23, p. 218–230.

KRYNINE, P. D., 1935, Arkose deposits in the humid tropics—a study of sedimentation in southern Mexico: Am. Jour. Science, series 5, v. 29, p. 353–363.

———, 1948, The megascopic study and field classification of sedimentary rocks: Jour. Geology, v. 56, p. 130–165.

———, 1949, The origin of red beds: N. Y. Acad. Science Trans., series 2, v. 2, p. 60–68.

KUENEN, PH. H., 1953, Significant features of graded bedding: Am. Assoc. Petroleum Geologists Bull., v. 37, p. 1044–1066.

——, and MIGLIORINI, C. I., 1950, Turbidity currents as a cause of graded bedding: Jour. Geology, v. 58, p. 91–126.

LEVORSEN, A. I., 1954, Geology of petroleum: San Francisco, W. H. Freeman and Co.

MILLER, D. J., 1953, Late Cenozoic marine glacial sediments and marine terraces of Middleton Island, Alaska: Jour. Geology, v. 61, p. 17–40.

ORIEL, S. S., 1949, Definition of arkose: Am. Jour. Sci., v. 247, p. 824–829.

ORR, W. L., and EMERY, K. O., 1956, Composition of organic matter in marine sediments—preliminary data on hydrocarbon distribution in basins off Southern California: Geol. Soc. America Bull., v. 67, p. 1247–1258.

PACKHAM, G. H., 1954, Sedimentary structures as an important factor in the classification of sandstones: Am. Jour. Sci., v. 252, p. 466–476.

PETTIJOHN, F. J., 1926, Intraformation phosphate pebbles of the Twin-City Ordovician: Jour. Geology, v. 34, p. 361–373.

——, 1943, Archean sedimentation: Geol. Soc. America Bull., v. 54, p. 925–972.

——, 1949, Sedimentary rocks (1st ed.): New York, Harper & Bros.

——, 1954, Classification of sandstones: Jour. Geology, v. 62, p. 360–365.

——, 1957, Sedimentary rocks (2nd ed.): New York, Harper & Bros.,

PIRSSON, L. V., and SCHUCHERT, C., 1920, Introductory geology: New York, John Wiley & Sons, Inc.

RUBEY, W. W., 1929, Origin of siliceous Mowry Shale of the Black Hills region:

U. S. Geol. Survey Prof. Paper 154D, p. 153–170.

SHEPARD, F. P., 1954, Nomenclature based on sand-silt-clay ratios: Jour. Sed. Petrology, v. 24, p. 151–158.

TALLMAN, S. L., 1949, Sandstone types—their abundance and cementing agents: Jour. Geology, v. 57, p. 582–591.

THIESSEN, R., 1920, Compilation and composition of bituminous coals: Jour. Geology, v. 28, p. 185–209.

TRASK, P. D., and PATNODE, H. W., 1942, Source beds of petroleum: Tulsa, Am. Assoc. Petroleum Geologists.

TWENHOFEL, W. H., 1937, Terminology of the fine-grained mechanical sediments: Rept. Comm. Sedimentation, 1936–1937, Nat. Research Council, p. 81–104.

——, 1950, Principles of sedimentation (2nd ed.): New York, McGraw-Hill Book Co., Inc.

WELLER, J. M., 1960, Stratigraphic principles and practice: New York, Harper & Bros.

WENTWORTH, C. K., and WILLIAMS, H., 1932, The classification and terminology of the pyroclastic rocks: Rept. Comm. Sedimentation, 1930–1932, Nat. Research Council.

WENTWORTH, C. K., 1935, The terminology of the coarse sediments: Rep. Comm. Sedimentation, 1932–1934, Nat. Research Council.

WILLIAMS, H., TURNER, F. J., and GILBERT, C. M., 1954, Petrography—an introduction to the study of rocks in thin sections: San Francisco, W. H. Freeman & Co.

WILLMAN, H. B., 1942, Geology and mineral resources of the Marseilles, Ottawa, and Streator Quadrangles: Illinois State Geol. Survey Bull. 66.

WOLF, K. H., 1960, Simplified limestone classification: Am. Assoc. Petroleum Geologists Bull., v. 44, p. 1414–1415.

Chapter 6. Sedimentary Processes

ADAMS, J. E., et al., 1951, Starved Pennsylvanian Midland Basin: Am. Assoc. Petroleum Geologists Bull., v. 35, p. 2600–2607.

BAGNOLD, R. A., 1941, The physics of blown sand and desert dunes: London,

Wm. Morrow & Co.

BASS, N. W., 1936, Origin of the shoestring sands of Greenwood and Butler Counties, Kansas: Kansas State Geol. Survey Bull. 23.

BATES, C. C., 1953, Rational theory of delta

formation: Am. Assoc. Petroleum Geologists Bull., v. 37, p. 2119–2162.

BELL, H. S., 1942, Density currents as agents for transporting sediments: Jour. Geology, v. 50, p. 512–547.

BOSWELL, P. G. H., 1960, The term graywacke: Jour. Sed. Petrology, v. 30, p. 154–156.

BRADLEY, J. S., 1957, Differentiation of marine and sub-aerial sedimentary environments by volume percentage of heavy minerals, Mustang Island, Texas: Jour. Sed. Petrology, v. 27, p. 116–125.

BRIGGS, L. I., 1958, Evaporite facies: Jour. Sed. Petrology, v. 28, p. 46–56.

CLARKE, F. W., 1924, The data of geochemistry: U. S. Geol. Survey Bull. 770.

CURRAY, J. R., 1960, Tracing sediment masses by grain size modes: 21st Internat. Geol. Cong. Rpt., pt. 23, p. 119–130.

DAPPLES, E. C., 1955, General lithofacies relationship of St. Peter Sandstone and Simpson Group: Am. Assoc. Petroleum Geologists Bull., v. 39, p. 444–467.

DUNBAR, C. O., and RODGERS, J., 1957, Principles of stratigraphy: New York, John Wiley & Sons, Inc.

EATON, J. E., 1929, The by-passing and discontinuous deposition of sedimentary materials: Am. Assoc. Petroleum Geologists Bull., v. 13, p. 713–762.

EINSTEIN, H. A., and CHIEN, N., 1953, Transport of sediment mixtures with large ranges of grain sizes: Univ. of Calif. Inst. of Eng. Research, Missouri River Division Sediment Series No. 2.

EMERY, K. O., 1956, Sediments and water of Persian Gulf: Am. Assoc. Petroleum Geologists Bull., v. 40, p. 2354–2383.

FINKEL, H. J., 1959, The barchans of southern Peru: Jour. Geology, v. 67, p. 614–647.

FLEMING, R. H., and REVELLE, R., 1939, Physical processes in the ocean, p. 95–102, in Recent marine sediments: Tulsa, Am. Assoc. Petroleum Geologists.

FOLK, R. L., 1951, Stages of textural maturity in sedimentary rocks: Jour. Sed. Petrology, v. 21, p. 127–130.

———, and WARD, W. C., 1957, Brazos River bar—a study in the significance of grain size parameters: Jour. Sed. Petrology, v. 27, p. 3–26.

GARRELS, R. M., 1960, Mineral equilibria: New York, Harper & Bros.

GILBERT, G. K., 1914, The transportation of debris by running water: U. S. Geol. Survey Prof. Paper 86.

GLASS, H. D., POTTER, P. E., and SIEVER, R., 1956, Clay mineralogy of some basal Pennsylvanian sandstones, clays and shales: Am. Assoc. Petroleum Geologists Bull., v. 40, p. 750–754.

GRIM, R. E., 1951, The depositional environment of red and green shales: Jour. Sed. Petrology, v. 21, p. 226–232.

———, 1953, Clay mineralogy: New York, McGraw-Hill Book Co., Inc.

———, 1958, Concept of diagenesis in argillaceous sediments: Am. Assoc. Petroleum Geologists Bull., v. 42, p. 246–253.

HJULSTROM, F., 1939, Transportation of detritus by moving water, p. 5–31, in Trask, P. D. (ed.), Recent marine sediments: Tulsa, Am. Assoc. Petroleum Geologists.

INMAN, D. L., 1949, Sorting of sediments in the light of fluid mechanics: Jour. Sed. Petrology, v. 19, p. 51–70.

JAFFE, G., and HUGHES, J. H., 1953, The radioactivity of bottom sediments in Chesapeake Bay: Am. Geophys. Union Trans., v. 34, p. 539–542.

JOHNS, W. D., and GRIM, R. E., 1958, Clay mineral composition of recent sediments from the Mississippi River delta: Jour. Sed. Petrology, v. 28, p. 186–199.

KALINSKE, A. A., and VAN DRIEST, E. R., 1938, Application of statistical theory of turbulence to hydraulic problems, p. 416–421, in Proc. 5th Internat. Cong. of Applied Mechanics: New York, John Wiley & Sons, Inc.

KALINSKE, A. A., 1942, Criteria for determining sand-transport by surface-creep and saltation: Am. Geophys. Union, Trans., 2, p. 639–643.

KELLER, W. D., 1945, Size distribution of sand in some dunes, beaches, and sandstone: Am. Assoc. Petroleum Geologists Bull., v. 29, p. 215–221.

———, 1955, The principles of chemical weathering: Columbia, Mo., Lucas Bros.

———, 1956, Clay minerals as influenced by environments of their formation: Am. Assoc. Petroleum Geologists Bull., v. 40, p. 2689–2710.

KNAPP, R. T., 1943, Density currents—their mixing characteristics and their effect on the turbulence structure of the associated flow: Iowa Inst. Hydraulic Research Bull. 27, p. 289–306.

KNILL, J. L., 1959, Axial and marginal sedimentation in geosynclinal basins: Jour. Sed. Petrology, v. 29, p. 317–325.

KRUMBEIN, W. C., 1951, Occurrence and lithologic associations of evaporites in the United States: Jour. Sed. Petrology, v. 21, p. 63–81.

———, and GARRELS, R. M., 1952, Origin and classification of chemical sediments in terms of pH and oxidation-reduction potentials: Jour. Geology, v. 60, p. 1–33.

KUENEN, PH. H., 1953, Significant features of graded bedding: Am. Assoc. Petroleum Geologists Bull., v. 37, p. 1044–1066.

———, 1956, The difference between sliding and turbidity flow: Deep-sea Research, v. 3, p. 134–139.

———, 1958, Problems concerning source and transportation of flysch sediments: Geologie en Mijnbouw, v. 20, p. 329–339.

———, 1959, Transport and sources of marine sediments: Geologie en Mijnbouw, v. 21, p. 191–196.

———, and MIGLIORINI, C. I., 1950, Turbidity currents as a cause of graded bedding: Jour. Geology, v. 58, p. 91–126.

LEIGHLY, J., 1934, Turbulence and the transportation of rock debris by streams: Geog. Review, v. 24, p. 453–464.

LEOPOLD, L. B., 1953, Downstream change of velocity in rivers: Am. Jour. Sci., v. 251, p. 606–624.

LLOYD, E. R., 1929, Capitan Limestone and associated formations of New Mexico and Texas: Am. Assoc. Petroleum Geologists Bull., v. 13, p. 645–658.

LYMAN, J., and FLEMING, R. H., 1940, Composition of sea water: Jour. Marine Research, v. 3, p. 134–146.

MASON, C. C., and FOLK, R. L., 1958, Differentiation of beach, dune, and aeolian flat environments by size analysis, Mustang Island, Texas: Jour. Sed. Petrology, v. 28, p. 211–226.

MCINTYRE, D. D., 1959, The hydraulic equivalence and size distributions of some mineral grains from a beach: Jour. Geology, v. 67, p. 278–301.

MCKEE, E. D., 1957, Flume experiments on the production of stratification and cross-stratification: Jour. Sed. Petrology, v. 27, p. 129–134.

MCKEE, E. D., and STERRETT, T. S., 1961, Laboratory experiments of form and structure of longshore bars and beaches, p. 13–28, in PETERSON, J. A., and OSMUND, J. C. (eds.), Geometry of sandstone bodies: Tulsa, Am. Assoc. Petroleum Geologists.

MENARD, H. W., and LUDWICK, J. C., 1951, Applications of hydraulics to the study of marine turbidity currents, p. 2–13, in Turbidity currents: Soc. Econ. Paleontologists and Mineralogists Spec. Publ. no. 2.

MORRIS, R. C., and DICKEY, P. A., 1957, Modern evaporite deposition in Peru: Am. Assoc. Petroleum Geologists Bull., v. 41, p. 2467–2474.

NEVIN, C., 1946, Competency of moving water to transport debris: Geol. Soc. America Bull., v. 57, p. 651–674.

O'BRIEN, M. P., 1933, Review of the theory of turbulent flow and its relation to sediment-transportation: Am. Geophys. Union 14th Ann. Meeting, Trans., p. 487–491.

PETTIJOHN, F. J., 1957, Sedimentary rocks (2nd ed.): New York, Harper & Bros.

PLUMLEY, W. J., 1948, Black Hills terrace gravels, a study in sediment transport: Jour. Geology, v. 56, p. 526–577.

POTTER, P. E., and OLSON, J. S., 1954, Variance components of cross-bedding direction in some basal Pennsylvania sandstones of the Eastern Interior Basin, geological application: Jour. Geology, v. 62, p. 50–73.

POTTER, P. E., and PRYOR, W. A., 1961, Dispersal centers of Paleozoic and later clastics of the upper Mississippi Valley and adjacent areas: Geol. Soc. America Bull., v. 72, p. 1195–1250.

REICHE, P., 1950, A survey of weathering processes and products: Univ. of New Mexico Publ. in Geol. no. 3 (revised ed.).

REVELLE, R., and FAIRBRIDGE, R., 1957, Carbonates and carbon dioxide, p. 239–

296, *in* Treatise on marine ecology and paleoecology, v. 1: Geol. Soc. America Memoir 67.

RITTENHOUSE, G., 1943, The transportation and deposition of heavy minerals: Geol. Soc. America Bull., v. 54, p. 1725–1780.

RUBEY, W. W., 1933, The size-distribution of heavy minerals within a waterlaid sandstone: Jour. Sed. Petrology, v. 3, p. 3–29.

————, 1937, The force required to move particles of a stream bed: U. S. Geol. Survey Prof. Paper 189E, p. 121–140.

RUSNAK, G. A., 1957, The orientation of sand under conditions of "unidirectional" fluid flow, (1) theory and experiment: Jour. Geology, v. 65, p. 384–409.

SCHEIDEGGER, A. E., 1961, Theoretical geomorphology: Englewood Cliffs, Prentice-Hall, Inc.

SCHWARZACHER, W., 1951, Grain orientation in sands and sandstones: Jour. Sed. Petrology, v. 21, p. 162–172.

SCRUTON, P. C., 1953, Deposition of evaporites: Am. Assoc. Petroleum Geologists Bull., v. 37, p. 2498–2512.

SHEPARD, F. P., 1961, Deep-sea sands: 21st Internat. Geol. Cong. Rept., pt. 23, p. 26–42.

————, and MOORE, D. G., 1954, Sedimentary environments differentiated by coarse fraction studies: Am. Assoc. Petroleum Geologists Bull., v. 38, p. 1792–1802.

SIEVER, R., 1951, The Mississippian-Pennsylvanian unconformity in southern Illinois: Am. Assoc. Petroleum Geologists Bull., v. 35, p. 542–581.

SLOSS, L. L., 1953, The significance of evaporites: Jour. Sed. Petrology, v. 23, p. 143–161.

SMITH, G. D., 1942, Illinois loess—Variations in its properties and distribution: Univ. of Ill. Agr. Expt. Sta. Bull. 490.

STRAUB, L. G., 1940, Approaches to the study of the mechanics of bed movement: Univ. of Iowa Studies in Eng. Bull. 20, p. 178–192.

SVERDRUP, H. U., JOHNSON, M. W., and FLEMING, R. H., 1942, The oceans—their physics, chemistry and general biology: New York, Prentice-Hall, Inc.

TWENHOFEL, W. H., 1950, Principles of sedimentation (2nd ed.): New York, McGraw-Hill Book Co., Inc.

VAN HOUTEN, F. B., 1953, Clay minerals in sedimentary rocks and derived soils: Am. Jour. Sci., v. 251, p. 61–82.

WEAVER, C. E., 1958, Geologic interpretation of argillaceous sediments, pts. 1 and 2: Am. Assoc. Petroleum Geologists Bull., v. 42, p. 254–271.

WELLER, J. M., 1960, Stratigraphic principles and practice: New York, Harper & Bros.

Chapter 7. Sedimentary Environments

BATHURST, R. G. C., 1959, Diagenesis in Mississippian calcilutites and pseudobreccias: Jour. Sed. Petrology, v. 29, p. 365–376.

BIEDERMAN, E. W., JR., 1962, Distinction of shoreline environments in New Jersey: Jour. Sed. Petrology, v. 32, p. 181–200.

BOKMAN, J., 1953, Lithology and petrology of the Stanley and Jackfork Formations: Jour. Geology, v. 61, p. 152–170.

BRADLEY, W. H., 1948, Limnology and the Eocene lakes of the Rocky Mountain region: Geol. Soc. America Bull., v. 59, p. 635–648.

BYRNE, J. V., and EMERY, K. O., 1960, Sediments of the Gulf of California: Geol. Soc. America Bull., v. 71, p. 933–1010.

DAPPLES, E. C., 1959, The behavior of silica in diagenesis, p. 36–54, *in* Silica in sediments: Soc. Econ. Paleontologists and Mineralogists Spec. Publ. 7.

DUNBAR, C. O., and RODGERS, J., 1957, Principles of stratigraphy: New York, John Wiley & Sons, Inc.

ELIAS, M. K., 1937, Depth of deposition of the Big Blue (late Paleozoic) sediments in Kansas: Geol. Soc. American Bull., v. 48, p. 403–432.

EMERY, K. O., and Rittenberg, S. C., 1952, Early diagenesis of California Basin sediments in relation to origin of oil; Am. Assoc. Petroleum Geologists Bull., v. 36, p. 735–806.

FISK, H. N., 1944, Geological investigation

on the alluvial valley of the Lower Mississippi River: Vicksburg, U. S. Corps Engineers, Miss. River Comm.

——, 1961, Bar-finger sands of Mississippi delta, p. 29–52, *in* Peterson, J. A., and Osmond, J. C. (eds.), Geometry of sandstone bodies: Tulsa, Am. Assoc. Petroleum Geologists.

——, et al., 1954, Sedimentary framework of the modern Mississippi delta, Louisiana: Jour. Sed. Petrology, v. 24, p. 76–99.

GINSBURG, R. N., 1957, Early diagenesis and lithification of shallow-water carbonate sediments in south Florida, p. 80–100, *in* Regional aspects of carbonate deposition: Soc. Econ. Paleontologists and Mineralogists Spec. Publ. 5.

GRIFFITHS, J. C., 1962, Uses of computers and statistics in exploration and development of mineral resources: Univ. of Arizona, College of Mines Symp., v. 1, p. EI-1-19.

HARRIS, S. A., 1958, Probability curves and the recognition of adjustment to depositional environment: Jour. Sed. Petrology, v. 28, p. 151–163.

IRELAND, H. A. (ed.), 1959, Silica in sediments, a symposium: Soc. Econ. Paleontologists and Mineralogists Spec. Publ. 7.

KRAUSKOPF, K. B., 1959, The geochemistry of silica in sedimentary environments, p. 4–19, *in* Silica in sediments: Soc. Econ. Paleontologists and Mineralogists Spec. Publ. 7.

KRUMBEIN, W. C., 1941, Principles of sedimentation and the search for stratigraphic traps: Econ. Geology, v. 36, p. 786–810.

——, 1942, Physical and chemical changes in sediments after deposition: Jour. Sed. Petrology, v. 12, p. 111–117.

——, and GARRELS, R. M., 1952, Origin and classification of chemical sediments in terms of pH and oxidation-reduction potentials: Jour. Geology, v. 60, p. 1–33.

LANKFORD, R. R., 1959, Distribution and ecology of foraminifera from east Mississippi delta margin: Am. Assoc. Petroleum Geologists Bull., v. 43, p. 2068–2099.

LE BLANC, R. J., and BREEDING, J. G. (eds.), 1957, Regional aspects of carbonate deposition, a symposium: Soc. Econ. Paleontologists and Mineralogists Spec. Publ. 5.

MASON, C. C., and FOLK, R. L., 1958, Differentiation of beach, dune, and aeolian flat environments by size analysis, Mustang Island, Texas: Jour. Sed. Petrology, v. 28, p. 211–226.

MC MASTER, R. L., 1960, Mineralogy as an indicator of beach sand movement along the Rhode Island shore: Jour. Sed. Petrology, v. 30, p. 404–413.

MILLER, R. L., and OLSON, E. C., 1955, The statistical stability of quantitative properties as a fundamental criterion for the study of environments: Jour. Geology, v. 63, p. 376–387.

MILLER, R. L., and ZEIGLER, J. M., 1958, A model relating dynamics and sediment pattern in equilibrium in the region of shoaling waves, breaker zone, and foreshore: Jour. Geology, v. 66, p. 417–441.

MOORE, R. C., 1929, Environment of Pennsylvanian life in North America: Am. Assoc. Petroleum Geologists Bull., v. 13, p. 459–487.

MURRAY, R. C., 1960, Origin of porosity in carbonate rocks: Jour. Sed. Petrology, v. 30, p. 59–84.

PACKHAM, G. H., and CROOK, K. A. W., 1960, The principle of diagenetic facies and some of its implications: Jour. Geology, v. 68, p. 392–407.

PETERSON, J. A., and OSMOND, J. C. (eds.), 1961, Geometry of sandstone bodies: Tulsa, Am. Assoc. Petroleum Geologists.

PETTIJOHN, F. J., 1957, Sedimentary rocks (2nd ed.): New York, Harper & Bros.

PHLEGER, F. B., JR., 1954, Ecology of foraminifera and associated micro-organisms from Mississippi Sound and environs: Am. Assoc. Petroleum Geologists Bull., v. 38, p. 584–647.

——, 1960, Recent sedimentology, northwest Gulf of Mexico, retrospect and prospect, p. 365–381, *in* Recent Sediments, Northwest Gulf of Mexico: Tulsa, Am. Assoc. Petroleum Geologists.

RICH, J. L., 1951, Three critical environments of deposition, and criteria for recognition of rocks deposited in each of them: Geol. Soc. America Bull., v. 62, p. 1–20.

SCRUTON, P. C., 1956, Oceanography of

Mississippi Delta sedimentary environments: Am. Assoc. Petroleum Geologists Bull., v. 40, p. 2864–2952.

SHEPARD, F. P., 1956, Marginal sediments of Mississippi Delta: Am. Assoc. Petroleum Geologists Bull., v. 40, p. 2537–2623.

————, and MOORE, D. G., 1954, Sedimentary environments differentiated by coarse fraction studies: Am. Assoc. Petroleum Geologists Bull., v. 38, p. 1792–1802.

————, PHLEGER, F .B., and VAN ANDEL, TJ. H. (eds.), 1960, Recent sediments, northwest Gulf of Mexico: Tulsa, Am. Assoc. Petroleum Geologists.

SIEVER, R., 1959, Petrology and geochemistry of silica cementation in some Pennsylvanian sandstones, p. 55–79, in Silica in sediments: Soc. Econ. Paleontologists and Mineralogists Spec. Publ. 7.

————, 1962, Silica solubility, 0°–22° C., and the diagenesis of siliceous sediments: Jour. Geology, v. 70, p. 127–150.

STEHLI, F. G., and HOWER, J., 1961, Mineralogy and early diagenesis of carbonate sediments: Jour. Sed. Petrology, v. 31, p. 358–371.

TOWE, K. M., 1962, Clay mineral diagenesis as a possible source of silica cement in sedimentary rocks: Jour. Sed. Petrology, v. 32, p. 26–28.

TWENHOFEL, W. H., 1950, Principles of sedimentation (2nd ed.): New York, McGraw-Hill Book Co., Inc.

VAN ANDEL, TJ. H., and POSTMA, H., 1954, Recent sediments of the Gulf of Paria, in Rpts. of the Orinoco Shelf expedition, v. 1: Kon. Nederl. Akad. Wetensch. Verh., v. 20, no. 5.

VAN HOUTEN, F. B., 1955, Inheritance factor in origin of clay minerals in soil: Nat. Acad. Sciences, Nat. Research Council Pub. 359, Highway Research Board Bull, 108.

WALDSCHMIDT, W. A., 1941, Cementing materials in sandstones and their probable influence on migration and accumulation of oil and gas: Am. Assoc. Petroleum Geologists Bull., v. 25, p. 1839–1879.

WASKOM, J. D., 1958, Roundness as an indicator of environment along the coast of panhandle Florida: Jour. Sed. Petrology, v. 28, p. 351–360.

WELLER, J. M., 1959, Compaction of sediments: Am. Assoc. Petroleum Geologists Bull., v. 43, p. 273–310.

————, 1960, Stratigraphic principles and practice: New York, Harper & Bros.

ZOBELL, C. E., 1946, Studies on redox potential of marine sediments: Am. Assoc. Petroleum Geologists Bull., v. 30, p. 477–513.

Chapter 8. Stratigraphic Paleontology

ALLEE, W. C., EMERSON, A. E., PARK, T., and SCHMIDT, K. P., 1951, Principles of animal ecology: Philadelphia, W. B. Saunders Co.

ARKELL, W. J., 1950, A classification of the Jurassic ammonites: Jour. Paleontology, v. 24, p. 354–364.

BURMA, B. H., 1948, Studies in quantitative paleontology: Jour. Paleontology, v. 22, p. 725–761.

————, 1949, Studies in quantitative paleontology—2. Multivariate analysis, a new analytical tool for paleontology and geology: Jour. Paleontology, v. 23, p. 95–103

CAIN, A. J., 1954, Animal species and their evolution: London, Hutchinson's University Library.

CLARK, B. L., 1945, Problems of speciation and correlation as applied to mollusks of the marine Cenozoic: Jour. Paleontology, v. 19, p. 158–172.

DAVIES, J. H., and TRUEMAN, A. E., 1927, A revision of the non-marine lamellibranchs of the Coal Measures and a discussion of their zonal sequence: Quart. Jour. Geol. Soc. London, v. 83, p. 210–259.

GLAESSNER, M. F., 1947, Principles of micropaleontology: New York, John Wiley & Sons, Inc.

HEDGPETH, J. W. (ed.), 1957, Treatise on marine ecology and paleoecology, v. 1—Ecology: Geol. Soc. America Memoir 67.

HENBEST, L. G. (ed.), 1952, Symposium on

distribution of evolutionary explosions in geologic time: Jour. Paleontology, v. 26, p. 297–394.

IMBRIE, J., 1957, The species problem with fossil animals, in Mayr, E. (ed.), The species problem: Am. Assoc. Adv. Sci. Publ. 50.

LADD, H. S. (ed.), 1957, Treatise on marine ecology and paleoecology, v. 2—Paleoecology: Geol. Soc. America Memoir 67.

LANKFORD, R. R., 1959, Distribution and ecology of foraminifera from east Mississippi Delta margin: Am. Assoc. Petroleum Geologists Bull., v. 43, p. 2068–2099.

MAYR, E. (ed.), 1957, The species problem: Am. Assoc. Adv. Science Publ. 50.

MOORE, R. C., 1948, Stratigraphical paleontology: Geol. Soc. America Bull., v. 59, p. 301–326.

NATLAND, M. L., 1957, Paleoecology of west coast Tertiary sediments, p. 543–572, in Ladd, H. S. (ed.), Treatise on marine ecology and paleoecology, v. 2—Paleoecology: Geol. Soc. America Memoir 67.

ROWE, A. W., 1899, An analysis of the genus *Micraster* as determined by rigid zonal collecting from the Zone of *Rhynchonella cuvieri* to that of *Micraster coranguinum:* Geol. Soc. London Quart. Jour., v. 55, p. 494–546.

SCHENCK, H. G., 1936, Marine molluscan provinces of western North America:

Am. Phil. Soc. Proc., v. 76, p. 921–938.

———, 1940, Applied paleontology: Am. Assoc. Petroleum Geologists Bull., v. 24, p. 1752–1758.

SIMPSON, G. G., 1943, Criteria for genera, species, and subspecies in zoology and paleozoology: N. Y. Acad. Sci. Annals, v. 44, p. 105–188.

———, 1944, Tempo and mode in evolution: New York, Columbia Univ. Press.

———, and ROE, A., 1939, Quantitative zoology: New York, McGraw-Hill Book Co., Inc.

SLOSS, L. L., 1950, Rates of evolution: Jour. Paleon., v. 24, p. 131–139.

SYLVESTER-BRADLEY, P. C. (ed.), 1956, The species concept in paleontology: Systematics Assoc. Publ. 2.

THOMAS, G., 1956, The species conflict— abstractions and their applicability, p. 17–31, in Sylvester-Bradley, P. C. (ed.), The species concept in paleontology: Systematics Assoc. Publ. 2.

TROMP, S. W., 1949, The determination of the Cretaceous-Eocene boundary by means of quantitative, generic, microfaunal determinations and the conception "Danian" in the Near East: Jour. Paleontology, v. 23, p. 673–676.

WALTON, W. R., 1955, Ecology of living benthonic foraminifera, Todos Santos Bay, Baja California: Jour. Paleontology v. 29, p. 952–1018.

Chapter 9. Stratigraphic Relationships

BAILEY, T. L., 1935, Lateral changes of fauna in the lower Pleistocene: Geol. Soc. America Bull., v. 46, p. 489–502.

BARRELL, J., 1917, Rhythms and the measurement of geologic time: Geol. Soc. America Bull., v. 28, p. 745–904.

BATES, R. L., 1942, Lateral gradation in the Seven Rivers Formation, Rocky Arroyo, Eddy county, New Mexico: Am. Assoc. Petroleum Geologists Bull., v. 26, p. 80–99.

BRADLEY, W. H., 1929, The varves and climate of the Green River epoch: U. S. Geol. Survey Prof. Papers 158, p. 87–110.

———, 1948, Limnology and the Eocene lakes of the Rocky Mountain region: Geol. Soc. America Bull., v. 59, p. 635–648.

BRIDGE, J., 1930, Geology of the Eminence and Cardareva Quadrangles: Missouri Bureau of Geol. and Mines, 2nd Ser., v. 24.

CASTER, K. E., 1934, The stratigraphy and paleontology of northwestern Pennsylvania: Bull. Am. Paleont., v. 21, p. 1–185.

CLIFTON, R. L., 1944, Paleoecology and environments inferred for some marginal Middle Permian marine strata: Am. Assoc. Petroleum Geologists Bull., v. 28, p. 1012–1031.

COOPER, B. N., and COOPER, G. A., 1946, Lower Middle Ordovician stratigraphy of the Shenandoah Valley, Virginia: Geol. Soc. America Bull., v. 57, p. 35–114.

CROOK, K. A. W., 1959, Unconformities in turbidite sequences: Jour. Geology, v. 67, p. 710–713.

CROSBY, W. O., 1912, Dynamic relations and terminology of stratigraphic conformity and unconformity: Jour. Geology, v. 20, p. 289–299.

DUBOIS, E. P., 1945, Subsurface relations of the Maquoketa and "Trenton" Formations in Illinois: Ill. Geol. Survey Rpt. Inv. 105–I.

DUNBAR, C. O., 1941, Permian faunas—a study in facies: Geol. Soc. America Bull., v. 52, p. 313–332.

———, and RODGERS, J., 1957, Principles of stratigraphy: New York, John Wiley & Sons, Inc.

ELIAS, M. K., 1937, Depth of deposition of the Big Blue (Late Paleozoic) sediments in Kansas: Geol. Soc. America Bull., v. 48, p. 403–432.

ESKOLA, P., 1915, Om Sambandet mellan kemisk och mineralogisk sammansättning hos Orijärvitraktens metamorfa bergarter: Commission Géol. Finlande Bull. 44, p. 1–45.

———, 1922, The mineral facies of rocks: Norsk Geol. Tidsskrift, Bd. 6, p. 142–194.

GRABAU, A. W., 1905, Physical character and history of some New York Formations: Science, n. s., v. 22, p. 534.

GRESSLY, A., 1838, Observation Géologiques sur le Jura Soleurois: Neue Denkschr. Allg. Schweizerische Gesellsch. ges. Naturw., v. 2, p. 1–112.

HAUG, E., 1907, Traité de géologie: Paris, Armand Cohn.

HEIM, A., 1908, Die Nummuliten und Flyschbildungen der Schweizer Alpen: Schweiz. Paläont. Gesell. Abb., v. 35, p. 173–174.

ISRAELSKY, M. C., 1949, Oscillation chart: Am. Assoc. Petroleum Geologists Bull., v. 33, p. 92–98.

KAY, M., 1948, Summary of Middle Ordovician bordering Allegheny synclinorium: Am. Assoc. Petroleum Geologists Bull., v. 32, p. 1397–1416.

KRUMBEIN, W. C., 1942, Criteria for subsurface recognition of unconformities: Am. Assoc. Petroleum Geologists Bull., v. 26, p. 36–62.

KRYNINE, P. D., 1948, The megascopic study and field classification of sedimentary rocks: Jour. Geology, v. 56, p. 130–165.

LAHEE, F. H., 1961, Field geology: New York, McGraw-Hill Book Co., Inc.

LOMBARD, A., 1956, Géologie sédimentaire: Les séries marines: Paris, Masson & Cie.

LONGWELL, C. R. (chairman), 1949, Sedimentary facies in geologic history: Geol. Soc. America Memoir 39.

LOVELY, H. R., 1948, Onlap and strike-overlap: Am. Assoc. Petroleum Geologists Bull., v. 32, p. 2295–2297.

LOWMAN, S. W., 1949, Sedimentary facies in Gulf Coast: Am. Assoc. Petroleum Geologists Bull., v. 33, p. 1939–1997.

LOZO, F. E., JR., 1944, Biostratigraphic relations of some North Texas Trinity and Fredericksburg (Comanchean) foraminifera: Am. Midl. Naturalist, v. 31, p. 513–582.

MC KEE, E. D., 1938, The environment and history of the Toroweap and Kaibab Formations of northern Arizona and southern Utah: Carnegie Inst. Washington Publ. 492.

———, 1949, Facies changes in the Colorado Plateau, p. 35–48, in Geol. Soc. America Memoir 39.

MELTON, F. A., 1947, Onlap and strike-overlap: Am. Assoc. Petroleum Geologists Bull., v. 31, p. 1868–1878.

MOORE, R. C., 1949, Meaning of facies, p. 1–34, in Geol. Soc. America Memoir 39.

———, 1957, Modern methods of Paleoecology: Am. Assoc. Petroleum Geologists Bull., v. 41, p. 1775–1801.

NALIVKIN, D. V., 1955–1956, Uchenie o Fatsiyakh, Isdatel'stvo: Moscow-Leningrad, Akad. Nauk USSR.

NATLAND, M. L., 1933, Temperature and depth distribution of some recent and fossil foraminifera in the southern California region: Bull. Scripps Inst. Oceanography, Univ. Calif. tech. ser. 3(10), p. 225–230.

NICOL, D., 1944, Paleoecology of three faunules in the Permian Kaibab Formation at Flagstaff, Arizona: Jour. Paleontology, v. 18, p. 553–557.

PIKE, W. S., JR., 1947, Intertonguing marine and non-marine Upper Cretaceous deposits of New Mexico, Arizona, and southwestern Colorado: Geol. Soc. America Memoir 24.

PIRSSON, L. V., and SCHUCHERT, C., 1920,

Introductory geology: New York, John Wiley & Sons, Inc.

SANDERS, J. E., 1957, Discontinuities in the stratigraphic record: N. Y. Acad. Science Trans., ser. 2, v. 19, p. 287–297.

SCHENCK, H. G., 1945, Geologic application of biometrical analysis of molluscan assemblages: Jour. Paleontology, v. 19, p. 504–521.

SELK, E. L., 1948, Problem of the "Mayes" in Oklahoma: Jour. Geology, v. 56, p. 303–307.

SHROCK, R. R., 1948, Sequence in layered rocks: New York, McGraw-Hill Book Co., Inc.

SIEVER, R., 1951, The Mississippian–Pennsylvanian unconformity in southern Illinois: Am. Assoc. Petroleum Geologists Bull., v. 35, p. 542–581.

SLOSS, L. L., 1956, Location of petroleum accumulation by facies studies: 4th World Petrol. Cong. Proc., sec. 1/B, p. 315–335.

———, 1960, Concepts and applications of stratigraphic facies in North America: 21st Internat. Geol. Cong. Rept., pt. 12, p. 7–18.

———, KRUMBEIN, W. C., and DAPPLES, E. C., 1949, Integrated facies analysis, p. 91–124, in Geol. Soc. America Memoir 39.

———, and LAIRD, W. M., 1947, Devonian System in central and northwestern Montana: Am. Assoc. Petroleum Geologists Bull., v. 31, p. 1404–1430.

SPIEKER, E. M., 1949, Sedimentary facies and associated diastrophism in the Upper Cretaceous of central and eastern Utah, p. 55–82, in Geol. Soc. America Memoir 39.

SWAIN, F. M., 1949, Onlap, offlap, overstep and overlap: Am. Assoc. Petroleum Geologists Bull., v. 33, p. 634–636.

TEICHERT, C., 1958, Some biostratigraphical concepts: Geol. Soc. America Bull., v. 69, p. 99–120.

TWENHOFEL, W. H., 1926, Treatise on sedimentation: Baltimore, Williams & Williams.

WALTERS, R. F., 1946, Buried Pre-Cambrian hills in northeastern Barton County, central Kansas: Am. Assoc. Petroleum Geologists Bull., v. 30, p. 660–710.

WALTHER, J., 1893–1894, Einleitung in die Geologie als historische Wissenschaft. Beobachtungen über die Bildung der Gesteine und ihrer organischen Einschlüsse, bd. 1: Jena, G. Fischer.

WELLER, J. M., 1960, Stratigraphic principles and practice: New York, Harper & Bros.

WELLS, J. W., 1947, Provisional paleoecological analysis of Devonian rocks of the Columbus region: Ohio Jour. Sci. v. 47, p. 119–126.

WHEELER, H. E., 1958, Primary factors in biostratigraphy: Am. Assoc. Petroleum Geologists Bull., v. 42, p. 640–655.

———, and MALLORY, S. V., 1956, Factors in lithostratigraphy: Am. Assoc. Petroleum Geologists Bull., v. 40, p. 2711–2723.

Chapter 10. Principles of Correlation

ALLAN, R. S., 1948, Geological correlation and paleoecology: Geol. Soc. America Bull., v. 59, p. 1–10.

ANDERSON, R. Y., and KIRKLAND, D. W., 1960, Origin, varves, and cycles of Jurassic Todilto Formation, New Mexico: Am. Assoc. Petroleum Geologists Bull., v. 44, p. 37–52.

ARKELL, W. J., 1946, Standard of the European Jurassic: Geol. Soc. America Bull., v. 57, p. 1–34.

BAILEY, E. B., 1930, New light on sedimentation and tectonics: Geol. Mag., v. 67, p. 77–92.

CHENEY, M. G., 1947, Pennsylvanian classification and correlation problems in north-central Texas: Jour. Geology, v. 55, p. 202–219.

COBBAN, W. A., 1951, Scaphitoid cephalopods of the Colorado group: U. S. Geol. Survey Prof. Paper 239.

———, and REESIDE, J. B., 1952, Correlation of the Cretaceous formations of the Western Interior of the United States: Geol. Soc. America Bull., v. 63, p. 1011–1044.

COOKE, C. W., et al., 1943, Correlation of Cenozoic formations of Atlantic and Gulf Coastal Plain and the Caribbean region: Geol. Soc. America Bull., v. 54, p. 1713–1724.

COOPER, G. A., et al., 1942, Correlation of

the Devonian sedimentary formations of North America: Geol. Soc. America Bull., v. 53, p. 1729–1793.

DUNBAR, C. O. (chairman), 1960, Correlation of the Permian formations of North America: Geol. Soc. America Bull., v. 71, p. 1763–1806.

———, and RODGERS, J., 1957, Principles of stratigraphy: New York, John Wiley & Sons, Inc.

DUNLAP, R. C., JR., 1956, Geophysical data for geological study: Am. Assoc. Petroleum Geologists Bull., v. 40, p. 1462–1472.

ELIAS, M. K., 1937, Depth of deposition of the Big Blue (Late Paleozoic) sediments in Kansas: Geol. Soc. America Bull., v. 48, p. 403–432.

FAIRBRIDGE, R. W., 1954, Stratigraphic correlation by microfacies: Am. Jour. Sci., v. 252, p. 683–694.

FAUST, L. Y., 1951, Seismic velocity as a function of depth and geologic time: Geophysics, v. 16, p. 192–206.

FLOWER, R. H., 1956, Montoya-Bighorn-Richmond correlations (Abstract): Geol. Soc. America Bull., v. 67, p. 1793–1794.

FORGOTSON, J. M., JR., 1957, Nature, usage, and definition of marker-defined vertically segregated rock units: Am. Assoc. Petroleum Geologists Bull., v. 41, p. 2108–2113.

———, 1957, Stratigraphy of Comanchean Cretaceous Trinity Group: Am. Assoc. Petroleum Geologists Bull., v. 41, p. 2328–2361.

FREBOLD, H., 1953, Correlation of the Jurassic formations of Canada: Geol. Soc. America Bull., v. 64, p. 1229–1246.

GRABAU, A .W., 1906, Types of sedimentary overlap: Geol. Soc. America Bull., v. 17, p. 567–636.

GUTSTADT, A. M., 1958, Upper Ordovician stratigraphy in Eastern Interior region: Am. Assoc. Petroleum Geologists Bull., v. 42, p. 513–547.

HAUN, J. D., and LE ROY, L. W., 1958, Subsurface geology in petroleum exploration: Golden, Colorado School of Mines.

HENDRIX, W. E., 1959, A new method of foraminiferal correlation: Jour. Paleontology, v. 33, p. 588–605.

HOUGH, J. L., 1953, Pleistocene climatic record in a Pacific Ocean core sample: Jour. Geology, v. 61, p. 252–262.

HOWELL, B. F., et al, 1944, Correlation of the Cambrian formations of North America: Geol. Soc. America Bull., v. 55, p. 993–1004.

IMLAY, R. W., 1944, Correlation of the Cretaceous formations of the Greater Antilles, Central America, and Mexico: Geol. Soc. America Bull., v. 55, p. 1005–1045.

———, 1952, Correlation of the Jurassic formations of North America exclusive of Canada: Geol. Soc. America Bull., v. 63, p. 953–992.

———, and REESIDE, J. B., 1954, Correlation of the Cretaceous formations of Greenland and Alaska: Geol. Soc. America Bull., v. 65, p. 223–246.

ISRAELSKY, M. C., 1949, Oscillation chart: Am. Assoc. Petroleum Geologists Bull., v. 33, p. 92–98.

KLEINPELL, R. M., 1938, Miocene stratigraphy of California: Tulsa, Am. Assoc. Petroleum Geologists.

KULP, J. L., 1961, Geologic time scale: Science, v. 133, p. 1105–1114.

LOWENSTAM, H. A., and EPSTEIN, S., 1954, Paleotemperature of the post-Aptian Cretaceous as determined by the oxygen method: Jour. Geology, v. 62, p. 207–248.

LOWMAN, S. W., 1949, Sedimentary facies in Gulf Coast: Am. Assoc. Petroleum Geologists Bull., v. 33, p. 1939–1997.

MALLORY, V. S., 1959, Lower Tertiary biostratigraphy of the California Coast Ranges: Tulsa, Am. Assoc. Petroleum Geologists.

MAYNE, K. I., LAMBERT, R. ST. J., and YORK, D., 1959, The geological time scale: Nature, v. 183, p. 212–214.

MILNER, H. B., 1962, Sedimentary petrography, v. 2, Principles and applications: New York, The Macmillan Co.

MOORE, P. F., 1958, Nature, usage, and definition of marker-defined vertically segregated rock units: Am. Assoc. Petroleum Geologists Bull., v. 42, p. 447–450.

MOORE, R. C. (chairman), 1944, Correlation of Pennsylvanian formations of North America: Geol. Soc. America Bull., v. 55, p. 657–706.

MULLER, S. W., and SCHENCK, H. G., 1943, Standard of Cretaceous System: Am. Assoc. Petroleum Geologists Bull., v. 27, p. 262–278.

MURRAY, G. E., 1952, Vicksburg Stage and Mosley Hill Formation: Am. Assoc. Petroleum Geologists Bull., v. 36, p. 700–707.

————, 1955, Midway Stage, Sabine Stage, and Wilcox Group: Am. Assoc. Petroleum Geologists Bull., v. 39, p. 671–696.

————, and WILBERT, L. J., JR., 1950, Jacksonian Stage: Am. Assoc. Petroleum Geologists Bull., v. 34, p. 1990–1997.

MC LEARN, F. H. (chairman), 1953, Correlation of the Triassic formations of Canada: Geol. Soc. America Bull., v. 64, p. 1205–1228.

PORTER, J. W., and FULLER, J. G. C. M., 1959, Lower Paleozoic rocks of northern Williston Basin and adjacent areas: Am. Assoc. Petroleum Geologists, v. 43, p. 124–189.

PROKOPOVICH, N., 1955, The nature of corrosion zones in the Middle Ordovician of Minnesota: Jour. Sed. Petrology, v. 25, p. 207–215.

REEDY, F., JR., 1949, Stratigraphy of Frio Formation, Orange and Jefferson Counties, Texas: Am. Assoc. Petroleum Geologists Bull., v. 33, p. 1830–1858.

REESIDE, J. B., JR., 1944, Cretaceous of the Western Interior: U. S. Geol. Survey Oil and Gas Investig. Ser. Prelim. Map 10.

———— (chairman), 1957, Correlation of the Triassic formations of North America exclusive of Canada: Geol. Soc. America Bull., v. 68, 1451–1513.

RENZ, H. H., 1948, Stratigraphy and fauna of the Agua Salada Group, State of Falcon, Venezuela: Geol. Soc. America Memoir 32.

RODGERS, J., 1959, The meaning of correlation: Am. Jour. Sci., v. 257, p. 684–691.

SARMIENTO, R., 1957, Microfossil zonation of Mancos Group: Am. Assoc. Petroleum Geologists Bull., v. 41, p. 1683–1693.

SCHENCK, H. G., 1945, Geologic application of biometrical analysis of molluscan assemblages: Jour. Paleontology, v. 19, p. 504–521.

SCHUCHERT, C., 1923, Sites and natures of North American geosynclines: Geol. Soc. America Bull., v. 34, p. 151–239.

SEARS, J. D., HUNT, C. B., and HENDRICKS, T. A., 1941, Transgressive and regressive Cretaceous deposits in southern San Juan Basin, New Mexico: U. S. Geol. Survey Prof. Paper 193F, p. 101–121.

SOC. ECON. PALEONTOLOGISTS AND MINERALOGISTS RESEARCH COMM., 1959, Symposium on concepts of stratigraphic classification and correlation: Am. Jour. Sci. v. 257, p. 673–778.

SPIEKER, E. M., 1949, Sedimentary facies and associated diastrophism in the Upper Cretaceous of central and eastern Utah, p. 55–82, in Geol. Soc. America Memoir 39.

STEPHENSON, L. W., et al, 1942, Correlation of the outcropping Cretaceous formations of the Atlantic and Gulf Coastal Plain and trans-Pecos Texas: Geol. Soc. America Bull., v. 53, p. 435–448.

SUTTON, R. G., 1959, Use of flute casts in stratigraphic correlation: Am. Assoc. Petroleum Geologists Bull., v. 43, p. 230–237.

SWARTZ, C. K., et al, 1942, Correlation of the Silurian formations of North America: Geol. Soc. America Bull., v. 53, p. 533–538.

TROMP, S. W., 1949, The determination of the Cretaceous-Eocene boundary by means of quantitative, generic, microfaunal determinations and the conception "Danian" in the Near East: Jour. Paleontology, v. 23, p. 673–676.

TWENHOFEL, W. H., et al, 1954, Correlation of the Ordovician formations of North America: Geol. Soc. America Bull., v. 65, p. 247–298.

WANLESS, H. R., 1952, Studies of field relations of coal beds: 2nd Conf. on the origin and constitution of coal, Crystal Cliffs, Nova Scotia, p. 148–175.

————, and SHEPARD, F. P., 1936, Sea level and climatic changes related to Late Paleozoic cycles: Geol. Soc. America Bull., v. 47, p. 1177–1206.

WEAVER, C. E., et al, 1944, Correlation of the Marine Cenozoic formations of western North America: Geol. Soc. America Bull., v. 55, p. 569–598.

WEAVER, C. E., 1958, Geologic interpretation of argillaceous sediments, parts 1 and 2: Am. Assoc. Petroleum Geologists Bull., v. 42, p. 254–271.

WEIMER, R. J., 1960, Upper Cretaceous stratigraphy, Rocky Mountain area: Am. Assoc. Petroleum Geologists Bull., v. 44, p. 1–20.

WELLER, J. M., et al, 1948, Correlation of the Mississippian formations of North America: Geol. Soc. America Bull., v. 59, p. 91–196.

WELLER, J. M., 1960, Stratigraphic principles and practice: New York, Harper & Bros.

WHEELER, H. E., 1958a, Primary factors in biostratigraphy: Am. Assoc. Petroleum Geologists Bull., v. 42, p. 640–655.

———, 1958b, Time stratigraphy: Am. Assoc. Petroleum Geologists Bull., v. 42, p. 1047–1063.

———, and MALLORY, V. S., 1953, Designation of stratigraphic units: Am. Assoc. Petroleum Geologists Bull., v. 37, p. 2407–2421.

———, and MURRAY, H. H., 1957, Base-level control patterns in cyclothemic

sedimentation: Am. Assoc. Petroleum Geologists Bull., v. 41, p. 1985–2011.

WILLS, L. J., 1929, Physiographical evolution of Britain: London, E. Arnold & Co.

WISEMAN, J. D. H., 1959, The relation between paleotemperatures and carbonate content in a deep-sea core, a discussion: Jour. Geol., v. 67, p. 572–573.

WOMACK, J. L., 1956, Aylesworth field, p. 373–391, in Petroleum geology of southern Oklahoma, v. 1: Tulsa, Am. Assoc. Petroleum Geologists.

WOOD, H. E., 2nd, et al, 1941, Nomenclature and correlations of the North American Continental Tertiary: Geol. Soc. America Bull., v. 52, p. 1–48.

ZELLER, E. J., 1954, Thermoluminescence as a radiation damage method of geologic age determination in carbonate sediments: 19th Internat. Geol. Cong. Rept., pt. 12, p. 365–373.

———, WRAY, J. L., and DANIELS, F., 1957, Factors in age determination of carbonate sediments by thermoluminescence: Am. Assoc. Petroleum Geologists Bull., v. 41, p. 121–129.

Chapter 11. Sedimentary Tectonics

ADAMS, J. E., et al., 1951, Starved Pennsylvanian Midland Basin: Am. Assoc. Petroleum Geologists Bull., v. 35, p. 2600–2607.

BAILEY, E. B., 1930, New light on sedimentation and tectonics: Geol. Mag., v. 67, p. 77–92.

BARRELL, J., 1913, The Upper Devonian delta of the Appalachian geosyncline: Am. Jour. Sci. v. 36, p. 429–472; v. 37, p. 87–109.

———, 1917, Rhythms and the measurement of geologic time: Geol. Soc. America Bull., v. 28, p. 745–904.

BARTON, D. C., 1933, Gulf Coast geosyncline: Am. Assoc. Petroleum Geologists Bull., v. 17, p. 1446–1458.

———, 1945, Pre-Permian axes of maximum deposition in West Texas: Am. Assoc. Petroleum Geologists Bull., v. 29, p. 1336–1348.

BILLINGS, M. P., 1960, Diastrophism and mountain building: Geol. Soc. America Bull., v. 71, p. 363–398.

BUBNOFF, S. VON, 1931, Grundprobleme der Geologie: Berlin, Borntraeger.

CADY, W. M., 1950, Classification of geotectonic elements: Am. Geophys. Union Trans., v. 31, p. 780–785.

DANA, J. D., 1873, On some results of the earth's contraction from cooling, including a discussion of the origin of mountains, and the nature of the earth's interior: Am. Jour. Sci., Ser. 3, v. 5, p. 423–443; v. 6, p. 6–14, 104–115, 161–172.

DAPPLES, E. C., KRUMBEIN, W. C., and SLOSS, L. L., 1948, Tectonic control of lithologic associations: Am. Assoc. Petroleum Geologists Bull., v. 32, p. 1924–1947.

DAPPLES, E. C., 1955, General lithofacies relationship of St. Peter Sandstone and Simpson Group: Am. Assoc. Petroleum Geologists Bull., v. 39, p. 444–467.

DEEKE, W., 1912, Die alpine Geosynklinale: Neu. Jahrb. Min.u. Petr., Beil. Bd., v. 33, p. 831–858.

DOTT, R. H., JR., 1955, Pennsylvanian stratigraphy of Elko and Northern Diamond ranges, northeastern Nevada: Am. Assoc. Petroleum Geologists Bull., v. 39, p. 2211–2305.

DUNBAR, C. O., and RODGERS, J., 1957, Principles of stratigraphy: New York, John Wiley and Sons, Inc.

FISCHER, G., 1933, Die Petrographie der Grauwacken: Jahrb. Preuss. Geol. Landesanstalt, v. 54, p. 320–343.

GLAESSNER, M. F., and TEICHERT, C., 1947, Geosynclines: a fundamental concept in geology: Am. Jour. Sci., v. 245, p. 465–482; 571–591.

GOGUEL, J., 1952, Traité de tectonique: Paris, Masson et Cie.

———, 1961, Tectonics: San Francisco, W. H. Freeman and Co.

HAUG, E., 1900, Les geosynclinaux et les aires continentales: Geol. Soc. France Bull., ser. 3, v. 28, p. 617–711.

HESS, H. H., 1938, Gravity anomalies and island arc structure with particular reference to the West Indies: Am. Philos. Soc. Proc., v. 79, p. 71–94.

———, 1948, Major structural features of the western North Pacific, an interpretation of H. O. 5485, bathymetric chart, Korea to New Guinea: Geol. Soc. America Bull., v. 59, p. 417–446.

JONES, O. T., 1938, On the evolution of a geosyncline: Geol. Soc. London, Proc., v. 94, p. 62–66.

KAY, M., 1942, Development of the northern Allegheny synclinorium and adjoining regions: Geol. Soc. America Bull., v. 53, p. 1601–1658.

———, 1944, Geosynclines in continental development: Science, v. 99, p. 461–462.

———, 1945, Paleogeographic and palinspastic maps: Am. Assoc. Petroleum Geologists Bull., v. 29, p. 426–450.

———, 1947, Geosynclinal nomenclature and the craton: Am. Assoc. Petroleum Geologists Bull., v. 31, p. 1289–1293.

———, 1951, North American geosynclines: Geol. Soc. America Memoir 48.

———, 1955, Sediments and subsidence through time: Geol. Soc. America Special Paper 62, p. 665–684.

KING, P. B., 1950, Tectonic framework of southeastern United States: Am. Assoc. Petroleum Geologists Bull., v. 34, p. 635–671.

KNOPF, A., 1948, The geosynclinal theory:

Geol. Soc. America Bull., v. 59, p. 649–670.

———, 1960, Analysis of some recent geosynclinal theory: Am. Jour. Sci., Bradley volume, v. 258–A, p. 126–136.

KRUMBEIN, W. C., SLOSS, L. L., and DAPPLES, E. C., 1949, Sedimentary tectonics and sedimentary environments: Am. Assoc. Petroleum Geologists Bull., v. 33, p. 1859–1891.

KRYNINE, P. D., 1941, Triassic sediments of Connecticut (abstract): Geol. Soc. America Bull., v. 52, p. 1919.

———, 1948, The megascopic study and field classification of sedimentary rocks: Jour. Geology, v. 56, p. 130–165.

———, 1951, A critique of geotectonic elements: Trans. Am. Geophys. Union, v. 32, p. 743–747.

KUENEN, PH. H., 1935, Geological interpretation of bathymetrical results: The Snellius Expedition, v. 5, pt. 1.

———, 1958, Problems concerning source and transportation of flysch sediments: Geol. en Mijnbouw, v. 20, p. 329–339.

MARTIN, L. J., 1959, Stratigraphy and depositional tectonics of north Yukon-lower Mackenzie area, Canada: Am. Assoc. Petroleum Geologists Bull., v. 43, p. 2399–2455.

PETTIJOHN, F. J., 1949, Sedimentary rocks: New York, Harper & Bros.

———, 1957, Sedimentary rocks (2d ed.): New York, Harper & Bros.

———, 1960, Some contributions of sedimentology to tectonic analysis: 21st Internat. Geol. Cong. Rept., pt. 18, p. 446–454.

SCHUCHERT, C., 1923, Sites and nature of the North American geosynclines: Geol. Soc. America Bull., v. 34, p. 151–230.

SLOSS, L. L., 1956, Location of petroleum accumulation by facies studies: 4th World Petroleum Cong. Proc., Sec. 1/B, p. 315–335.

STEELE, G., 1960, Pennsylvanian-Permian stratigraphy of east-central Nevada and adjacent Utah: Intermountain Assoc. Petroleum Geologists 11th ann. field conf., Guidebook, p. 91–113.

STILLE, H., 1936, Wege und ergebnisse der geologisch-tektonischen Forschung, Festschr., 25 Jahre K.-Wilhelm Gesellsch, Förd, Wiss., Bd. 2.

———, 1940, Einfuhrung in den bau Amerikas: Berlin, Borntraeger.

TERCIER, J., 1940, Dépots marins actuels et séries géologiques: Eclogae Geologicae Helvetiae, v. 32, p. 47–100.

UMBGROVE, J. H. F., 1947, The pulse of the earth: The Hague, Martinus Nijhoff.

VOISEY, A. H., 1959, Australian geosyn-clines: Australian Jour. Sci., v. 22, p. 188–198.

WEEKS, L. G., 1952, Factors of sedimentary basin development that control oil oc-currence: Am. Assoc. Petroleum Geolo-gist Bull., v. 36, p. 2071–2124.

WELLER, J. M., 1960, Stratigraphic prin-ciples and practice: New York, Harper & Bros.

Chapter 12. Stratigraphic Maps

ALLEN, P., and KRUMBEIN, W. C., 1962, Sec-ondary trend components in the Top Ashdown Pebble Bed—a case history: Jour. Geol., v. 70, p. 507–538.

AMSDEN, T. W., 1955, Lithofacies map of Lower Silurian deposits in central and eastern United States and Canada: Am. Assoc. Petroleum Geologists Bull., v. 39, p. 60–74.

ANDRESEN, M. J., 1962, Paleodrainage pat-terns—their mapping from subsurface data, and their paleogeographic value: Am. Assoc. Petroleum Geologists Bull., v. 46, p. 398–405.

ANDRICHUK, J. M., 1951, Regional strati-graphic analysis of Devonian System in Wyoming, Montana, southern Saskatche-wan, and Alberta: Am. Assoc. Petroleum Geologists Bull., v. 35, p. 2368–2408.

———, 1960, Facies analysis of Upper Devonian Wabamun Group in west-central Alberta, Canada: Am. Assoc. Petroleum Geologists Bull., v. 44, p. 1651–1681.

BAILLIE, A. D., 1955, Devonian System of Williston Basin: Am. Assoc. Petroleum Geologists Bull., v. 39, p. 575–629.

BISHOP, M., 1960, Subsurface mapping: New York, John Wiley & Sons, Inc.

BRILL, K. B., 1952, Stratigraphy in the Permo-Pennsylvania zeugogeosyncline of Colorado and northern New Mexico: Geol. Soc. America Bull., v. 63, p. 809–880.

CHAYES, F., 1960, On correlation between variables of constant sum: Jour. Geo-phys. Research, v. 65, p. 4185–4193.

DICKEY, P. A., and ROH, R. E., 1955, Facies control of oil occurrence: Am. Assoc. Petroleum Geologists Bull., v. 39, p. 2306–2320.

FORGOTSON, J. M., JR., 1954, Regional stratigraphic analysis of Cotton Valley Group of upper Gulf Coastal Plain: Am. Assoc. Petroleum Geologists Bull., v. 38, p. 2476–2499.

———, 1960, Review and classification of quantitative mapping techniques: Am. Assoc. Petroleum Geologists Bull., v. 44, p. 83–100.

GOODLET, G. A., 1957, Lithological varia-tion in the Lower Limestone Group in the Midland Valley of Scotland: Geol. Survey of Great Britain Bull., v. 12, p. 52–65.

GRABAU, A. W., 1913, Principles of stratig-raphy: New York, A. G. Seiler & Co.

GRANT, F., 1957, A problem in the analysis of geophysical data: Geophysics, v. 22, p. 309–344.

GROSSMAN, W. L., 1944, Stratigraphy of the Genesee Group of New York: Geol. Soc. America Bull., v. 55, p. 41–76.

IMBRIE, J., 1955, Biofacies analysis: in Geol. Soc. America Special Paper 62, p. 449–464.

———, 1955, Quantitative lithofacies and biofacies study of Florena Shale (Per-mian) of Kansas: Am. Assoc. Petroleum Geologists Bull., v. 39, p. 649–670.

KAY, M., 1945, Paleogeographic and palin-spastic maps: Am. Assoc. Petroleum Geologists Bull., v. 29, p. 426–450.

———, 1952, Paleozoic North American geosynclines and island arcs: 18th In-ternat. Geol. Cong. Rept., pt. 13, p. 150–153.

———, 1954, Isolith, isopach, and palin-spastic maps: Am. Assoc. Petroleum Geologists Bull., v. 38, p. 916–917.

KING, P. B., 1942, Permian of west Texas and southeastern New Mexico: Am. Assoc. Petroleum Geologists Bull., v. 26, p. 535–763.

KRUMBEIN, W. C., 1948, Lithofacies maps and regional sedimentary-stratigraphic analysis: Am. Assoc. Petroleum Geologists Bull., v. 32, p. 1909–1923.

———, 1952, Principles of facies map interpretation: Jour. Sed. Petrology, v. 22, p. 200–211.

———, 1954, The tetrahedron as a facies mapping device: Jour. Sed. Petrology, v. 24, p. 3–19.

———, 1955, Composite end members in facies mapping: Jour. Sed. Petrology, v. 25, p. 115–122.

———, 1956, Regional and local components in facies maps: Am. Assoc. Petroleum Geologists Bull., v. 40, p. 2163–2194.

———, 1957, Comparison of percentage and ratio data in facies mapping: Jour. Sed. Petrology, v. 27, p. 293–297.

———, 1958, Measurement and error in regional stratigraphic analysis: Jour. Sed. Petrology, v. 28, p. 175–185.

———, 1959, Trend surface analysis of contour-type maps with irregular control-point spacing: Jour. Geophys. Research, v. 64, p. 823–834.

———, 1960, Stratigraphic maps from data observed at outcrop: Yorkshire Geol. Soc. Proc., v. 32, p. 353–366.

———, 1962, The computer in geology: Science, v. 136, p. 1087–1092.

———, and LIBBY, W. G., 1957, Application of moments to vertical variability maps of stratigraphic units: Am. Assoc. Petroleum Geologists Bull., v. 41, p. 197–211.

———, and NAGEL, F. G., 1953, Regional stratigraphic analysis of "Upper Cretaceous" rocks of Rocky Mountain region: Am. Assoc. Petroleum Geologists Bull., v. 37, p. 940–960.

———, and SLOSS, L. L., 1958, High-speed digital computers in stratigraphic and facies analysis: Am. Assoc. Petroleum Geologists Bull., v. 42, p. 2650–2669.

LEE, W., 1954, Thickness maps as criteria of regional structural movement: Kansas State Geol. Survey Bull. 109, p. 65–80.

LEVORSEN, A. I., 1927, Convergence studies in the Mid-Continent region: Am. Assoc. Petroleum Geologists Bull., v. 11, p. 657–682.

———, 1931, Pennsylvanian overlap in United States: Am. Assoc. Petroleum Geologists Bull., v. 15, p. 113–148.

———, 1933, Studies in paleogeology: Am. Assoc. Petroleum Geologists Bull., v. 17, p. 1107–1132.

———, 1943, Discovery thinking: Am. Assoc. Petroleum Geologists Bull., v. 27, p. 887–928.

———, 1960, Paleogeologic maps: San Francisco, W. H. Freeman and Co.

LIPPITT, L., 1959, Statistical analysis of regional facies changes in Ordovician Cobourg Limestone in northwestern New York and southern Ontario: Am. Assoc. Petroleum Geologists Bull., v. 43, p. 807–816.

MC COY, A. W., 1934, An interpretation of local structural development in Mid-Continent areas associated with deposits of petroleum, p. 581–627, in Problems of petroleum geology: Tulsa, Am. Assoc. Petroleum Geologists.

MC KEE, E. D., et al., 1956, Paleotectonic maps—Jurassic system: U. S. Geological Survey, Map I–175.

———, 1959, Paleotectonic maps—Triassic system: U. S. Geological Survey, Map I–300.

MILLER, R. L., 1956, Trend surfaces—their application to analysis and description of environments of sedimentation: Jour. Geology, v. 64, p. 425–446.

PELLETIER, B. R., 1958, Pocono paleocurrents in Pennsylvania and Maryland: Geol. Soc. America Bull., v. 69, p. 1033–1064.

PELTO, C. R., 1954, Mapping of multicomponent systems: Jour. Geology, v. 62, p. 501–511.

PETTIJOHN, F. J., 1957, Paleocurrents of Lake Superior Pre-Cambrian quartzites: Geol. Soc. America Bull., v. 68, p. 469–480.

———, 1957, Sedimentary rocks (2nd ed.): New York, Harper & Bros.

PIKE, W. S., JR., 1947, Intertonguing marine and non-marine Upper Cretaceous deposits of New Mexico, Arizona, and southwestern Colorado: Geol. Soc. America Memoir 24.

POTTER, P. E., and SIEVER, R., 1955, A comparative study of upper Chester and lower Pennsylvanian stratigraphic variability: Jour. Geol., v. 63, p. 429–451.

POTTER, P. E., et al, 1958, Chester cross-bedding and sandstone trends in Illinois Basin: Am. Assoc. Petroleum Geologists Bull., v. 42, p. 1013–1046.

POTTER, P. E., and PRYOR, W. A., 1961, Dispersal centers of Paleozoic and later clastics of the upper Mississippi Valley and adjacent areas: Geol. Soc. America Bull., v. 72, p. 1195–1250.

PROBST, D. A., 1953, Stratigraphic studies, Greater Oficina, Venezuela: Am. Assoc. Petroleum Geologists Bull., v. 37, p. 2073–2092.

PYE, W. D., 1944, Petrology of Bethel Sandstone of south-central Illinois: Am. Assoc. Petroleum Geologists Bull., v. 28, p. 63–122.

READ, C. B., and WOOD, G. H., 1947, Distribution and correlation of Pennsylvanian rocks in Late Paleozoic sedimentary basins of northern New Mexico: Jour. Geology, v. 55, p. 220–235.

SLOSS, L. L., DAPPLES, E. C., and KRUMBEIN, W. C., 1960, Lithofacies maps—an atlas of the United States and southern Canada: New York, John Wiley & Sons.

SWANN, D. H., 1951, Waltersburg sandstone oil pools of lower Wabash area, Illinois and Indiana: Am. Assoc. Petroleum Geologists Bull., v. 35, p. 2561–2581.

VAN ANDEL, TJ. H., 1960, Sources and dispersion of Holocene sediments, northern Gulf of Mexico, p. 34–55, in Recent sediments, northwest Gulf of Mexico: Tulsa, Am. Assoc. Petroleum Geologists.

———, and CURRAY, J. R., 1960, Regional aspects of modern sedimentation in northern Gulf of Mexico and similar basins, and paleogeographic significance, p. 345–364, in Recent sediments, northwest Gulf of Meixco: Tulsa, Okla., Am. Assoc. Petroleum Geologists.

VAN ANDEL, TJ. H., and POOLE, D. M., 1960, Sources of recent sediments in the northwest Gulf of Mexico: Jour. Sed. Petrology, v. 30, p. 91–122.

VER WIEBE, W. A., 1930, Ancestral Rocky Mountains: Am. Assoc. Petroleum Geologists Bull., v. 14, p. 765–788.

WELLER, J. M., 1960, Stratigraphic principles and practice: New York, Harper & Bros.

Chapter 13. Stratigraphic Analysis

ADAMS, J. E., et al., 1951, Starved Pennsylvanian Midland Basin: Am. Assoc. Petroleum Geologists Bull., v. 35, p. 2600–2607.

ALLING, H. L., and BRIGGS, L. I., 1961, Stratigraphy of Upper Silurian Cayugan evaporites: Am. Assoc. Petroleum Geologists Bull., v. 45, p. 515–547.

ANDRICHUK, J. M., 1955, Mississippian Madison Group stratigraphy and sedimentation in Wyoming and southern Montana. Am. Assoc. Petroleum Geologists Bull., v. 39, p. 2170–2210.

———, 1958a, Cooking Lake and Duvernay (Late Devonian) sedimentation in Edmonton area of central Alberta, Canada: Am. Assoc. Petroleum Geologists Bull., v. 42, p. 2182–2222.

———, 1958b, Stratigraphy and facies analysis of Upper Devonian reefs in Leduc, Stettler, and Redwater areas, Alberta: Am. Assoc. Petroleum Geologists Bull., v. 42, p. 1–93.

———, 1961, Stratigraphic evidence for tectonic and current control of Upper Devonian reef sedimentation, Duhamel area, Alberta, Canada: Am. Assoc. Petroleum Geologists Bull., v. 45, p. 612–632.

———, and WONFOR, J. S., 1954, Late Devonian geologic history in Stettler area, Alberta, Canada: Am. Assoc. Petroleum Geologists Bull., v. 38, p. 2500–2536.

BAILLIE, A. D., 1955, Devonian System of Williston Basin Area: Am. Assoc. Petroleum Geologists Bull., v. 39, p. 575–629.

BASS, N. W., 1936, Origin of the shoestring sands of Greenwood and Butler Counties, Kansas: Geol. Survey Kansas Bull. 23.

BASSETT, D. A., and WALTON, E. K., 1960, The Hell's Mouth Grits: Cambrian greywackes in St. Tudwal's Peninsula, North Wales: Quart. Jour. Geol. Soc. London, v. 116, p. 85–110.

BEALES, F. W., 1953, Dolomitic mottling in Palliser (Devonian) Limestone, Banff and Jasper National Parks, Alberta: Am. Assoc. Petroleum Geologists Bull., v. 37, p. 2281–2293.

BELL, W. C., BERG, R. R., and NELSON, C. A., 1956, Croixan type area—upper Mississippi Valley: 20th Internat. Geol. Cong., Symposium on the Cambrian System, v. 2, Pt. 2, p. 415–466.

BISSELL, H. J., and CHILDS, O. E., 1958, The Weber Formation of Utah and Colorado: Rocky Mountain Assoc. Geol., Symposium on Pennsylvanian Rocks of Colorado and Adjacent Areas, p. 26–30.

BOUMA, A. H., 1961, Sedimentology of some flysch deposits: a graphic approach to facies interpretation: Amsterdam, Elsevier Publishing Co.

BRIGGS, L. I., 1957, Quantitative aspects of evaporite deposition: Mich. Acad. Sci. Papers, v. 42, p. 115–123.

———, 1958, Evaporite facies: Jour. Sed. Petrology, v. 28, p. 46–56.

BURNSIDE, R. J., 1959, Geology of part of the Horseshoe Atoll in Borden and Howard Counties, Texas: U. S. Geol. Survey Prof. Paper 315-B.

BUSCH, D. A., 1961, Prospecting for stratigraphic traps, p. 220–232, in Peterson, J. A., and Osmond, J. C., (eds.), Geometry of Sandstone Bodies: Tulsa, Am. Assoc. Petroleum Geologists.

CHAMBERLIN, T. C., 1897, The method of multiple working hypotheses: Jour. Geology, v. 5, p. 837–848.

CLAIR, J. R., 1958, Subsurface stratigraphy of the Pennsylvanian of the Paradox Basin: Rocky Mountain Assoc. Geol., Symposium on Pennsylvanian Rocks of Colorado and Adjacent Areas, p. 31–46.

CLARK, J., 1962, Field interpretation of red beds: Geol. Soc. America Bull., v. 73, p. 423–428.

CLINE, L. M., 1960, Late Paleozoic rocks of the Ouachita Mountains: Okla. Geol. Survey Bull., v. 85.

CUMINGS, E. R., 1932, Reefs or bioherms: Geol. Soc. America Bull., v. 43, p. 331–352.

———, and SHROCK, R. R., 1928, Niagaran coral reefs of Indiana and adjacent states and their stratigraphic relations: Geol. Soc. America Bull., v. 39, p. 579–620.

DAPPLES, E. C., 1955, General lithofacies relationship of St. Peter Sandstone and

Simpson Group: Am. Assoc. Petroleum Geologists Bull., v. 39, p. 444–467.

———, KRUMBEIN, W. C., and SLOSS, L. L., 1948, Tectonic control of lithologic associations: Am. Assoc. Petroleum Geologists Bull., v. 32, p. 1924–1947.

DICKEY, P. A., 1943, Natural potentials in sedimentary rocks: Am. Inst. Mining and Met. Eng., Tech. Publ. 1625, Petrol. Tech., v. 6.

DILLARD, W. R., 1941, Olympic pool, Hughes and Okfuskee Counties, Oklahoma, p. 456–472 in Levorsen, A. I. (ed.), Stratigraphic type oil fields: Tulsa, Am. Assoc. Petroleum Geologists.

———, OAK, D. P., and BASS, N. W., 1941, Chanute oil pool, Neosho County, Kansas—a water-flooding operation, p. 57–77, in Levorsen, A. I. (ed.), Stratigraphic type oil fields: Tulsa, Am. Assoc. Petroleum Geologists.

DUNHAM, K. C., 1953, Red coloration in desert formations of Permian and Triassic age in Britain: 19th Internat. Geol. Cong., Comptes rendus, sec. 7, p. 25–32.

DUNNINGTON, H. V., 1958, Generation, migration, accumulation, and dissipation of oil in northern Iraq, p. 1194–1257, in Weeks, L. G. (ed.), Habitat of Oil: Tulsa, Am. Assoc. Petroleum Geologists.

DZULYNSKI, S., KSIAZKIEWICZ, M., and KUENEN, PH. H., 1959, Turbidites in flysch of the Polish Carpathian Mountains: Geol. Soc. America Bull., v. 70, p. 1089–1118.

EDIE, R. W., 1958, Mississippian sedimentation and oil fields in southeastern Saskatchewan: Am. Assoc. Petroleum Geologists Bull., v. 42, p. 95–126.

EDWARDS, A. R., 1959, Facies changes in Pennsylvanian rocks along north flank of Wichita Mountains, p. 142–155, in Petroleum Geology of Southern Oklahoma, v. 2: Tulsa, Am. Assoc. Petroleum Geologists.

FAIRBRIDGE, R. W., 1957, The dolomite question, p. 125–178, in Regional aspects of carbonate deposition: Tulsa, Soc. Econ. Paleontologists and Mineralogists.

———, 1958, What is a consanguineous association?: Jour. Geology, v. 66, p. 319–324.

FISK, H. N., 1955, Sand facies of recent Mississippi Delta deposits: 4th World

Petroleum Cong., Proc., sec. 1, p. 377–398.

————, 1961, Bar-finger sands of Mississippi Delta, p. 29–52, *in* Peterson, J. A., and Osmond, J. C. (eds.), Geometry of Sandstone Bodies: Tulsa, Am. Assoc. Petroleum Geologists.

————, et al., 1954, Sedimentary framework of the modern Mississippi Delta, La.: Jour. Sed. Petrology, v. 24, p. 76–99.

FOLK, R. L., 1960, Petrography and origin of the Tuscarora, Rose Hill, and Keefer formations, Lower and Middle Silurian of eastern West Virginia: Jour. Sed. Petrology, v. 30, p. 1–58.

FULLER, J. G. C. M., 1961, Ordovician and contiguous formations in North Dakota, South Dakota, Montana, and adjoining areas of Canada and United States: Am. Assoc. Petroleum Geologists Bull., v. 45, p. 1334–1363.

GINSBURG, ROBERT N., 1956, Environmental relationships of grain size and constituent particles in some south Florida carbonate sediments: Am. Assoc. Petroleum Geologists Bull., v. 40, p. 2384–2427.

GOGUEL, J., 1952, Traité de Tectonique: Paris, Masson et Cie.

————, 1961, Tectonics: San Francisco, W. H. Freeman and Co.

GOODELL, H. G., 1957, The petrology and petrogenesis of the Frontier Sandstone of Wyoming: Ph.D. thesis, Northwestern University.

————, 1962, The stratigraphy and petrology of the Frontier Formation of Wyoming, p. 173–210, *in* Symposium on Early Cretaceous Rocks: Wyoming Geological Assoc., Guidebook 17th Annual Field Conference.

GORSLINE, D. S., and EMERY, K. O., 1959, Turbidity-current deposits in San Pedro and Santa Monica Basins off Southern California: Geol. Soc. America Bull. v. 70, p. 279–290.

HARBAUGH, J. W., 1957, Mississippian bioherms in northeast Oklahoma: Am. Assoc. Petroleum Geologists Bull., v. 41, p. 2530–2544.

HENSON, F. R. S., 1950, Cretaceous and Tertiary reef formations and associated sediments in Middle East: Am. Assoc. Petroleum Geologists Bull., v. 34, p. 215–238.

HERMAN, G., and BARKELL, C. A., 1957, Pennsylvanian stratigraphy and productive zones, Paradox Salt Basin: Am. Assoc. Petroleum Geologists Bull., v. 41, p. 861–881.

HOLLENSHEAD, C. T., and PRITCHARD, R. L., 1961, Geometry of producing Mesaverde sandstones, San Juan Basin, p. 98–118, *in* Peterson, J. A., and Osmond, J. C. (eds.), Geometry of Sandstone Bodies: Tulsa, Am. Assoc. Petroleum Geologists.

*INGELS, J. J. C., 1960, Thornson reef complex in the Silurian of northeastern Illinois: Ph.D. thesis, Northwestern University.

JAMES, H. L., 1954, Sedimentary facies of iron-formation: Econ. Geology, v. 49, p. 235–293.

JONES, O. T., 1938, On the evolution of a geosyncline: Geol. Soc. London, Proc., v. 94, p. 62–66.

KAY, M., 1951, North American geosynclines: Geol. Soc. America Memoir 48.

KING, P. B., 1942, Permian of west Texas and southeastern New Mexico: Am. Assoc. Petroleum Geologists Bull., v. 26, p. 535–763.

————, 1948, Geology of the Southern Guadalupe Mountains, Texas: U. S. Geol. Survey Prof. Paper 215.

————, 1959, The evolution of North America: Princeton University Press.

KING, R. H., 1947, Sedimentation in Permian Castile Sea: Am. Assoc. Petroleum Geologists Bull., v. 31, p. 470–477.

KRUMBEIN, W. C., 1951, Occurrence and lithologic associations of evaporites in the United Sttaes: Jour. Sed. Petrology, v. 21, p. 63–81.

————, SLOSS, L. L., and DAPPLES, E. C., 1949, Sedimentary tectonics and sedimentary environments: Am. Assoc. Petroleum Geologists Bull., v. 33, p. 1859–1891.

KRYNINE, P. D., 1942, Differential sedimentation and its products during one complete geosynclinal cycle: 1° Congreso Panamericano Ing. Minas y Geologia, tomo 2, geologia, pt. 1, p. 537–561.

* Published (1933): Am. Assoc. Petroleum Geologists Bull., v. 47, p. 405–440.

————, 1949, The origin of red beds: N. Y. Acad. Sci. Trans., series II, v. 2, p. 60–68.

KUENEN, PH. H., 1959, Experimental abrasion 3: fluviatile action on sand: Am. Jour. Sci., v. 257, p. 172–190.

————, 1959, Sand: its origin, transportation, abrasion and accumulation: Geol. Soc. South Africa, publ. no. 134, p. 1–33.

————, 1959, Turbidity currents a major factor in flysch deposition: Eclogae Geol. Helv., v. 51, p. 1009–1021.

————, 1960, Experimental abrasion of sand grains: 21st Internat. Geol. Cong. Rept., pt. 10, p. 50–53.

LADD, H. S., 1950, Recent reefs: Am. Assoc. Petroleum Geologists Bull., v. 34, p. 203–214.

LANG, W. B., 1937, The Permian formations of the Pecos Valley of New Mexico and Texas: Am. Assoc. Petroleum Geologists Bull., v. 21, p. 853–898.

LEVORSEN, A. I., 1931, Pennsylvanian overlap in United States: Am. Assoc. Petroleum Geologists Bull., v. 15, p. 113–148.

LINK, T. A., 1950, Theory of transgressive and regressive reef (bioherm) development and origin of oil: Am. Assoc. Petroleum Geologists Bull., v. 34, p. 263–294.

LOMBARD, A., 1956, Géologie sédimentaire, les séries marines: Paris, Masson et Cie.

LOWENSTAM, H. A., 1948, Marine pool, Madison County, Illinois, Silurian reef producer, p. 153–188, in Structure of typical American oilfields, v. 3: Tulsa, Am. Assoc. Petroleum Geologists.

————, 1950, Niagaran reefs of the Great Lakes area: Jour. Geology, v. 58, p. 430–487.

LOWMAN, S. W. 1949, Sedimentary facies in Gulf Coast: Am. Assoc. Petroleum Geologists Bull., v. 33, p. 1939–1997.

MAC NEIL, F. S., 1954, Organic reefs and banks and associated detrital sediments: Am. Jour. Sci., v. 252, p. 385–401.

MARCHETTI, M. P., 1957, The occurrence of slide and flowage materials (Olistostromes) in the Tertiary Series of Sicily: 20th Internat. Geol. Cong., Sec. 5, Relaciones entre la Tectonica y la Sedimentacion, pt. 1, p. 209–225.

MELHORN, W. N., 1958, Stratigraphic analysis of Silurian rocks in Michigan Basin: Am. Assoc. Petroleum Geologists Bull., v. 42, p. 816–838.

MALLORY, W. W., 1958, Pennsylvanian coarse arkosic redbeds and associated mountains: Rocky Mountain Assoc. Geol., Symposium on Pennsylvanian Rocks of Colorado and Adjacent Areas, p. 17–20.

MC CABE, H. R., 1961, Regional Stratigraphic Analysis of the Mississippian Madison Group, Williston Basin Area: Ph.D. thesis, Northwestern University.

MILLER, R. L., 1954, A model for the analysis of environments of sedimentation: Jour. Geology, v. 62, p. 108–113.

MOORE, R. C., 1931, Pennsylvanian cycles in the northern Mid-Continent region: III. Geol. Survey Bull., v. 60, p. 247–257.

MURRAY, G. E., 1961, Geology of the Atlantic and Gulf Coastal Province of North America: New York, Harper & Bros.

MURRAY, H. F., 1958, Pennsylvanian stratigraphy of the Maroon trough: Rocky Mountain Assoc. Geol., Symposium on Pennsylvanian Rocks of Colorado and Adjacent Areas, p. 47–58.

MYERS, D. A., STAFFORD, P. T., and BURNSIDE, R. J., 1956, Geology of the late Paleozoic Horseshoe Atoll in West Texas: Bureau of Econ. Geology, Univ. of Texas, publ. no. 5607.

NANZ, R. H., JR., 1954, Genesis of Oligocene sandstone reservoir, Seeligson field, Jim Wells and Kleberg Counties, Texas: Am. Assoc. Petroleum Geologists Bull., v. 38, p. 96–117.

NATLAND, M. L., and KUENEN, P.H., 1951, Sedimentary history of the Ventura Basin, California, and the action of turbidity currents, p. 76–107, in Turbidity currents and the transportation of coarse sediments to deep water—a symposium: Soc. Econ. Paleontologists and Minerologists Special Publ., no. 2.

NEWELL, N. D., ET AL., 1953, The Permian reef complex of the Guadalupe Mountains region, Texas and New Mexico—a study in paleoecology: San Francisco, W. H. Freeman and Co.

NEWELL, N. D., PURDY, E. G., and IMBRIE, J., 1960, Bahamian oolitic sand: Jour. Geology, v. 68, p. 481–497.

PELLETIER, B. R., 1958, Pocono paleocurrents in Pennsylvania and Maryland: Geol. Soc. America Bull., v. 69, p. 1033–1064.

PEPPER, J. F., DEWITT, W. J., and DEMAREST, D. F., 1954, Geology of the Bedford Shale and Berea Sandstone in the Appalachian Basin: U. S. Geol. Survey Prof. Paper 259.

PETTIJOHN, F. J., 1941, Persistence of heavy minerals and geologic age: Jour. Geology, v. 49, p. 610–625.

———, 1943, Archean sedimentation, Geol. Soc. America Bull., v. 54, p. 925–972.

———, 1957, Sedimentary rocks: New York, Harper & Bros.

———, 1960, Some contributions of sedimentology to tectonic analysis: 21st Internat. Geol. Cong. Rept., pt. 18, p. 446–454.

PORTER, J. W., and FULLER, J. G. C. M., 1959, Lower Paleozoic rocks of northern Williston Basin and adjacent areas: Am. Assoc. Petroleum Geologists Bull., v. 43, p. 124–189.

POTTER, P. E., 1959, Facies model conference: Science, v. 129, p. 1292–1294.

———, and PRYOR, W. A., 1961, Disposal centers of Paleozoic and later clastics of the upper Mississippi Valley and adjacent areas: Geol. Soc. America Bull., v. 72, p. 1195–1250.

———, and SIEVER, R., 1956, Sources of basal Pennsylvanian sediments in the Eastern Interior Basin; pt. 1, crossbedding: Jour. Geology, v. 64, p. 225–244.

PROBST, D. A., 1953, Stratigraphic studies, Greater Officina, Venezuela: Am. Assoc. Petroleum Geologists Bull., v. 37, p. 2073–2092.

PRYOR, W. A., 1961, Sand trends and paleoslope of Illinois Basin and Mississippi Embayment, p. 119–134, in Peterson, J. A., and Osmond, J. C. (eds.), Geometry of sandstone bodies: Tulsa, Am. Assoc. Petroleum Geologists.

RICH, J. L., 1923, Shoestring sands of eastern Kansas: Am. Assoc. Petroleum Geologists Bull., v. 7, p. 103–113.

———, 1951a, Three critical environments of deposition and criteria for recognition of rocks deposited in each of them: Geol. Soc. America Bull., v. 62, p. 1–19.

———, 1951b, Probable fondo origin of Marcellus-Ohio-New Albany-Chattanoo-

ga bituminous shales: Am. Assoc. Petroleum Geologists Bull., v. 35, p. 2017–2040.

ROBERTS, R. J., HOLTZ, P. E., GILLULY, J., and FERGUSON, H. G., 1958, Paleozoic rocks of north-central Nevada: Am. Assoc. Petroleum Geologists Bull., v. 42, p. 2813–2857.

Rocky Mountain Association of Geologists, 1958, Symposium on the Pennsylvanian rocks of Colorado and adjacent areas: Tulsa, Am. Assoc. Petroleum Geologists.

SCRUTON, P. C., 1953, Deposition of evaporites: Am. Assoc. Petroleum Geologists Bull., v. 37, p. 2498–2512.

———, 1960, Delta building and the deltaic sequence, p. 82–102, in Recent sediments northwest Gulf of Mexico: Tulsa, Am. Assoc. Petroleum Geologists.

———, 1961, Rocky Mountain Cretaceous stratigraphy and regressive sandstones: Wyoming Geol. Assoc. Guidebook, 16th Ann. Field Conf., p. 241–249.

SHEPARD, F. P., and MOORE, D. G., 1955, Central Texas coast sedimentation: characteristics of sedimentary environment, recent history and diagenesis: Am. Assoc. Petroleum Geologists Bull., v. 39, p. 1463–1593.

SHEPARD, F. P., PHLEGER, F. B., and VAN ANDEL, TJ. H. (eds.), 1960, Recent sediments, northwest Gulf of Mexico: Tulsa, Am. Assoc. Petroleum Geologists.

SIEVER, R., 1951, The Mississippian-Pennsylvanian unconformity in southern Illinois: Am. Assoc. Petroleum Geologists Bull., v. 35, p. 542–581.

SLOSS, L. L., 1953, The significance of evaporites: Jour. Sed. Petrology, v. 23, p. 143–161.

———, 1962, Stratigraphic models in exploration: Am. Assoc. Petroleum Geologists Bull., v. 46, p. 1050–1057.

———, 1963, Sequences in the cratonic interior of North America: Geol. Soc. America Bull., v. 74, p. 93–114.

———, DAPPLES, E. C., and KRUMBEIN, W. C., 1960, Lithofacies maps: an atlas of the United States and southern Canada: New York, John Wiley & Sons, Inc.

STAFFORD, P. T., 1959, Geology of part of the Horseshoe Atoll in Scurry and Kent

Counties, Texas: U. S. Geol. Survey Prof. Paper 315-A.

STOCKDALE, P. B., 1931, Bioherms in the Borden Group of Indiana: Geol. Soc. America Bull., v. 42, p. 708–718.

STORM, L. W., 1945, Resumé of facts and opinions on sedimentation in the Gulf coast region of Texas and Louisiana: Am. Assoc. Petroleum Geologists Bull., v. 29, p. 1304–1335.

SWINEFORD, A., 1955, Petrography of Upper Permian rocks in south-central Kansas: Kansas State Geol. Survey Bull. 111.

TAYLOR, J. R., 1958, Pennsylvanian stratigraphy and history of the north Denver Basin, p. 64–68, in Rocky Mountain Assoc. Geol. Symposium on Pennsylvanian rocks of Colorado and adjacent areas.

THOMPSON, W. O., 1949, Lyons Sandstone of Colorado Front Range: Am. Assoc. Petroleum Geologists Bull., v. 33, p. 52–72.

TOMLINSON, C. W., and MC BEE, W., JR., 1959, Pennsylvanian sediments and orogenies of Ardmore district, Oklahoma, p. 3–52, in Petroleum geology of southern Oklahoma, v. 2: Tulsa, Am. Assoc. Petroleum Geologists.

TRASK, P. D. (ed), 1950, Applied sedimentation: New York, John Wiley & Sons.

VAN ANDEL, TJ. H., 1959, Reflections on the interpretation of heavy mineral analyses: Jour. Sed. Petrology, v. 29, p. 153–163.

VAN HOUTEN, F. B., 1948, Origin of red-banded early Cenozoic deposits in Rocky Mountain region: Am. Assoc. Petroleum Geologists Bull., v. 32, p. 2083–2126.

WAHLSTROM, E. E., 1948, Pre-Fountain and recent weathering of Flagstaff Mountain near Boulder, Colorado: Geol. Soc. America Bull., v. 59, p. 1173–1189.

WANLESS, H. R., 1931, Pennsylvania cycles in western Illinois: Geol. Soc. America Bull., v. 42, p. 801–812.

————, and SHEPARD, R. P., 1936, Sea level and climatic changes related to late

Paleozoic cycles: Geol. Soc. America Bull., v. 47, p. 1177–1206.

WARING, W. W., and LAYER, D. B., 1950, Devonian dolomitized reef D3 reservoir, Leduc field, Alberta, Canada: Am. Assoc. Petroleum Geologists Bull., v. 34, p. 295–312.

WASSOJEWITSCH, N., 1959, Der Flysch—eine geo-historische Formation, Eclogae Geol. Helv., v. 51, p. 1152–1154.

WATERS, J. A., MC FARLAND, P. W., and LEA, J. W., 1955, Geologic framework of Gulf Coastal Plain of Texas: Am. Assoc. Petroleum Geologists Bull., v. 39, p. 1821–1850.

WEAVER, C. E., 1958, Geologic interpretation of argillaceous sediments, part I and II: Am. Assoc. Petroleum Geologists Bull., v. 42, p. 254–271.

WELLER, J. M., 1930, Cyclical sedimentation of the Pennsylvanian Period and its significance: Jour. Geology, v. 38, p. 97–135.

————, 1960, Stratigraphic principles and practice: New York, Harper & Bros.

WHEELER, H. E., and MURRAY, H. H., 1957, Base-level control pattern in cyclothemic sedimentation: Am. Assoc. Petroleum Geologists Bull., v. 41, p. 1985–2011.

WILLIAMS, H., TURNER, F. J., and GILBERT, C. M., 1954, Petrography—an introduction to the study of rocks in thin sections: San Francisco, W. H. Freeman and Co.

WILLMAN, H. B., and PAYNE, J. N., 1942, Geology and mineral resources of the Marseilles, Ottawa, and Streator quadrangles: Ill. State Geol. Survey Bull. 66.

WOOD, A., and SMITH, A. J., 1959, Sedimentation and sedimentary history of the Aberystwyth Grits (Upper Llandoverian): Quart. Jour. Geol. Soc. London, v. 114, pt. 2, p. 163–195.

YEAKEL, L. S., 1962, Tuscarora, Juniata, and Bald Eagle paleocurrents and paleogeography in the central Appalachians: Geol. Soc. America Bull., v. 73, p. 1515–1540.

Appendix

Code of Stratigraphic Nomenclature*

American Commission on Stratigraphic Nomenclature

*Reprinted, with permission, from Am. Assoc. Petroleum Geologists Bull., v. 45, no. 5 (May 1961), p. 645–660.

PREAMBLE

Article 1.—The American Commission on Stratigraphic Nomenclature,[1] recognizing the desirability of uniform usage in stratigraphic classification and terminology throughout the continent of North America, proposes the following code. The prime purpose is (i) to formulate a usefully comprehensive, yet explicit statement of principles and practices for classifying and naming stratigraphic units, and (ii) to secure the greatest possible uniformity in applying these principles and practices. This code is applicable to all kinds of rocks, sedimentary, igneous, and metamorphic. The Commission has been guided by the philosophy expressed in its reports[2] on the

nature, usage, and nomenclature of rock-stratigraphic, biostratigraphic, and time-stratigraphic units. The Articles of this code are recommendations that can not be generally mandatory, but geological organizations may adopt these articles as their rules of nomenclatorial procedure.

CATEGORIES OF STRATIGRAPHIC UNITS

Article 2.—Categories of stratigraphic units are multiple. According to different concepts and criteria, they comprise various mutually overlapping but distinct types of stratigraphic units. This code provides regulations and recommendations relating to (i) rock-stratigraphic units, (ii) soil-stratigraphic units, (iii) biostratigraphic units, and (iv) time-stratigraphic units. The code also treats two categories of units that are not in themselves stratigraphic units but are closely related. These are (v) geologic-time units, which are fundamentally related in concept to time-stratigraphic units, and (vi) geologic-climate units, which are based on Quaternary stratigraphic units.

Remark. (a) Homotaxis.—Rock-stratigraphic units or

---

[1] American Commission on Stratigraphic Nomenclature, 1947, Note 1—Organization and objectives of the Stratigraphic Commission: Am. Assoc. Petroleum Geologists Bull., v. 31, no. 3 (Mar.), p. 513–518, summarizes the history leading to its formation. In 1932 a committee of representatives from four organizations, the American Association of Petroleum Geologists, the Geological Society of America, the Association of American State Geologists, and the United States Geological Survey, formulated rules for the "Classification and nomenclature of rock units." When the committee had completed its code, which was published in 1933 (see Article 3, footnote), it disbanded. The four organizations severally continued to be concerned with the problems of stratigraphic nomenclature in the United States, and at least one such problem was referred to the Committee on Stratigraphy of the National Research Council. Note 1 of the Commission on Stratigraphic Nomenclature describes its founding, proposed in 1941 and achieved in 1946, with representatives from five organizations: Geological Survey of Canada, American Association of Petroleum Geologists, Geological Society of America, Association of American State Geologists, and United States Geological Survey. The Commission became more substantially American in 1955, when it was joined by representatives of three Mexican organizations: Asociación Mexicana de Geólogos Petroleros, Sociedad Geológica Mexicana, and Instituto de Geología de la Universidad Nacional Autónoma de México.

[2] American Commission on Stratigraphic Nomenclature, 1949, Report 1—Declaration on naming of sub-

surface stratigraphic units: Am. Assoc. Petroleum Geologists Bull., v. 33, no. 7 (July), p. 1280–82.

—— 1952, Report 2—Nature, usage, and nomenclature of time-stratigraphic and geologic-time units: Am. Assoc. Petroleum Geologists Bull., v. 36, no. 8 (Aug.), p. 1627–1638.

—— 1955, Report 3—Nature, usage, and nomenclature of time-stratigraphic and geologic-time units as applied to the Precambrian: Am. Assoc. Petroleum Geologists Bull., v. 39, no. 9 (Sept.), p. 1859–1861.

—— 1956, Report 4—Nature, usage, and nomenclature of rock-stratigraphic units: Am. Assoc. Petroleum Geologists Bull., v. 40, no. 8 (Aug.), p. 2003–2014.

—— 1957, Report 5—Nature, usage, and nomenclature of biostratigraphic units: Am. Assoc. Petroleum Geologists Bull., v. 41, no. 8 (Aug.), p. 1877–1889.

—— 1959, Report 6—Application of stratigraphic classification and nomenclature to the Quaternary: Am. Assoc. Petroleum Geologists Bull., v. 43, no. 3 (Mar.), p. 663–673.

biostratigraphic units that have a similar order of arrangement in different locations but are not necessarily contemporaneous are said to be homotaxial.

FORMAL AND INFORMAL NAMES AND UNITS

Article 3.—The code is a systematic collection of rules of formal stratigraphic classification and nomenclature. A stratigraphic unit of one of the categories mentioned in Article 2 and its name are classified as formal if they are proposed in publication in conformance with Article 13 and meet other requirements specified in the code. (See also Articles 10, 11, and 12.) Its valid name is then pre-empted from use as the name of any other formal unit in the same category. A stratigraphic unit and its name are classified as informal if they are not formally proposed. (See Articles 4fghi, 5c, 7a, 8ab, 10gh, 13cde, 20a, 23b, 24, 37ab, 38ac, and 40b.) The geologic vocabulary of North America contains a great many formal names of stratigraphic units, which have been proposed more or less in accordance with these rules and the rules of the previous code.[3] Many formal names antedate the rules. The names and nomenclatural history of formal units are recorded in compendia maintained by the Geologic Names Committee of the United States Geological Survey, Washington, D. C., by the Committee on Stratigraphic Nomenclature of the Geological Survey of Canada, Ottawa, Ontario, by the Instituto de Geologia, Ciudad Universitaria, México, D. F., and by some state geological surveys. Information as to the status or availability of names can be obtained from these organizations on request.

ROCK-STRATIGRAPHIC (LITHOSTRATIGRAPHIC) UNITS

NATURE OF ROCK-STRATIGRAPHIC UNITS

Article 4.—A rock-stratigraphic unit is a subdivision of the rocks in the earth's crust distinguished and delimited on the basis of lithologic characteristics.

Remarks. (*a*) *Recognition and definition.*—Rock-stratigraphic units are recognized and defined by observable physical features rather than by inferred geologic history; boundaries may be placed at sharp contacts or drawn arbitrarily within a zone of gradation. Rock-stratigraphic units are essentially the practical units of general geologic work that serve as a foundation for describing and studying lithology, local and regional structure, stratigraphy, economic resources, and geologic history.

(*b*) *Type section and extent.*—The definiton of a rock-stratigraphic unit should be based on as full knowledge as possible of its lateral and vertical variations, but for purposes of nomenclatural stability a type section should be designated. Extension of a defined unit to separated bodies of rock is permissible only where they are homotaxial (Article 2a).

(*c*) *Independence from inferred geologic history.*—Concepts based on inferred geologic history or biologic sequence properly play no part in the definition or differentiation of a rock-stratigraphic unit. Nevertheless, fossils may be valuable as physical criteria in defining a rock-stratigraphic unit in the same way as other physical constituents; for example, oyster-rich sandstone, coquina, algal reef.

(*d*) *Independence from time concepts.*—A rock-stratigraphic unit may possess approximately isochronous boundaries, or its boundaries may transgress time horizons. Concepts of time-spans, however measured, properly play no part in differentiating or determining the boundaries of any rock-stratigraphic unit. Either relatively short or relatively long intervals of time may be represented by a single rock unit, whether it be sedimentary, igneous, or metamorphic, but this factor is irrelevant to recognition of the unit. The accumulation of material assigned to a particular unit may have begun or ended earlier in some localities than in others; also removal of rock material by erosion, either within the time span of deposition of the unit or later, may reduce the time-span represented by the unit. The entire thickness of a body in some places may be younger than the entire thickness of the same body in other places. The definition of rock units is thus completely independent of time concepts.

(*e*) *Surface form.*—In surficial deposits, the constructional morphologic character, or primary surface form, of a rock-stratigraphic unit may be a factor in its definition, but should be subsidiary to the character of the rock itself. In any rock-stratigraphic unit, erosional morphology or secondary surface form may be a factor in the recognition of the unit but properly should play no part in the definition.

(*f*) *Aquifers, oil sands, coal beds,* and *quarry layers* are examples of informal units even though named. (See Articles 8a and 10gh.) Unnamed units such as "formation A" or "map unit 1" are informal.

(*g*) *Zone.*—As applied to the designation of rock-stratigraphic units, the term "zone" is informal. Examples are "producing zone," "mineralized zone," "metamorphic zone," and "heavy-mineral zone" (see Article 20a). A zone is set off as distinct from surrounding parts and may include all or parts of a bed, a member, a formation, or even a group.

(*h*) *Cyclothems.*—Cyclical sedimentary sequences called cyclothems have been widely recognized in the Mid-Continent and other regions. Geographic names have been given to many cyclothems. Because the criteria for the recognition of cyclothems are irrelevant to those for recognition of a formation, cyclothems can not be regarded as a part of rock-stratigraphic classification. The designation "cyclothem" should always be applied, if a geographic term is used in this way. Never-

---

[3] Committee on Stratigraphic Nomenclature, 1933, Classification and nomenclature of rock units: Geol. Soc. America Bull., v. 44, pt. 2 (30 Apr.), p. 423–459; Am. Assoc. Petroleum Geologists Bull., v. 17, no. 7 (July), p. 843–863; Am. Assoc. Petroleum Geologists Bull., v. 23, no. 7 (July, 1939), p. 1068–1088.

theless, the boundaries of an individual cyclothem may actually coincide with those of a particular formation.

(*i*) *Soil* is a layer composed of products of weathering of pre-existing rocks, which may be of diverse character and geologic age. A soil differs in several respects from a rock-stratigraphic unit and should not be given formal status in the standard rock-stratigraphic classification. (See Article 18.)

Article 5.—Boundaries of rock-stratigraphic units are placed at positions of lithologic change. Boundaries are placed at sharp contacts or may be fixed arbitrarily within zones of gradation. Both vertical and lateral boundaries are based on the lithologic criteria that provide the greatest unity and practical utility.

Remarks. (*a*) *Boundary in a gradational sequence.*— Where one rock unit passes vertically or laterally into another by intergrading or interfingering of two or more kinds of rock, the boundary is necessarily arbitrary and should be selected to provide the most practical units. For example, where a shale unit overlies a unit of interbedded limestone and shale, the boundary commonly is placed at the top of the highest readily traceable limestone bed; where a sandstone unit grades upward into shale, the boundary may be so gradational as to require completely arbitrary treatment. Because of creep, it is generally best to define such arbitrary boundaries by the highest occurrence of a particular lithologic type, rather than the lowest.

(*b*) *Key beds used for boundaries.*—Key beds may be used as boundaries for formal rock-stratigraphic units over an area where the internal lithologic characteristics of the units remain relatively constant. Even though key beds may be traceable beyond the area of the diagnostic over-all lithology, an extension of the potential boundary markers does not alone justify geographic extension of a rock-stratigraphic unit. Where the rock between key beds becomes drastically different from that of the type locality, a new unit should be recognized, even though key beds are continuous. (See Article 8b.)

(*c*) *Mechanically defined boundaries.*—The continuing development and application of geophysical, geochemical, and mineralogic techniques have given rise to problems concerning both the vertical and lateral boundaries of units defined and identified by these techniques. Marker horizons based on electrical and other mechanically recorded logs may coincide with the boundaries of rock-stratigraphic units and help to delineate them (see Articles 6b and 13b). Such horizons may be discordant vertically or laterally with those of formal rock stratigraphic units. Units established by these techniques are considered informal.

(*d*) *Obscure unconformity.*—A sequence of closely similar rocks may not represent continuous deposition, but may include an obscure unconformity so that a separation into two units may be desirable. If, however, no lithologic distinction adequate to define a boundary can be made, only one unit should be recognized even though it may include rock deposited in different epochs, periods, or eras.

(*e*) *Boundaries in facies change.*—Where a unit changes laterally through abrupt gradation into or intertonguing with a markedly different kind of rock, it may be desirable to propose a new unit. An arbitrary boundary may be placed between the two units. Where the area of intergradation or intertonguing is sufficiently extensive, the rocks of mixed lithology may constitute a third independent unit.

RANKS OF ROCK-STRATIGRAPHIC UNITS

Article 6.—The formation is the fundamental unit in rock stratigraphic classification. A formation is a body of rock characterized by lithologic homogeneity; it is prevailingly but not necessarily tabular and is mappable at the earth's surface or traceable in the subsurface.

Remarks. (*a*) *Content.*—A formation should possess some degree of internal lithologic homogeneity or distinctive lithologic features. It may contain between its upper and lower limits (i) rock of one lithologic type, (ii) repetitions of two or more lithologic types, or (iii) extreme heterogeneity of constitution which in itself may constitute a form of unity compared to the adjacent rock units.

(*b*) *Distinctive lithologic characteristics* may include chemical composition and such supplementary features as ripple marks, mud cracks, cross-bedding, the presence of fossils or unusual minerals, schistose or gneissic structure in metamorphic rocks, and texture in igneous rocks. A unit distinguishable only by its fossils is not a rock-stratigraphic unit but is properly classified as a biostratigraphic unit (see Article 4c). Lithology may be distinctively reflected by electrical, radioactive, seismic, or other properties (see Articles 5c and 13b).

(*c*) *Fundamental unit.*—Formations are the basic rock-stratigraphic units used in describing and interpreting the geology of a region. The limits of a formation normally are those boundaries of lithologic change that give it the greatest practicable unity of constitution. A formation may represent a long or short time interval, may be composed of materials from one or several sources, and may include breaks in the time-stratigraphic sequence.

(*d*) *Mappability.*—Practicability of surface or subsurface mapping is essential in establishing a formation. Mappability at the surface is considered as delineation at scales of the order of 1:25,000. In general, the definition of a new formation should be based upon tested mappability, rather than upon a type section alone, however completely exposed the type section may be.

(*e*) *Thickness* of a formation is not a determining feature in its classification. A formation has three dimensions, and its thickness may range from a featheredge at its margin to 5,000 feet or more elsewhere. Also, a formation 10 feet thick may be adjacent to another 1,000 feet thick. Exceptionally a formation may be mapped as a single line, but obviously a sequence of formations so thin becomes impractical because unmappable.

(*f*) *Sedimentary rock and extrusive igneous rock* that are intricately interbedded may be assembled into a formation under one name.

(*g*) *Volcanic rock.*—Cartographically distinguishable sequences of volcanic rock should be treated as formations like any stratified sequence of sedimentary rocks. (See Articles 9f and 30d.)

(*h*) *Intrusive igneous rock.*—Units composed of intrusive igneous rock that are discriminated by mineralogic or textural characteristics, or chemical composition, may be classed as formations. (See Article 10i.)

(*i*) *Metamorphic rock.*—Formations composed of metamorphic rock are, like other formations, distinguished primarily by lithologic composition. The mineral facies may differ from place to place, but these variations do not necessarily require definition of a new formation. Metamorphic rocks with relict textures and structures that enable the geologist to recognize mappable units should be classified just as any normal stratigraphic sequence. Metamorphic and metasomatic rocks not classifiable by normal stratigraphic methods have to be discriminated primarily on their petrographic and structural features. (See Article 10j.)

(*j*) *Complex.*—If a mass of rock is composed of diverse types of any class or classes or is characterized by highly complicated structure, the word "complex" may be used as part of the formal name instead of a lithologic or rank term; for example, Crooks Complex.

Article 7.—A member is a part of a formation; it is not defined by specified shape or extent. A geographically restricted member that terminates on all sides within a formation may be called a lentil. A member that extends outward beyond the main body of a formation may be called a tongue.

Remarks. (*a*) *Designation of members.*—Formations may be divided into formally defined and named members. In some formations, one or more formal members are established, while the remainder of the formation is undivided or is treated as one or more unnamed members. If formations are divided into members designated solely by lithology (for example, siliceous shale member), or by letter or number, the usage is informal. Although members normally are in vertical sequence, laterally equivalent parts of a formation that differ recognizably may also be considered members; for example, the gravel member and the silt member of the Bonneville Formation.

(*b*) *Mapping of members.*—A member is established when it is advantageous to recognize a specially developed part of a varied formation. A member, whether named or unnamed, need not be mappable at the scale required for formations. Even though all members of a formation are locally mappable, it does not follow that they should be raised to formational rank, because multiplicity of formation names may obscure rather than clarify relations with other areas. A named member may extend from one formation into another.

(*c*) *Subdivision of members.*—Members may contain beds but never members of members.

Article 8.—A bed is the smallest rock-stratigraphic unit recognized in classification.

Remarks. (*a*) *Informal status of most beds.*—The designation of individual beds as formally named rock-stratigraphic units should generally be limited to certain distinctive beds which are particularly useful to recognize. Coal beds, oil sands, and other beds of economic importance are commonly named, but such units and their names are not usually a part of formal stratigraphic nomenclature. (See Article 4f and 10gh.)

(*b*) *Key or marker beds.*—Widely distributed key beds may be named, but these likewise are usually considered informal units. Individual key beds may be traced beyond the lateral limits of a particular formal unit. (See Article 5b.)

Article 9.—A group is the rock-stratigraphic unit next higher in rank than a formation; a group consists of two or more associated formations.

Remarks. (*a*) *Use and composition.*—Groups are recognized for the purpose of expressing the natural relations of associated formations having significant lithologic features in common. A group consists wholly of divisions defined as formations; in this respect, it contrasts with a formation and its members, for a formation need not be divided into members, and, even if a formation contains members, not every part of it need be assigned to any member. In some reconnaissance work, the term "group" has been applied to stratigraphic units that appear to be divisible into formations but have not yet been so divided.

(*b*) *Change in component formations.*—The component formations of a group are not necessarily everywhere the same. For example, in the upper part of Glen Canyon, Utah, the Glen Canyon Group comprises three formations, the Wingate Sandstone, the Kayenta Formation, and the Navajo Sandstone. At Serpents Trail, Colorado, it is composed of Wingate and Kayenta.

(*c*) *Change in rank.*—The wedge-out of a component formation or formations may justify the reduction of the group to formation rank, retaining the same name. When a group is extended laterally beyond where it is divided into formations, it becomes in effect a formation, even if it is still called a group. When a previously established formation is broken down into two or more component units that are formally given formation rank, the old formation, with its old geographic name, should be raised to group status. Raising the rank of the unit is preferable to restricting the old name to a part of its former limits, because a change in rank leaves the sense of the geographic part of the name unchanged. (See Article 14b.)

(*d*) *Subgroup.*—The hierarchy of rock-stratigraphic units (group, formation, member) does not always provide a sufficient number of categories for the proper relative assignment of all units. In certain areas stratigraphers have named and defined assemblages of formations within already established useful groups and called these assemblages subgroups.

(*e*) *Supergroup.*—In certain areas stratigraphers need a supergroup; that is, a formal assemblage of related groups or of formations and groups.

(*f*) *Misuse of "series" for group or supergroup.*—The term "series" has been employed for an assemblage of formations or an assemblage of formations and groups, especially in the Precambrian, but should no longer be so used. These are groups or supergroups. The term "series" has also been applied to a sequence of rocks resulting from a succession of eruptions or intrusions. In this usage "series" is usually preceded by an adjective such as eruptive, intrusive, or volcanic to indicate the origin of the rock. Here, as elsewhere in rock-stratigraphy, group should replace "series." Series is a time-stratigraphic term that should not be used in a rock-stratigraphic sense. (See Articles 6g and 30d.)

NOMENCLATURE OF ROCK-STRATIGRAPHIC UNITS

Article 10.—The formal name of a rock-stratigraphic unit of any rank is binomial, consisting of a geographic name combined with a descriptive lithologic term or with the appropriate rank term alone. Capitalization of the initial letters of all words used in forming the names of formal rock-stratigraphic units is recommended.

Remarks. (*a*) *Source of geographic name.*—The geographic name should be the name of a natural or artificial feature at or near which the rock-stratigraphic unit is typically developed. Names derived from such changeable sources as the names of farms or ranches, churches, schools, crossroads, and small communities, are not entirely satisfactory but are acceptable if no others are available. Names for formations or other important rock units may be selected from those that can be found in an ordinary atlas, or on state or provincial, county, forest service, topographic, or similar maps. If a name that does not meet this test is used, precise description of the place from which the name is derived should be given. A subsurface unit may be given a farm name, if its type locality happens to be in some sparsely populated area with few geographic names. A unit should not be named from the source of its materials; for example, a deposit supposedly derived from the Keewatin center should not be called "Keewatin Drift."

(*b*) *Omission of part of name.*—Where frequent repetition would make a cumbersome style, and omission is compatible with clarity, the geographic name, the lithologic term, or the rank term may be used alone; as the Burlington," "the limestone," or "the formation," for the Burlington Limestone.

(*c*) *Use of simple lithologic term.*—Where a lithologic term is used in the name of a rock-stratigraphic unit, the simplest generally acceptable term is recommended (for example, limestone, sandstone, shale, tuff, granite, quartzite, serpentine). Compound terms (for example, clay shale, hornblende-microcline-oligoclase granite gneiss) and terms that are not in common usage (for example, calcirudite, orthoquartzite) should be avoided. Combined terms, such as sand and clay, should not be used for the lithologic part of the names of rock-stratigraphic units, nor should an adjective be used between the geographic and the lithologic terms, as "Chattanooga Black Shale" and "Biwabik Iron-bearing Formation."

(*d*) A *group name* customarily combines a geographic name with the term "group," and no lithologic designation is included; for example, San Rafael Group.

(*e*) A *formation name* consists of the geographic name followed by a lithologic designation or by the word "formation." Examples: Dakota Sandstone, Mitchell Mesa Rhyolite, Monmouth Formation, Fort Covington Till.

(*f*) A *member name* combines a geographic term followed by the term "member." Where a lithologic designation is useful, it should be included as part of the name (Wedington Sandstone Member of the Fayetteville Shale).

(*g*) *Capitalization.*—When geographic names (see remark h) are applied to such informal units as oil sands coal beds, mineralized zones, and informal members (see Articles 4f and 8a), the unit term should not be capitalized. A name is not necessarily formal because it is capitalized, nor does failure to capitalize a name render it informal. Geographic names should be combined with the terms "formation" or "group" only in formal nomenclature.

(*h*) *Informal usage of identical geographic names.*— The application of identical geographic names to several minor units in one vertical sequence is considered informal nomenclature (lower Mount Savage coal, Mount Savage fireclay, upper Mount Savage coal, Mount Savage rider coal, and Mount Savage sandstone). The application of identical geographic names to the several lithologic units constituting a cycle of sedimentation is likewise considered informal.

(*i*) *Intrusive igneous rock.*—In some areas formal stratigraphic terminology is needed for intrusive igneous rocks (see Article 6h). The formal name of an intrusive rock body properly consists of a geographic term and the petrographic name of the dominant rock type; for example, Goose Lake Granodiorite. "Dike," "stock," "pluton," "batholith," and other similar names, or more general terms such as "intrusion," are not stratigraphic terms; accordingly, the names of such intrusive igneous bodies as the Idaho batholith or the Loon Lake pluton are not stratigraphic names.

(*j*) *Metamorphic rock* recognized as a normal stratified sequence should be classified as named groups, formations, and members, such as the Deception Rhyolite, a formation of the Ash Creek Group. Metamorphic or metasomatic rocks, not classifiable by normal stratigraphic methods, should be given a suitable geographic name followed by the petrographic term for the dominant rock of the unit; for example, Baltimore Gneiss. (See Article 6i.)

(*k*) *Misuse of well known name.*—A name that suggests some well known locality, region, or political division should not, in general, be applied to a unit typically developed in another less well known locality of the same name. For example, it would not be advisable to use the name "Chicago Formation" for a unit in California.

Article 11.—The rule of priority should be observed in applying names to rock-stratigraphic units.

Remarks. (*a*) *Priority* is defined as priority of date of publication. Page precedence should decide, as in other sets of rules governing scientific nomenclature.

(*b*) *Preservation of well established name.*—A name that has become well established should not be displaced, merely on account of priority, by one not well known or only occasionally used. The term "well established" is difficult to define, but acceptance of a name by several authors is generally taken as establishing it.

(*c*) *Duplication of names* should be avoided throughout North America. A name previously applied to any unit should not later be applied to another, unless alternative names are lacking, and then only if geographic and stratigraphic separation preclude confusion. Furthermore, a group and a formation within it should not bear the same name (see Article 16d), nor a formation and a member within it; for example, the lower member of the Pruett Formation should not be called the "lower Pruett member."

Article 12.—The geographic component of an established rock-stratigraphic name should not be changed.

Remarks. (*a*) *Difference in spelling of geographic name.* —A stratigraphic name repeatedly published with spelling different from that of its geographic source should nevertheless be retained. For example, Bennett Shale, uniformly used for more than thirty years, should not be altered to Bennet Shale on the grounds that the town is named Bennet. Stratigraphic names that have been spelled variously should be made uniform by adopting the form accepted by a majority, whatever the local spelling or the original spelling in geological literature. This remark should not be construed to require geologists of one native tongue to continue to use names proposed for their region by geologists of a different tongue if these names are absurd or in violation of good taste.

(*b*) *Change in the name of a geographic feature* does **not** entail change of the corresponding name of a stratigraphic unit. The original name of the unit should be maintained. For example, Mauch Chunk Shale should not be changed to Jim Thorpe Shale because the former town of Mauch Chunk is now called Jim Thorpe.

(c) *Disappearance of a geographic feature* does not entail the disappearance of the corresponding name of a stratigraphic unit. For example, Thurman Sandstone, named from a former village in Pittsburg County, Oklahoma, does not require renaming.

(d) *Names in different countries and different languages.*—Spelling of the geographic component of a rock-stratigraphic name should conform to the usage recognized in the country that contains the type locality. It should not be altered by conversion into equivalent but different words in other languages. For example, Cuchillo should not be translated to Knife, and La Peña should retain the tilde; on the other hand, Canyon should not be translated as Cañon. Moreover, a rock unit should not be named Montchauve after Bald Mountain in Wyoming; the name Bald Mountain is preoccupied, and translation is not a proper recourse. It is proper, however, to translate the lithologic term or rank term; thus, the Edwards Limestone may be called Caliza Edwards, and Formación La Casita, the La Casita Formation.

PROCEDURE IN ESTABLISHING FORMAL ROCK-STRATIGRAPHIC UNITS

Article 13.—Establishing a formal rock-stratigraphic unit requires publication in some recognized scientific medium of a definition that includes: (i) statement of intention to designate a formal unit; (ii) selection of name; (iii) definition of unit in the type area with specific location of the type section; (iv) distinguishing characteristics; (v) definition of boundaries and contact relationships; (vi) dimensions and shape; and, as far as possible, (vii) geologic age and correlation.

Remarks. (a) *Specific requirements.*—The proposed unit should be described and defined so clearly that any subsequent worker can, without doubt, recognize the same unit. The intent to introduce a new name and the important facts that led to the discrimination of the unit should be clearly stated. The definition should cite the geographic feature from which the name is taken. It should cite, also, the specific location of one or more representative sections near the geographic feature. One of these sections should be designated the type section, and its description should be included. Specific reference to location in section, township, and range, or other land divisions should be included. An accurate map showing the location of the type section is desirable. Where necessary, reference sections may be designated to supplement the type section, or, when the type section is no longer exposed, a principal reference section should be established. (See remark i.) The morphological expression of the unit should be described. In defining the boundaries of a unit, it is not sufficient merely to state that the top of the *X* Formation is the base of the *Y* Formation; the criteria used in drawing the boundary should be discussed explicitly, where possible with reference to specific points in the type section or in typical sections.

(b) *Additional requirements for subsurface units.*—

Subsurface rock units are given formal names only if such names are useful in describing the geology of the region and if the subsurface section differs materially from the equivalent rocks in outcrop. In proposing a new name for a subsurface unit, the well or mine in which the type section is present becomes the type locality. Subsurface units defined on the basis of exposures in mines should be treated similarly to other subsurface units. The following additional data are desirable:

(i) Location of the type well or mine by written description and map; name of operating company or individual; name of farm or lease; date of drilling; total depth; surface elevation; and depths to top and bottom of the new unit or mine level where it is exposed. If all the data needed to establish a type section cannot be furnished from one well, two or more wells should be used.

(ii) Sample logs of the well, or wells, maps and cross-sections of the mine, in written or graphic form, or both. The boundaries and subdivisions, if any, of the new unit should be indicated clearly on logs or charts.

(iii) Electrical or other mechanically recorded logs, preferably of several wells. The boundaries and subdivisions of the new unit should be shown at a scale large enough to permit full appreciation of detail.

(iv) Location of the depository where sets of cuttings or samples and fossil material are available for study. Such depositories may be federal, provincial, or state geological surveys, universities, and museums with proper facilities.

(c) *Form of publication.*—The phrase "recognized scientific medium" is difficult to define. Availability to the scientific public is the chief determining factor regardless of size of edition or form of publication, such as type printing, mimeographing, or lithography. A publication must be generally available either on request or by purchase. Any well-known regularly issued, numbered series meets this requirement. Many independent or irregularly issued publications also meet it, though some notice should appear in a nationally circulated scientific journal. Names proposed in informal or restricted media such as letters, company reports unavailable to the public, or unpublished addresses, theses or dissertations, have no status in stratigraphic literature. Microfilming or publication in newspaper and commercial or trade journals is not valid publication.

(d) *Casual mention of name insufficient.*—Casual mention, such as "the formation at Jonesville schoolhouse," does not establish a new name, nor does mere use as in a table or columnar section or on a map. To be valid, a new name should be duly proposed as outlined in remark *a*.

(e) *Publication in abstracts and guidebooks.*—New stratigraphic names should not be included in an abstract published separately in advance of a more complete report, as the essential conciseness of abstracts does not permit full definitions. New stratigraphic names should not be introduced in guidebooks.

(f) *References for names already established.*—Authors should refer to federal and state records of stratigraphic names to determine whether a name has been previously used. (See Article 3.)

(g) *Surface vs. subsurface names.*—It may be possible to correlate a named subsurface unit with a named surface unit. If the characteristics of both are so similar that two names are unnecessary, priority and usage should determine which is to be applied.

(h) *Type section never changed.*—Type sections can

not be changed. There may be more than one typical section but only one type section.

(*i*) *Reference localities* may be established to supplement the type locality. For example, in naming weakly consolidated rocks it may be necessary to designate a type area within which the diagnostic relations are widely represented, because good exposures are evanescent. Thus the type locality contains the type section, and the type area contains the type locality. Many early definitions of stratigraphic units indicate a type area or type region without specifying a type section.

REVISION OF ROCK-STRATIGRAPHIC CLASSIFICATION AND NOMENCLATURE

Article 14.—Redefining a rock-stratigraphic unit without changing its name requires as much justification as establishing a new unit.

Remarks. (*a*) *Redefinition* is justifiable where a minor change in boundary will make a unit more natural and useful. Where revision removes only a minor part of a previously established unit, the original name may be retained for the major part.

(*b*) *Undesirable restriction.*—When a unit is divided into two or more of the same rank as the original, the original name should not be employed for any of the divisions. The retention of the old name for one of the units would preclude use of the name in a term of higher rank. In order to understand an author's meaning, a later reader must know about the modification and its date, and whether the author is following the original or the modified usage. For this reason it should be normal practice to raise the rank of a unit when it becomes everywhere subdivisible into mappable units. (See Article 9c.)

Article 15.—A change in the lithologic term applied to a rock-stratigraphic unit does not require a new geographic term.

Remark. (*a*) *Change in lithologic designation.*—Priority should not prevent more exact lithologic designation if the original designation is not everywhere applicable; for example, the term "limestone" in such names as Galena Limestone and Leadville Limestone may locally be inapplicable and therefore changed to "dolomite," even though the type section may have been correctly named. If the lithologic variation warrants neither name the term "formation" may be preferable.

Article 16.—Change in rank of a rock-stratigraphic unit does not require redefinition of its boundaries or alteration of the geographic part of its name.

Remarks. (*a*) *Change in rank.*—It is possible for a member to become a formation or vice versa, and for a formation to become a group or vice versa.

(*b*) *Examples of changes from area to area.*—The Conasauga Shale is recognized as a formation in Georgia and as a group in eastern Tennessee; the Osgood Formation, Laurel Limestone, and Waldron Shale of Indiana are classed as members of the Wayne Formation in a part of Tennessee; the Virgelle Sandstone is a formation in western Montana and a member of the Eagle Sandstone in central Montana.

(*c*) *Example of change in single area.*—It often becomes desirable to change the rank of a unit without changing its content of rocks. For example, the Madison Limestone of early work in Montana became in later work the Madison Group, containing several formations.

(*d*) *Different geographic name for unit and its parts.*—In changing the rank of a unit, the same name should not continue to be applied both to the unit as a whole and to a part of it. For example, the Astoria Group should not contain an Astoria Sandstone, nor the Washington Formation, a Washington Sandstone Member. (See Article 11c.)

Article 17.—A name for a stratigraphic unit once applied and then abandoned is available for some other unit only if the name was introduced casually, or if it has been published only once in the last several decades and is not in current usage, and if its reintroduction will cause no confusion.

Remarks. (*a*) *Obsolete names.*—Authors should refer to federal and state records of stratigraphic names to determine whether a name is obsolete. (See Article 3.)

(*b*) *Reference to abandoned names.*—When it seems useful to refer to an obsolete or abandoned formal name, its status is made clear by some such term as "abandoned" or "obsolete," or by using a phrase such as "La Plata Sandstone of Cross (1898)."

SOIL-STRATIGRAPHIC UNITS

Article 18.—A soil-stratigraphic unit is a soil with physical features and stratigraphic relations that permit its consistent recognition and mapping as a stratigraphic unit. Soil-stratigraphic units are distinct from both rock-stratigraphic and pedologic units.

Remarks. (*a*) *Distinction from rock-stratigraphic units.*—A soil-stratigraphic unit differs from a rock-stratigraphic unit in that it is formed for the most part *in situ* from underlying rock-stratigraphic units, which may be of diverse composition and geologic age. (See Article 4i.) Further, the characteristic features of soil-stratigraphic units are the products of surficial weathering and of the action of organisms at a later time and under ecologic conditions independent of those that prevailed while the parent rocks were formed.

(*b*) *Distinction from pedologic units.*—Stratigraphic relations are an essential element in defining a soil-stratigraphic unit but are irrelevant in defining a pedologic unit. A soil-stratigraphic unit may comprise one or more pedologic units or parts of units.

(*c*) *Requirements for formal status.*—A soil-stratigraphic unit should be defined on the basis of observable physical features and stratigraphic relations at a type locality and may be extended as far as it can be recognized. Boundaries may be placed at sharp contacts or within zones of gradation. The definition of a soil-stratigraphic unit should be based on as full knowledge as possible of its lateral variations and should be independent of concepts based on geologic history. Soil-stratigraphic units may parallel or transgress time horizons.

(*d*) *Rank.*—The single rank of soil-stratigraphic classification is the soil.

(*e*) *Names.*—Formal names of soil-stratigraphic units should be chosen in accordance with the rules that govern naming of rock-stratigraphic units, and should not conflict with rock-stratigraphic or pedologic names. Names based on subjacent and superjacent rock units, for example the post-Wilcox pre-Claiborne soil, are informal.

BIOSTRATIGRAPHIC UNITS

NATURE OF BIOSTRATIGRAPHIC UNITS

Article 19.—A biostratigraphic unit is a body of rock strata characterized by its content of fossils contemporaneous with the deposition of the strata.

Remarks. (a) *Fossil remains,* both plant and animal, are widespread in sedimentary rocks, and they provide several different kinds of stratigraphic information. Because of their complexity and variety, they are particularly distinctive and identifiable rock constituents. Fossils, as the remains of once-living forms, are sensitive indicators of environment of deposition. Finally, owing to the progressive and more or less orderly evolution of organisms throughout the Phanerozoic Eon, fossils are particularly valuable in time correlation of strata and are essential in placing rocks in a world-wide geologic-time scale.

(b) *Contemporaneity of rock and contained fossils.*—Normally, all fossils contained in a biostratigraphic unit are remains of organisms that lived when the sediment surrounding them was deposited. The organisms may have been buried *in situ* or transported to their place of burial, but in either case they are indigenous in the sense of belonging to the deposit as contemporaneous original constituents. For example, well preserved leaves of land plants are associated with nearly complete articulated crinoids and other marine invertebrates in the Keasey Formation (Oligocene?) of northwestern Oregon.

(c) *Reworked fossils.*—Some sedimentary strata, however, contain reworked" fossils derived from older rocks. Examples of fossils clearly not indigenous to the rock that contains them are: (i) worn silicified Ordovician fossils in Mississippian deposits of southeastern Missouri; (ii) a mixture of weathered and nearly perfect Late Cretaceous foraminifers in the Claytone Limestone (Paleocene) of southern Alabama; and (iii) abundant Cretaceous pelecypods (*Gryphaea*) mingled with Miocene vertebrates in the Oakville Sandstone (Miocene) of southwestern Texas. These adventitious fossils may be significant from certain points of view, but they are clearly distinct from indigenous remains; they may be relevant in identifying a rock-stratigraphic unit, but are not relevant in defining a biostratigraphic unit.

(d) *"Leaked" fossils.*—Much less commonly organic remains have "leaked" from younger sources. Such fossils are younger than the strata that contain them. Although stratigraphic leaks are usually easy to recognize, not all are obvious, and failure to recognize them may cause serious errors. Examples are: (i) shells of Cenozoic mollusks that have burrowed into Cretaceous and even into Paleozoic strata; (ii) both microfossils and macrofossils that have been carried from younger formations through crevices into solution-made cavities in older rocks, wherein they are sealed by mineral deposits or sediment.

(e) *Relation of biostratigraphic units to rock-stratigraphic units.*—Biostratigraphic units are fundamentally different from rock-stratigraphic units. The boundaries of the two may coincide or lie at quite different stratigraphic horizons or cross each other. Where fossil remains are so abundant that in themselves they become lithologically important, a biostratigraphic unit may also be a rock-stratigraphic unit. Moreover, the lithologic changes that bound rock-stratigraphic units may represent changes in depositional environment that are.likewise reflected in changes of fossil assemblage so that the limits of both kinds of units closely correspond. Similarly, unconformities or breaks in deposition tend to concentrate range-zone (biozone) limits at horizons of lithologic change.

(f) *Relation of biostratigraphic units to time-stratigraphic units.*—A biostratigraphic unit is physically bounded and extends no farther than the limits of strata characterized by a certain fossil or assemblage of fossils. Commonly, biostratigraphic evidence is the most useful means for determining time-stratigraphic boundaries, but criteria for defining biostratigraphic and time-stratigraphic units differ fundamentally.

(g) *Ecologic and evolutionary significance.*—Because fossils reflect both irreversible evolutionary change and adaptation to environment, all biostratigraphic units are records of both time and facies.

Article 20.—A zone is the general basic unit in biostratigraphic classification. It is defined as a stratum or body of strata characterized by the occurrence of a fossil taxon or taxa from one or more of which it receives its name.

Remarks. (a) *Kinds of zone.*—The unmodified term "zone" does not define a formal biostratigraphic unit, because it has been used indiscriminately for several different concepts and does not distinguish between them. Moreover, the term "zone" is not confined to biostratigraphy, for it is used in other kinds of stratigraphic classification and in other branches of geology (for example, cherty zone, concretionary zone, fault zone, zone of flowage, zone of saturation; see Article 4g). Nevertheless, reference to biostratigraphic zones claims great antiquity, if not priority. More specific definition of zones is needed to express biostratigraphic concepts accurately.

(b) *Definition.*—A biostratigraphic zone is defined solely by the fossils it contains, without reference to lithology, inferred environment, or concepts of time.

(c) *Scope of term "zone."*—A biostratigraphic zone may be based on all its fossils, or it may be based solely on the fossils of one phylum, or one class, or one order, etc. Thus it is possible to have differing and overlapping systems of zones variously based on foraminifers, or mollusks, or diatoms, or vertebrates, or land plants, or combinations of two or more kinds of organic remains.

(d) *Dimensions of zone.*—The scale of zone classification is indefinite and extremely variable. At one extreme, a zone may be a single local bed with a characteristic fossil assemblage; at the other, it is even possible to consider all Cenozoic deposits as constituting a "Zone of Mammals" and all Mesozoic deposits as constituting a "Zone of Reptiles."

(e) *Subzone.*—In places it may be feasible and desirable to recognize and define zonal units of lower rank. These may be designated subzones, and classified as subdivisions of the zone. It is not necessary that an entire zone should be divided into subzones.

(f) *Zonule.*—The smallest recognized subdivision of a zone is a zonule. Generally it consists of a single stratum or small thickness of strata. Zonules need not be vertically contiguous biostratigraphic units. A zonule may be distinguished as a minor component of a zone without dividing the zone into subzones. In this respect, classification and nomenclature of zonules correspond to the rock-stratigraphic usage in naming members or beds (see Articles 7a and 8a).

(g) *Peak zone.*—A peak zone is a special kind of zone, characterized by the exceptional abundance of some one taxon for which it is named. Peak zones are informal. They may represent one or more episodes of exceptional proliferation of a taxon, not only in number of individuals, but commonly in such respects as great lateral spread, or dominance in the entire organic assemblage. Various other terms, such as epibole, acme zone, and flood zone, have essentially the same meaning as peak zone.

Article 21.—An assemblage zone is a body of strata characterized by a certain assemblage of fossils without regard to their ranges; it receives its name from one or more of these fossils.

Remarks. (a) *Nature.*—The bases for recognizing assemblage zones include variations in the fossil taxa, in abundance of specimens, or in both. Such variations are usually in response to environment though evolutionary change may be a factor. The assemblage zone may indicate ecologic facies or age or both. It is, however, primarily a grouping of strata according to directly observable fossil content. Assemblage zones may be based on all the fossils or only on specific kinds. The assemblage on which a specific unit is based should be defined in a specified section.

(b) *Naming.*—The assemblage zone is usually named from one or more taxa particularly prominent or diagnostic of the assemblage, although name-givers need not be confined to the zone or found in every part of it.

(c) *Example.*—The *Heterostegina* Assemblage Zone of the Gulf Coast is an example.

(d) *History.*—The faunizone and florizone of Buckman are close in concept to the assemblage zone but these names are not generally accepted, and their correct definitions are in dispute. Some consider a faunizone (or florizone) as formed by the overlap of biozones (see Article 22h) and as having dominantly time-stratigraphic significance; others consider a faunizone (or florizone) as a body of strata characterized by a particular fauna or flora, regardless of whether it is inferred to have time or only environmental significance. Assemblage zone as here defined is used without any implications as to either time or facies. (See also Article 23.)

(e) *Guide fossils.*—The fossil or fossils most characteristic of an assemblage-zone, and those chosen to name it, as well as other characteristic fossils in the assemblage, are termed guide fossils. Neither the name-givers nor the other guide fossils are necessarily restricted to the zone, nor are they found in every part of it.

Article 22.—A range zone is a body of strata comprising the total horizontal and vertical range of occurrence of a specified taxon.

Remarks. (a) *Nature.*—Each taxon has its own individual range zone and thus there are as many range zones as there are recognized species, genera, etc.

(b) *Extent.*—A range zone comprises the rocks that contain the taxon whose name it bears.

(c) *Example.*—The *Cardioceras cordatum* Range Zone is the total body of rock bounded by the vertical (stratigraphic) and horizontal (geographic) limits of occurrence of *Cardioceras cordatum*. Range zones do not

usually coincide with assemblage zones named for the same fossil.

(d) *Application.*—Range zones are much used in time-correlation of strata and have furnished a basis for placing rocks in the standard geologic time scale. Because the taxa on which range zones are based are arbitrarily defined, the range zones themselves are equally arbitrary and far from precise. Obviously, moreover, they do not lend themselves to systematic partitioning of a stratigraphic section into units without gaps and overlaps, because there are inevitable gaps and overlaps in ranges.

(e) *Time value.*—The time represented by a range zone may be referred to as its time value; for example, the time value of the *Cardioceras cordatum* Range Zone, differs from the time value of the Assemblage Zone of *Cardioceras cordatum*.

(f) *Scope.*—There are no units of lesser or greater rank than the range zone to form a hierarchy of terms in this kind of biostratigraphic classification, although the range zone of a genus is likely to be greater than the range zone of any of its constituent species, the range zone of a family greater than that of any of its constituent genera, and so on.

(g) *Local range zone.*—The range of a taxon in any local section or area is unlikely to be its maximum range. A local range zone can be referred to simply as the range zone of the taxon in a specific, geographically located section or area; for example, "Range zone of *Dorothia bulleta* in Denmark"; "*Megalodon* Range zone in the Exshaw Creek section." The use of the German term "teilzone" or other special terms for a local range zone seems unnecessary. Obviously, the summation of all the local range zones is the range zone of the taxon. There are considerable differences in the span of local range zones in different areas because of variations in facies, migration time, and other factors. Because all local range zones can never be known, the true range zone cannot be determined.

(h) *Synonyms.*—In 1902 Buckman coined the term "biozone" as a time term indicating the range of a particular taxon in geologic time. Arkell[4] pointed out that H. S. Williams in 1901 had already coined the term "biochron" for this meaning. Arkell preferred to use biozone for the deposits formed during the life-span of the taxon, but whether the biozone includes all deposits equivalent in age to the life-span of the taxon or only those in which the taxon is actually found is a controversial question. The term "biozone" has been used with all three meanings; hence, it is somewhat confusing, and the term "range zone" is more readily understood. The term "teilzone" proposed by Pompeckj is replaced by the term "local range zone" (see Remark g).

Article 23.—A concurrent-range zone is a zone defined by the overlapping ranges of specified taxa from one or more of which it takes its name.

Remarks. (a) *Nature.*—The concurrent-range zone is one of the most useful kinds of zones. It is the principal basis of time correlation of strata. The specified taxa are only those that form a distinctive association because their ranges overlap; that is, some taxa range no higher than the zone, others range no lower, and some taxa may be confined to it. To have useful significance the concurrent-range zone must be defined explicitly by naming the taxa on whose overlap the unit is based. It is helpful to cite reference localities where the unit is

[4] Arkell, W. J., 1933, The Jurassic System in Great Britain: Oxford, p. 22–23.

exposed and the chosen taxa are adequately represented.

(b) *History.*—The concurrent-range zone as here defined is the zone generally recognized by stratigraphers when they use fossils in attempting time-correlation of strata. Such zones are formal zones. Historically this usage is derived from Oppel[b] who, described "zone" as ". . . marked in any one place by a number of species that are constant for it. . . . " (See also Article 21d.)

(c) *Example.*—The *Bulimina excavata* Concurrent-range Zone (Paleocene of California) contains the lowest known occurrences of *Anomalina judas, Bulimina excavata, Cibicides fortunatus,* plus 73 additional species, and the highest known occurrences of *Ammodiscus glabratus, Bulimina exigua, Gyrodina depressa,* plus 20 additional species (V. S. Mallory, 1959).

NOMENCLATURE OF BIOSTRATIGRAPHIC UNITS

Article 24.—The name of a zone, subzone, or zonule consists of the names of the characteristic fossil or fossils combined with the appropriate zone term.

Remarks. (a) *Ambiguity of the unmodified term "zone."* —The formal name of any biostratigraphic unit should specify the kind of zone, for the meaning of the unmodified term is indefinite. In later references in the same paper, however, it is permissible to combine the biologic name with the unmodified term "zone," if the meaning is obvious.

(b) *Capitalization.*—The initial letter of formal unit terms, except the names of species, used in biostratigraphic classification should be capitalized when part of a named unit, in conformity with the usage adopted for rock-stratigraphic and time-stratigraphic units. (See Articles 10g and 32.) Examples are the *Cardioceras cordatum* Concurrent-range Zone or Zone of *Cardioceras cordatum;* the *Bolivina* Range Zone or Range Zone of *Bolivina;* the *Bifericeras bifer* Subzone and *Oxynoticeras lymense* Subzone of the *Oxynoticeras oxynotum* Concurrent-range Zone, Sinemurian, Lower Jurassic of England.

(c) *Generic name.*—The formal name of a zone or subzone that is based upon a certain species should always include the generic name also. In later references to the zone in the same paper, however, it is permissible to use only the initial letter of the genus preceding the specific name; for example, *C. cordatum* Zone.

(d) *Formal and informal names.*—Biostratigraphic units, like those of other categories (rock-stratigraphic, time-stratigraphic) may be either formal or informal (see Article 3). Formally designated units should be distinguished by use of an initial capital letter for the zone term (see Remark b), whereas an informal unit should not be so capitalized; for example, *Cardioceras cordatum* zone.

(e) *Duplication of names.*—The name of the same fossil should not be used for both a zone and a subdivision of that zone.

Article 25.—Names of biostratigraphic units should be changed to conform with changes in names of taxa required by international rules of biologic nomenclature.

[b] Oppel, A., 1856–1858, Die Juraformation Englands, Frankreichs und des Südwestlichen Deutschlands: Stuttgart, p. 3.

Remark. (a) *Reason for change.*—The names of biostratigraphic units should be modified whenever the name of the taxon is changed to conform to the international rules of nomenclature; otherwise, the biologic part of the biostratigraphic name would disagree with the name recognized by paleobotanists and paleozoologists. Until the changed name of the taxon becomes well known, it is desirable to cite both old and new names; for example, *Hyracotherium* ("*Eohippus*") Concurrent-range Zone, *Merycoidodon* ("*Oreodon*") Range Zone.

TIME-STRATIGRAPHIC (CHRONOSTRATIGRAPHIC) UNITS

NATURE OF TIME-STRATIGRAPHIC UNITS

Article 26.—A time-stratigraphic unit is a subdivision of rocks considered solely as the record of a specific interval of geologic time.

Remarks. (a) *Definition.*—Time-stratigraphic units depend fundamentally for definition on actual sections or sequences of rock, and without these standards they are meaningless. They are material units. Each is the record of an interval of time that extended from the beginning to the ending of its deposition or intrusion. In actual practice, the scope of a time-stratigraphic unit in its type section or type area usually is made to coincide with that of some other kind of stratigraphic unit, such as a biostratigraphic or a rock-stratigraphic unit, which thus serves as an objective reference. As time-stratigraphic units depend for definition on actual sections of rock, care should be taken to define geologic-time units in terms of time-stratigraphic units and not vice versa.

(b) *Principal purposes.*—Two principal purposes are served by time-stratigraphic classification: (i) correlation of rocks in one section or area with those of others on the basis of age equivalence or contemporaneity of origin; and (ii) placing the rocks of the earth's crust in a systematic geochronologic sequence, so as to indicate their relative position and age with respect to earth history as a whole.

Article 27.—Boundaries of time-stratigraphic units at the type locality or area are defined by objective criteria.

Remarks. (a) *Definition.*—The upper and lower limits of all time-stratigraphic units should be defined in the rock succession at a type section within the type area in order to provide a standard for the unit. In the type area the boundaries may be based on any features thought to be stratigraphically useful or may be designated arbitrarily. Preferably, they should set the unit apart as representing a significant geologic episode. Preferably also, the limits should coincide with such horizons in the type section as boundaries of formations or biostratigraphic zones. The better these objective criteria can be extended laterally as guides to placement of the rocks in time, the greater is the geographic extent of the area in which the unit can be identified accurately. Boundaries of time-stratigraphic units in other than the type area may fall within rock-stratigraphic or biostratigraphic units.

(b) *Historic boundaries.*—Boundaries of many of the older time-stratigraphic units were selected to coincide with hiatuses in the rock succession; others were based on lithologic change. Further, Lyell used the relative proportions of living forms among the fossil species for classifying Cenozoic rocks into time-stratigraphic units.

Article 28.—Geographic extension of a time-stratigraphic unit from its type section or area can be accomplished only as criteria of time equivalence are available, and then only within the limits of accuracy imposed by physical (including isotopic) or paleontologic criteria.

Remarks. (a) Physical criteria.—Physically based criteria are (i) generally more useful and often more precise in local time-correlation and (ii) seldom if ever surpass paleontologic criteria for world-wide correlation. Many physical criteria may be useful; for example, isotopes, products of radioactivity, lithologic similarity, paleomagnetism, thermoluminescence, relation to adjacent strata, relation to unconformities and to intrusions.

(b) Paleontologic criteria.—Paleontologic criteria may be (i) as useful and precise as physical for local time-correlation; (ii) by virtue of progressive organic evolution, they remain the most successful means of world-wide correlation of all ranks of Phanerozoic time-stratigraphic units.

(c) Ideal boundaries.—Ideally the boundaries of time-stratigraphic units, as extended geographically from the type section, are isochronous surfaces, representing everywhere the same horizon in time; thus, ideally these boundaries are independent of lithology, fossil content, or any other material bases of stratigraphic division. In actual practice, the geographic extension of a time-stratigraphic unit is influenced and generally controlled by stratigraphic features.

(d) Radiometry and isotopes.—Age determinations by means of isotopic ratios are useful in time-stratigraphic correlation. Radiometric and isotope methods are applicable to sedimentary rocks that contain a suitable authigenic mineral. The radiocarbon method is applicable to Quaternary rocks that contain suitable carbon. Isotope methods are applicable to igneous rocks that contain a suitable primary mineral in which the normal ratio of decay products has not been altered through contamination, metamorphism, or other changes. Thus some time-stratigraphic units of sedimentary or igneous rocks can be approximately extended from their type localities.

(e) Indirect radiometric and isotope methods.—Radiometry and the study of isotopes may also be used where the rock and the dated mineral are not coeval; thus, assemblages of volcanic rock and nonvolcanic sedimentary rock may be placed within maximum and minimum age limits. The maximum age and minimum age of an assemblage may be determined in relation (i) to veins, faults, intrusive rocks, and other transecting features, (ii) to overriding metamorphism, (iii) to detrital minerals within the rock, and (iv) to unconformably subjacent igneous and metamorphic rocks. Thus it may be possible to group separate bodies of rock, not necessarily of the same age, into larger time-stratigraphic units.

(f) Precambrian divisions.—Because of difficulties of interregional correlation it is not yet possible to divide the Precambrian rocks of North America into widely applicable time-stratigraphic units. Several students prefer to limit classification and nomenclature of the Precambrian to rock-stratigraphic units. Others advocate that major time-stratigraphic divisions be used in a relative sense for a particular region (Lower Precambrian, Upper Precambrian). But some have extended such terms, intended for local use, over large areas as major time-stratigraphic units (Lower, Middle, and Upper Precambrian); and still others have defined major time-stratigraphic units at a type locality and have attempted to extend them geographically, basing their correlations on lithologic similarity, structural similarity, comparison of sequences, and relations to adjacent strata, to unconformities, and to intrusions (Archaean, Proterozoic). New Precambrian time-stratigraphic units should be introduced only when they can be useful for interregional time-stratigraphy and for geochronology.

RANKS OF TIME-STRATIGRAPHIC UNITS

Article 29.—The system is the fundamental unit of world-wide time-stratigraphic classification of Phanerozoic rocks.

Remarks. (a) Definition and extent.—The bases for original definition of the generally adopted geologic systems are remarkably varied and haphazard. The definition of any time-stratigraphic unit should properly depend on a clear original designation of a type sequence of rocks. This has not been true of the original definitions of any of the recognized systems. Almost all systems began as rather local units and many of them have been extended more or less successfully throughout the world on a time-stratigraphic basis, mainly through their fossil content. They have been revised and supplemented by work in the type areas and elsewhere. As a result the rocks included in the several systems as now recognized are only partly, or even indirectly, related to the sections originally designated.

(b) Precambrian systems.—In the Precambrian, systems still have only local significance. They have not been placed in widely accepted orderly succession and do not serve as the fundamental units of time-stratigraphic classification.

(c) Subsystem.—Some systems established in Europe have been later divided elsewhere into parts for each of which the rank of system has been claimed. As a solution to some of the resulting difficulties in nomenclature, the term "subsystem" has been proposed for these parts.

Article 30.—Series is a time-stratigraphic unit next in rank below system.

Remarks. (a) Definition.—The basis for definition of a series should be a clearly designated stratigraphic interval in a type area, but many of these units have come to be adopted quite generally without explicit indication of their limits.

(b) Extent.—The series may constitute a major unit in time correlation, within a province, between provinces, or between continents. Some are recognized as world-wide time-stratigraphic units; others are only provincial.

(c) Intrusive rock.—The term "series" is not restricted to stratified rocks but may be applied to intrusive rocks in the same time-stratigraphic sense.

(d) "Misuse of term series."—In stratigraphic terminology "series" should not be applied to rock-stratigraphic units. (See Article 9f.)

Article 31.—Stage is a time-stratigraphic unit next in rank below series.

Remarks. (a) Use of stage.—The stage is an important

working unit in time-stratigraphic correlation and classification. Commonly it is based on a succession of biostratigraphic zones; the zones may differ in different geographic areas. Stages are often employed to relate the various kinds of minor stratigraphic units in one geologic section or area to those in another with respect to time of origin.

(*b*) *Misuse of term "stage."*—The terms "stage" and "substage" were authorized for climatic subdivisions of the Quaternary Period by the 1933 Code. This usage has led to confusion and is here specifically rejected. "Stage" and "substage" are time-stratigraphic terms and should be used for Quaternary rocks as for other parts of the column.

NOMENCLATURE OF TIME-STRATIGRAPHIC UNITS

Article 32.—A formal time-stratigraphic unit is given a binomial name, and the initial letter of both terms should be capitalized.

Remarks. (*a*) *System names.*—The existing names that are generally accepted for systems have diverse origins, and they also have different sorts of endings; for example, Cambrian, Cretaceous, Jurassic, Tertiary.

(*b*) *Series names.*—Series are commonly known either by geographic names, for example, Waucoban Series, Niagaran Series, or by names of their encompassing systems modified by the capitalized adjectives Upper, Middle, Lower, for example, Lower Cretaceous Series, Middle Devonian Series. In general a geographic name is preferable because it may be tied to a type area. For names of geographic origin the adjectival endings -*an* or -*ian* have been widely used, for example, Cincinnatian Series, but it is permissible to use the geographic name without any special ending, for example, Cincinnati Series.

(*c*) *Stage names.*—The great majority of stage names already in use have been based on rock-stratigraphic units (groups, formations, members) and bear the names of these units, for example, Chemung Stage, Maestrichtian Stage, Claiborne Stage. Preferably a stage should have a geographic name not previously used in stratigraphic nomenclature, for example, Refugian Stage.

(*d*) *New names.*—Geographic names proposed for new time-stratigraphic units should not duplicate those used for rock-stratigraphic units. Moreover, two names should not be derived from the same place, for example, the stage names Bathonian and Bathian. The later variant should be regarded as a "stillborn homonym."

Article 33.—Doubt in the assignment of rocks to time-stratigraphic units should be made explicit if criteria of time equivalence are inconclusive or lacking. (See Article 28.)

Remark. (*a*) *Expression of doubt.*—Doubt can be expressed in several ways. (i) If the balance of evidence seems to favor one age assignment, the rock may be assigned to a specific time-stratigraphic unit with the doubt expressed by a question mark or by the words "probably" or "possibly." (ii) If the evidence suggests a position athwart a time-stratigraphic boundary, the doubt may be expressed (with or without question marks) by coupling the names of the two time-stratigraphic units with "or," "and," or a hyphen. (iii) If the evidence indicates only an upper or a lower limit, the assignment should be indicated by the prefix

"pre-" or "post-," for example, pre-Cretaceous, post-Cambrian. (iv) It is not necessary to make formal time-stratigraphic assignments if evidence of age equivalence with established units is lacking.

PROCEDURE IN ESTABLISHING TIME-STRATIGRAPHIC UNITS

Article 34.—Requirements for establishing a time-stratigraphic unit include (i) statement of intention to designate such a unit; (ii) selection of name; (iii) definition of boundaries of the unit in the type area with specific reference to designated sections; (iv) distinguishing characteristics including fossils if present; (v) correlation and age relationships; and (vi) publication in a recognized scientific medium as specified in Article 13.

Remark. (*a*) *Invalid names.*—Naming a time-stratigraphic unit simply by adding "-an" of "-ian" to the name of a rock stratigraphic name is improper and does not constitute definition of a time-stratigraphic unit. A new name so proposed should be considered invalid.

REVISION OF TIME-STRATIGRAPHIC CLASSIFICATION AND NOMENCLATURE

Article 35.—Redefinition of a time-stratigraphic unit without changing its name is allowable but requires as much justification as the establishment of a new unit and demands conservatism. Redefinition of systems calls for international agreement.

Remark. (*a*) *Supplementary sections.*—If definition of a time-stratigraphic unit is inadequate, it may be redefined and revised by reference to supplementary sections. (See Article 34.)

GEOLOGIC-TIME (GEOCHRONOLOGIC) UNITS

NATURE OF GEOLOGIC-TIME UNITS

Article 36.—Geologic-time units are divisions of time distinguished on the basis of the rock record, particularly as expressed by time-stratigraphic units. They are not material units.

Remarks. (*a*) *Boundaries.*—Historically the definition of a period as a unit of geologic time depended on chosen sections in the type area of the system, which is the corresponding time-stratigraphic unit. The period comprised an interval of time defined by the beginning and ending of the deposition of the system. To define periods rigorously in this manner is to create unnamed time units between periods, in other words, gaps in formal geologic time. By later work supplementary sections largely or wholly filling the hiatuses have been found elsewhere in the world and their rocks, by common consent, have been assigned to one or another of the contiguous systems. Many of the gaps have thereby been essentially filled. Today it is probable that formal geologic time as referred to actual rocks is continuous or even (as now classified) duplicated. In practice, placement of boundaries of time units is imprecise because of imperfect correlation.

(b) *Validity of geologic-time units.*—The units of geologic time are no more valid than the time-stratigraphic units on which they are based. (See Articles 26, 27, and 28.)

RANKS OF GEOLOGIC-TIME UNITS

Article 37.—Ranks of geologic-time units in order of decreasing magnitude are eon, era, period, epoch, and age.

Remarks. (a) *Period, epoch, and age.*—A period is defined as the time during which the corresponding system was deposited. Epochs are similarly related to series, and ages (in the formal sense), to stages. Because some of these words, particularly "age," are often used informally, wherever they are used formally in conjunction with a proper name they should be capitalized as noted in Article 38a.

(b) *Era and eon.*—Time-stratigraphic units composed of combined systems lack generally accepted formal names, but three such combinations of systems are the time-stratigraphic bases of the three geologic-time units called the Paleozoic Era, the Mesozoic Era, and the Cenozoic Era. These three combinations are combined in turn into a single unnamed combination of systems, which is the time-stratigraphic basis of the Phanerozoic Eon. Precambrian eras, because of difficulties in establishing a chronologic succession of periods, may be formed independently.

NOMENCLATURE OF GEOLOGIC-TIME UNITS

Article 38.—Geographic or other names used for period, epoch, and age are identical with those of the corresponding time-stratigraphic units; the names of eras and eons are independently formed.

Remarks. (a) *Capitalization.*—In naming a formal unit of geologic time the initial letter of each term is capitalized, as Devonian Period. (See Article 37a.)

(b) *Names of epochs.*—If a series name consists of the system name preceded by Lower, Middle, or Upper, the corresponding epoch name should consist of the period name preceded by Early, Middle, or Late; for example, Early Devonian Epoch.

(c) *Time intervals* represented by unconformities should not receive formal names. They should, in general, be referred to preceding or succeeding stratigraphic units by the prefixes *pre-* and *post-*; for example, post-Laramie interval. Where such convenient names for time intervals as "Laramide revolution" are used, they should have no part in formal stratigraphic nomenclature. Similarly, the naming of time intervals represented by cycles of erosion that are expressed in present-day land forms, for example, "Elk Valley erosion cycle" is permissible, but such physiographic names have no part in formal stratigraphic nomenclature. It is generally undesirable to use the same geographic name for an erosion cycle or erosion surface and for a rock unit; for example, "Fremont erosion cycle" in Wyoming and "Fremont Limestone" in Colorado.

GEOLOGIC CLIMATE UNITS (FOR USE IN THE QUATERNARY)

Article 39.—A geologic-climate unit is an inferred widespread climatic episode defined from a subdivision of Quaternary rocks.

Remarks. (a) *Definition.*—A geologic-climate unit is defined from its records, which are bodies of rock, soil, and organic material. At any single place the time boundaries of the geologic-climate unit are defined by the boundaries of some kind of stratigraphic unit. These local stratigraphic boundaries may be isochronous surfaces, but the different stratigraphic boundaries that define the limits of the geologic-time unit in different latitudes are not likely to be isochronous. In this respect geologic-climate units differ from geologic-time units, which are based on time-stratigraphic units. The locality where the geologic-climate unit is first defined is its type locality.

(b) *Principal purposes.*—Geologic-climate units are used (i) in correlating episodes of deposition of Quaternary rocks in different areas, and (ii) in determining the historical sequence of events in the Quaternary Period.

(c) *Extent.*—Geologic-climate units may be extended geographically as far as the record of the geologic climate can be identified, regardless of changes of facies of the rocks, soils, or other materials that constitute the record.

Article 40.—Glaciation and interglaciation are fundamental units of geologic-climate classification; stade and interstade are subdivisions of a glaciation.

Remarks. (a) *Definitions.*—(i) A glaciation was a climatic episode during which extensive glaciers developed, attained a maximum extent, and receded. (ii) An interglaciation was an episode during which the climate was incompatible with the wide extent of glaciers that characterized a glaciation. (iii) A stade was a climatic episode within a glaciation during which a secondary advance of glaciers took place. (iv) An interstade was a climatic episode within a glaciation during which a secondary recession or a stillstand of glaciers took place.

(b) *Nomenclature.*—Formal names of geologic-climate units should be chosen in accordance with the rules (see Article 13) that govern the naming of rock-stratigraphic units. A geologic-climate unit may be named after a rock-stratigraphic unit, a soil-stratigraphic unit, or some other geographically named stratigraphic unit. In the type locality of the geologic-climate unit the record of its major climatic characteristics should be plain, and the evidence of climatic change at the lower and upper limits should be manifest.

PROCEDURE FOR AMENDMENT

Article 41.—Additions or amendments to this code may be proposed to the Commission by any geologist in writing at any time. If accepted for consideration by a majority vote of the Commission, they may be adopted by a two-thirds vote of the Commission at an annual meeting not less than a year after publication of the proposal.

Index